[CONTAC

98th edition published by Spotlight
t: 020 7437 7631 f: 020 7437 5881

What is Contacts?

Contacts is the essential handbook for everyone working or wanting to work in the entertainment industry. It has been published by Spotlight since 1947. It contains over 5000 listings for companies, services and individuals across all branches of Television, Stage, Film and Radio. These are updated annually to bring you the most accurate information available.

Also watch out for the 'information pages', designed to tell you more about those listed and why you might want to contact them. They include valuable advice from key industry figures - especially helpful if you are just starting out in the industry.

As ever, please send any feedback or suggestions for the next edition to marketing@spotlight.com

How can I / my company appear in the next edition of Contacts?

Contacts is published annually. If you would like to appear in the next edition, either with an advert or a free, text-only listing, please visit: www.contactshandbook.com

How do I buy copies of Contacts?

To purchase additional copies of Contacts,
visit www.contactshandbook.com, e-mail sales@spotlight.com,
or call 020 7440 5026. It is also available from most good bookshops.

SPOTLIGHT

Contents

Index To Advertisers

[CONTACTS 2009]

A

C

D

F

G

H

A

Accountants, Insurance & Law
Agents
Agents & Personal Managers
Children's & Teenagers'
Concert & Concert Promoters
Dance
Literary & Play
Presenters
Voice-Over
Walk-On & Supporting Artists

PMA: For information regarding membership of the
Personal Managers' Association please contact
PO Box 63819, London N1P 1HL
t. 0845 6027191 w. www.thepma.com

CPMA: For information regarding membership of the
Co-operative Personal Management Association
please contact
The Secretary, CPMA
c/o 1 Mellor Road, Leicester LE3 6HN
t. 07984 345310 w. www.cpma.co.uk

NASAA: For information regarding membership of
the **National Association of Supporting Artistes**
Agents please see
w. www.nasaa.org.uk

Members of the above organisations are
clearly marked as such in the following listings.

Animals
Arts Centres
Arts Councils

[CONTACTS 2009]

AON Ltd (Trading as AON/ALBERT G. RUBEN)
(Insurance Brokers)
Pinewood Studios, Pinewood Road
Iver, Bucks SL0 0NH
Website: www.aon.co.uk
Fax: 01753 785861   Tel: 01753 785859

ATKINS Chris & COMPANY
(Accountants & Business Consultants)
Astra House, Arklow Road, London SE14 6EB
e-mail: info@chrisatkins.co.uk   Tel: 020-8691 4100

BLACKMORE Lawrence
(Production Accountant)
Suite 5, 26 Charing Cross Road
London WC2H 0DG
Fax: 020-7836 3156   Tel: 020-7240 1817

BLAKE LAPTHORNE TARLO LYONS
(Solicitors)
Watchmaker Court
33 St John's Lane, London EC1M 4DB
Website: www.bllaw.co.uk
e-mail: info@bllaw.co.uk
Fax: 020-7814 9421   Tel: 020-7405 2000

BOWKER ORFORD
(Chartered Accountants)
15-19 Cavendish Place, London W1G 0DD
e-mail: rparmar@bowkerorford.com
Fax: 020-7580 3909   Tel: 020-7636 6391

BREBNERS
(Chartered Accountants)
180 Wardour Street, London W1F 8LB
Website: www.brebners.com
e-mail: partners@brebners.com
Fax: 020-7287 5315   Tel: 020-7734 2244

BRECKMAN & COMPANY
(Chartered Certified Accountants)
49 South Molton Street, London W1K 5LH
Website: www.breckmanandcompany.co.uk
                                     Tel: 020-7499 2292

CARR Mark & Co Ltd
(Chartered Accountants)
Garrick House, 26-27 Southampton Street
Covent Garden, London WC2E 7RS
Website: www.markcarr.co.uk
e-mail: mark@markcarr.co.uk   Tel: 020-7717 8474

COUNT AND SEE Ltd
(Tax, Accountancy & Book-keeping Services)
219 Macmillan Way, London SW17 6AW
Website: www.countandsee.com
e-mail: info@countandsee.com
Fax: 0845 004 3454   Tel: 020-8767 7882

EQUITY INSURANCE SERVICES
131-133 New London Road
Chelmsford, Essex CM2 0QZ
Website: www.equity-ins-services.com
e-mail: enquiries@equity-ins-services.com
Fax: 01245 491641   Tel: 01245 357854

FISHER BERGER & ASSOCIATES
(Chartered Accountants)
57 Elmcroft Crescent, London NW11 9TA
e-mail: nik@fisherberger.com
Fax: 020-8458 9776   Tel: 020-8458 9770

Why might I need this section?

This section contains listings for a number of companies and services which exist to help performers with the day-to-day administration of their working lives. Performers need to manage their business affairs personally, in ways that those in 'normal' jobs do not. For example, unlike most employees, a performer does not have an accounts department to work out their tax and national insurance, or an HR department to take care of contracts or health insurance on their behalf. On top of which, performers can often be away on tour or on set for many months and unable to attend to these matters themselves.

Areas covered in this section include:

Accountants and other financial services

Dedicated companies exist which can help you to manage key financial issues, including national insurance, taxation, benefits, savings and pensions. Specialist mortgage companies also exist for performers and other self-employed workers within the entertainment industry. See overleaf for specific information about accountancy services. If you are a member of Equity you can also ask them for free financial advice, and an Equity pension scheme exists into which the BBC, ITV, PACT, TV companies and West End Theatre producers will pay when you have a main part with one of them. Similar schemes also exist for dancers and other performers.

Insurance

Performers may often need specialist insurance for specific jobs, as well as the standard life and health insurance policies held by most people. A number of specialist insurers are listed in the pages overleaf. Equity also offers a specialist backstage/accident and public liability insurance policy to all of its members.

Legal

There may be times in a performer's career when he/she needs specialist legal advice or representation. Legal advisors and solicitors are listed in this section. In addition, as part of their membership, Equity performers can also obtain free legal advice regarding professional engagements or personal injury claims.

How should I use these listings?

As when looking to hire any company or individual, contact a number of different companies and carefully compare the services they offer. Ask others in the industry for recommendations. If you are an Equity member, don't forget to check first that the service isn't already available free of charge, as part of your annual membership.

BRECKMAN & COMPANY
chartered certified accountants

BRECKMAN & COMPANY Chartered Certified Accountants have been dubbed "leading showbusiness accountants" by The Stage. They offer some useful tips and advice for performers and others who are self-employed in the arts/entertainment industry.

All self-employed individuals need to submit a tax return to 5th April each year. This has to be completed by 31st October in the same year if submitting a paper return, or by 31st January of the following year if filing online.

Tax is payable on 31st January and 31st July. In an ideal world we would all have put aside enough to settle our liabilities, but often the payment due on 31st January is the killer. It invariably consists of two ingredients: the shortfall on a previous year and a payment on account for the current year. For the actor, whose income can fluctuate from year to year, this creates real hardship. A payment on account, which is based on a previous year's income, usually bears no relation to the actual income earned in the current year. The amount to put aside could be anywhere between 10-40% of current and expected earnings. If a performer has had a rotten year, they can make a claim to reduce the payments on account. If they propose a lesser payment than the ultimate figure, they are then penalised and charged interest on the shortfall.

Under the self-assessment tax system the taxpayer does all the work for the taxman and the taxman then merely sends out tax demands based on figures that the taxpayer has provided. From time to time the taxman may decide to embark on an investigation into an individual taxpayer's affairs. There are a number of reasons why the taxman may start an investigation such as an actor receiving tax refunds year after year, figures seeming inconsistent with previous years, or merely an investigation at random.

Just starting out?
If you are just starting out as self-employed then you need to register with the Inland Revenue within three months of commencement or you may incur a £100 late notification penalty. This is done by completing a form CWF1 or visiting an accountant who, as well as completing the form for you, can advise you on various other issues such as National Insurance Contributions, VAT, record keeping and what expenses can be claimed.

VAT (Value added tax)
If your turnover is in excess of £67,000 in any cumulative 12 month period then you should notify the VAT man and will probably have to register for VAT. This means you then have to add VAT to all your fees and account for these to the VAT man. If notification is not made within one month the individual may incur a penalty based on the tax due. There are also more strict rules for accounting and penalties for late returns.

Allowable expenses
The performer has many facets to their discipline. The descriptions of the various expense headings can be modified according to the role it plays in the performer's repertoire. One is restricted somewhat by the all-embracing interpretation that the taxman puts upon his own definitions of what expenses can be claimed. The legal mantra is that expenses claimed are to be "wholly and exclusively incurred in the performance of the business", but this is not always clear-cut.

Broadly speaking, everything a performer does can be related to their work. For example, the taxman would not generally allow clothing as an expense, but if an actor were to buy clothing for a particular performance or for rehearsals then this expenditure would be allowable. Alternatively, if a performer were required to attend a film premiere where they are likely to be photographed for publicity purposes, the outfit they bought for that occasion could also be allowable. However, the claiming of expenditure has to be done with care and not abused. Over-claiming may lead to problems later on, if the taxman does decide to investigate.

For further advice and all your accountancy and taxation needs contact Kevin Beale, Graham Berry or Richard Nelson at Breckman & Company on 020-7499 2292 or visit our website www.breckmanandcompany.co.uk.

FORD Jonathan & Co
(Chartered Accountants)
The Coach House, 31 View Road
Rainhill, Merseyside L35 OLF
Website: www.jonathanford.co.uk
e-mail: info@jonathanford.co.uk   Tel: 0151-426 4512

GLOBAL MOBILITY LAW
Contact: Julia de Cadenet
(US Legal & Visa Consultancy. Advice on all aspects of work
visas and US green cards). Offices in California with
liaisons in London & Paris
Website: www.globalmobilitylaw.com
e-mail: info@legalbrain.eu
Tel: +44 33 1 58 64 05 53   Tel: 020-8940 1310

GORDON LEIGHTON
(Chartered Accountants, Business Advisers)
3rd Floor, 20-23 Greville Street, London EC1N 8SS
Website: www.gordonl.co.uk
e-mail: malcolms@gordonl.com
Fax: 020-7831 0500   Tel: 020-7831 8300

HARVEYS LLP
(Accountants)
The Old Winery, Lamberhurst Vineyard
Lamberhurst, Kent TN3 8ER
Fax: 01892 891892   Tel: 01892 890388

HILL DICKINSON LLP
1 St Paul's Square, Old Hall Street, Liverpool L3 9SJ
Website: www. hilldickinson.com
e-mail: mediateam@hilldickinson.com   Tel: 0161-817 7200

HOMEMATCH PROPERTY FINANCE
(Mortgages for Entertainers)
Eagle Place, Pheasant Street, Worcester WR1 2EE
e-mail: chrisjcatchpole@aol.com
Fax: 01905 22121   Tel: 01905 22007

KERR John CHARTERED ACCOUNTANTS
369-375 Eaton Road, West Derby, Liverpool L12 2AH
e-mail: advice@jkca.co.uk
Fax: 0151-228 3792   Tel: 0151-228 8977

LARK INSURANCE BROKING GROUP
(Insurance Brokers)
Wigham House, Wakering Road, Barking, Essex IG11 8PJ
e-mail: mailbox@larkinsurance.co.uk
Fax: 020-8557 2430   Tel: 020-8557 2300

LONGREACH INTERNATIONAL Ltd
(Specialist Insurance Brokers)
20-21 Tooks Court, London EC4A 1LB
Website: www.longreachint.com/theatre
e-mail: info@longreachint.com
Fax: 020-7421 7550   Tel: 020-7421 7555

NYMAN LIBSON PAUL
(Chartered Accountants)
Regina House, 124 Finchley Road, London NW3 5JS
Website: www.nlpca.co.uk
e-mail: entertainment@nlpca.co.uk
Fax: 020-7433 2401   Tel: 020-7433 2400

PLANISPHERES
(Business & Legal Affairs)
Sinclair House, 2 Sinclair Gardens, London W14 0AT
Website: www.planispheres.com
e-mail: info@planispheres.com   Tel/Fax: 020-7602 2038

SUMMERS David & COMPANY
(Chartered Accountants)
Argo House
Kilburn Park Road
London NW6 5LF
e-mail: dsummersfca@hotmail.com
Fax: 020-7644 0678   Tel: 0800 328 8741

TODS MURRAY LLP
(Richard Findlay Entertainment Lawyer)
Edinburgh Quay
133 Fountainbridge
Edinburgh EH3 9AG
e-mail: richard.findlay@todsmurray.com
Fax: 0131-656 2023   Tel: 0131-656 2000

VANTIS
(Accountants, Business & Tax Advisers)
Torrington House
47 Holywell Hill
St Albans
Hertfordshire AL1 1HD
Website: www.vantisplc.com/stalbanshh
e-mail: stalbans@vantisplc.com
Fax: 01727 861052   Tel: 01727 838255

WIDDOWSON Alexis CHARTERED ACCOUNTANTS
1 High Street
Welford
Northants NN6 6HT
e-mail: alexiswiddowson@aol.com   Tel/Fax: 01858 575734

Treating people with respect will gain one acceptance and improve business.

Tao Zhu Gong, 500BC

Brebners offers much more than accountancy services and business advice. We offer trust, reliability and a truly personal service.

Whether you are just starting out or are more established, our committed and specialist team offers a full range of services to help your business succeed.

Please call Michael Burton, Raef Gregory or Hazel Milne on 020 7734 2244 for a free and confidential discussion.

BREBNERS

CHARTERED ACCOUNTANTS
& BUSINESS ADVISERS

THE QUADRANGLE 180 WARDOUR STREET LONDON W1F 8LB TEL: 020 7734 2244
EMAIL: PARTNERS@BREBNERS.COM WEB: WWW.BREBNERS.COM

Who are agents and personal managers?

There are hundreds of Agents and Personal Managers in the UK, representing thousands of actors and artists. It is their job to promote their clients to casting opportunities and negotiate contracts on their behalf. In return they take commission ranging from 10-15%. Larger agencies can have hundreds of clients on their books, smaller ones may only have a handful. Agents usually try to represent a good range of artists (age, sex, type) to fill the diverse role types required by casting directors. A personal manager is someone who manages an artist's career on a more one-on-one basis.

What is a co-operative agency?

Co-operative agencies are staffed by actors themselves, who take turns to handle the administrative side of the agency and promote themselves to casting opportunities as a team. If you want more control over your career and can handle the pressures and responsibility that an agent takes away from you, then you might consider joining a co-operative agency. However it is very important that you think carefully about what you are signing up for. You will be responsible for the careers of others as well as yourself, so you must first of all be able to conduct yourself well when speaking to casting professionals. You will also have to commit some of your time to administrative jobs. You must be prepared to deal with finances and forms - all the boring paperwork you usually hand over to your agent! You must also be aware that the other actors in the agency will want to interview you and, if you are successful, to give you a trial period working with them.

Why do I need an agent?

Your agent will have contacts and authority in the entertainment industry that you, as an individual actor, cannot have. Agents, if you want them to, can also deal with paperwork such as Equity and Spotlight membership renewal. They can offer you advice on which headshot would be best to send out to casting directors, what to include or exclude in your CV as you build on your skills and experience, what a particular casting director might expect when you are invited to an audition, and so on.

How should I use these listings?

If you are an actor getting started in the industry, or looking to change your agent, the following pages will supply you with up-to-date contact details for many of the UK's leading agencies. Every company listed is done so by written request to us. Members of the Personal Managers' Association (PMA) and the Co-operative Personal Management Association (CMPA) have indicated their membership status under their name. Some agencies have also chosen to list other information such as relevant contact names, their preferred method of contact from new applicants, whether or not they will accept showreels and/or voicereels with your CV and headshot, the number of performers represented by the agency, the number of agents working for the company, and/or a description of the performance areas they cover. Use this information to narrow down your search for a suitable agent.

How do I choose a new agent?

When writing to agencies, try to research the different companies instead of just sending a 'blanket' letter to every single one. This way you can target your approaches to the most suitable agencies and avoid wasting their time (and yours). As well as using the listing information provided here, look at agency websites and ask around for personal recommendations. Unfortunately Spotlight is not able to offer personalised advice on choosing an agent, nor is it in a position to handle any financial or contractual queries or complaints, but we have prepared some useful career advice on our website: www.spotlight.com/artists/advice. Click on our Frequently Asked Questions page for general guidance regarding agents, or you may wish to try consulting our list of Independent Advisory Services if you want one-to-one tailored advice. You can also contact The Agents' Association www.agents-uk.com or The Personal Managers' Association (PMA) www.thepma.com. If you are a member of Equity then you can contact their legal and welfare department with general information about issues including commissions, fees and contracts. However, Equity is not able to recommend specific agencies or agents.

How do I approach agencies?

Once you have made a list of suitable agencies, consult the listings again. Some agencies have indicated their preferred method of initial contact, whether by post, email or telephone. Do not email them if they have stated that they wish to receive your headshot, CV and covering letter by post. If they have not given a preference, you should send your CV by post as this is the traditional method of contacting agents. You should always include a stamped-addressed envelope (SAE) big enough to contain your 10 x 8 photo and with sufficient postage. This will increase your chances of getting a reply. Write your name and telephone number on the back of your headshot in case it gets separated from your CV.

Remember that agents receive hundreds of letters each week, so try to keep your communication concise, and be professional at all times. We also recommend that your covering letter has some kind of focus: perhaps you can tell them about your next showcase, or where they can see you currently appearing on stage. Ideally this should be addressed to an individual, not "To whom it may concern" or "Dear Sir or Madam". Some agents have provided a contact name in their listing.

Some agents have indicated that they are happy to receive a showreel and/or voicereel with your CV, but it would be best to exclude these from your correspondence if they are not mentioned. Point out in your covering letter that one is available and the agent can contact you if they want to find out more.

Should I pay an agent to join their books?
Or sign a contract?

Equity (the actors' trade union) does not recommend that artists pay an agent to join their client list. Before signing a contract, you should be very clear about the terms and commitments involved. For advice on both of these issues, or if you experience any problems with a current agent, we recommend that you contact Equity www.equity.org.uk. They also publish the booklet You and your Agent which is free to all Equity members.

How do I become an agent?

Budding agents will need to get experience of working in an agent's office; usually this is done by working as an assistant. It can be extremely hard work, and you will be expected to give up a lot of your evenings to attend productions. There are two organisations you may find it useful to contact: the Agents' Association www.agents-uk.com and the Personal Managers' Association www.thepma.com

Mark Ward has worked throughout the entertainment industry as a performer, teacher and agent. He has taught and lectured at numerous colleges, including Arts Educational London, LIPA and Performers College. Mark was the Senior Agent at Re|animator, a leading UK dance agency, for five years before joining the team at BBA Ltd in 2005.

Preparation, preparation, preparation. That should be a motto for anyone carving out a career in theatre, TV or film. The pace of the industry is getting faster. We live in a world of reality TV shows and talent shows that can provide fast-track opportunities for people who might normally struggle to get on. There are more people than ever looking for work in the entertainment business, so attention to detail on how you promote yourself can be the deciding factor in achieving a consistent career with longevity. Here are some pointers worth considering...

If you are looking for representation, ask for personal recommendations. An agent is only as good as the clients they represent so look for a list that seems to work consistently and in the areas that you are interested in. Does the agent have actual experience in the entertainment business outside of being an agent? What are their qualifications? How are they perceived in the business? If your agent rubs people up the wrong way this can have a direct effect on your career.

Invest in your career. It saddens me how often artists settle for 'favours' from friends who dabble in photography, vocal coaching or making showreels. You should never submit a photograph that looks amateur as that makes you look amateur. Your photograph is actually your first audition and you are not even there for it! There are reasonable photographers out there and most offer a discount for students. Showing your agent that you take your career seriously will encourage them to work harder for you.

I find the 'skills' section on artists' CVs the most interesting. I try and persuade people to acquire certified skills as much as possible. This proves you are highly proficient in them. Things you tried once at college or on holiday are not relevant and could cause more harm than good if picked up on. Think about the sort of jobs you would like to be offered and work backwards from there.

The lines are blurring between straight theatre, musical theatre, TV and film and performers today switch between them more and more. However you should be careful not to jump too far, too soon. Your agent should have good advice on how to make the move from one genre to another and be able to protect you from appearing unprepared in front of casting professionals.

There are more styles of musicals now than ever before and choosing songs for auditions has never been more important. You should have designated songs to demonstrate vocal range, vocal ability, diction and performance. I cannot stress how important it is to have regular vocal coaching sessions with a qualified singing teacher. If you are a trained dancer make sure you attend regular dance classes to keep up your ability to retain routines and pick up different styles quickly.

You should be informed as much as possible about the people and projects you are auditioning for. What other projects have they worked on? Do they have a certain style or method of working? There is so much information available via the media and the internet as well as your agent. One of the best ways to get a broad handle on the industry is go and see as much as possible! You can pick up a lot from watching other people perform.

Lastly, a few words that may seem obvious, but are often forgotten. Always be polite: no matter how talented you are nobody likes to deal with overblown ego or a demanding personality. Think before you ask a question or make an observation. I try to have an ongoing dialogue with all of my clients. We discuss anything from what they wear, what they sing, what job they are interested in doing next and indeed what they want to be doing in the next few years and the best way for us to go about attaining it. It should be a professional relationship where both of you are working toward a similar goal. Be pro-active! Sitting around waiting for your mobile to ring is not going to give you the career or life you have worked hard for. Working with your agent should be based on teamwork and more often than not...fun!

Please visit www.buchanan-associates.co.uk for further information.

PMA: For information regarding membership of the **Personal Managers' Association** please contact
PO Box 63819, London N1P 1HL
t. 0845 6027191 w. www.thepma.com

CPMA: For information regarding membership of the **Co-operative Personal Management Association** please contact
The Secretary, CPMA
c/o 1 Mellor Road, Leicester LE3 6HN
t. 07984 345310 w. www.cpma.co.uk

Members of the above organisations are clearly marked as such in the following listings.

1984 PERSONAL MANAGEMENT Ltd
(Personal Manager) (CPMA Member)
24 Performers. Contact: David Meyer. By Post
Accepts Showreels
Suite 508
Davina House
137 Goswell Road
London EC1V 7ET
Website: www.1984pm.com
e-mail: info@1984pm.com
Fax: 020-7250 3031   Tel: 020-7251 8046

21ST CENTURY ACTORS MANAGEMENT Ltd
(CPMA Member)
15 Performers. Contact: By Post
Commercials. Film. Singers. Stage. Television
206 Panther House
38 Mount Pleasant
London WC1X 0AN
Website: www.21stcenturyactors.co.uk
e-mail: mail@21stcenturyactors.co.uk   Tel: 020-7278 3438

2MA Ltd
Sports. Stunts
Spring Vale, Tutland Road
North Baddesley
Hants SO52 9FL
Website: www.2ma.co.uk
e-mail: info@2ma.co.uk
Fax: 023-8074 1355   Tel: 023-8074 1354

A-LIST LOOKALIKES & ENTERTAINMENTS Ltd
4th Floor Calls Landing
36-38 The Calls, Leeds LS2 7EW
Website: www.alistlookalikes.co.uk
e-mail: info@alistlookalikes.co.uk   Tel: 0113-243 6245

A & B PERSONAL MANAGEMENT Ltd
(Personal Manager) (PMA Member)
Contact: By Post
Suite 330, Linen Hall
162-168 Regent Street
London W1B 5TD
e-mail: billellis@aandb.co.uk
Fax: 020-7038 3699   Tel: 020-7434 4262

paulcable
photography & design

www.paulcable.com
info@paulcable.com
07958 932 764

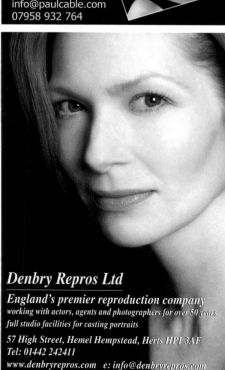

Denbry Repros Ltd

England's premier reproduction company
working with actors, agents and photographers for over 50 years
full studio facilities for casting portraits

57 High Street, Hemel Hempstead, Herts HP1 3AF
Tel: 01442 242411
www.denbryrepros.com e: info@denbryrepros.com

Photo: Nadia Cameron-Blakey by Dan Harwood-Stamper

A & J MANAGEMENT
242A The Ridgeway
Botany Bay
Enfield EN2 8AP
Website: www.ajmanagement.co.uk
e-mail: info@ajmanagement.co.uk
Fax: 020-8342 0842   Tel: 020-8342 0542

A@B (AGENCY AT BODYWORK)
25-29 Glisson Road
Cambridge CB1 2HA
e-mail: agency@bodyworkds.co.uk
Fax: 01223 358923   Tel: 01223 309990

ABA (ABACUS ADULTS)
The Studio, 4 Bailey Road
Westcott, Dorking, Surrey RH4 3QS
e-mail: aba@abacusagency.co.uk
Fax: 01306 877813   Tel: 01306 877144

ABBOTT June ASSOCIATES
55 East Road
London N1 6AH
e-mail: jaa@thecourtyard.org.uk
Fax: 020-7251 6018   Tel: 020-7250 0520

ACADEMY CASTINGS
Blue Square
272 Bath Street
Glasgow G2 4JR
Website: www.academycastings.co.uk
e-mail: robert@academycastings.co.uk
Fax: 0141-354 8876   Tel: 0141-354 8873

ACCESS ARTISTE MANAGEMENT Ltd
Contact: Sarah Bryan. By Post/email
Accepts Showreels
PO Box 39925
London EC1V 0WN
Website: www.access-associates.co.uk
e-mail: mail@access-associates.co.uk   Tel: 020-8505 1094

ACROBAT PRODUCTIONS
Advisors. Artists
12 Oaklands Court
Hempstead Road, Watford WD17 4LF
Website: www.acrobatproductions.com
e-mail: roger@acrobatproductions.com   Tel: 01923 224938

ACT OUT AGENCY
22 Greek Street
Stockport
Cheshire SK3 8AB
e-mail: ab22actout@aol.com   Tel/Fax: 0161-429 7413

ACTING ASSOCIATES
(Personal Manager)
Contact: Fiona Farley. By Post
Accepts Showreels /Voicereels
1 Agent represents 40 Performers. Commercials.
Corporate. Film. Musicals. Radio. Stage. Television
71 Hartham Road, London N7 9JJ
Website: www.actingassociates.co.uk
e-mail: fiona@actingassociates.co.uk
                    Tel/Fax: 020-7607 3562

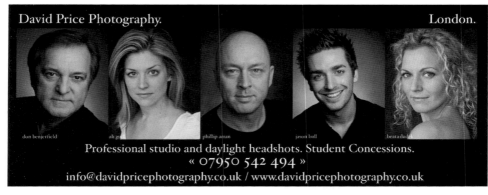
ACTOR MUSICIANS @ ACCESS
(Personal Manager) *Contact: Sarah Bryan. By Post/email*
Actor/Musician Productions. Commercials. Musicals. Stage
PO Box 39925, London EC1V OWN
Website: www.access-associates.co.uk
e-mail: musicians@access-associates.co.uk
                                    Tel: 020-8505 1094

ACTORS AGENCY
1 Glen Street
Tollcross, Edinburgh EH3 9JD
Website: www.stivenchristie.co.uk
e-mail: info@stivenchristie.co.uk
Fax: 0131-228 4645   Tel: 0131-228 4040

ACTORS ALLIANCE
(CPMA Member) *18 Performers. Contact: By Post*
Commercials. Corporate. Film. Stage. Television
Disney Place House, 14 Marshalsea Road
London SE1 1HL
e-mail: actors@actorsalliance.co.uk Tel/Fax: 020-7407 6028

ACTORS' CREATIVE TEAM
(CPMA Member)
Panther House
38 Mount Pleasant, London WC1X OAN
Website: www.actorscreativeteam.co.uk
e-mail: office@actorscreativeteam.co.uk
Fax: 020-7833 5086   Tel: 020-7278 3388

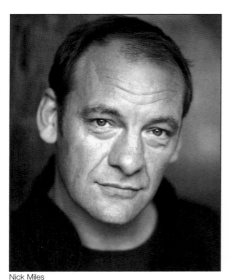

Nick Miles

Lucy-Jo Hudson

Joanna Page

Nigel Harman

chris
baker

photographer

www.chrisbakerphotographer.com

020 8441 3851

e: chrisbaker@photos2000.demon.co.uk

"Still the best!"

ACTORS DIRECT Ltd
Gainsborough House
109 Portland Street, Manchester M1 6DN
Website: www.actorsdirect.org.uk
e-mail: info@actorsdirect.org.uk
Mobile: 07985 760226   Tel/Fax: 0161-237 1904

ACTORS FILE The
(Personal Manager) (CPMA Member)
Contact: By Post/email
Spitfire Studios
63-71 Collier Street, London N1 9BE
Website: www.theactorsfile.co.uk
e-mail: mail@theactorsfile.co.uk
Fax: 020-7278 0364   Tel: 020-7278 0087

ACTORS' GROUP The (TAG)
(Personal Manager) (CPMA Member)
21-31 Oldham Street
Manchester M1 1JG
Website: www.theactorsgroup.co.uk
e-mail: enquiries@theactorsgroup.co.uk
    Tel/Fax: 0161-834 4466

ACTORS IN SCANDINAVIA
Tarkk'ampujankatu 14
00150 Helsinki, Finland
Website: www.actors.fi
e-mail: laura@actors.fi
Fax: 00 358 9 68 40 4422   Tel: 00 358 9 68 40 440

ACTORS INTERNATIONAL Ltd
Conway Hall
25 Red Lion Square, London WC1R 4RL
e-mail: mail@actorsinternational.co.uk
Fax: 020-7831 8319   Tel: 020-7242 9300

ACTORS IRELAND
Crescent Arts Centre
2-4 University Road, Belfast BT7 1NH
Website: www.actorsireland.net
e-mail: actorsireland@aol.com   Tel: 028-9024 8861

ACTOR'S TEMPLE The
13 Warren Street
London W1T 5LG
Website: www.actorstemple.com
e-mail: info@actorstemple.com
Mobile: 07771 734670   Tel: 020-3004 4537

ACTORS WORLD CASTING
13 Briarbank Road, London W13 0HH
Website: www.actors-world-production.com
e-mail: katherine@actors-world-production.com
    Tel: 020-8998 2579

ACTORUM Ltd
(Personal Manager)
9 Bourlet Close, London W1W 7BP
Website: www.actorum.com
e-mail: info@actorum.com
Fax: 020-7636 6975   Tel: 020-7636 6978

ADAMS Juliet MODELS & TALENT CASTINGS AGENCY
19 Gwynne House
Challice Way, London SW2 3RB
Website: www.julietadams.co.uk
e-mail: bookingdesk@julietadams.co.uk
Fax: 020-8671 9314   Tel: 020-8671 7673

Artist Management
adults   children

Byron's Management
Tel: 020 8444 4445
Fax: 020 8444 4040
byronsmanagement@aol.com
www.byronsmanagement.co.uk

AFFINITY MANAGEMENT
The Coach House, Down Park
Turners Hill Road
Crawley Down
West Sussex RH10 4HQ
e-mail: jstephens@affinitymanagement.co.uk
Fax: 01342 715800   Tel: 01342 715275

AGENCY Ltd The
Contact: Teri Hayden
47 Adelaide Road
Dublin 2, Ireland
Website: www.the-agency.ie
e-mail: admin1@tagency.ie
Fax: 00 353 1 6760052   Tel: 00 353 1 6618535

AGENCY PLANITOLOGY
Studio G7, Shakespeare Business Centre
245A Coldharbour Lane, London SW9 8RR
Website: www.agencyplanitology.co.uk
e-mail: info@agencyplanitology.co.uk
Fax: 020-7326 5768   Tel: 020-7733 2995

AHA
(See HOWARD Amanda ASSOCIATES Ltd)

AIM (ASSOCIATED INTERNATIONAL MANAGEMENT)
(PMA Member)
Fairfax House, Fulwood Place, London WC1V 6HU
Website: www.aimagents.com
e-mail: info@aimagents.com
Fax: 020-7242 0810   Tel: 020-7831 9709

Reece Dinsdale

Linda John-Pierre

ALANDER AGENCY
10 Ingram Close, Stanmore
Middlesex HA7 4EW   Tel: 020-8954 7685

ALEXANDER PERSONAL MANAGEMENT Ltd
Pinewood Studios, Pinewood Road
Iver Heath, Bucks SL0 0NH
Website: www.apmassociates.net
e-mail: apm@apmassociates.net
Fax: 01753 639205   Tel: 01753 639204

ALL TALENT UK
Contact: Kay Gannon, Sonia Scott Mackay
By Post/email/Telephone
Accepts Showreels/Voicereels
2 Agents represent 40 Performers. Film. Modelling.
Television. Voice Overs. Walk-on & Supporting Artists
Central Chambers
93 Hope Street, Glasgow G2 6LD
Website: www.alltalentuk.co.uk
e-mail: enquiries@alltalentuk.co.uk
Fax: 0141-221 8883   Tel: 0141-221 8887

ALLSORTS AGENCY
Suite 1 & 2 Marlborough Business Centre
96 George Lane, London E18 1AD
Website: www.allsortsagency.com
e-mail: bookings@allsortsagency.com
Fax: 020-8989 5600   Tel: 020-8989 0500

ALLSORTS DRAMA FOR CHILDREN
(In Association with Sasha Leslie Management)
34 Pember Road
London NW10 5LS
e-mail: sasha@allsortsdrama.com   Tel/Fax: 020-8969 3249

ALLSTARS CASTING
Apartment 4
66 Hope Street, Liverpool L1 9BZ
Website: www.allstarsweb.co.uk
e-mail: allstarsweb@hotmail.co.uk
Mobile: 07739 359737   Tel/Fax: 0151-476 1135

ALPHA PERSONAL MANAGEMENT Ltd
(Personal Manager) (CPMA Member)
Studio B4, 3 Bradbury Street, London N16 8JN
Website: www.alphaactors.com
e-mail: alpha@alphaactors.com
Fax: 020-7241 2410   Tel: 020-7241 0077

ALRAUN Anita REPRESENTATION
(PMA Member)
Contact: By Post (SAE)
5th Floor, 28 Charing Cross Road
London WC2H 0DB
e-mail: anita@cjagency.demon.co.uk
Fax: 020-7379 6865   Tel: 020-7379 6840

ALTARAS Jonathan ASSOCIATES Ltd
(PMA Member)
11 Garrick Street
Covent Garden, London WC2E 9AR
e-mail: info@jaa.ndirect.co.uk
Fax: 020-7836 6066   Tel: 020-7836 8722

ALVAREZ MANAGEMENT
(Personal Manager)
Contact: By Post
1 Agent represents 48 Performers
Commercials. Corporate. Film. Musicals. Singers. Stage
Television. Voice Overs
33 Ludlow Way
London N2 0JZ
e-mail: sga@alvarezmanagement.fsnet.co.uk
          Tel: 020-8883 2206

ALW ASSOCIATES
1 Grafton Chambers
Grafton Place
London NW1 1LN
e-mail: alw_carolpaul@talktalk.net
Fax: 020-7813 1398   Tel: 020-7388 7018

A M ENTERTAINMENTS
Specialising in Stand-up Comedians who Act
Suite 1, Townsend House
22-25 Dean Street, London W1D 3RY
e-mail: hilsjago@amentertainments.com
Mobile: 07970 524234   Tel: 020-7734 4588

AMBER PERSONAL MANAGEMENT Ltd
(PMA Member)
28 St Margaret's Chambers
5 Newton Street, Manchester M1 1HL
Website: www.amberltd.co.uk
e-mail: info@amberltd.co.uk
Fax: 0161-228 0235   Tel: 0161-228 0236
London   Tel: 020-7734 7887

AMC MANAGEMENT
Contact: Anna McCorquodale
31 Parkside
Welwyn
Herts AL6 9DQ
e-mail: anna@amcmanagement.co.uk
Fax: 01483 718669   Tel: 01483 714652

AMCK MANAGEMENT Ltd
103 Westbourne Studios
242 Acklam Road
Notting Hill
London W10 5JJ
Website: www.amck.tv
e-mail: info@amck.tv
Fax: 020-7524 7789   Tel: 020-7524 7788

AMERICAN AGENCY The
Contact: By Post
3 Agents represent 70-80 Performers. Commercials
Corporate. Film. Musicals. Television
Voice Overs (American)
14 Bonny Street, London NW1 9PG
Website: www.americanagency.tv
e-mail: americanagency@btconnect.com
Fax: 020-7482 4666   Tel: 020-7485 8883

ANA (Actors Network Agency)
(Personal Manager) (CPMA Member)
55 Lambeth Walk, London SE11 6DX
Website: www.ana-actors.co.uk
e-mail: info@ana-actors.co.uk
Fax: 020-7735 8177   Tel: 020-7735 0999

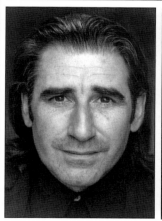

John Colclough Advisory

Practical independent guidance for actors and actresses

t: 020 8873 1763   **e:** john@johncolclough.org.uk   www.johncolclough.co.uk

ANDREWS Amanda AGENCY
30 Caverswall Road
Blythe Bridge
Stoke-on-Trent
Staffordshire ST11 9BG
e-mail: amanda.andrews.agency@tesco.net
Mobile: 07711 379770   Tel/Fax: 01782 393889

ANGEL Susan & FRANCIS Kevin Ltd
(PMA Member)
Contact: By Post
1st Floor
12 D'Arblay Street
London W1F 8DU
e-mail: agents@angelandfrancis.co.uk
Fax: 020-7437 1712   Tel: 020-7439 3086

ANTONY Christopher ASSOCIATES
The Old Dairy
164 Thames Road
London W4 3QS
Website: www.christopherantony.co.uk
e-mail: info@christopherantony.co.uk
Fax: 020-8742 8066   Tel: 020-8994 9952

A.P.M. ASSOCIATES (Linda French)
(See ALEXANDER PERSONAL MANAGEMENT Ltd)

ARAENA/COLLECTIVE
10 Bramshaw Gardens
South Oxhey
Herts WD19 6XP   Tel/Fax: 020-8428 0037

ARC ENTERTAINMENTS
Contact: By email.
1 Agent represents 300 Active Performers
10 Church Lane
Redmarshall, Stockton on Tees
Cleveland TS21 1EP
Website: www.arcents.co.uk
e-mail: arcents@hotmail.com   Tel: 01740 631292

ARCADIA ASSOCIATES
18B Vicarage Gate
London W8 4AA
e-mail: info.arcadia@btopenworld.com
                    Tel/Fax: 020-7937 0264

ARENA ENTERTAINMENT CONSULTANTS
Corporate Entertainment
Regent's Court
39 Harrogate Road
Leeds LS7 3PD
Website: www.arenaentertainment.co.uk
e-mail: info@arenaentertainment.co.uk
Fax: 0113-239 2016   Tel: 0113-239 2222

ARENA PERSONAL MANAGEMENT Ltd
(Co-operative)
Room 11
East Block
Panther House
38 Mount Pleasant
London WC1X 0AP
Website: www.arenapmltd.co.uk
e-mail: arenapmltd@aol.com   Tel/Fax: 020-7278 1661

A R G (ARTISTS RIGHTS GROUP Ltd)
(PMA Member)
4 Great Portland Street
London W1W 8PA
e-mail: argall@argtalent.com
Fax: 020-7436 6700   Tel: 020-7436 6400

ARGYLE ASSOCIATES
(Personal Manager)
Contact: Richard Argyle. By Post (SAE)
St John's Buildings
43 Clerkenwell Road
London EC1M 5RS
e-mail: argyle.associates@virgin.net
Fax: 0871 4336130   Tel: 020-7608 2095

ARTIST MANAGEMENT UK Ltd
PO Box 96
Liverpool L9 8WY
Website: www.artistmanagementuk.com
e-mail: chris@artistmanagementuk.com
Mobile: 07948 793552   Tel: 0151-523 6222

ARTS MANAGEMENT
First Floor
10 Goddard Place
Maidenbower
West Sussex RH10 7HR
Website: www.artsmanagement.co.uk
e-mail: artsmanagementltd@hotmail.com
Mobile: 07764 801167   Tel: 01293 885746

ARUN Jonathan Ltd
Studio 9
33 Stannary Street
London SE11 4AA
e-mail: jonathan@jonathanarun.com
Fax: 020-8249 0310   Tel: 020-7840 0123

ASHCROFT Sharron MANAGEMENT Ltd
Dean Clough Mills
Halifax HX3 5AX
Website: www.sharronashcroft.com
e-mail: info@sharronashcroft.com
Fax: 01422 343417   Tel: 01422 343949

AM LONDON

ACTORS HEADSHOTS

SIMON PEGG

CONNIE FISHER

JEREMY EDWARDS

JOHN BARROWMAN

CATHERINE TATE

PETER SERAFINOWICZ

HOLLY DAVIDSON

JAMES SUTTON

MODEL, DANCE & PERFORMER PORTFOLIOS

WWW.AM-LONDON.COM

PHOTOGRAPHERS CLAIRE ALEXANDER & CASEY MOORE

 STUDIO: 020 7193 1868   MOBILE: 07974 188 105

ASQUITH & HORNER
(Personal Manager)
Contact: By Post (SAE)
The Studio, 14 College Road
Bromley, Kent BR1 3NS
Fax: 020-8313 0443   Tel: 020-8466 5580

ASSOCIATED ARTS
Designers. Directors. Lighting Designers
8 Shrewsbury Lane
London SE18 3JF
Website: www.associated-arts.co.uk
e-mail: karen@associated-arts.co.uk
Fax: 020-8856 8189   Tel: 020-8856 4958

ASSOCIATED SPEAKERS
Lecturers & Celebrity Speakers
24A Park Road
Hayes, Middlesex UB4 8JN   Tel: 020-8848 9048

ASTRAL ACTORS MANAGEMENT
7 Greenway Close
London NW9 5AZ
Website: www.astralactors.com
e-mail: info@astralactors.com   Tel: 020-8728 2782

AVALON MANAGEMENT GROUP Ltd
4A Exmoor Street
London W10 6BD
Website: www.avalonuk.com
e-mail: enquiries@avalonuk.com
Fax: 020-7598 7300   Tel: 020-7598 8000

AVENUE ARTISTES Ltd
PO Box 1573
Southampton S016 3XS
Website: www.avenueartistes.com
e-mail: info@avenueartistes.com   Tel: 023-8076 0930

AWA - ANDREA WILDER AGENCY
23 Cambrian Drive
Colwyn Bay, Conwy LL28 4SL
Website: www.awagency.co.uk
e-mail: casting@awagency.co.uk
Fax: 07092 249314   Mobile: 07919 202401

AXM
(Actors' Exchange Management)
(Co-operative) (PMA Member)
308 Panther House
38 Mount Pleasant
London WC1X 0AN
Website: www.axmgt.com
e-mail: info@axmgt.com
Fax: 020-7837 7215   Tel: 020-7837 3304

BALLROOM, LONDON THEATRE OF
Ballroom/Social Dancers for Film/TV/Theatre
24 Montana Gardens
Sutton
Surrey SM1 4FP
Website: www.londontheatreofballroom.com
e-mail: office@londontheatreofballroom.com
Mobile: 07958 784462   Tel: 020-8722 8798

B A M ASSOCIATES
Benets Cottage
Dolberrow
Churchill, Bristol BS25 5NT
Website: www.ebam.tv
e-mail: casting@ebam.tv   Tel: 01934 852942

BANANAFISH MANAGEMENT
85-89 Duke Street
Liverpool L1 5AP
Website: www.bananafish.co.uk
e-mail: info@bananafish.co.uk
Mobile: 07974 206622   Tel: 0151-324 2222

BARKER Gavin ASSOCIATES Ltd
(PMA Member)
Contact: Gavin Barker, Michelle Burke
2d Wimpole Street
London W1G 0EB
Website: www.gavinbarkerassociates.co.uk
e-mail: steven@gavinbarkerassociates.co.uk
Fax: 020-7499 3777   Tel: 020-7499 4777

BASHFORD Simon
(See GLOBAL ARTISTS)

B.A.S.I.C./JD AGENCY
3 Rushden House
Tatlow Road
Glenfield
Leicester LE3 8ND
e-mail: jonny.dallas@ntlworld.com   Tel/Fax: 0116-287 9594

BELCANTO LONDON ACADEMY/BLA MANAGEMENT
Children & Adults
Performance House
20 Passey Place
Eltham, London SE9 5DQ
e-mail: agent@belcantolondonacademy.com
Fax: 020-8850 9944   Tel: 020-8850 9888

BELFRAGE Julian ASSOCIATES
(PMA Member)
Adam House
14 New Burlington Street
London W1S 3BQ
Fax: 020-7287 8832   Tel: 020-7287 8544

BELL Olivia Ltd
(PMA Member)
Contact: By Post
2 Agents represent 100 Performers. Commercials. Film.
Musicals. Stage. Television
189 Wardour Street, London W1F 8ZD
e-mail: info@olivia-bell.co.uk
Fax: 020-7439 3485   Tel: 020-7439 3270

BENJAMIN Audrey AGENCY
278A Elgin Avenue
Maida Vale, London W9 1JR
e-mail: a.benjamin@btconnect.com
Fax: 020-7266 5480   Tel: 020-7289 7180

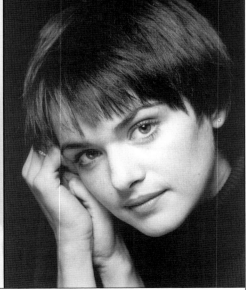

BERLIN ASSOCIATES
(PMA Member)
14 Floral Street
London WC2E 9DH
Website: www.berlinassociates.com
e-mail: agents@berlinassociates.com
Fax: 020-7632 5296   Tel: 020-7836 1112

BETTS Jorg ASSOCIATES
(PMA Member)
Gainsborough House
81 Oxford Street
London W1D 2EU
e-mail: agents@jorgbetts.com
Fax: 020-7903 5301   Tel: 020-7903 5300

BILLBOARD PERSONAL MANAGEMENT
Unit 5
11 Mowll Street
London SW9 6BG
Website: www.billboardpm.com
e-mail: billboardpm@btconnect.com
Fax: 020-7793 0426   Tel: 020-7735 9956

BILLY MARSH DRAMA Ltd
(Actors & Actresses)
(See MARSH Billy DRAMA Ltd)

BIRD AGENCY
(Personal Performance Manager)
Birkbeck Centre, Birkbeck Road
Sidcup, Kent DA14 4DE
Fax: 020-8308 1370   Tel: 020-8308 6994

BLOND Rebecca ASSOCIATES
69A Kings Road
London SW3 4NX
e-mail: info@rebecccablondassociates.com
Fax: 020-7351 4600   Tel: 020-7351 4100

BLOOMFIELDS MANAGEMENT
(PMA Member)
77 Oxford Street
London W1D 2ES
Website: www.bloomfieldsmanagement.com
e-mail: emma@bloomfieldsmanagement.com
Fax: 020-7659 2101   Tel: 020-7659 2001

BLUE STAR ASSOCIATES
Apartment 8
132 Charing Cross Road
London WC2H 0LA
Website: www.barriestacey.com
e-mail: hopkinstacey@aol.com
Fax: 020-7836 2949   Tel: 020-7836 6220

BLUE WAND MANAGEMENT
(Personal Manager)
Contact: By Post/email/Telephone
*Accepts Showreels. Commercials. Corporate. Dancers. Film.
Modelling. Musicals. Singers. Stage. Television. Voice Overs.
Walk-on & Supporting Artists*
2nd Floor, 12 Weltje Road
Hammersmith, London W6 9TG
e-mail: bluewand@btinternet.com   Tel: 020-8741 2038

BMA MODELS
346 High Street
Marlow House
Berkhamsted, Herts HP4 1HT
Website: www.bmamodels.com
e-mail: info@bmamodels.com
Fax: 01442 879879   Tel: 01442 878878

BODENS AGENCY
(Personal Manager)
Contact: Adam Boden. By Post/email
3 Agents represent 520 Performers
*Children. Commercials. Television. Walk-on & Supporting
Artists*
Bodens Studios & Agency
99 East Barnet Road
New Barnet, Herts EN4 8RF
Website: www.bodensagency.com
e-mail: info@bodensagency.com
Fax: 020-8449 5212   Tel: 020-8447 0909

BOSS CREATIVE ENTERTAINMENT
Top Floor
81 Overhill Road
London SE22 0PQ
Website: www.bosscreativeentertainment.com
e-mail: enquiries@bosscreativeentertainment.com
Fax: 020-8516 1867   Tel: 020-8299 0478

BOSS MODEL MANAGEMENT Ltd
Half Moon Chambers
Chapel Walk
Manchester M2 1HN
Website: www.bossmodelmanagement.co.uk
e-mail: info@bossmodels.co.uk   Tel: 0161-834 3403

BOYCE Sandra MANAGEMENT
(PMA Member)
1 Kingsway House, Albion Road
London N16 0TA
Website: www.sandraboyce.com
e-mail: info@sandraboyce.com
Fax: 020-7241 2313   Tel: 020-7923 0606

Steve Lawton

PHOTOGRAPHY LONDON

07973 307487

www.stevelawton.com

Student rates

Steven Webb, Gerard McCarthy, Helen Koya

Kerry Ellis, Robert Kazinsky, Natalie Anderson

Trey Farley, Natalie Cox, Adam-Jon Fiorentino

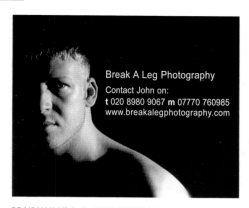

Break A Leg Photography
Contact John on:
t 020 8980 9067 **m** 07770 760985
www.breakalegphotography.com

BRAIDMAN Michelle ASSOCIATES Ltd
(PMA Member)
2 Futura House
169 Grange Road
London SE1 3BN
e-mail: info@braidman.com
Fax: 020-7231 4634   Tel: 020-7237 3523

BRAITHWAITE'S THEATRICAL AGENCY
8 Brookshill Avenue
Harrow Weald
Middlesex HA3 6RZ   Tel: 020-8954 5638

BREAK A LEG MANAGEMENT Ltd
Units 2/3 The Precinct
Packington Square
London N1 7UP
Website: www.breakalegman.com
e-mail: agency@breakalegman.com
Fax: 020-7359 3660   Tel: 020-7359 3594

BROADCASTING AGENCY
Unit 36
Pall Mall Deposit
124-128 Barlby Road
London W10 6BL
Website: www.broadcastingagency.co.uk
e-mail: info@broadcastingagency.co.uk
Fax: 020-8960 9689   Tel: 020-8960 5020

BROOD MANAGEMENT
Contact: By email
1 Agent represents 40 Performers
High Street Buildings, 134 Kirkdale, London SE26 4BB
Website: www.broodmanagement.com
e-mail: broodmanagement@aol.com
Fax: 020-8699 8787   Tel: 020-8699 1757

BROOK Dolly AGENCY
PO Box 5436, Dunmow CM6 1WW
e-mail: dollybrookcasting@btinternet.com
Fax: 01371 875996   Tel: 01371 875767

BROOK Valerie AGENCY
10 Sandringham Road, Cheadle Hulme, Cheshire SK8 5NH
e-mail: colinbrook@freenetname.co.uk
Fax: 0161-488 4206   Tel: 0161-486 1631

BROOKS Claude ENTERTAINMENTS
19 Sussex Place, Slough, Berks SL1 1NH
Fax: 01753 520424   Tel: 01753 520717

BROWN & SIMCOCKS
(PMA Member)
1 Bridgehouse Court, 109 Blackfriars Road, London SE1 8HW
e-mail: mail@brownandsimcocks.co.uk
Fax: 020-7928 1909   Tel: 020-7928 1229

BROWN Suzanna MANAGEMENT
Lower Ground
15-16 Margaret Street, London W1W 8RW
Website: www.suzannabrown.co.uk
e-mail: suzanna@suzannabrown.co.uk
Fax: 020-7907 1150   Tel: 020-7436 8506

BRUNSKILL MANAGEMENT Ltd
(Personal Manager) (PMA Member)
Contact: Aude Powell. By email
Accepts Showreels/Voicereels
Commercials. Corporate. Film. Musicals. Radio. Stage
Television. Voice Overs
Suite 8A, 169 Queen's Gate, London SW7 5HE
e-mail: contact@brunskill.com
Fax: 020-7589 9460   Tel: 020-7581 3388

The Courtyard, Edenhall
Penrith, Cumbria CA11 8ST
Fax: 01768 881850   Tel: 01768 881430

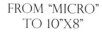

BSA Ltd
(See HARRISON Penny BSA Ltd)

BSA MANAGEMENT
First Floor
75 Brownlow Road, London N11 2BN
Website: www.bsa-management.co.uk
e-mail: info@bsa-management.co.uk   Tel: 020-3240 1064

BUCHANAN Bronia ASSOCIATES Ltd
(PMA Member)
First Floor, 23 Tavistock Street
London WC2E 7NX
Website: www.buchanan-associates.co.uk
e-mail: info@buchanan-associates.co.uk
Fax: 020-7379 5560   Tel: 020-7395 1400

BURNETT GRANGER CROWTHER Ltd
(PMA Member)
Contact: Barry Burnett, Lindsay Granger, Lizanne Crowther
3 Clifford Street, London W1S 2LF
Website: www.bgcltd.org
e-mail: associates@bgcltd.org
Fax: 020-7287 3239   Tel: 020-7437 8008

BWH AGENCY Ltd The
(PMA Member)
Contact: By Post/email. Accepts Showreels. 4 Agents
Barley Mow Business Centre
10 Barley Mow Passage, Chiswick, London W4 4PH
Website: www.thebwhagency.co.uk
e-mail: info@thebwhagency.co.uk
Fax: 020-8996 1662   Tel: 020-8996 1661

BYRON'S MANAGEMENT
(Personal Manager)
Contact: By Post/email
Accepts Showreels
Children. Commercials. Corporate. Dancers. Film. Musicals.
Singers. Stage. Television
76 St James Lane
Muswell Hill
London N10 3DF
Website: www.byronsmanagement.co.uk
e-mail: byronsmanagement@aol.com
Fax: 020-8444 4040   Tel: 020-8444 4445

C.A. ARTISTES MANAGEMENT
26-28 Hammersmith Grove, London W6 7BA
Website: www.caartistes.com
e-mail: casting@caartistes.com   Tel: 020-7967 8067

CAM
(Personal Manager) (PMA Member)
Contact: By Post
First Floor, 55-59 Shaftesbury Avenue
London W1D 6LD
Website: www.cam.co.uk
e-mail: tn@cam.co.uk
Fax: 020-7734 3205   Tel: 020-7292 0600

CAMBELL JEFFREY MANAGEMENT
Set, Costume, Lighting Directors
11A Greystone Court, South Street
Eastbourne BN21 4LP
e-mail: cambell@theatricaldesigners.co.uk
Fax: 01323 411373   Tel: 01323 411444

CAMPBELL Alison MODEL & PROMOTION AGENCY
381 Beersbridge Road
Belfast BT5 5DT
Website: www.alisoncampbellmodels.com
e-mail: info@alisoncampbellmodels.com
Fax: 028-9080 9808   Tel: 028-9080 9809

CANONGATE
(Personal Manager)
Contact: Shona Campbell. By email Accepts Showreels.
1 Agent represents 5 Performers Commercials. Modelling.
Radio. Television
9 Waters Close, Leith, Edinburgh EH6 6RB
Website: www.canongate.com
e-mail: shona@canongate.com
Fax: 0131-555 2021   Tel: 0131-555 4455

CAPITAL VOICES
Contact: Anne Skates
Film. Session Singers. Stage. Studio. Television
PO Box 364
Esher, Surrey KT10 9XZ
Website: www.capitalvoices.com
e-mail: capvox@aol.com
Fax: 01372 466229   Tel: 01372 466228

Claire Murphy

Paris Jefferson
PHOTOGRAPHER
PARISJEFFERSON.COM
07876 586601

CARAVANSERAI ASSOCIATES Ltd
Unit 30
Grand Union Centre
West Row, London W10 5AS
e-mail: info@cserai.co.uk   Tel: 05601 534892

CARDIFF CASTING
(CPMA Member) Now Known As OREN
Chapter Arts Centre
Market Road
Cardiff CF5 1QE
Website: www.oren20.com
e-mail: admin@oren20.com   Tel: 029-2023 3321

CAREY Roger ASSOCIATES
(Personal Manager) (PMA Member)
Suite 909
The Old House
Shepperton Film Studios
Studios Road
Shepperton
Middlesex TW17 0QD
e-mail: info@rogercarey.f2s.com
Fax: 01932 569602   Tel: 01932 582890

CARNEY Jessica ASSOCIATES
(Personal Manager) (PMA Member)
4th Floor
23 Golden Square
London W1F 9JP
e-mail: info@jcarneyassociates.co.uk
Fax: 020-7434 4173   Tel: 020-7434 4143

CAROUSEL EVENTS
Entertainment for Corporate & Private Events
Ivy House, 35 High Street
Bushey, Herts WD23 1BD
Website: www.carouselevents.co.uk
e-mail: enquiries@carouselevents.co.uk
Fax: 020-8421 9537   Tel: 020-8421 7172

CARR Norrie AGENCY
Holborn Studios
49-50 Eagle Wharf Road
London N1 7ED
Website: www.norriecarr.com
e-mail: info@norriecarr.com
Fax: 020-7253 1772   Tel: 020-7253 1771

CASAROTTO MARSH Ltd
Film Technicians
Waverley House
7-12 Noel Street
London W1F 8GQ
Website: www.casarotto.co.uk
e-mail: casarottomarsh@casarotto.co.uk
Fax: 020-7287 9128   Tel: 020-7287 4450

CASTAWAY ACTORS AGENCY
30-31 Wicklow Street
Dublin 2, Ireland
Website: www.irish-actors.com
e-mail: castaway@clubi.ie
Fax: 00 353 1 6719133   Tel: 00 353 1 6719264

DIRECT PERSONAL MANAGEMENT

formerly Direct Line Personal Management
Personal Manager: Daphne Franks

e-mail: daphne.franks@directpm.co.uk
website: www.directpm.co.uk

LONDON
St. John's House
16 St. John's Vale
London SE8 4EN
Tel/fax 020 8694 1788

LEEDS
Park House
62 Lidgett Lane
Leeds LS8 1PL
Tel/fax 0113 266 4036

CASTCALL
Casting & Consultancy Service
106 Wilsden Avenue, Luton LU1 5HR
Website: www.castcall.co.uk
e-mail: casting@castcall.co.uk
Fax: 01582 480736   Tel: 01582 456213

CASTING DEPARTMENT The
277 Chiswick Village
London W4 3DF
Website: www.thecastingdept.co.uk
e-mail: thecastingdpt@aol.com   Tel: 020-8582 5523

CASTING SUITE AGENCY The
8-10 Lower James Street
London W1F 9EL
Website: www.thecastingsuite.com
e-mail: agency@thecastingsuite.com
Fax: 020-7494 0803   Tel: 020-7534 5757

CASTING UK
26-34 Emerald Street
London WC1N 3QA
Website: www.castinguk.com
e-mail: info@castinguk.com   Tel: 020-7400 1250

CAVAT AGENCY
16A Mook Hill, South Croydon, Surrey CR2 0LA
Website: www.cavatagency.co.uk
Mobile: 07764 673916   Tel: 020-8651 1099

C B A INTERNATIONAL
Contact: Cindy Brace
166 Waverley Avenue, Twickenham TW2 6DL
e-mail: cba_office@yahoo.co.uk   Mobile: 07789 991032

31 rue Milton, 75009 Paris, France
Website: www.cindy-brace.com
e-mail: c_b_a@club-internet.fr
Fax: 00 33 148 74 51 42   Tel: 00 33 145 26 33 42

C C A MANAGEMENT
(Personal Manager) (PMA Member)
Contact: By Post
Actors. Technicians
Garden Level
32 Charlwood Street
London SW1V 2DY
e-mail: actors@ccamanagement.co.uk
Fax: 020-7630 7376   Tel: 020-7630 6303

CCM
(CPMA Member)
Panther House
38 Mount Pleasant
London WC1X 0AP
Website: www.ccmactors.com
e-mail: casting@ccmactors.com   Tel: 020-7278 0507

CDA
(PMA Member)
Contact: Belinda Wright
125 Gloucester Road
London SW7 4TE
e-mail: cda@cdalondon.com
Fax: 020-7373 1110   Tel: 020-7373 3323

CELEBRITY GROUP The
13 Montagu Mews South
London W1H 7ER
Website: www.celebrity.co.uk
e-mail: info@celebrity.co.uk   Tel: 0871 2501234

CENTRAL LINE
(Personal Manager) (CPMA Member)
Contact: By Post
11 East Circus Street
Nottingham NG1 5AF
Website: www.the-central-line.co.uk
e-mail: centralline@btconnect.com   Tel: 0115-941 2937

Picture Credits Sinitta *actresss and singer*, Natalie Palys *Madness of King George*, Sir Richard Branson *Duo Magazine*, Andy Hamilton *Whitbread*, Anabel Kutay *ballerina and dancer Phantom of the Opera*, Miss Pinto and Rat, Benjamin and Rebecca Green *dancers*

Will C specialises in actors, actresses and personalities in advertising, editorial, film and television. He has been principal photographer on over 30 major films and 40 commercials. Actors and actresses portraits can be taken in our fully equipped film and digital studio in NW2 - just 15 minutes from Marble Arch or Baker Street.

Tokyo • New York • Amsterdam • Paris • London

DAVID BONNICK

Gemma Mount Photography

Student Discount Available

Tel: 07976 824923

www.gemmamountphotography.com

Craig Sugden Photography

www.craigsugden.com

07967 380568

Studio/location/student rates

St Martin's Court, London WC2N 4AL

1 min from L Sq tube

CENTRE STAGE AGENCY
(Personal Manager) (PMA Member)
Contact: By email
Accepts Showreels
50 Performers
Commercials. Film. Singers. Television
7 Rutledge Terrace
South Circular Road, Dublin 8, Ireland
e-mail: geraldinecenterstage@eircom.net
Tel/Fax: 00 353 1 4533599

CENTURY MODELS
Unit D, Well House
23A Benwell Road, London N7 7BL
Website: www.centurym.com
e-mail: models@centurym.com
Mobile: 07984 055638   Tel: 020-7619 8235

CHALICE PERSONAL MANAGEMENT Ltd
Temple Court
Cathedral Road
Cardiff CF11 9HA
Website: www.chalicepersonalmanagement.co.uk
e-mail: agent@chalicepersonalmanagement.co.uk
Fax: 029-2078 6666   Tel: 029-2078 6537

PO Box 59291
London NW3 9JW
e-mail: gemma@chalicepersonalmanagement.co.uk
Mobile: 07591 503980

CHAMBERS MANAGEMENT
23 Long Lane
Barbican, London EC1A 9HL
Website: www.chambersmgt.co.uk
e-mail: hannah@chambersmgt.com
Fax: 020-7796 3676   Tel: 020-7796 3588

CHAPMAN AGENCY
BSA
Millennium Point
Curzon Street
Birmingham B4 7XG
e-mail: chapmanagency@bsa.bcu.ac.uk
Fax: 0121-331 7221   Tel: 0121-331 7220

CHARLESWORTH Peter & ASSOCIATES
68 Old Brompton Road
London SW7 3LQ
e-mail: info@petercharlesworth.co.uk
Fax: 020-7589 2922   Tel: 020-7581 2478

CHATTO & LINNIT Ltd
123A Kings Road, London SW3 4PL
e-mail: info@chattolinnit.com
Fax: 020-7352 3450   Tel: 020-7352 7722

CHP (CHARLOTTE HAMILTON PRODUCTIONS)
(Personal Manager)
Contact: By email
Comedians. Commercials. Corporate. Film. Presenters
Radio. Television. Writers
Website: www.chproductions.org.uk
e-mail: charlotte@chproductions.org.uk
Mobile: 07976 560580

Robert Kilroy-Silk

Ruth Shephard

Anthony Marsh

Michelle C

Howard Sayer Photographer
www.howardsayer.com   m: 07860 559891   howard@howardsayer.com

CHRYSTEL ARTS AGENCY
6 Eunice Grove, Chesham, Bucks HP5 1RL
e-mail: chrystelarts@waitrose.com
Mobile: 07799 605489   Tel/Fax: 01494 773336

CINEL GABRAN MANAGEMENT
(Personal Manager) (PMA Member)
Contact: By Post. Accepts Showreels
60 Performers
Commercials. Corporate. Film. Musicals. Presenters. Radio
Stage. Television. Voice Overs
PO Box 5163, Cardiff CF5 9BJ
Website: www.cinelgabran.co.uk
e-mail: info@cinelgabran.co.uk
Fax: 0845 0666601   Tel: 0845 0666605

PO Box 101, Newholm
Whitby, North Yorkshire YO21 3WT

CIRCUIT PERSONAL MANAGEMENT Ltd
Contact: By Post/email
Accepts Showreels
22 Performers
Commercials. Corporate. Film. Stage. Television
Suite 71 S.E.C.
Bedford Street, Shelton
Stoke-on-Trent, Staffs ST1 4PZ
Website: www.circuitpm.co.uk
e-mail: mail@circuitpm.co.uk
Fax: 01782 206821   Tel: 01782 285388

CIRCUS MANIACS AGENCY
Corporate. Physical Artistes
Office 8A
The Kingswood Foundation
Britannia Road
Kingswood, Bristol BS15 8DB
Website: www.circusmaniacsagency.com
e-mail: agency@circusmaniacs.com
Mobile: 07977 247287   Tel/Fax: 0117-947 7042

CITY ACTORS' MANAGEMENT
(Personal Manager) (CPMA Member)
Oval House
52-54 Kennington Oval
London SE11 5SW
Website: www.cityactors.co.uk
e-mail: info@cityactors.co.uk
Fax: 020-7820 0990   Tel: 020-7793 9888

C.K.K. ENTERTAINMENT
PO Box 24550
London E17 9FG
e-mail: ckk.entertainment@virgin.net
Fax: 020-7515 6373   Tel: 020-7531 6300

CLARENDON ARTIST MANAGEMENT
6 Old Lodge Place
St. Margarets
Twickenham TW1 1RQ
e-mail: info@clarendonam.com   Tel: 020-8831 7221

Established in 1995
JPA Management offers
personal management to
professional actors for work in
all aspects of the
entertainment industry
including Television, Film,
Theatre, Musical Theatre,
Radio & Commercials.

Visit our website:
www.jpamanagement.co.uk

Address: 30 Daws Hill Lane,
High Wycombe, HP11 1PW
Tel: 01494 520 978

CLARKE AND JONES Ltd
28 Fordwych Court
Shoot Up Hill, London NW2 3PH
e-mail: mail@clarkeandjones.plus.com
Fax: 0870 1313391   Tel: 020-8438 0185

CLASS - CARLINE LUNDON ASSOCIATES
25 Falkner Square
Liverpool L8 7NZ
e-mail: carline.lundon@ukonline.co.uk
    Mobile: 07853 248957

CLAYMAN Tony PROMOTIONS Ltd
Vicarage House
58-60 Kensington Church Street
London W8 4DB
Website: www.tonyclayman.com
e-mail: tony@tonyclayman.com
Fax: 020-7368 3338   Tel: 020-7368 3336

CLAYPOLE MANAGEMENT
PO Box 123 DL3 7WA
Website: www.claypolemanagement.co.uk
e-mail: info@claypolemanagement.co.uk
Fax: 0870 1334784   Tel: 0845 6501777

CLIC AGENCY
Rhoslwyn
Rhoslsaf, Nr. Caernarfon
Gwynedd LL54 7NF
Website: www.clicagency.co.uk
e-mail: clic@btinternet.com   Tel: 01286 831001

CLOUD NINE AGENCY
96 Tiber Gardens
Treaty Street
London N1 0XE
Website: www.cloudnineagency.co.uk
e-mail: cloudnineagency@blueyonder.co.uk
    Tel/Fax: 020-7278 0029

CMP MANAGEMENT
8-30 Galena Road
Hammersmith
London W6 0LT
e-mail: info@ravenscourt.net
Fax: 020-8741 1786   Tel: 020-8741 3400

COCHRANE Elspeth PERSONAL MANAGEMENT
(PMA Member)
Contact: Tony Barlow. By Post
Accepts Showreels
Commercials. Dancers. Film. Musicals. Singers. Stage
Television. Writers
16 Trinity Close
The Pavement, London SW4 0JD
e-mail: elspethcochrane@talktalk.net   Tel: 020-7622 3566

COLE KITCHENN PERSONAL MANAGEMENT Ltd
(PMA Member)
212 Strand
London WC2R 1AP
Website: www.colekitchenn.com
e-mail: stuart@colekitchenn.com
Fax: 020-7353 9639   Tel: 020-7427 5681

COLLINS Shane ASSOCIATES
(PMA Member)
11-15 Betterton Street
Covent Garden
London WC2H 9BP
Website: www.shanecollins.co.uk
e-mail: info@shanecollins.co.uk
Fax: 0870 460 1983   Tel: 020-7470 8864

COLLIS MANAGEMENT
182 Trevelyan Road
London SW17 9LW
e-mail: marilyn@collismanagement.co.uk
Fax: 020-8682 0973   Tel: 020-8767 0196

COMEDY CLUB Ltd The
2nd Floor
28-31 Moulsham Street
Chelmsford
Essex CM2 0HX
Website: www.hahaheehee.com
e-mail: info@hahaheehee.com
Fax: 01245 255507   Tel: 0870 0425656

COMIC VOICE MANAGEMENT
2nd Floor
28-31 Moulsham Street
Chelmsford, Essex CM2 0HX
Website: www.comicvoice.com
e-mail: info@comicvoice.com
Fax: 01245 255507   Tel: 0870 0425656

COMMERCIAL AGENCY The
(See TCA)

CONTI Italia AGENCY Ltd
Contact: By Post/Telephone
23 Goswell Road, London EC1M 7AJ
e-mail: agency@italiaconti.co.uk
Fax: 020-7253 1430   Tel: 020-7608 7500

CONWAY Clive CELEBRITY PRODUCTIONS Ltd
32 Grove Street
Oxford OX2 7JT
Website: www.celebrityproductions.info
e-mail: info@celebrityproductions.org
Fax: 01865 514409   Tel: 01865 514830

CONWAY VAN GELDER GRANT Ltd
(Personal Manager) (PMA Member)
3rd Floor, 18-21 Jermyn Street, London SW1Y 6HP
Website: www.conwayvangeldergrant.com
Fax: 020-7287 1940   Tel: 020-7287 0077

COOKE Howard ASSOCIATES
(PMA Member)
Contact: Howard Cooke. By Post
2 Agents represent 50 Performers
Commercials. Film. Stage. Television
19 Coulson Street, Chelsea, London SW3 3NA
Fax: 020-7591 0155   Tel: 020-7591 0144

COOPER Tommy AGENCY The
Comedy. Magicians
8 Chapman Square, Harrowgate HG1 2SL
Website: www.tommycooperremembered.co.uk
      Mobile: 07860 290437

CORNER Clive ASSOCIATES
Contact: Duncan Stratton
By Post. Accepts Showreels
3 Agents represent 80 Performers
Commercials. Film. Musicals. Stage. Television
3 Bainbridge Close
Ham, Middlesex TW10 5JJ
e-mail: cornerassociates@aol.com   Tel/Fax: 020-8332 1910

CORNISH Caroline MANAGEMENT Ltd
Technicians Only
12 Shinfield Street
London W12 0HN
Website: www.carolinecornish.co.uk
e-mail: carolinecornish@btconnect.com
Fax: 020-8743 7887   Tel: 020-8743 7337

COULSON Lou ASSOCIATES Ltd
(PMA Member)
1st Floor, 37 Berwick Street
London W1F 8RS
e-mail: info@loucoulson.co.uk
Fax: 020-7439 7569   Tel: 020-7734 9633

COULTER MANAGEMENT AGENCY Ltd
(PMA Member)
Contact: Anne Coulter
333 Woodlands Road, Glasgow G3 6NG
e-mail: cmaglasgow@btconnect.com
Fax: 0141-357 6676   Tel: 0141-357 6666

Icon Actors Management
Tel: **0161 273 3344** Fax: 0161 273 4567
Tanzaro House, Ardwick Green North, Manchester. M12 6FZ.
info@iconactors.net   www.iconactors.net

COVENT GARDEN MANAGEMENT
5 Denmark Street
London WC2H 8LP
Website: www.coventgardenmanagement.com
e-mail: agents@coventgardenmanagement.com
Fax: 020-7240 8409   Tel: 020-7240 8400

CPA MANAGEMENT
The Studios
219B North Street
Romford, Essex RM1 4QA
Website: www.cpamanagement.co.uk
e-mail: lindsay@cpamanagement.co.uk
Fax: 01708 766077   Tel: 01708 766444

CRAWFORDS
PO Box 44394
London SW20 0YP
Website: www.crawfords.tv
e-mail: cr@wfords.com
Fax: 020-3258 5037   Tel: 020-8947 9999

CREATIVE MEDIA MANAGEMENT
(PMA Member)
No Actors. Film, TV & Theatre Technical Personnel only
Ealing Studios, Ealing Green
London W5 5EP
Website: www.creativemediamanagement.com
e-mail: enquiries@creativemediamanagement.com
Fax: 020-8566 5554   Tel: 020-8584 5363

CREDITS ACTORS AGENCY Ltd
29 Lorn Road
London SW9 0AB
e-mail: credits@actors29.freeserve.co.uk
                                     Tel: 020-7737 0735

CRESCENT MANAGEMENT
(Personal Manager) (CPMA Member)
10 Barley Mow Passage
Chiswick, London W4 4PH
e-mail: mail@crescentmanagement.co.uk
Fax: 020-8987 0207   Tel: 020-8987 0191

CROWD PULLERS
Street Performers
14 Somerset Gardens, London SE13 7SY
e-mail: jhole@crowdpullers.co.uk
Fax: 020-8469 2147   Tel: 020-8469 3900

CRUICKSHANK CAZENOVE Ltd
(PMA Member)
Contact: Sky Macaskill. By Post
Accepts Showreels
2 Agents
Choreographers. Designers. Directors
97 Old South Lambeth Road
London SW8 1XU
e-mail: office@cruickshankcazenove.com
Fax: 020-7582 6405   Tel: 020-7735 2933

CS MANAGEMENT
The Croft
7 Cannon Road
Southgate, London N14 7HE
Website: www.csmanagementuk.com
e-mail: carole@csmanagementuk.com
Fax: 020-8886 7555   Tel: 020-8886 4264

C.S.A.
(Christina Shepherd Advertising)
4th Floor
45 Maddox Street, London W1S 2PE
e-mail: csa@shepherdmanagement.co.uk
Fax: 020-7499 7535   Tel: 020-7499 7534

CSM (ARTISTS)
Contact: By Post
77 Oxford Street, London W1D 2ES

CURTIS BROWN GROUP Ltd
(PMA Member)
Haymarket House
28-29 Haymarke, London SW1Y 4SP
e-mail: actorsagents@curtisbrown.co.uk
Fax: 020-7393 4401   Tel: 020-7393 4400

DALY PEARSON ASSOCIATES
Contact: David Daly, Paul Pearson
586 King's Road, London SW6 2DX
Website: www.dalypearson.co.uk
e-mail: agent@dalypearson.co.uk
Fax: 020-7610 9512   Tel: 020-7384 1036

DALY PEARSON ASSOCIATES (MANCHESTER)
16 King Street, Knutsford WA16 6DL
Website: www.dalypearson.co.uk/manchester
e-mail: north@dalypearson.co.uk
Fax: 01565 755334   Tel: 01565 631999

BLUE WAND MANAGEMENT
The Agency for Actors, Dancers, Singers & Models

2nd Floor, 12 Weltje Road, Hammersmith, London W6 9TG
Tel/Fax: 020 8741 2038 Mobile: 07525 187468 E-mail: bluewand@btinternet.com

DALZELL & BERESFORD Ltd
26 Astwood Mews, London SW7 4DE
e-mail: mail@dbltd.co.uk
Fax: 020-7341 9412   Tel: 020-7341 9411

DANCERS
1 Charlotte Street, London W1T 1RD
Website: www.features.co.uk
e-mail: info@features.co.uk
Fax: 020-7636 1657   Tel: 020-7636 1473

DARRELL Emma MANAGEMENT
Directors. Producers. Writers
Hazelbank, 3 Chalfont Lane, Chorleywood, Herts WD3 5PR
e-mail: emma.mc@virgin.net
Fax: 01923 284064   Tel: 01923 284061

DAVID ARTISTES MANAGEMENT AGENCY Ltd The
26-28 Hammersmith Grove
London W6 7BA
Website: www.davidagency.net
e-mail: casting@davidagency.net   Tel: 020-7967 7001

DAVIS Chris MANAGEMENT Ltd
(PMA Member)
Tenbury House
36 Teme Street
Tenbury Wells
Worcestershire WR15 8AA
Website: www.cdm-ltd.com
e-mail: info@cdm-ltd.com
Fax: 01584 819076   Tel: 01584 819005

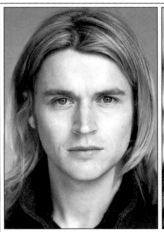

Lindsey Coulson

Martin Freeman

Adele Silva

Claire Grogan
P h o t o g r a p h y

020 7272 1845

mobile 07932 635381
www.clairegrogan.co.uk
student rates

DAVIS Lena, JOHN BISHOP ASSOCIATES
(Personal Manager)
Contact: By Post
2 Agents
Cotton's Farmhouse
Whiston Road
Cogenhoe, Northants NN7 1NL
e-mail: admin@cottonsfarmhouse.freeserve.co.uk
Tel: 01604 891487

DEALERS AGENCY BELFAST
22-31 Waring Street
Belfast BT1 2DX
Website: www.dealersagency.co.uk
e-mail: patrickduncan609@msn.com
Tel: 028-9043 6639   Tel: 028-9024 2726

DENMAN CASTING AGENCY
Contact: By Post/Telephone.
2 Agents represent 100+ Performers
Burgess House
Main Street, Farnsfield
Notts NG22 8EF   Tel/Fax: 01623 882272

DENMARK STREET MANAGEMENT
(Personal Manager) (CPMA Member)
Contact: By Post (SAE)
Suite 4, Clarendon Buildings
25 Horsell Road
Highbury N5 1XL
Website: www.denmarkstreet.net
e-mail: mail@denmarkstreet.net
Fax: 020-7607 8085   Tel: 020-7700 5200

DENNIS Lisa MANAGEMENT Ltd
Summit House
London Road
Bracknell RG12 2AQ
e-mail: agents@lisad.co.uk
Fax: 01344 643568   Tel: 01344 707342

DEREK'S HANDS AGENCY
Hand & Foot Modelling
26-28 Hammersmith Grove
London W6 7BA
Website: www.derekshands.com
e-mail: casting@derekshands.com   Tel: 020-8834 1609

de WOLFE Felix
(Personal Manager) (PMA Member)
Contact: By Post
Accepts Showreels
3 Agents
Film. Musicals. Radio. Stage. Television
Kingsway House, 103 Kingsway
London WC2B 6QX
e-mail: info@felixdewolfe.com
Fax: 020-7242 8119   Tel: 020-7242 5066

DIAMOND MANAGEMENT
(PMA Member)
31 Percy Street
London W1T 2DD
e-mail: agents@diman.co.uk
Fax: 020-7631 0500   Tel: 020-7631 0400

Personal Management

(Formerly known as Michael Garrett Associates)

Agents:
Simon Bashford
Michael Garrett
Niki Winterson

GLOBAL ARTISTS
23 Haymarket London SW1Y 4DG
Tel: 020 7839 4888 Fax: 020 7839 4555
email: info@globalartists.co.uk
www.globalartists.co.uk
www.theatricalagent.co.uk

Members of the Personal Managers' Association

Michael Garrett Associates Ltd. Registered No. 4404385
Registered Office: 23 Haymarket, London SW1Y 4DG

DIESTENFELD Lily
(Personal Manager for 50+ ages)
No unsolicited Mail/Calls from Actors
28B Alexandra Grove
London N12 8HG   Tel: 020-8446 5379

DIMPLES THEATRICAL ACADEMY
84 Kirkhall Lane
Leigh, Lancs WN7 5QQ
e-mail: info@dimples-models.com
Fax: 01942 262232   Tel: 01942 262012

DIRECT PERSONAL MANAGEMENT
(Personal Manager) (CPMA Member)
Contact: Daphne Franks
St John's House
16 St John's Vale
London SE8 4EN
Website: www.directpm.co.uk
e-mail: daphne.franks@directpm.co.uk
                                  Tel/Fax: 020-8694 1788
Park House
62 Lidgett Lane
Leeds LS8 1PL   Tel/Fax: 0113-266 4036

DOE John ASSOCIATES
26 Noko
3-6 Banister Road, London W10 4AR
Website: www.johndoeassociates.com
e-mail: johndoemgt@yahoo.co.uk
Mobile: 07957 114175   Tel: 020-8960 2848

DON CAPO ENTERTAINMENT PRODUCTIONS
Suite B
5 South Bank Terrace
Surbiton
Surrey KT6 6DG
Website: www.doncapo.com
e-mail: doncapoandco@aol.com
Mobile: 07787 995604   Tel/Fax: 020-8390 8535

DOUBLE ACT CELEBRITY LOOK ALIKES
PO Box 25574
London NW7 3GB
Website: www.double-act.co.uk
e-mail: info@double-act.co.uk
Fax: 020-8201 1795   Tel: 020-8381 0151

DOUBLEFVOICES
Singers
1 Hunters Lodge
Bodiam, East Sussex TN32 5UE
e-mail: rob@doublefvoices.com
Mobile: 07976 927764   Tel: 01580 830071

DOWNES PRESENTERS AGENCY
96 Broadway
Bexleyheath
Kent DA6 7DE
Website: www.presentersagency.com
e-mail: downes@presentersagency.com Tel: 020-8304 0541

DP MANAGEMENT
Contact: Danny Pellerini. By Post.
Accepts Showreels/Voicereels.
1 Agent represents 60 Performers
1 Euston Road
London NW1 2SA
e-mail: danny@dpmanagement.org
Fax: 020-7278 3466   Tel: 020-7843 4331

DQ MANAGEMENT
Suite 21, Kingsway House
134-140 Church Road
Hove
East Sussex BN3 2DL
Website: www.dqmanagement.com
e-mail: dq.management1@googlemail.com
Fax: 01273 779065   Tel: 01273 721221

DREW Bryan Ltd
(Personal Manager)
Contact: By Post
Mezzanine, Quadrant House
80-82 Regent Street
London W1B 5AU
e-mail: bryan@bryandrewltd.com
Fax: 020-7437 0561   Tel: 020-7437 2293

EARLE Kenneth PERSONAL MANAGEMENT
214 Brixton Road
London SW9 6AP
Website: www.entertainment-kennethearle.co.uk
e-mail: kennethearle@agents-uk.com
Fax: 020-7274 9529   Tel: 020-7274 1219

EARNSHAW Susi MANAGEMENT
(Personal Manager)
68 High Street
Barnet
Herts EN5 5SJ
Website: www.susiearnshaw.co.uk
e-mail: casting@susiearnshaw.co.uk
Fax: 020-8364 9618   Tel: 020-8441 5010

EDEN Shelly ASSOCIATES Ltd
The Old Factory
Minus One House
Lyttelton Road
London E10 5NQ
e-mail: shellyeden@aol.com   Tel/Fax: 020-8558 3536

EDLER Debbie MANAGEMENT Ltd (DEM)
Little Friars Cottage
Lombard Street
Eynsham
Oxon OX29 4HT
Website: www.demagency.co.uk
e-mail: info@demagency.co.uk   Tel: 01865 884203

EJA ASSOCIATES
150 Tooley Street
London SE1 2TU
e-mail: ejaassociates@aol.com
Mobile: 07891 632946   Tel: 020-7564 2688

EKA ACTOR MANAGEMENT
(Personal Manager)
Contact: Rebecca Keeley
By Post/email.
Accepts Showreels
6 Agents
Commercials. Film. Television. Voice Overs
The Warehouse Studios
Glaziers Lane
Culcheth
Warrington WA3 4AQ
Website: www.eka-agency.com
e-mail: castings@eka-agency.com
Fax: 01925 767563   Tel: 01925 761088

ELLIOTT AGENCY Ltd The
10 High Street
Shoreham-by-Sea BN43 5DA
Website: www.elliottagency.co.uk
e-mail: elliottagency@btconnect.com   Tel: 01273 454111

ELLIS Bill Ltd
(See A & B PERSONAL MANAGEMENT Ltd)

ELLITE MANAGEMENT
Contact: By Post/email
Accepts Showreels
3 Agents represent 40 Performers. Dancers
The Dancer
8 Peterson Road
Wakefield WF1 4EB
Website: www.elliteproductions.co.uk
e-mail: enquiries@ellitemanagement.co.uk
Mobile: 07957 631510   Tel: 0845 6525361

James Mann
Photographer
T: 07742814160   www.j-mann.com
Headshots, Publicity Shots, Production Stills

EMPTAGE HALLETT
(PMA Member)
14 Rathbone Place, London W1T 1HT
e-mail: mail@emptagehallett.co.uk
Fax: 020-7580 2748   Tel: 020-7436 0425

2nd Floor
3-5 The Balcony, Castle Arcade, Cardiff CF10 1BU
e-mail: claire.lincoln@emptagehallett.co.uk
Fax: 029-2034 4206   Tel: 029-2034 4205

ENGLISH Doreen '95
Contact: By Post/Telephone
4 Selsey Avenue
Aldwick, Bognor Regis
West Sussex PO21 2QZ   Tel/Fax: 01243 825968

EPSTEIN June ASSOCIATES
Contact: By Post
Flat 1, 62 Compayne Gardens, London NW6 3RY
e-mail: june@june-epstein-associates.co.uk
Fax: 020-7328 0684   Tel: 020-7328 0864

ESOTERIC ENTERTAINMENTS Ltd
Mystics. Psychics
PO Box 582, Rochester ME1 9LF
Website: www.esoteric-e.co.uk
e-mail: info@esoteric-e.co.uk   Tel: 01634 323376

ESSANAY
(Personal Manager) (PMA Member)
Contact: By Post
PO Box 44394, London SW20 0YP
e-mail: info@essanay.co.uk
Fax: 020-3258 5037   Tel: 020-8549 4472

ET-NIK-A PRIME MANAGEMENT & CASTINGS Ltd
Contact: Aldo Arcilla
By Post
Accepts Showreels/Voicereels
30 Great Portland Street
London W1W 8QU
Website: www.etnikapmc.com
e-mail: info@etnikapmc.com
Fax: 020-7299 3558   Tel: 020-7299 3555

ETHNICS ARTISTE AGENCY
86 Elphinstone Road
Walthamstow, London E17 5EX
e-mail: info@ethnicsaa.co.uk
Fax: 020-8523 4523   Tel: 020-8523 4242

EUROKIDS CASTING AGENCY
Contact: Rebecca Keeley. By Post/email
Accepts Showreels
6 Agents
Children. Commercials. Film. Television. Walk-on &
Supporting Artists
The Warehouse Studios
Glaziers Lane, Culcheth, Warrington WA3 4AQ
Website: www.eka-agency.com
e-mail: castings@eka-agency.com
Fax: 01925 767563   Tel: 01925 761088

EVANS & REISS
(PMA Member)
100 Fawe Park Road, London SW15 2EA
e-mail: marcia@evansandreiss.co.uk
Fax: 020-8877 0307   Tel: 020-8877 3755

EVANS Jacque MANAGEMENT Ltd
Top Floor Suite
14 Holmesley Road
London SE23 1PJ
Website: www.jacqueevansltd.com
Fax: 020-8699 5192   Tel: 020-8699 1202

EVANS Stephanie ASSOCIATES
Rivington House
82 Great Eastern Street
London EC2A 3JF
Website: www.stephanie-evans.com
e-mail: steph@stephanie-evans.com Tel/Fax: 0870 6092629

EVOLUTION TALENT MANAGEMENT
The Truman Brewery Building
Studio 21
91 Brick Lane
London E1 6QL
Website: www.evolutionmngt.com
e-mail: info@evolutionmngt.com
Fax: 020-7375 2752   Tel: 020-7770 6128

EXPRESSIONS CASTING AGENCY
3 Newgate Lane
Mansfield
Nottingham NG18 2LB
Website: www.expressionsperformingarts.co.uk
e-mail: expressions-uk@btconnect.com
Fax: 01623 647337   Tel: 01623 424334

EYE MODELS The
Tower Room, The Bath House
8 Chapel Place
Rivington Street
London EC2A 3DQ
Website: www.theeyecasting.com
e-mail: bayo@theeyecasting.com   Tel: 020-7729 9705

FARNES Norma MANAGEMENT
9 Orme Court
London W2 4RL
Fax: 020-7792 2110   Tel: 020-7727 1544

FAWKES Irene MANAGEMENT
2nd Floor
91A Rivington Street
London EC2A 3AY
e-mail: irenefawkes@btconnect.com
Fax: 020-7613 0769   Tel: 020-7729 8559

FBI AGENCY The
PO Box 250
Leeds LS1 2AZ
Website: www.fbi-agency.co.uk
e-mail: casting@fbi-agency.co.uk   Mobile: 07050 222747

FD MANAGEMENT
Contact: By email
Accepts Showreels
1 Agent represents 20 Performers
18C Marine Square
Brighton BN2 1DN
e-mail: vivienwilde@mac.com
Mobile: 07730 800679   Tel: 01273 245195

Laurence Jeffcoate

Sophia Di Martino

michael pollard
photographer
manchester

tel : 0161 456 7470
email : info@michaelpollard.co.uk
website : www.michaelpollard.co.uk

studio/location/student rates

luke varley / photo
www.lukevarley.com
+44 (0) 7711 183 631

left to right:
Samuel James
Charlotte Lucas
Zawe Ashton

FEA MANAGEMENT
(Ferris Entertainment)
Number 8
132 Charing Cross Road
London WC2H 0LA
Website: www.ferrisentertainment.com
e-mail: info@ferrisentertainment.com   Tel: 08454 724725

FEAST MANAGEMENT Ltd
(PMA Member)
1st Floor
34 Upper Street
London N1 0PN
e-mail: office@feastmanagement.co.uk
Fax: 020-7354 8995   Tel: 020-7354 5216

FEATURES
1 Charlotte Street, London W1T 1RD
Website: www.features.co.uk
e-mail: info@features.co.uk
Fax: 020-7636 1657   Tel: 020-7637 1487

FETCH
c/o Mad Dog Casting Ltd
15 Leighton Place
London NW5 2QL
Website: www.fetchactors.com
e-mail: fetchtalent@maddogcasting.com
Fax: 020-7284 2689   Tel: 020-7482 0477

FIELD Alan ASSOCIATES
(Personal Manager)
Contact: By email
1 Agent represents 5 Performers
Musicals. Presenters. Singers
3 The Spinney, Bakers Hill
Hadley Common, Herts EN5 5QJ
e-mail: alan@alanfield.com
Fax: 020-8447 0657   Tel: 020-8441 1137

FILM RIGHTS Ltd
(Personal Manager)
Contact: By Post
Mezzanine, Quadrant House
80-82 Regent Street
London W1B 5AU
Fax: 020-7734 0044   Tel: 020-7734 9911

FINCH & PARTNERS
6 Heddon Street
London W1B 4BS
Website: www.finchandpartners.com
e-mail: kat@finchandpartners.com
Fax: 020-7287 6420   Tel: 020-7851 7140

FIRST ACT PERSONAL MANAGEMENT
(Personal Manager)
Contact: John Burton. By Post
3 Agents represent 27-45 Performers
Commercials. Corporate. Film. Stage. Television
2 Saint Michaels
New Arley
Coventry
Warwickshire CV7 8PY
Website: www.spotlightagent.info/firstact
e-mail: firstactpm@aol.com
Fax: 01676 542777   Tel: 01676 540285

FIRST ARTIST MANAGEMENT
3 Tenterden Street
Hanover Square
London W1S 1TD
Website: www.firstartist.co.uk
e-mail: info@firstartist.co.uk
Fax: 020-3205 2140   Tel: 020-7096 9999

FIRST CALL MANAGEMENT
29-30 Dame Street
Dublin 2, Ireland
e-mail: fcm@indigo.ie
Fax: 00 353 1 679 8353   Tel: 00 353 1 679 8401

FITZGERALD Sheridan MANAGEMENT
Contact: By Post (SAE). No Phone Calls
87 Western Road
Upton Park
London E13 9JE   Tel: 020-8471 9814

FLAIR TALENT
46 Barry Road
East Dulwich
London SE22 0HU
Website: www.flairtalent.com
e-mail: aaron@flairtalent.com   Tel: 020-8693 8649

vin diesel | giovanna falconi | spike lee | aishwarya rai

verity-rae martin | matt roberts | natalie holiday | martin scorsese

kevin power | francesca kingdon | sean bean | kelly clarkson

guy porritt | dennis quaid | thora birch | michael burke

isabella cave | kurt russell | grant orviss | james haslam

jamiehughesphotography

m: 07850-122977 jamie@jamiehughesphotography.com
www.jamiehughesphotography.com

ETHNICS ARTISTE AGENCY
Talent of Colour. Talent of Foreign Language.

| Film | TV | Radio | Commercials | Theatre
| Photographic Work | Voice Overs

T: 020-8523 4242
F: 020-8523 4523

FLETCHER ASSOCIATES
(Personal Manager)
Contact: Francine Fletcher. By email/Telephone
1 Agent represents 15 Performers. Corporate. Experts.
Radio. Stage. Television
25 Parkway
London N20 0XN
Website: www.fletcherassociates.net
Fax: 020-8361 8866   Tel: 020-8361 8061

FLETCHER JACOB
(Artist Management)
Tower Room
Bath House
8 Chapel Place
Rivington Street, London EC2A 3DQ
e-mail: info@fletcherjacob.co.uk   Tel: 020-7617 7181

FORMULA LIVE PRODUCTIONS
Hurlingham Studios
Unit 19A
Ranelagh Gardens
Fulham, London SW6 3PA
Website: www.formulaliveproductions.com
e-mail: info@formulaliveproductions.com
Fax: 020-7731 3422   Tel: 020-7371 0300

FOSTER Sharon MANAGEMENT
15A Hollybank Road
Birmingham B13 0RF
Website: www.sharonfoster.co.uk
e-mail: mail@sharonfoster.co.uk   Tel: 0121-443 4865

FOX Clare ASSOCIATES
Set, Lighting & Sound Designers
9 Plympton Road, London NW6 7EH
Website: www.clarefox.co.uk
e-mail: cimfox@yahoo.co.uk   Tel/Fax: 020-7328 7494

FRENCH Linda
(See ALEXANDER PERSONAL MANAGEMENT Ltd)

FRESH AGENTS Ltd
Suite 5
Saks House
19 Ship Street
Brighton BN1 1AD
Website: www.freshagents.co.uk
e-mail: info@freshagents.co.uk   Tel: 0845 4080998

FRESH PARTNERS Ltd
19-21 Nile Street
London N1 7LL
Website: www.fresh-partners.com
e-mail: hello@fresh-partners.com
Fax: 020-7251 2749   Tel: 020-7566 1774

FRONTLINE ACTORS AGENCY DUBLIN
30-31 Wicklow Street
Dublin 2, Ireland
Website: www.frontlineactors.com
e-mail: frontlineactors@eircom.net   Tel: 00 353 1 6359882

FUNKY BEETROOT CELEBRITY MANAGEMENT Ltd
(Personal Manager)
Actors. Television Celebrities
PO Box 143
Faversham
Kent ME13 9LP
Website: www.funky-beetroot.com
e-mail: info@funky-beetroot.com
Fax: 01227 752300   Tel: 01227 751549

FUSHION PUKKA BOSH
(Personal Manager) (London & New York)
Contact: Jamie Lowe, Rachel Davis. By Post
4 Agents represent 25 Performers
Film. Presenters. Recording Artistes. Television. Writers
27 Old Gloucester Street
London WC1N 3XX
Website: www.fushionpukkabosh.com
e-mail: enquirieslondon@fushion-uk.com
Fax: 08700 111020   Tel: 08700 111100

GAELFORCE 10 MANAGEMENT
14 Bowmont Gardens
Glasgow G12 9LR
Website: www.gaelforce10.com
e-mail: info@gaelforce10.com
Mobile: 07778 296002   Tel/Fax: 0141-334 6246

GAGAN Hilary ASSOCIATES
(Personal Manager) (PMA Member)
187 Drury Lane
London WC2B 5QD
e-mail: hilary@hgassoc.freeserve.co.uk
Fax: 020-7430 1869   Tel: 020-7404 8794

GALLOWAYS ONE
15 Lexham Mews
London W8 6JW
e-mail: hugh@gallowaysone.com
Fax: 020-7376 2416   Tel: 020-7376 2288

GARDNER HERRITY Ltd
(PMA Member)
Contact: Kerry Gardner, Andy Herrity
24 Conway Street
London W1T 6BG
Website: www.gardnerherrity.co.uk
e-mail: info@gardnerherrity.co.uk
Fax: 020-7388 0688   Tel: 020-7388 0088

Nick Gregan
PHOTOGRAPHY

**The easiest and the best headshot you'll ever have -
By one of London's premier theatrical photographers.**

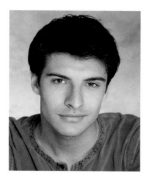  

For contemporary, natural headshots for the acting profession, contact Nick on
Tel: 020 8533 3003 | Mobile: 07774 421878 | www.nickgregan.com
email:info@nickgregan.com

GARRETT Michael
(See GLOBAL ARTISTS)

GARRICKS
(PMA Member)
Angel House
76 Mallinson Road, London SW11 1BN
e-mail: info@garricks.net
Fax: 020-7801 0088   Tel: 020-7738 1600

GAY Noel
19 Denmark Street
London WC2H 8NA
Website: www.noelgay.com
Fax: 020-7287 1816   Tel: 020-7836 3941

GILBERT & PAYNE
Room 236
2nd Floor, Linen Hall
162-168 Regent Street
London W1B 5TB
e-mail: ee@gilbertandpayne.com
Fax: 020-7494 3787   Tel: 020-7734 7505

GILLMAN Geraldine ASSOCIATES
Malcolm House
Malcolm Primary School
Malcolm Road
Penge
London SE20 8RH
e-mail: geraldi.gillma@btconnect.com
Mobile: 07799 791586   Tel: 0844 8005328

GLASS Eric Ltd
25 Ladbroke Crescent
Notting Hill, London W11 1PS
e-mail: eglassltd@aol.com
Fax: 020-7229 6220   Tel: 020-7229 9500

GLOBAL ARTISTS
(PMA Member)
Contact: By Post/email
Accepts Showreels/Voicereels
5 Agents
23 Haymarket, London SW1Y 4DG
Website: www.globalartists.co.uk
e-mail: info@globalartists.co.uk
Fax: 020-7839 4555   Tel: 020-7839 4888

GLYN MANAGEMENT
The Old School House
Brettenham
Ipswich IP7 7QP
e-mail: glyn.management@tesco.net
Fax: 01449 736117   Tel: 01449 737695

GO ENTERTAINMENTS Ltd
Circus Artistes, Chinese State Circus, Cirque Surreal,
Bolshoi Circus "Spirit of The Horse"
The Arts Exchange
Congleton
Cheshire CW12 1JG
Website: www.arts-exchange.com
e-mail: info@arts-exchange.com
Fax: 01260 270777   Tel: 01260 276627

GOLD AGENCY
Contact: By email
Accepts Showreels
32 Performers
Britannia House
Lower Road, Northfleet, Kent DA11 9BL
Website: www.goldagency.co.uk
e-mail: ann@goldagency.co.uk   Tel/Fax: 01474 561200

GOLDMAN KING
Actors. Comedians. Comic Performers. Studio Warm-ups.
Voice Overs
21 Red Lion Street
London WC1R 4PS
Website: www.goldmanking.com
e-mail: contacts@goldmanking.com   Mobile: 07980 241505

GORDON & FRENCH
(PMA Member)
Contact: By Post
12-13 Poland Street
London W1F 8QB
e-mail: mail@gordonandfrench.net
Fax: 020-7734 4832   Tel: 020-7734 4818

GRAHAM David PERSONAL MANAGEMENT (DGPM)
The Studio
107A Middleton Road, London E8 4LN
e-mail: infodgpm@aol.com   Tel/Fax: 020-7241 6752

GRANTHAM-HAZELDINE Ltd
Suite 315, The Linen Hall
162-168 Regent Street
London W1B 5TD
e-mail: agents@granthamhazeldine.com
Fax: 020-7038 3739   Tel: 020-7038 3737

GRAY Darren MANAGEMENT
Specialising in representing/promoting Australian Artists
2 Marston Lane
Portsmouth, Hampshire PO3 5TW
Website: www.darrengraymanagement.co.uk
e-mail: darren.gray1@virgin.net
Fax: 023-9267 7227   Tel: 023-9269 9973

DarkSide

A company offering high quality work with personal attention at very competitive prices.

FREE COPY NEG & CAPTION FOR 50 PRINTS OR MORE

GENUINE PHOTOGRAPHIC REPROS

PRINTS FROM NEGATIVES, ORIGINALS AND DIGITAL MEDIA

GLOSS OR MATT FINISH IN A RANGE OF SIZES

RE-ORDERS BY TELEPHONE

POSTAL AND COURIER SERVICES AVAILABLE

ALL MAJOR CREDIT CARDS ACCEPTED

DISCOUNTS FOR SCHOOLS & COLLEGES

020 7250 1200

DarkSide Photographic Ltd.
4 Helmet Row, London EC1V 3QJ
email: info@darksidephoto.co.uk
www.darksidephoto.co.uk

mobile:
0792 1182055 www.galaxy-casting.com/photographer lenki13@yahoo.co.uk
lenka photography

GRAYS MANAGEMENT & ASSOCIATES
(Personal Manager)
Panther House
38 Mount Pleasant, London WC1X 0AP
Website: www.graysman.com
e-mail: grays.man@btconnect.com
Fax: 020-7278 1091   Tel: 020-7278 1054

GREEN & UNDERWOOD
(Personal Manager)
Contact: By Post
PO Box 44394, London SW20 0YP
e-mail: info@greenandunderwood.com
Fax: 020-3258 5037   Tel: 020-8546 2614

GREGOR Katherine ASSOCIATES
Contact: By email
1 Agent represents 40 Performers
Commercials. Film. Radio. Stage. Television
The Colombo Centre
34-68 Colombo Street, London SE1 8DP
Website: www.katherinegregorassociates.co.uk
e-mail: agent@katherinegregorassociates.co.uk
                          Tel/Fax: 020-7261 9466

GRESHAM Carl GROUP
PO Box 3, Bradford
West Yorkshire BD1 4QN
Website: www.carlgresham.com
e-mail: gresh@carlgresham.co.uk
Fax: 01274 827161   Tel: 01274 735880

GRIDMODELS Ltd
Contact: Becky Ferdinando
By email/Telephone
2 Agents represent 300 Performers
Modelling
25 Charter Road
Kingston On Thames, Surrey KT1 3PY
Website: www.gridmodels.com
e-mail: info@gridmodels.com
Fax: 020-7993 5758   Tel: 020-7993 6512

GRIFFIN Sandra MANAGEMENT
6 Ryde Place
Richmond Road
East Twickenham, Middlesex TW1 2EH
e-mail: office@sandragriffin.com
Fax: 020-8744 1812   Tel: 020-8891 5676

GUBBAY Louise ASSOCIATES
26 Westmore Road
Tatsfield, Kent TN16 2AX
Website: www.louisegubbay.com
e-mail: louise@louisegubbay.com   Tel: 01959 573080

GURNETT J. PERSONAL MANAGEMENT Ltd
12 Newburgh Street
London W1F 7RP
Website: www.jgpm.co.uk
e-mail: mail@jgpm.co.uk
Fax: 020-7287 9642   Tel: 020-7440 1850

HALL JAMES PERSONAL MANAGEMENT
PO Box 604, Pinner
Middlesex HA5 9GH
Website: www.halljames.co.uk
e-mail: agents@halljames.co.uk
Fax: 020-8868 5825   Tel: 020-8429 8111

HALLY Yvette MANAGEMENT
121 Grange Road
Rathfarnham
Dublin 14
Ireland
e-mail: yhmgt@eircom.net
Fax: 00 353 1 4933076   Tel: 00 353 1 4933685

HAMBLETON Patrick MANAGEMENT
Top Floor
136 Englefield Road
London N1 3LQ
e-mail: patrick@phm.uk.com
Fax: 0870 2848554   Tel: 020-7226 0947

HAMILTON HODELL Ltd
(PMA Member)
5th Floor
66-68 Margaret Street
London W1W 8SR
Website: www.hamiltonhodell.co.uk
e-mail: info@hamiltonhodell.co.uk
Fax: 020-7636 1226   Tel: 020-7636 1221

HandE CASTING ADVERTISING AGENCY
Epping Film Studios
Brickfield Business Centre
Thornwood High Road
Epping
Essex CM16 6TH
Website: www.hande.org
e-mail: caa@hande.org
Fax: 01992 570601   Tel: 01992 570662

HARGREAVES Alison MANAGEMENT
Designers
27 Hamilton Road
London NW10 1NS
Website: www.alisonhargreaves.co.uk
e-mail: agent@alisonhargreaves.co.uk   Tel: 020-8438 0112

HARRIS AGENCY Ltd The
(PMA Member)
PO Box 308
Northwood, Middlesex HA6 9DT
e-mail: theharrisagency@btconnect.com
Fax: 01923 822253   Tel: 01923 822744

HARRISON Penny BSA Ltd
Trinity Lodge
25 Trinity Crescent, London SW17 7AG
e-mail: harrisonbsa@aol.com
Fax: 020-8672 8971   Tel: 020-8672 0136

HARVEY VOICES
4th Floor
52-53 Margaret Street, London W1W 8SQ
Website: www.harveyvoices.co.uk   Tel: 020-7952 4361

HAT MANAGEMENT
Contact: Neil Howarth
24 Thornley Rise
Audenshaw, Manchester M34 5JX
e-mail: hat.mgmt@hotmail.co.uk
Mobile: 07775 744438 — Tel: 0161-370 8648

HATTON McEWAN
(Personal Manager) (PMA Member)
Contact: Stephen Hatton, Aileen McEwan, James Penford
By Post
PO Box 37385, London N1 7XF
Website: www.hattonmcewan.com
e-mail: mail@hattonmcewan.com
Fax: 020-7251 9081 — Tel: 020-7253 4770

H C A
(See COOKE Howard ASSOCIATES)

HEADNOD TALENT AGENCY
2nd Floor
18 Kingsland Road, London E2 8DA
Website: www.headnodagency.com
e-mail: info@headnodagency.com — Tel: 020-7502 9478

HENRIETTA RABBIT CHILDREN'S ENTERTAINMENTS AGENCY Ltd
Balloonologists. Face Painters, Jugglers, Magiciennes
Punch & Judy. Stiltwalkers
The Warren
12 Eden Close, York YO24 2RD
Website: www.henriettarabbit.co.uk
e-mail: info@henriettarabbit.co.uk — Tel: 0800 0965653

HENRY'S AGENCY
53 Westbury
Rochford, Essex SS4 1UL
Website: www.henrysagency.co.uk
e-mail: info@henrysagency.co.uk — Tel/Fax: 01702 541413

HICKS Jeremy ASSOCIATES
(Personal Manager)
Contact: By Post/email
Accepts Showreels
2 Agents represent 25 Performers
Chefs. Comedians. Presenters. Writers
114-115 Tottenham Court Road
London W1T 5AH
Website: www.jeremyhicks.com
e-mail: info@jeremyhicks.com
Fax: 020-7383 2777 — Tel: 020-7383 2000

HILL Edward MANAGEMENT
Dolphin House
2-5 Manchester Street BN2 1TF
e-mail: info@edagent.com
Tel: 01273 906781 — Tel: 020-7558 8153

HILTON Elinor ASSOCIATES
2nd Floor
28 Charing Cross Road
London WC2H 0DB
Website: www.elinorhilton.com
e-mail: info@elinorhilton.com
Fax: 020-7836 3982 — Tel: 020-7240 2555

HINDIN Dee ASSOCIATES
Existing Clients only
9B Brunswick Mews
Great Cumberland Place
London W1H 7FB
Fax: 020-7258 0651 — Tel: 020-7723 3706

HIRED HANDS
12 Cressy Road
London NW3 2LY
Website: www.hiredhandsmodels.com
e-mail: hiredhandsagency@aol.com — Tel: 020-7267 9212

HOBBS Liz GROUP Ltd
Artiste Management
65 London Road
Newark, Notts NG24 1RZ
Website: www.lizhobbsgroup.com
e-mail: casting@lizhobbsgroup.com
Fax: 0870 3337009　　　　　　　　Tel: 0870 0702702

HOBSON'S ACTORS
62 Chiswick High Road
Chiswick, London W4 1SY
Website: www.hobsons-international.com
e-mail: actors@hobsons-international.com
Fax: 020-8996 5350　　　　　　　　Tel: 020-8995 3628

HOLLOWOOD Jane ASSOCIATES Ltd
Apartment 17, 113 Newton Street, Manchester M1 1AE
e-mail: janehollowood@ukonline.co.uk
Fax: 0161-237 9142　　　　　　　　Tel: 0161-237 9141

HOLLY Dave ARTS MEDIA SERVICES
The Annexe, 23 Eastwood Gardens
Felling, Tyne & Wear NE10 0AH
Fax: 0191-438 2722　　　　　　　　Tel: 0191-438 2711

**HOLMES Kim SHOWBUSINESS
ENTERTAINMENT AGENCY Ltd**
8 Charles Close
Ilkeston, Derbyshire DE7 5AF
Fax: 0115-930 9636　　　　　　　　Tel: 0115-930 5088

HOPE Sally ASSOCIATES
(PMA Member)
108 Leonard Street
London EC2A 4XS
Website: www.sallyhope.biz
e-mail: casting@sallyhope.biz
Fax: 020-7613 4848
Tel: 020-7613 5353

HORSEY Dick MANAGEMENT Ltd
(Personal Manager)
Contact: By Post/email/Telephone
Accepts Showreels/Voicereels
2 Agents represent 40 Performers
Corporate. Musicals. Stage. Television
Suite 1
Cottingham House
Chorleywood Road
Rickmansworth, Herts WD3 4EP
Website: www.dhmlimited.co.uk
e-mail: roger@dhmlimited.co.uk
Mobile: 07850 112211
Tel: 01923 710614

HOWARD Amanda ASSOCIATES Ltd
(PMA Member)
Contact: By Post
21 Berwick Street
London W1F 0PZ
Website: www.amandahowardassociates.co.uk
e-mail: mail@amandahowardassociates.co.uk
Fax: 020-7287 7785
Tel: 020-7287 9277

HOWARD Richard ASSOCIATES
6 Upper Hollingdean Road
Brighton BN1 7GA
Website: www.richardhowardassociates.co.uk
e-mail: info@richardhowardassociates.co.uk
Tel/Fax: 01273 539530

HOWE Janet
(Personal Manager)
4 Agents
Children. Modelling. Television. Walk-on & Supporting
Artists
58 High Street
Newcastle-under-Lyme
Staffordshire ST5 1QE
Tel/Fax: 01782 661777

The Pie Factory
101 Broadway
Salford Quays, Manchester M50 2EQ
e-mail: info@janethowe.com
Tel/Fax: 0161-263 0633

The Works Media Centre
36 White House Street
Hunslet, Leeds LS10 1AD
Tel/Fax: 0113-242 5225

HOWELL Philippa
(See PHPM)

HUDSON Nancy ASSOCIATES Ltd
PO Box 1344
High Wycombe North
Bucks HP11 9ER
Website: www.nancyhudsonassociates.com
e-mail: agents@nancyhudsonassociates.com
Tel: 020-7499 5548

HUNTER Bernard ASSOCIATES
13 Spencer Gardens
London SW14 7AH
Fax: 020-8392 9334
Tel: 020-8878 6308

HUNWICK HUGHES Ltd
(Personal Manager)
(PMA Member)
Contact: By Post/email
Accepts Showreels/Voicereels
Commercials. Film. Musicals. Radio. Stage. Television
Suite 2F
45A George Street
Edinburgh EH2 2HT
Website: www.hunwickhughes.com
e-mail: maryam@hunwickhughes.com
Fax: 0131-225 4535
Tel: 0131-225 3585

I-MAGE CASTINGS
Regent House Business Centre
Suite 22
24-25 Nutford Place
Marble Arch
London W1H 5YN
Website: www.i-mage.uk.com
e-mail: jane@i-mage.uk.com
Fax: 020-7725 7004
Tel: 020-7725 7003

ICON ACTORS MANAGEMENT
Tanzaro House
Ardwick Green North
Manchester M12 6FZ
Website: www.iconactors.net
e-mail: info@iconactors.net
Fax: 0161-273 4567
Tel: 0161-273 3344

I.M.L.
(Personal Manager) (CPMA Member)
The White House
52-54 Kennington Oval
London SE11 5SW
Website: www.iml.org.uk
e-mail: info@iml.org.uk
Tel/Fax: 020-7587 1080

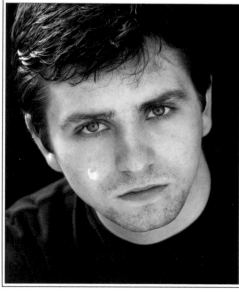

IMPACT INTERNATIONAL MANAGEMENT
(Personal Manager)
Contact: Cornelia Hefti
By email. Accepts Showreels/Voicereels
1 Agent represents 10 Performers. Commercials. Dancers
Film. Musicals. Singers. Walk-on & Supporting Artists
1st Floor Danceworks
16-18 Balderton Street
London W1K 6TN
Website: www.impact-london.co.uk
e-mail: info@impact-london.co.uk
Fax: 020-7495 6515   Tel: 020-7495 6655

IMPERIAL PERSONAL MANAGEMENT Ltd
102 Kirkstall Road
Leeds
West Yorkshire LS3 1JA
Website: www.ipmcasting.com
e-mail: katie_ross@btinternet.com   Tel: 0113-244 3222

INDEPENDENT TALENT GROUP Ltd
(Formerly ICM, London) (PMA Member)
Oxford House
76 Oxford Street
London W1D 1BS
Website: www.independenttalent.com
Fax: 020-7323 0101   Tel: 020-7636 6565

INDEPENDENT THEATRE WORKSHOP The
2 Mornington Road
Ranelagh
Dublin 6
Ireland
Website: www.independent-theatre-workshop.com
e-mail: info@independent-theatre-workshop.com
                         Tel/Fax: 00 353 1 4968808

INDUSTRY ARTISTS
332 Royal Exchange
Manchester M2 7BR
Website: www.industryactors.co.uk
e-mail: mark@industryactors.co.uk
Fax: 0161-839 1661   Tel: 0161-839 1551

INSPIRATION MANAGEMENT
(Personal Manager)
Room 227
The Aberdeen Centre
22-24 Highbury Grove
London N5 2EA
Website: www.inspirationmanagement.org.uk
e-mail: mail@inspirationmanagement.eclipse.co.uk
                         Tel: 020-7704 0440

INTER-CITY CASTING
(Personal Manager)
Contact: By Post
Accepts Showreels
2 Agents represent 60 Performers
Portland Tower
Portland Street
Manchester M1 3LF
Website: www.iccast.co.uk
e-mail: intercitycasting@btconnect.com
                         Tel/Fax: 0161-238 4950

INTERNATIONAL ARTISTES Ltd
(PMA Member)
4th Floor, Holborn Hall
193-197 High Holborn
London WC1V 7BD
e-mail: reception@internationalartistes.com
Fax: 020-7404 9865   Tel: 020-7025 0600

INTERNATIONAL COLLECTIVE ARTIST MANAGEMENT
Golden Cross House
8 Duncannon Street
The Strand
London WC2N 4JF
Website: www.internationalcollective.com
e-mail: enquiries@internationalcollective.co.uk
Fax: 020-7484 5100   Tel: 020-7484 5080

INTERNATIONAL MODEL MANAGEMENT Ltd
(Incorporating Yvonne Paul Management)
Elysium Gate, Unit 15
126-128 New Kings Road
London SW6 4LZ
e-mail: info@immmodels.com
Fax: 020-7736 2221   Tel: 020-7610 9111

INTERNATIONAL MODELS & TALENT AGENCY
1901 Avenue of The Stars
Suite #200
Century City, CA 90067
e-mail: int.talent@hotmail.com
Fax: (323) 644-5440   Tel: (310) 461-1550

INTERNATIONAL THEATRE & MUSIC Ltd
Contact: Piers Chater Robinson
Garden Studios
11-15 Betterton Street
Covent Garden
London WC2H 9BP
Website: www.it-m.co.uk
e-mail: info@it-m.co.uk
Fax: 020-7379 0801   Tel: 020-7470 8786

ROSIE STILL (PHOTOGRAPHER)

Zoe Heyes

Christopher Parker

Bella Emberg

John Judd

Liz Fraser

Charlie Clements

Maureen Sweeney

Robert Gray

Mia McKenna-Bruce

Michael Barber

Debra Stephenson

Chris Jarvis

*Special SPOTLIGHT price*Student rates*Free prints*Free airbrushing*
Very relaxed atmosphere in my own South London studio
*View work instantly*Whole shoot put onto CD*

020 8857 6920 ** www.rosiestillphotography.com

STAND UP DRAMA® PRESENTS
London's leading acting showcase...

LONDON BITES ™

DIGESTIBLE DRAMA WITH A DRINK!
Where actors, writers, casting directors and agents meet.
The first Wednesday, Thursday of every month.
For actors looking for industry exposure, performance experience or to secure representation.

WHY CHOOSE LONDON BITES?
- **AWARD WINNING** Winner of "Best Producer" at The Fringe Report Awards.
- **2 NIGHTS** Actors perform on 2 nights for increased exposure.
- **HIGH STANDARDS** All actors are pre-auditioned and rehearsed.
- **REPUTATION** Founded 2005 Stand Up Drama has earned an unrivalled reputation.
- **PROFESSIONAL SHOW** London Bites is an entertaining and interactive performance.
- **UNIQUE ATMOSPHERE** Our shows take place in a beautiful bar, where audience can enjoy a drink whilst being entertained.
- **LIVE AUDIENCE** Industry can see first hand how each of our actors communicate with our theatre-going audience.
- **INFORMATION** Every actor is listed on our website, with a link to their Spotlight page, so they can always be found by industry.
- **INDUSTRY** We invite industry through our sponsors Spotlight.

AND I QUOTE

"..a resounding success. Well done." - THE STAGE

"Stand Up Drama is a most welcome venture by actors, for actors".
- FRONTLINE MANAGEMENT

"I am doing great since my appearance in London Bites. I got a show from it, which led to an agent, which led to a job on TV this year. So Stand Up Drama does work."
Past Performer

"Professionally every thing is going really well thanks to London Bites. I had a meeting with 2 different agents and they both offered me a place. Past Performer

"Highly entertaining, professional performances, great ambience"
Audience member

AND NOW: STAND UP DRAMA® PRESENTS

'The Casting Director Workshops' - put yourself in front of the people that matter with our new initiative. Meet six new Casting Directors in six weeks, or work intensely on your craft with one. See web for info.

WWW.STANDUPDRAMA.COM
SPONSORED BY

Representing:-
- Dancers, Choreographers and Singers in all aspects of TV, Film, Video, Theatre, Commercial and Cruise work.
- Specialising in Musical Theatre.
- Full Production Team available for Trade, Fashion & Corporate Events.
- Select actors' personal management service available.

Visit our website: www.kmcagencies.co.uk

PO Box 122
48 Great Ancoats Street
Manchester M4 5AB
t: 0161 237 3009
f: 0161 237 9812
e: casting@kmcagencies.co.uk

Garden Studios
11-15 Betterton Street
London WC2H 9BP
t: 0870 460 4868
f: 0870 442 1780
e: london@kmcagencies.co.uk

JAA
(See ALTARAS Jonathan ASSOCIATES Ltd)

JABBERWOCKY AGENCY
Contact: Christina Yates
By email
4 Agents represent 135 Performers
Children. Teenagers
Glassenbury Hill Farm
Glassenbury Road
Cranbrook, Kent TN17 2QF
Website: www.jabberwockyagency.com
e-mail: info@jabberwockyagency.com
Fax: 01580 714346   Tel: 01580 714306

JAFFREY MANAGEMENT Ltd
(Personal Manager) (PMA Member)
Contact: Jennifer Jaffrey
By Post/email
Accepts Showreels/Voicereels (SAE)
2 Agents represent 60 Performers
Commercials. Film. Stage. Television
The Double Lodge
Pinewood Studios
Iver Heath
Bucks SL0 0NH
Website: www.jaffreyactors.co.uk
e-mail: castings@jaffreyactors.co.uk
Fax: 01753 785163   Tel: 01753 785162

JAMES Susan
(See SJ MANAGEMENT)

JAMESON Joy Ltd
(Personal Manager)
21 Uxbridge Street
Kensington, London W8 7TQ
e-mail: joy@jote.freeuk.com
Fax: 020-7985 0842   Tel: 020-7221 0990

JAY Alex PERSONAL MANAGEMENT
8 Higher Newmarket Road
Newmarket
Gloucestershire GL6 0RP
e-mail: alexjay@alex-jay-pm.freeserve.co.uk
    Tel/Fax: 01453 834783

JB ASSOCIATES
(Personal Manager) (PMA Member)
Contact: John Basham
By Post/email
Accepts Showreels/Voicereels
2 Agents represent 60 Performers
Commercials. Radio. Stage. Television
4th Floor, Manchester House
84-86 Princess Street
Manchester M1 6NG
Website: www.j-b-a.net
e-mail: info@j-b-a.net
Fax: 0161-237 1809   Tel: 0161-237 1808

ANTHONY BRITTON
PHOTOGRAPHER
www.anthonybritton.co.uk
Email anthony-britton@btconnect.com
Tel: 01784-488343

JEFFREY & WHITE MANAGEMENT Ltd
(Personal Manager) (PMA Member)
Suite 1803
16-19 Southampton Place
London WC1A 2AJ
e-mail: info@jeffreyandwhite.co.uk — Tel: 020-7745 7181

JERMIN Mark MANAGEMENT
8 Heathfield
Swansea SA1 6EJ
Website: www.markjermin.co.uk
e-mail: info@markjermin.co.uk
Fax: 01792 458844 — Tel: 01792 458855

J.G.M.
15 Lexham Mews, London W8 6JW
Website: www.jgmtalent.com
e-mail: mail@jgmtalent.com
Fax: 020-7376 2416 — Tel: 020-7376 2414

JLM PERSONAL MANAGEMENT
(Personal Manager) (PMA Member)
Contact: Sharon Henry, Sarah Lee
By Post
Accepts Showreels
2 Agents
Commercials. Film. Radio. Stage. Television
4th Floor, Holborn Hall
193-197 High Holborn, London WC1V 7BD
e-mail: info@jlmpm.co.uk
Fax: 020-7404 9865 — Tel: 020 7025 0630

J.M. MANAGEMENT
Personal representation to a small number of
Actors/Actresses in film work
20 Pembroke Road
North Wembley
Middlesex HA9 7PD — Tel/Fax: 020-8908 0502

JOHNSON WHITELEY Ltd
12 Argyll Mansions
Hammersmith Road, London W14 8QG
e-mail: johnsonwhiteley@btconnnect.com
Fax: 020-7348 0164 — Tel: 020-7348 0163

JOHNSTON & MATHERS ASSOCIATES Ltd
PO Box 3167
Barnet EN5 2WA
Website: www.johnstonandmathers.com
e-mail: johnstonmathers@aol.com
Fax: 020-8449 2386 — Tel: 020-8449 4968

JPA MANAGEMENT
30 Daws Hill Lane
High Wycombe
Bucks HP11 1PW
Website: www.jpamanagement.co.uk
e-mail: jackie.palmer@btinternet.com
Fax: 01494 510479 — Tel: 01494 520978

K TALENT
(Personal Manager)
Contact: By Post/email
Accepts Showreels/Voicereels
3 Agents represent 45 Performers
Children. Commercials. Dancers. Film. Musicals. Singers
Stage. Television
1st Floor
28 Grays Inn Road, London WC1X 8HR
Website: www.ktalent.co.uk — Tel: 0844 5672470

KAL MANAGEMENT
Contact: By Post
95 Gloucester Road
Hampton
Middlesex TW12 2UW
Website: www.kaplan-kaye.co.uk
e-mail: kaplan222@aol.com
Fax: 020-8979 6487 — Tel: 020-8783 0039

KANAL Roberta AGENCY
82 Constance Road
Twickenham
Middlesex TW2 7JA
e-mail: roberta.kanal@dsl.pipex.com
Tel/Fax: 020-8894 7952 — Tel: 020-8894 2277

KARUSHI MANAGEMENT
Contact: By email
3 Agents represent 29 Performers
Unit 10
7 Wenlock Road
London N1 7SL
Website: www.karushi.com
e-mail: lisa@karushi.com
Fax: 0845 9005522 — Tel: 0845 9005511

KD ASSOCIATES
12 The Drive
Northampton NN1 4SH
Website: www.kdassociates.biz
e-mail: kd.associates@virgin.net — Tel: 01604 715598

KEDDIE SCOTT ASSOCIATES Ltd
(Personal Manager) (PMA Member)
Contact: By Post
Accepts Showreels/Voicereels
4 Agents represent 145 Performers
Commercials. Corporate. Dancers. Film. Musicals
Presenters. Radio. Singers. Stage. Television. Writers
Studio 1, 17 Shorts Gardens
Covent Garden, London WC2H 9AT
Website: www.ks-ass.co.uk
e-mail: fiona@ks-ass.co.uk
Fax: 020-7147 1326   Tel: 020-7836 6802

KSA - SCOTLAND
Contact: Paul Michael. By Post/email
Accepts Showreels/Voicereels
2 Agents represent 15 Performers
Film. Musicals. Stage. Television
(0/1) 430 Tantallon Road, Glasgow G41 3HR
e-mail: scotland@ks-ass.co.uk
Fax: 020-7147 1326   Mobile: 07980 121728

KSA - WALES
Studio 1, 17 Shorts Gardens
Covent Garden, London WC2H 9AT
e-mail: wales@ks-ass.co.uk
Mobile: 07917 272298   Tel: 020-7836 6802

KELLY MANAGEMENT Ltd
3rd Floor
50 South Molton Street
Mayfair, London W1K 5SB
Website: www.kelly-management.com
e-mail: assistant@kelly-management.com
Fax: 020-7495 5212   Tel: 020-7495 5211

KELLY'S KIND
Actors. Choreographers. Dance. Make-up Artists. Models.
Various Alternative Specialist Skills
Third Floor
17-18 Margaret Street
London W1W 8RP
Website: www.kellyskind.co.uk
e-mail: suzie@kellyskind.co.uk   Tel: 0870 8701299

KENIS Steve & Co
(PMA Member)
Royalty House
72-74 Dean Street, London W1D 3SG
e-mail: sk@sknco.com
Fax: 020-7287 6328   Tel: 020-7434 9055

KENT Tim ASSOCIATES Ltd
(Personal Manager)
Contact: Tim Kent
By Post/email
Accepts Showreels/Voicereels
4 Agents represent 70 Performers
The Coach House, Pinewood Studios
Pinewood Road, Iver Heath, Bucks SL0 0NH
e-mail: castings@tkassociates.co.uk
Fax: 01753 655622   Tel: 01753 655517

KEW PERSONAL MANAGEMENT
PO Box 53974
London SW15 2SQ
Website: www.kewpersonalmanagement.com
e-mail: info@kewpersonalmanagement.com
Tel: 020-8871 3697

KEYLOCK MANAGEMENT
Contact: By Post
Accepts Showreels
2 Agents represent 77 Performers
Commercials. Film. Stage. Television
16 Bulbecks Walk
South Woodham Ferrers
Essex CM3 5ZN
Website: www.keylockmanagement.com
e-mail: agency@keylockmanagement.com
Fax: 01245 328625   Tel: 01245 321638

KING Adrian ASSOCIATES
(PMA Member)
Contact: Adrian King
By Post/email
Accepts Showreels
2 Agents represent 50 Performers
Commercials. Directors. Musicals. Stage. Television
33 Marlborough Mansions
Cannon Hill, London NW6 1JS
e-mail: akassocs@aol.com
Fax: 020-7435 4100   Tel: 020-7435 4600

K M C AGENCIES
Garden Studios
11-15 Betterton Street, London WC2H 9BP
e-mail: london@kmcagencies.co.uk
Fax: 0870 4421780   Tel: 0870 4604868

PO Box 122
48 Great Ancoats Street
Manchester M4 5AB
e-mail: casting@kmcagencies.co.uk
Fax: 0161-237 9812   Tel: 0161-237 3009

KNIGHT AYTON MANAGEMENT
114 St Martin's Lane, London WC2N 4BE
Website: www.knightayton.co.uk
e-mail: info@knightayton.co.uk
Fax: 020-7836 8333   Tel: 020-7836 5333

KNIGHT Ray CASTING
21A Lambolle Place
London NW3 4PG
Website: www.rayknight.co.uk
e-mail: casting@rayknight.co.uk
Fax: 020-7722 2322   Tel: 020-7722 1551

KORT Richard MANAGEMENT Ltd
Theatre House
2-4 Clasketgate, Lincoln LN2 1JS
Website: www.richardkortassociates.com
e-mail: richardkort@dial.pipex.com
Fax: 01522 511116   Tel: 01522 526888

image
photographic
Number One in Repros
020 7602 1190
54 Shepherds Bush Road London W6 7PH

Full digital and retouching service available

Telephone : 020 **7602 1190** or 020 **7603 4463** **Fax :** 020 **7602 6219**

Website : www.imagephotographic.com *E-Mail :* sales@imagephotographic.com

MAGGIE DAVISON
DAVISON PICTURES
020 8579 7006   07917 758754
www.davisonpictures.co.uk   maggie@byronw7.freeserve.co.uk

David Black

Michael Strobel

KREATE
Unit 232
30 Great Guildford Street
London SE1 0HS
e-mail: web@kreate.co.uk
Fax: 020-7401 3003
Tel: 020-7401 9007

KREMER ASSOCIATES
(See MARSH Billy DRAMA Ltd)

KSA - SCOTLAND
(See KEDDIE SCOTT ASSOCIATES Ltd)

KSA - WALES
(See KEDDIE SCOTT ASSOCIATES Ltd)

L.A. MANAGEMENT
10 Fairoak Close
Kenley
Surrey CR8 5LJ
Website: www.lamanagement.biz
e-mail: info@lamanagement.biz
Mobile: 07963 573538

LADA MANAGEMEMENT
Sparkhouse Studios
Rope Walk, Lincoln LN6 7DQ
Website: www.lada.org.uk/agency
e-mail: management@lada.org.uk
Fax: 01522 837201
Tel: 01522 837243

LADIDA
Contact: By Post.
Accepts Showreels.
2 Agents represent 70 Performers.
Commercials. Creatives. Film. Musicals. Radio. Stage.
Television. Writers
Cambridge Theatre
Earlham Street
London WC2H 9HU
Website: www.ladidagroup.com
e-mail: m@ladidagroup.com
Tel: 020-7379 6199

LAINE MANAGEMENT Ltd
Laine House
131 Victoria Road
Hope, Salford M6 8LF
Website: www.lainemanagement.co.uk
e-mail: sam@lainemanagement.co.uk
Fax: 0161-787 7572
Tel: 0161-789 7775

LAINE Betty MANAGEMENT
The Studios
East Street, Epsom
Surrey KT17 1HH
e-mail: enquiries@betty-laine-management.co.uk
Tel/Fax: 01372 721815

LANGFORD ASSOCIATES Ltd
(Personal Manager)
Contact: Barry Langford
By Post/email
Commercials. Film. Stage. Television
17 Westfields Avenue
Barnes
London SW13 0AT
e-mail: barry.langford@btconnect.com
Fax: 020-8878 7078
Tel: 020-8878 7148

LAWRENCE Tonicha AGENCY
Serenissima
Church Hill
Thorner
Leeds LS14 3EG
Website: www.tonichalawrence.co.uk
e-mail: tonichalawrence@fastmail.co.uk
Mobile: 07766 415996
Tel/Fax: 0113-289 3433

LE BARS Tessa MANAGEMENT
(PMA Member)
Existing Clients only
54 Birchwood Road
Petts Wood
Kent BR5 1NZ
Website: www.galtonandsimpson.com
e-mail: tessa.lebars@ntlworld.com
Mobile: 07860 287255
Tel: 01689 837084

LEE Wendy MANAGEMENT
2nd Floor
6 Langham Street
London W1W 7AP
e-mail: wendy-lee@btconnect.com
Tel: 020-7703 5187

LEE GARRETT Anna MANAGEMENT
24-26 Arcadia Avenue
Finchley Central
London N3 2JU
Website: www.annaleegarrett.net
e-mail: contact@annaleegarrett.net
Tel: 020-8144 1142

LEHRER Jane ASSOCIATES
(Personal Manager)
(PMA Member)
Contact: By Post/email
2 Agents
100A Chalk Farm Road
London NW1 8EH
Website: www.janelehrer.co.uk
e-mail: janelehrer@aol.com
Fax: 020-7482 4899
Tel: 020-7482 4898

LEIGH MANAGEMENT
14 St David's Drive
Edgware
Middlesex HA8 6JH
e-mail: leighmanagement@aol.com   Tel/Fax: 020-8951 4449

LEIGH Mike ASSOCIATES
37 Marylebone Lane
London W1U 2NW
Website: www.mikeleighassoc.com
Fax: 020-7486 5886   Tel: 020-7935 5500

LESLIE Sasha MANAGEMENT
(In Association with Allsorts Drama for Children)
34 Pember Road
London NW10 5LS
e-mail: sasha@allsortsdrama.com   Tel/Fax: 020-8969 3249

LIME ACTORS AGENCY & MANAGEMENT Ltd
Contact: Georgina Andrew
By Post
Accepts Showreels
Nemesis House, 1 Oxford Court
Bishopsgate, Manchester M2 3WQ
Website: www.limemanagement.tv
e-mail: georgina@limemanagement.co.uk
Fax: 0161-228 6727   Tel: 0161-236 0827

LINKS MANAGEMENT
Contact: By Post
Accepts Showreels
20 Performers. Commercials. Film. Musicals. Stage
Television
34-68 Colombo Street
London SE1 8DP
Website: www.links-management.co.uk
e-mail: agent@links-management.co.uk
                            Tel/Fax: 020-7928 0806

LINKSIDE AGENCY
Contact: By Post
2 Agents represent 30 Performers
Dancers. Musicals. Singers. Stage. Television
21 Poplar Road
Leatherhead
Surrey KT22 8SF
e-mail: linkside_agency@yahoo.co.uk
Fax: 01372 378398   Tel: 01372 802374

LINTON MANAGEMENT
27-31 Clerkenwell Close
London EC1R 0AT
e-mail: london@linton.tv
Fax: 020-7785 7276   Tel: 020-7785 7275

3 The Rock, Bury BL9 0JP
e-mail: carol@linton.tv
Fax: 0161-761 1999   Tel: 0161-761 2020

LONDON ARTISTS AGENCY
Suite 108
315 Chiswick High Road
London W4 4HH
Website: www.londonartistsagency.co.uk
e-mail: info@londonartistsagency.co.uk Tel: 020-8487 9645

LONG Eva AGENTS
Contact: By Post/email
2 Agents represent 30 Performers
Commercials
Corporate. Film. Musicals. Radio. Singers. Stage. Television
Voice Overs
107 Station Road, Earls Barton
Northants NN6 0NX
Website: www.evalongagents.co.uk
e-mail: evalongagents@yahoo.co.uk
Fax: 01604 811921   Mobile: 07736 700849

LONGRUN ARTISTES AGENCY
Contact: Gina Long, Irene Wernli
3 Chelsworth Drive
Plumstead Common
London SE18 2RB
Website: www.longrunartistes.co.uk
e-mail: gina@longrunartistes.co.uk
Mobile: 07983 742022   Mobile: 07748 723228

LOOKALIKES
Contact: Susan Scott
106 Tollington Park
London N4 3RB
Website: www.lookalikes.info
e-mail: susan@lookalikes.info
Fax: 020-7281 1263   Tel: 020-7281 8029

LOOKS
Contact: By Post/email/Telephone
200 Performers
*Commercials. Corporate. Modelling. Presenters. Walk-on &
Supporting Artists*
PO Box 42783, London N2 0UF
Website: www.lookslondon.com
e-mail: lookslondonltd@btconnect.com
Fax: 020-8442 9190   Tel: 020-8341 4477

LOVETT Pat ASSOCIATES
(See PLA)

LSW PROMOTIONS
PO Box 31855
London SE17 3XP
e-mail: londonswo@hotmail.com   Tel/Fax: 020-7793 9755

LUXFACTOR GROUP (UK) The
(Personal Manager)
Contact: Michael D. Finch. By email
1 Agent represents 20+ Performers
*Creatives. Presenters. Television. Walk-on & Supporting
Artists*
Fleet Place
12 Nelson Drive
Petersfield, Hampshire GU31 4SJ
Website: www.luxfactor.co.uk/actors.htm
e-mail: info@luxfactor.co.uk
Fax: 0845 3700588   Tel: 0845 3700589

LYNE Dennis AGENCY
(PMA Member)
503 Holloway Road
London N19 4DD
e-mail: info@dennislyne.com
Fax: 020-7272 4790   Tel: 020-7272 5020

MACFARLANE CHARD ASSOCIATES Ltd
(PMA Member)
33 Percy Street
London W1T 2DF
Website: www.macfarlane-chard.co.uk
e-mail: enquiries@macfarlane-chard.co.uk
Fax: 020-7636 7751   Tel: 020-7636 7750

MACFARLANE CHARD ASSOCIATES IRELAND
7 Adelaide Street
Dun Laoghaire
Co Dublin, Ireland
e-mail: enquiries@macfarlane-chard.ie
Fax: 00 353 1 663 8649   Tel: 00 353 1 663 8646

MACNAUGHTON LORD REPRESENTATION
(PMA Member)
*Choreographers. Composers. Designers. Directors. Lighting
Designers. Lyricists. Musical Directors. Writers*
Unit 10
The Broomhouse Studios
50 Sulivan Road
London SW6 3DX
Website: www.mlrep.com
e-mail: info@mlrep.com
Fax: 020-7371 7563   Tel: 020-7384 9517

MADELEY Paul ASSOCIATES
17 Valley Road
Arden Park, Bredbury
Stockport
Cheshire SK6 2EA
e-mail: paulmadeley@amserve.com   Tel/Fax: 0161-430 5380

MAIDA VALE SINGERS
Singers for Recordings, Theatre, Film, Radio & Television
7B Lanhill Road
Maida Vale, London W9 2BP
Website: www.maidavalesingers.co.uk
e-mail: maidavalesingers@cdtenor.freeserve.co.uk
Mobile: 07889 153145   Tel/Fax: 020-7266 1358

MAIN ARTISTS
(Personal Manager)
Contact: Andrew Allen
By email
Accepts Showreels
2 Agents represent 60 Performers
Commercials. Film. Stage. Television
34 South Molton Street
London W1K 5BP
Website: www.mainartists.com
e-mail: andrew@mainartists.com
Fax: 0870 1280003   Tel: 020-7495 4955

MAITLAND MANAGEMENT
(Personal Manager)
Contact: Anne Skates
PO Box 364
Esher, Surrey KT10 9XZ
Website: www.maitlandmusic.com
e-mail: maitmus@aol.com
Fax: 01372 466229   Tel: 01372 466228

MAMBAB AGENCY
Contact: Nichola D. Hartwell
PO Box 51261, Kennington, London SE11 4SW
Website: www.mrandmissblackandbeautiful.com
e-mail: contacts@mrandmissblackandbeautiful.com
Mobile: 07868 728132   Tel: 020-7793 4848

MANAGEMENT 2000
Contact: Jackey Gekling
By Post
Accepts Showreels
1 Agent represents 40 Performers
Commercials. Film. Radio. Stage. Television
11 Well Street, Treuddyn, Flintshire CH7 4NH
Website: www.management-2000.co.uk
e-mail: jackey@management-2000.co.uk
                              Tel/Fax: 01352 771231

MANS Johnny PRODUCTIONS Ltd
PO Box 196, Hoddesdon, Herts EN10 7WG
Website: www.johnnymansproductions.co.uk
e-mail: johnnymansagent@aol.com
Fax: 01992 470516   Tel: 01992 470907

MANSON Andrew PERSONAL MANAGEMENT Ltd
(PMA Member)
288 Munster Road
London SW6 6BQ
Website: www.andrewmanson.com
e-mail: post@andrewmanson.com
Fax: 020-7381 8874   Tel: 020-7386 9158

MARCH MODELS
The Aberdeen Centre
22-24 Highbury Grove
London N5 2EA
Website: www.marchmodels.com
e-mail: hello@marchmodels.com
Fax: 020-7704 6085   Tel: 020-7704 6950

MARCUS & McCRIMMON MANAGEMENT
(Personal Manager)
Contact: By Post. Accepts Showreels
3 Agents represent 60 Performers
Film. Musicals. Stage Television
1 Heathgate Place
75 Agincourt Road
Hampstead, London NW3 2NU
Website: www.marcusandmccrimmon.com
e-mail: info@marcusandmccrimmon.com
Fax: 020-7485 5030   Tel: 020-7485 4040

MARKHAM & FROGGATT Ltd
(Personal Manager) (PMA Member)
Contact: By Post
4 Windmill Street
London W1T 2HZ
Website: www.markhamfroggatt.com
e-mail: admin@markhamfroggatt.co.uk
Fax: 020-7637 5233   Tel: 020-7636 4412

MARKHAM & MARSDEN Ltd
(PMA Member)
405 Strand
London WC2R 0NE
Website: www.markham-marsden.com
e-mail: info@markham-marsden.com
Fax: 020-7836 4222   Tel: 020-7836 4111

MARSH Billy ASSOCIATES Ltd
(PMA Member)
76A Grove End Road
St Johns Wood
London NW8 9ND
Website: www.billymarsh.co.uk
e-mail: talent@billymarsh.co.uk
Fax: 020-7449 6933   Tel: 020-7449 6930

MARSH Billy DRAMA Ltd
Actors & Actresses
11 Henrietta Street
Covent Garden, London WC2E 8PY
e-mail: info@billymarshdrama.co.uk
Fax: 020-7379 7272   Tel: 020-7379 4800

MARSH Sandra MANAGEMENT
Film Technicians
Waverley House
7-12 Noel Street, London W1F 8GQ
Website: www.casarotto.co.uk
e-mail: casarottomarsh@casarotto.co.uk
Fax: 020-7287 9128   Tel: 020-7287 4450

MARSHALL Ronnie AGENCY
Contact: Ronnie Marshall
By Post/Telephone
Accepts Showreels
1 Agent represents 25 Performers. Commercials. Film.
Musicals. Stage. Television
66 Ollerton Road
London N11 2LA   Tel/Fax: 020-8368 4958

MARSHALL Scott PARTNERS Ltd
(PMA Member)
2nd Floor
15 Little Portland Street, London W1W 8BW
e-mail: smpm@scottmarshall.co.uk
Fax: 020-7636 9728   Tel: 020-7637 4623

MARTIN Carol PERSONAL MANAGEMENT
19 Highgate West Hill
London N6 6NP
Fax: 020-8340 4868   Tel: 020-8348 0847

MAY John
Top Floor, 46 Golborne Road, London W10 5PR
e-mail: may505@btinternet.com   Tel: 020-8962 1606

MAYER Cassie Ltd
(PMA Member)
5 Old Garden House
The Lanterns
Bridge Lane, London SW11 3AD
e-mail: info@cassiemayerltd.co.uk
Fax: 020-7350 0890   Tel: 020-7350 0880

MBA (Formerly John Mahoney Management)
Concorde House
18 Margaret Street
Brighton BN2 1TS
Website: www.mbagency.co.uk
e-mail: mba.concorde@virgin.net
Fax: 01273 818306   Tel: 01273 685970

Abbie Osmon

Sophie Bould

Howard Grater

robin savage photography

www.robinsavage.co.uk

contact@robinsavage.co.uk

07901 927597

McKINNEY MACARTNEY MANAGEMENT Ltd
Technicians
The Barley Mow Centre
10 Barley Mow Passage
London W4 4PH
Website: www.mckinneymacartney.com
e-mail: mail@mckinneymacartney.com
Fax: 020-8995 2414   Tel: 020-8995 4747

McLEAN Bill PERSONAL MANAGEMENT
(Personal Manager)
Contact: By Post
23B Deodar Road
London SW15 2NP   Tel: 020-8789 8191

McLEAN-WILLIAMS MANAGEMENT
14 Rathbone Place
London W1T 1HT
Website: www.mclean-williams.com
e-mail: info@mclean-williams.com
Fax: 020-7631 3739   Tel: 020-7631 5385

McLEOD HOLDEN ENTERPRISES Ltd
Priory House
1133 Hessle Road
Hull HU4 6SB
Website: www.mcleod-holden.com
e-mail: alex.just@mcleod-holden.com
Fax: 01482 353635   Tel: 01482 565444

Anna Hull Photography

Laurence Mitchell

Nicole Davis

www.annahullphotography.com
t: 020 7498 5023

Artist and Photographer   ascha.co.uk

MCL MANAGEMENT
6 Ingestre Court
Ingestre Place, London W1F OJL
e-mail: info@mclmanagement.org   Mobile: 07826 609302

McREDDIE Ken ASSOCIATES Ltd
(Personal Manager) (PMA Member)
36-40 Glasshouse Street
London W1B 5DL
Website: www.kenmcreddie.com
e-mail: email@kenmcreddie.com
Fax: 020-7734 6530   Tel: 020-7439 1456

MCS AGENCY
47 Dean Street, London W1D 5BE
Website: www.mcsagency.co.uk
e-mail: info@mcsagency.co.uk   Tel: 020-7734 9995

MEDIA LEGAL
Existing Clients only
West End House
83 Clarendon Road
Sevenoaks, Kent TN13 1ET   Tel: 01732 460592

MF MANAGEMENT
55 Newman Street
London W1T 3EB
e-mail: mfmall@mfmanagement.com   Tel: 020-3291 2929

MHM
Heather Barn
Cryers Hill Lane
High Wycombe
Bucks HP15 6AA
Website: www.mhmagents.com
e-mail: mhmagents@gmail.com
Fax: 01494 716448   Tel: 01494 711400

MILNER David MANAGEMENT
40 Whitehall Road
London E4 6DH
e-mail: milner.agent@btinternet.com
    Tel/Fax: 020-8523 8086

MIME THE GAP
Mime Artistes. Physical Comedy Specialists
23 Manor Place
Staines, Middlesex TW18 1AE
Website: www.mimethegap.com   Mobile: 07970 685982

MINT MANAGEMENT
1 Sheencroft Cottages
Bessels Way, Blewbury
Didcot, Oxon OX11 9ED
e-mail: lisi@mintman.co.uk
Mobile: 07792 107644   Tel/Fax: 01235 851165

MITCHELL MAAS McLENNAN
MD 2000 Offices
Island Business Centre
Thomas Street
Woolich, London SE18 63F
Website: www.mmm2000.co.uk
e-mail: agency@mmm2000.co.uk   Tel/Fax: 01767 650020

MLR
(See MACNAUGHTON LORD REPRESENTATION)

MONDI ASSOCIATES Ltd
Unit 3 O, Cooper House
2 Michael Road
London SW6 2AD
Website: www.mondiassociates.com
e-mail: info@mondiassociates.com   Mobile: 07817 133349

MONTAGU ASSOCIATES
Ground Floor
13 Hanley Road
London N4 3DU
e-mail: montagus@btconnect.com   Tel: 020-7263 3883

MOORE Jakki MANAGEMENT
Ulpha Room
Millom Network Centre
Salthouse Road
Millom
Cumbria LA18 5AB
e-mail: jakki@jakkimoore.com
Mobile: 07967 612784   Tel: 01229 719656

MORGAN & GOODMAN
Mezzanine
Quadrant House
80-82 Regent Street
London W1B 5RP
e-mail: mg1@btinternet.com
Fax: 020-7494 3446   Tel: 020-7437 1383

MORGAN Lee MANAGEMENT
Cameo House
Suite 17
11 Bear Street
Leicester Square
London WC2H 7AS
Website: www.leemorganmanagement.co.uk
e-mail: leemorganmgnt@aol.com
Fax: 020-7839 1900   Tel: 020-7766 5234

MORRIS Andrew MANAGEMENT
Penthouse Offices
60 Reachview Close
Camden Town
London NW1 0TY
e-mail: morrisagent@yahoo.co.uk
Mobile: 07918 636775   Tel/Fax: 020-7482 0451

www.londonfaces.com

SOCRATES MITSIOS

studio and outdoor headshots   email@londonfaces.com ✉
for actors and performers   07903000017 ☎

MOUTHPIECE MANAGEMENT
PO Box 145, Inkberrow
Worcestershire WR7 4ZG
Website: www.mouthpiecemanagement.co.uk
e-mail: karin@mouthpiecemanagement.co.uk
Mobile: 07900 240904   Tel: 01527 850149

MPC ENTERTAINMENT
Contact: By Post/Telephone
MPC House, 15-16 Maple Mews
Maida Vale, London NW6 5UZ
Website: www.mpce.com
e-mail: mpc@mpce.com
Fax: 020-7624 4220   Tel: 020-7624 1184

MR.MANAGEMENT
(Personal Manager)
Contact: Ross Dawes, Mark Pollard
By Post/email. Accepts Showreels
2 Agents represent 60 Performers
Commercials. Film. Musicals. Stage. Television
29 Belton Road, Brighton, East Sussex BN2 3RE
e-mail: mr.management@ntlworld.com
Fax: 020-8579 6360   Tel: 01273 232381

MUGSHOTS AGENCY
153 Buckhurst Avenue, Carshalton, Surrey SM5 1PD
e-mail: becky@mugshots.co.uk
Fax: 020-8296 8056   Tel: 020-8296 0393

SIMON & HOW ASSOCIATES

t. 0845 064 6666   90-92 Ley Street
e. info@simon-how.com   Ilford Essex
w. www.simon-how.com   IG1 4BX

london based talent agency for tv, film, commercials, theatre & dance.

Fred Ledoux

Lucy Smith
photographer

www.thatlucy.co.uk

MURPHY Elaine ASSOCIATES
Suite 1
50 High Street
London E11 2RJ
e-mail: elaine@elainemurphy.co.uk
Fax: 020-8989 1400   Tel: 020-8989 4122

MUSIC INTERNATIONAL
13 Ardilaun Road
London N5 2QR
Website: www.musicint.co.uk
e-mail: music@musicint.co.uk
Fax: 020-7226 9792   Tel: 020-7359 5183

MV MANAGEMENT
*Clients must be graduates of Mountview Academy of
Theatre Arts*
Co-operative of 25 performers
Ralph Richardson Memorial Studios
Kingfisher Place
Clarendon Road, London N22 6XF
e-mail: theagency@mountview.org.uk
Fax: 020-8829 1050   Tel: 020-8889 8231

MYERS MANAGEMENT
63 Fairfields Crescent
London NW9 0PR   Tel/Fax: 020-8204 8941

NARROW ROAD COMPANY The
(PMA Member)
3rd Floor
76 Neal Street
London WC2H 9PL
e-mail: agents@narrowroad.co.uk
Fax: 020-7379 9777   Tel: 020-7379 9598

182 Brighton Road
Coulsdon, Surrey CR5 2NF
e-mail: coulsdon@narrowroad.co.uk
Fax: 020-8763 2558   Tel: 020-8763 9895

2nd Floor
Grampian House
144 Deansgate
Manchester M3 3EE
e-mail: manchester@narrowroad.co.uk
          Tel/Fax: 0161-833 1605

NE REPRESENTATION
3-5 Bakehouse Hill
Darlington
Co. Durham DL1 5QA
Website: www.nerepresentation.co.uk
e-mail: info@nerepresentation.co.uk
Fax: 01325 488390   Tel: 01325 488385

NELSON BROWNE MANAGEMENT Ltd
40 Bowling Green Lane
London EC1R 0NE
Website: www.nelsonbrowne.com
e-mail: enquiries@nelsonbrowne.com
Fax: 020-7837 7612   Tel: 020-7970 6010

NEVS AGENCY
Regal House
198 King's Road
London SW3 5XP
Website: www.nevs.co.uk
e-mail: getamodel@nevs.co.uk
Fax: 020-7352 6068   Tel: 020-7352 4886

NEW CASEY AGENCY
The Annexe
129 Northwood Way
Northwood HA6 1RF   Tel: 01923 823182

NEW FACES Ltd
(Personal Manager)
Contact: Val Horton
By Post/email
Accepts Showreels
*3 Agents represent 50 Performers. Children. Commercials
Film. Stage. Television*
2nd Floor
The Linen Hall
162-168 Regent Street
London W1B 5TB
Website: www.newfacestalent.co.uk
e-mail: info@newfacestalent.co.uk
Fax: 020-7287 5481   Tel: 020-7439 6900

NFD - THE FILM & TV AGENCY
PO Box 76
Leeds LS25 9AG
Website: www.film-tv-agency.com
e-mail: info@film-tv-agency.com   Tel/Fax: 01977 681949

NICHOLSON Jackie ASSOCIATES
(Personal Manager)
Contact: By Post
Suite 44, 2nd Floor
Morley House
320 Regent Street, London W1B 3BD
e-mail: jnalondon@aol.com
Fax: 020-7580 4489   Tel: 020-7580 4422

N M MANAGEMENT
16 St Alfege Passage
Greenwich
London SE10 9JS
e-mail: nmmanagement@hotmail.com   Tel: 020-8853 4337

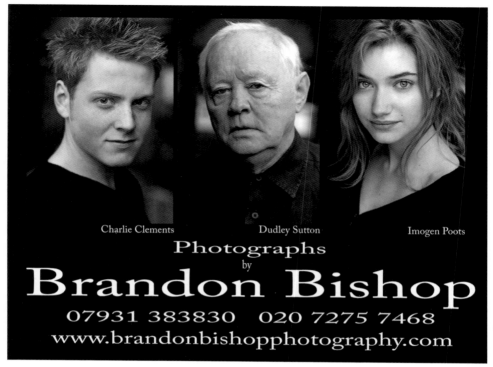

Charlie Clements   Dudley Sutton   Imogen Poots

Photographs
by
Brandon Bishop
07931 383830   020 7275 7468
www.brandonbishopphotography.com

NMP MANAGEMENT
(Personal Manager)
Contact: By email
2 Agents represent 10 Performers
Corporate. Presenters. Television
PO Box 981, Wallington, Surrey SM6 8JU
Website: www.nmpmanagement.co.uk
e-mail: management@nmp.co.uk
Fax: 020-8404 2621   Tel: 020-8669 3128

NORTH OF WATFORD ACTORS AGENCY
(Co-operative)
Bridge Mill, Hebden Bridge, West Yorks HX7 8EX
Website: www.northofwatford.com
e-mail: info@northofwatford.com
Fax: 01422 846503   Tel: 01422 845361

NORTH WEST ACTORS
(Personal Manager)
Contact: Richard White
By Post.
Accepts Showreels/Voicereels
Commercials. Film. Stage. Television
36 Lord Street
Radcliffe, Manchester M26 3BA
Website: www.northwestactors.co.uk
e-mail: info@northwestactors.co.uk   Tel/Fax: 0161-724 6625

NORTHERN LIGHTS MANAGEMENT Ltd
Dean Clough Mills
Halifax, West Yorks HX3 5AX
e-mail: northern.lights@virgin.net
Fax: 01422 330101   Tel: 01422 382203

URBAN TALENT
Actors for work in Film, Television, Theatre & Commercials

Nemesis House, 1 Oxford Court, Bishopsgate, Manchester M2 3WQ,
Tel: 0161 228 6866, Fax 0161 228 6727,
www.urbantalent.tv, liz@nmsmanagement.co.uk

NORTHERN PROFESSIONALS
Casting, Technicians, Action Safety, Boat & Diving
Equipment Hire
21 Cresswell Avenue, North Shields
Tyne & Wear NE29 9BQ
Website: www.northernprocasting.co.uk
e-mail: bill@northernprocasting.co.uk
Fax: 0191-296 3243   Tel: 0191-257 8635

NORTHONE MANAGEMENT
(CPMA Member)
HG08 Aberdeen Studios, Highbury Grove, London N5 2EA
Website: www.northone.co.uk
e-mail: actors@northone.co.uk   Tel/Fax: 020-7359 9666

NS ARTISTES MANAGEMENT
10 Claverdon House
Holly Bank Road
Billesley, Birmingham B13 0QY
Website: www.nsmanagement.co.uk
e-mail: nsmanagement@fsmail.net   Tel: 0121-684 5607

NSM
(Natasha Stevenson Management Ltd)
(Personal Manager) (PMA Member)
Contact: By Post/email/Telephone
3 Agents
Commercials. Film. Stage. Television
Studio 7C, Clapham North Arts Centre
Voltaire Road, London SW4 6DH
Website: www.natashastevenson.co.uk
e-mail: inbox@natashastevenson.co.uk
Fax: 020-7720 5565   Tel: 020-7720 3355

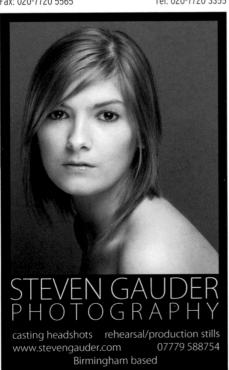

STEVEN GAUDER
PHOTOGRAPHY
casting headshots   rehearsal/production stills
www.stevengauder.com   07779 588754
Birmingham based

NUMBER ONE CASTING & MODEL MANAGEMENT Ltd
The Barn, Pasture Farm
Coventry Road
Solihull B92 0HH
Website: www.numberonemodelagency.co.uk
e-mail: info@numberonemodelagency.co.uk
                                      Tel: 01675 443900

NYLAND MANAGEMENT Ltd
20 School Lane
Heaton Chapel
Stockport SK4 5DG
e-mail: nylandmgmt@freenet.co.uk   Tel: 0161-442 2224

OFF THE KERB PRODUCTIONS
3rd Floor
Hammer House
113-117 Wardour Street
London W1F 0UN
Website: www.offthekerb.co.uk
e-mail: info@offthekerb.co.uk
Fax: 020-7437 0647   Tel: 020-7437 0607

OI OI AGENCY
2 Agents represent 300 Performers
Children. Commercials. Corporate. Dancers. Disabled. Film
Modelling. Musicals. Presenters. Radio. Singers. Stage
Television. Voice Overs
Pinewood Film Studios
Pinewood Road
Iver Heath, Bucks SL0 0NH
Website: www.oioi.org.uk
e-mail: info@oioi.org.uk
Fax: 01753 655622   Tel: 01753 655514

OLIVER & OLIVER
Contact: Oliver Hume. By Post/email
Co-operative of 8 Performers
33 Coleridge Road
Walthamstow
London E17 6QX
e-mail: olivernoliver@gmail.com   Tel: 08712 775090

ONE MAKE UP/ONE PHOTOGRAPHIC Ltd
4th Floor
48 Poland Street, London W1F 7ND
Website: www.onemakeup.com
e-mail: info@onemakeup.com
Fax: 020-7287 2313   Tel: 020-7287 2311

ONSCREEN AGENCY.COM
Contact: By email
Accepts Showreels
3 Agents represent 20 Performers
Commercials. Ethnic Artistes. Film. Television
No 199
Lansdowne Row
Mayfair, London W1J 6HL
Website: www.onscreenagency.com
e-mail: info@onscreenagency.com
Fax: 020-7493 4935   Tel: 020-7193 7547

OPERA & CONCERT ARTISTS
Musicals. Opera
75 Aberdare Gardens
London NW6 3AN
e-mail: enquiries@opera-and-concert-artists.co.uk
Fax: 020-7372 3537   Tel: 020-7328 3097

ORDINARY PEOPLE
Actors. Modelling
16 Camden Road, London NW1 9DP
Website: www.ordinarypeople.co.uk
e-mail: info@ordinarypeople.co.uk
Fax: 020-7267 5677   Tel: 020-7267 7007

OREN
(See CARDIFF CASTING)

ORIENTAL CASTING AGENCY Ltd
Contact: Peggy Sirr
By email/Telephone
Accepts Showreels/Voicereels
1 Agent represents 200+ Performers
Afro/Asian Artists
1 Wyatt Park Road
Streatham Hill, London SW2 3TN
Website: www.orientalcasting.com
e-mail: peggy.sirr@btconnect.com
Fax: 020-8674 9303   Tel: 020-8671 8538

OTTO PERSONAL MANAGEMENT Ltd
(Personal Manager) (CPMA Member)
S.I.F.
5 Brown Street
Sheffield S1 2BS
Website: www.ottopm.co.uk
e-mail: admin@ottopm.co.uk
Fax: 0114-279 5225   Tel: 0114-275 2592

OUR COMPANY
Room 205
Channelsea House
Canning Road
Stratford, London E15 3ND
Website: www.our-company.co.uk
e-mail: info@our-company.co.uk
Fax: 020-8221 1167   Tel: 020-8221 1151

PADBURY David ASSOCIATES
44 Summerlee Avenue
Finchley, London N2 9QP
Website: www.davidpadburyassociates.com
e-mail: info@davidpadburyassociates.com
      Tel/Fax: 020-8883 1277

PAN ARTISTS AGENCY Ltd
Cornerways
34 Woodhouse Lane
Sale, Cheshire M33 4JX
Website: www.panartists.co.uk
e-mail: panartists@btconnect.com
Mobile: 07890 715115   Tel: 0800 6349147

PANTO PEOPLE
3 Rushden House, Tatlow Road
Glenfield, Leicester LE3 8ND
e-mail: jonny.dallas@ntlworld.com   Tel/Fax: 0116-287 9594

PARAMOUNT INTERNATIONAL MANAGEMENT
30 Performers. International Comedians
Talbot House
204-226 Imperial Drive
Harrow, Middlesex HA2 7HH
Website: www.ukcomedy.com
e-mail: mail@ukcomedy.com
Fax: 020-8868 6475   Tel: 020-8429 3179

PARKER Cherry MANAGEMENT (RSM)
(See RSM: Cherry Parker Management)

PARSONS & BROOK
Contact: By email. Accepts Showreels. 2 Agents represent
65 Performers. Commercials. Corporate. Film. Musicals.
Radio. Stage. Television
37 Berwick Street, London W1F 8RS
e-mail: info@parsonsandbrook.co.uk
Fax: 020-7287 8016   Tel: 020-7434 0398

PARSONS Cary MANAGEMENT
Set, Costume & Lighting Designers, Directors &
Choreographers
Goldicote Lodge, Goldicote Road
Loxley, Warwickshire CV35 9LF
e-mail: carylparsons@gmail.com   Tel/Fax: 01789 840453

P B J MANAGEMENT Ltd
(Personal Manager) (PMA Member)
Contact: Janette Linden. By email
Accepts Showreels
8 Agents represent 54 Performers
Comedians. Commercials. Corporate. Presenters. Radio.
Stage. Television. Voice Overs. Walk-on & Supporting
Artists. Writers
7 Soho Street, London W1D 3DQ
Website: www.pbjmgt.co.uk
e-mail: general@pbjmgt.co.uk
Fax: 020-7287 1191   Tel: 020-7287 1112

PC THEATRICAL, MODEL & CASTING AGENCY
Large Database of Twins
12 Carlisle Road
Colindale, London NW9 0HL
Website: www.twinagency.com
e-mail: twinagy@aol.com
Fax: 020-8933 3418   Tel: 020-8381 2229

PELHAM ASSOCIATES
(Personal Manager)
(PMA Member)
Contact: Peter Cleall
The Media Centre
9-12 Middle Street, Brighton BN1 1AL
Website: www.pelhamassociates.co.uk
e-mail: petercleall@pelhamassociates.co.uk
Fax: 01273 202492   Tel: 01273 323010

PEMBERTON ASSOCIATES Ltd
(PMA Member)
Contact: Barbara Pemberton
By Post/email
Showreels on request. 5 Agents represent 130 Performers
Film. Musicals. Radio. Singers. Stage. Television
Voice Overs
193 Wardour Street, London W1F 8ZF
Website: www.pembertonassociates.com
e-mail: general@pembertonassociates.com
Fax: 020-7734 2522   Tel: 020-7734 4144

Express Networks
1 George Leigh Street, Manchester M4 5DL
Fax: 0161-235 8442   Tel: 0161-235 8440

PEPPERPOT PROMOTIONS
Bands
Suite 20B
20-22 Orde Hall Street, London WC1N 3JW
e-mail: chris@pepperpot.co.uk
Fax: 01255 473107   Tel: 020-7405 9108

PERFORMANCE ACTORS AGENCY
(Co-operative) (CPMA Member)
137 Goswell Road, London EC1V 7ET
Website: www.performanceactors.co.uk
e-mail: info@performanceactors.co.uk
Fax: 020-7251 3974   Tel: 020-7251 5716

STAGEWORKS®
WORLDWIDE PRODUCTIONS

agency

SKATING
ICE DANCERS
FREE SKATERS
PAIR SKATERS
ADAGIO SKATERS
COMEDY SKATERS

DANCERS
ACTORS
SINGERS
MODELS

CIRCUS ARTISTS
SPECIALITY ACTS
MAGICIANS
ILLUSIONISTS
COSTUME CHARACTERS
STREET PERFORMERS

PROMOTIONAL PERSONNEL
HOSTS & HOSTESSES
GUEST SPEAKERS

SCRIPT WRITING

TECHNICAL STAGE MANAGEMENT

MUSIC PRODUCTION
PUBLISHING

MILLINERY AND COSTUMES

CHOREOGRAPHERS
DIRECTORS
PRODUCERS

00 44 **(0) 1253 342426**
00 44 **(0) 1253 336341**
info@stageworkswwp.com
stageworkswwp.com

PERFORMERS DIRECTORY
Actors. Dancers. Modelling. Walk-on & Supporting Artists
PO Box 29942
London SW6 1FL
Website: www.performersdirectory.co.uk
e-mail: performersdirectory@yahoo.com Tel: 020-7610 6677

PERFORMING ARTS
(Personal Manager) (PMA Member)
Contact: By Post/email
2 Agents represent 30 Performers Creative Team
Members Only
6 Windmill Street
London W1T 2JB
Website: www.performing-arts.co.uk
e-mail: info@performing-arts.co.uk
Fax: 020-7631 4631   Tel: 020-7255 1362

PERSONAL APPEARANCES
Contact: By email
Corporate. Presenters. Radio. Television. Voice Overs
20 North Mount, 1147-1161 High Road
Whetstone N20 0PH
Website: www.personalappearances.biz
e-mail: patsy@personalappearances.biz
                    Tel/Fax: 020-8343 7748

P F D
(PMA Member)
Drury House
34-43 Russell Street, London WC2B 5HA
Website: www.pfd.co.uk
e-mail: actors@pfd.co.uk
Fax: 020-7836 9544   Tel: 020-7344 1010

PHA ACTORS MANAGEMENT
Tanzaro House
Ardwick Green North, Manchester M12 6FZ
Website: www.pha-agency.co.uk
e-mail: casting@pha-agency.co.uk
Fax: 0161-273 4567   Tel: 0161-273 4444

PHD ARTISTS
24 Montana Gardens
Sutton, Surrey SM1 4FP
Website: www.phdartists.com
e-mail: office@phdartists.com   Tel/Fax: 020-7241 6601

PHILLIPS Frances
(Personal Manager)
(PMA Member)
Contact: Frances Zealander-Phillips
By email
2 Agents represent 40 Performers
89 Robeson Way
Borehamwood
Hertfordshire WD6 5RY
Website: www.francesphillips.co.uk
e-mail: derekphillips@talk21.com
Mobile: 07957 334328   Tel: 020-8953 0303

PHPM
(Philippa Howell Personal Management)
(Personal Manager)
Contact: By Post (SAE)/email
2 Agents represent 80 Performers
Commercials. Film. Musicals. Stage. Television
184 Bradway Road
Sheffield S17 4QX
e-mail: philippa@phpm.co.uk   Tel/Fax: 0114-235 3663

PHYSICK Hilda
(Personal Manager)
Contact: By Post
78 Temple Sheen Road
London SW14 7RR
Fax: 020-8876 5561   Tel: 020-8876 0073

PICCADILLY MANAGEMENT
(Personal Manager)
23 New Mount Street
Manchester M4 4DE
Website: www.piccadillymanagement.com
e-mail: info@piccadillymanagement.com
Fax: 0161-953 4001   Tel: 0161-953 4057

PINEAPPLE AGENCY
Montgomery House
159-161 Balls Pond Road
London N1 4BG
Website: www.pineappleagency.com
e-mail: pineapple.agency@btconnect.com
Fax: 020-7241 3006   Tel: 020-7241 6601

SMILE TALENT

AGENTS & PERSONAL MANAGERS ARE PROUD TO REPRESENT THE FOLLOWING ACTORS

Phone: 01799 531966 E-mail: info@smiletalent.com

Annie Aldington | Beinn Alec | Daryl Branch | James Bunyon

Alarna Carr | Michael Coghlan | Hugh Coleridge | Geoff Cotton

Claire G Conroy | Harold Gasnier | Maria Holmes | Michael Miller

Judith Quin | Monica Purcell | Katrina Sheffield | Caroline Short

Graham Smith | Dag Soerlie | Sam White | Henry Steele

Smile Talent, The Studio, Unit 16/17, Ickleton Riverside Barns, Frogge Street, Ickleton, Saffron Walden, Essex CB10 1SH
Fax: 01799 531476   Mobile: 07984 464748   www.smiletalent.biz

PLA
(LOVETT Pat ASSOCIATES)
(PMA Member)
5 Union Street, Edinburgh EH1 3LT
Website: www.pla-uk.com
e-mail: edinburgh@pla-uk.com
Fax: 0131-478 7070   Tel: 0131-478 7878

40 Margaret Street, London W1G 0JH
e-mail: london@pla-uk.com
Fax: 020-7495 6411   Tel: 020-7495 6400

PLAIN JANE
PO Box 2730
Romford, Essex RM7 1AB
Website: www.plain-jane.co.uk
e-mail: info@plain-jane.co.uk   Mobile: 07813 667319

PLATER Janet MANAGEMENT Ltd
Contact: By Post
D Floor, Milburn House
Dean Street
Newcastle upon Tyne NE1 1LF
Website: www.janetplatermanagement.co.uk
e-mail: magpie@tynebridge.demon.co.uk   Tel: 0191-221 2490

PLUNKET GREENE ASSOCIATES
(In conjunction with James Sharkey Associates Ltd)
Existing Clients only
PO Box 8365, London W14 0GL
Fax: 020-7603 2221   Tel: 020-7603 2227

POLLYANNA MANAGEMENT Ltd
1 Knighten Street
Wapping, London E1W 1PH
Website: www.pollyannatheatre.com
e-mail: aliceharwood@talktalk.net
Fax: 020-7480 6761   Tel: 020-7481 1911

POOLE Gordon AGENCY Ltd
The Limes, Brockley
Bristol BS48 3BB
Website: www.gordonpoole.com
e-mail: agents@gordonpoole.com
Fax: 01275 462252   Tel: 01275 463222

POWER MODEL MANAGEMENT CASTING AGENCY
PO Box 1198
Salhouse, Norwich NR13 6WD
Website: www.powermodel.co.uk
e-mail: info@powermodel.co.uk   Tel: 01603 777190

POWER PROMOTIONS
PO Box 61, Liverpool L13 0EF
Website: www.powerpromotions.com
e-mail: tom@powerpromotions.co.uk
Fax: 0870 7060202   Tel: 0151-230 0070

PREGNANT PAUSE AGENCY
Pregnant Models, Dancers, Actresses
11 Matham Road
East Molesey KT8 0SX
Website: www.pregnantpause.co.uk
e-mail: sandy@pregnantpause.co.uk   Tel: 020-8979 8874

PRESTON Morwenna MANAGEMENT
(See TAKE FLIGHT MANAGEMENT)

PRICE GARDNER MANAGEMENT
PO Box 59908
London SW16 5QH
Website: www.pricegardner.co.uk
e-mail: info@pricegardner.co.uk
Fax: 020-7381 3288   Tel: 020-7610 2111

PRINCIPAL ARTISTES
(Personal Manager)
Contact: By Post
4 Paddington Street
Marylebone
London W1U 5QE
Fax: 020-7486 4668   Tel: 020-7224 3414

PRODUCTIONS & PROMOTIONS Ltd
Apsley Mills Cottage
London Road
Hemel Hempstead
Herts HP3 9QU
Website: www.prodmotions.com
e-mail: reception@prodmotions.com   Tel: 01442 233372

PROSPECTS ASSOCIATIONS
Sessions. Singers. Voice Overs for Commercials,
Film & Television
28 Magpie Close
Forest Gate
London E7 9DE   Tel: 020-8555 3628

PURE ACTORS AGENCY & MANAGEMENT Ltd
44 Salisbury Road
Manchester M41 0RB
Website: www.pure-management.co.uk
e-mail: enquiries@pure-management.co.uk
Fax: 0161-746 9886   Tel: 0161-747 2377

PVA MANAGEMENT Ltd
Hallow Park
Worcestershire WR2 6PG
e-mail: clients@pva.co.uk
Fax: 01905 641842   Tel: 01905 640663

QUICK Nina ASSOCIATES
(See TAYLOR Brian ASSOCIATES)

NEXT STOP

NextStopLAˣ
+44 207 0961 301
+1 323.363.9933
info@nextstoplax.com
www.nextstoplax.com

RELOCATING ENTERTAINMENT INDUSTRY PROFESSIONALS
Flawlessly

"We at NextStopLAx are here to take care of the busy work for you. We know making the transition from your home to Los Angeles can be quite a challenge—and as glamorous as LA can be, we understand there's a lot of fluff, mistrust, and drama that comes with the city, too. That's why our relocation and concierge service are here for you, specializing in setting up entertainment industry professionals, like yourselves, comfortably in LA."

-Andy Newton Lee, Managing Director

SOME OF OUR SERVICES:
(For a complete list of services go to our website)

US VISAS   **AIRFARE**   **ACCOMMODATION**   **TRANSPORT**

CLIENTS INCLUDE:

Nadine Coyle (Girls Aloud)
Simon Cole (Hollyoaks)
Jon Lee (S Club 7)
Samantha Mumba (Singer)
Aaron Renfree (S Club 8)
Guy Burnett (Hollyoaks)

Sam Robertson (Coronation St.)
Louise Brady (TV Presenter)
Leilani Dowding (Model)
Calvin Goldspink (S Club 8)
Jason Smith (Home and Away)
Pooja Shah (EastEnders)

www.nextstoplax.com

LONDON LOS ANGELES SYDNEY

RAFFLES Tim ENTERTAINMENTS
(Personal Manager)
2 Agents represent 9 Performers
Corporate. Cruise Work. Singers. Television
Victoria House
29 Swaythling Road
West End, Southampton SO30 3AG
Website: www.timrafflesentertainments.co.uk
e-mail: info@timrafflesentertainments.co.uk
Tel/Fax: 023-8046 5843

RAGE MODELS
Tigris House
256 Edgware Road
London W2 1DS
Website: www.ragemodels.org
e-mail: ragemodels@ugly.org
Fax: 020-7402 0507   Tel: 020-7262 0515

RAMA GLOBAL Ltd
Contact: Rachael Pacey
By Post
Accepts Showreels
1 Agent represents 10 Performers
Children. Commercials. Film. Stage. Television.
Huntingdon House
278-290 Huntingdon Street
Nottingham NG1 3LY
Website: www.rama-global.co.uk
e-mail: admin@rama-global.co.uk
Fax: 0115-948 3696   Tel: 0845 0540255

RANDALL RICHARDSON ACTORS MANAGEMENT
2nd Floor
145-157 St John Street
London EC1V 4PY
Website: www.randallrichardson.co.uk
e-mail: mail@randallrichardson.co.uk
Fax: 0870 7623212   Tel: 020-7060 1645

RAPID TALENT Ltd
10 Cornfield Lane
Eastbourne
East Sussex BN21 4NE
Website: www.rapidtalent.co.uk
e-mail: enquiries@rapidtalent.co.uk
Fax: 01323 720342   Tel: 020-7734 5775

RAVENSCOURT MANAGEMENT
8-30 Galena Road
Hammersmith
London W6 0LT
Website: www.ravenscourt.net
e-mail: info@ravenscourt.net
Fax: 020-8741 1786   Tel: 020-8741 0707

RAW AGENCY
Studio 1, Bizzy House
73A Mayplace Road West
Bexleyheath
Kent DA7 4JL
Website: www.raw-agency.com   Tel: 020-8303 2627 Ext 24

RAY KNIGHT CASTING
(See KNIGHT Ray CASTING)

RAZZAMATAZZ MANAGEMENT
Mulberry Cottage
Park Farm
Haxted Road
Lingfield RH7 6DE
e-mail: razzamatazzmanagement@btconnect.com
Tel/Fax: 01342 835359

RbA MANAGEMENT Ltd
(Personal Manager) (CPMA Member)
Contact: By email
27 Performers. Accepts Showreels/Voicereels
37-45 Windsor Street
Liverpool L8 1XE
Website: www.rbamanagement.co.uk
e-mail: info@rbamanagement.co.uk   Tel: 0151-708 7273

RBM ACTORS
3rd Floor, 168 Victoria Street
London SW1E 5LB
Website: www.rbmactors.com
e-mail: info@rbmactors.com
Fax: 020-7630 6549   Tel: 020-7630 7733

RDF MANAGEMENT
(Personal Manager) (PMA Member)
Contact: Debi Allen
By Post/email
Accepts Showreels
5 Agents represent 135 Performers
Children. Presenters. Stage. Television. Writers
3-6 Kenrick Place
London W1U 6HD
e-mail: debi.allen@rdfmanagement.com
Fax: 020-7317 2245   Tel: 020-7317 2251

REACTORS AGENCY
Contact by Post/email
Accepts Showreels
Co-operative of 23 Performers
1 Eden Quay
Dublin 1, Ireland
Website: www.reactors.ie
e-mail: info@reactors.ie
Fax: 00 353 1 8783182   Tel: 00 353 1 8786833

Lime

Lime Actors Agency & Management Ltd

Nemesis House / 1 Oxford Court / Bishopsgate / Manchester / M2 3WQ
0161 236 0827 / www.limemanagement.tv / georgina@limemanagement.co.uk

REAL PEOPLE, REAL TALENT
Half Moon Chambers
Chapel Walks, Manchester M2 1HN
Website: www.realpeople4u.com
e-mail: info@realpeople4u.com
Fax: 0161-832 5219   Tel: 0161-832 8259

RE.ANIMATOR MANAGEMENT
(PMA Member)
3rd Floor, The Priory
Syresham Gardens
West Sussex RH16 3LB
Website: www.reanimator.co.uk
e-mail: management@reanimator.co.uk
Fax: 01444 447030   Tel: 01444 447020

RED&BLACK
Website: www.red-black.co.uk
e-mail: info@red-black.co.uk   Mobile: 07722 887277

RED CANYON MANAGEMENT
Website: www.redcanyon.co.uk
e-mail: info@redcanyon.co.uk
Mobile: 07939 365578   Mobile: 07931 381696

RED DOOR MANAGEMENT
The Pie Factory
101 Broadway
Media City
Manchester M50 2EQ
Website: www.the-reddoor.co.uk
e-mail: mail@the-reddoor.co.uk   Tel/Fax: 0161-425 6495

RED HOT ENTERTAINMENT
6 Farriers Mews
London SE15 3XP
Website: www.redhotentertainment.biz
e-mail: info@redhotentertainment.biz
Fax: 020-7635 8988   Tel: 020-7635 0403

RED ONION AGENCY
Session Fixer for Singers, Musicians and Gospel Choirs
26-28 Hatherley Mews, London E17 4QP
Website: www.redonion.uk.com
e-mail: studio@redonion.uk.com
Fax: 020-8521 6646   Tel: 020-8520 3975

REDDIN Joan
(Personal Manager)
Contact: By Post
Hazel Cottage, Frogg's Island, Wheeler End Common
Bucks HP14 3NL   Tel: 01494 882729

REDROOFS ASSOCIATES
Littlewick Green
Maidenhead, Berkshire SL6 3QY
Website: www.redroofs.co.uk
e-mail: agency@redroofs.co.uk
Fax: 01628 822461   Tel: 01628 822982

REGAN RIMMER MANAGEMENT
Contact: Debbie Rimmer
Suite 4, Little Russell House
22 Little Russell Street
London WC1A 2HS
e-mail: thegirls@regan-rimmer.co.uk
Fax: 020-7404 9958   Tel: 020-7404 9957

Contact: Leigh-Ann Regan
Ynyslas Uchaf Farm
Blackmill, Bridgend CF35 6DW
e-mail: regan-rimmer@btconnect.com
Fax: 01656 841815   Tel: 01656 841841

REGENCY AGENCY
25 Carr Road, Calverley
Leeds LS28 5NE   Tel: 0113-255 8980

REPRESENTATION UPSON EDWARDS
Voice Coaches only
23 Victoria Park Road
Stoke on Trent, Staffs ST6 6DX
Website: www.voicecoach.tv
e-mail: sarah.upson@voicecoach.tv
Fax: 01782 728004   Tel: 01782 827222

REYNOLDS Sandra AGENCY
Contact: By email
8 Agents represent 150 Performers
Children. Commercials. Modelling. Presenters. Television
Shakespeare House
168 Lavender Hill, London SW11 5TF
Website: www.sandrareynolds.co.uk
e-mail: info@sandrareynolds.co.uk
Fax: 020-7387 5848   Tel: 020-7387 5858

Bacon House
35 St Georges Street, Norwich NR3 1DA
Fax: 01603 219825   Tel: 01603 623842

RHINO PERSONAL MANAGEMENT
Studio House, Delamare Road
Cheshunt, Herts EN8 9SH
Website: www.rhino-management.co.uk
e-mail: rhinomanagement@hotmail.co.uk
Fax: 0845 3625457   Tel: 0845 3625456

RICHARDS Lisa AGENCY The
108 Upper Leeson Street
Dublin 4, Ireland
Website: www.lisarichards.ie
e-mail: info@lisarichards.ie
Fax: 00 353 1 667 1256   Tel: 00 353 1 637 5000

The Space, 57-61 Mortimer Street, London W1W 8HS
Website: www.lisarichards.ie
e-mail: rose@lisarichards.ie   Tel: 020-3170 6205

RICHARDS Stella MANAGEMENT
Contact: Stella Richards, Julia Lintott
Existing Clients Only
42 Hazlebury Road
London SW6 2ND
Website: www.stellarichards.com
e-mail: stellaagent@aol.com
Fax: 020-7731 5082   Tel: 020-7736 7786

RICHARD STONE PARTNERSHIP The
(See STONE Richard PARTNERSHIP The)

RIDGEWAY MANAGEMENT
Fairley House
Andrews Lane
Cheshunt, Herts EN7 6LB
e-mail: info@ridgewaystudios.co.uk
Fax: 01992 633844   Tel: 01992 633775

ROGUES & VAGABONDS MANAGEMENT Ltd
(Personal Manager) (CPMA Member)
The Print House
18 Ashwin Street, London E8 3DL
e-mail: rogues@vagabondsmanagement.com
Fax: 020-7249 8564   Tel: 020-7254 8130

ROLE MODELS
12 Cressy Road, London NW3 2LY
Website: www.rolemodelsagency.com
e-mail: info@rolemodelsagency.com   Tel: 020-7284 4337

ROSEBERY MANAGEMENT Ltd
(CPMA Member)
Contact: Alan Bell
By Post. Accepts Showreels
1 Agent represents 27 Performers
Commercials. Film. Musicals. Stage. Television. Voice Overs
Hoxton Hall
130 Hoxton Street, London N1 6SH
Website: www.roseberymanagement.com
e-mail: admin@roseberymanagement.com
Fax: 020-7503 0517   Tel: 020-7684 0187

ROSEMAN ORGANISATION The
51 Queen Anne Street, London W1G 9HS
Website: www.therosemanorganisation.co.uk
e-mail: info@therosemanorganisation.co.uk
Fax: 020-7486 4600   Tel: 020-7486 4500

Christine Adams

Carsten Hayes

Natasha Merchant - Greenberg
Photographer

020 8653 5399   www.natashamerchant.com   **07932 618 111**

ROSS BROWN ASSOCIATES
(Personal Manager)
Rosedale House, Rosedale Road, Richmond, Surrey TW9 2SZ
e-mail: sandy@rossbrown.eu
Fax: 020-8398 4111   Tel: 020-8398 3984

ROSS Frances MANAGEMENT
(Personal Manager)
Contact: Frances Ross
By Post/email/Telephone
1 Agent represents 11 Performers
Commercials. Corporate. Film. Stage. Television
Higher Leyonne, Golant, Fowey, Cornwall PL23 1LA
e-mail: francesross@btconnect.com
Mobile: 07918 648330   Tel/Fax: 01726 833004

ROSSMORE PERSONAL MANAGEMENT
(PMA Member)
70-76 Bell Street, London NW1 6SP
Website: www.rossmoremanagement.com
e-mail: agents@rossmoremanagement.com
Fax: 020-7258 0124   Tel: 020-7258 1953

ROUGH HANDS AGENCY The
29 James Street, Epping, Essex, London CM16 6RR
e-mail: roughhandsagency@yahoo.co.uk
Mobile: 07932 573228   Tel: 01992 578835

ROWE ASSOCIATES
33 Percy Street, London W1T 1DE
Website: www.growe.co.uk   e-mail: agents@growe.co.uk
Mobile: 07887 898220   Tel/Fax: 01992 308519

Theatrical Agents • **Actors** • **Dancers** • **Singers**
Models • **Presenters** • **Choreographers**

Room 236 Linen Hall 162-168 Regent Street London W1B 5TB
T 020 7734 3356 **F** 020 7494 3787
www.successagency.co.uk **e** ee@successagency.co.uk

ƒucceƒƒ

ROYCE MANAGEMENT
29 Trenholme Road
London SE20 8PP
Website: www.roycemanagement.co.uk
e-mail: office@roycemanagement.co.uk
Tel/Fax: 020-8778 6861

RSM (Cherry Parker Management)
Contact: Cherry Parker
15 The Fairway SS9 4QN
Website: www.rsm.uk.net
e-mail: info@rsm.uk.net
Mobile: 07976 547066　　Tel: 01702 522647

RUBICON MANAGEMENT
27 Inderwick Road
Crouch End, London N8 9LB
e-mail: rubiconartists@blueyonder.co.uk
Tel/Fax: 020-8374 1836

RUDEYE DANCE AGENCY
PO Box 38743
London E10 5WN
Website: www.rudeye.com
e-mail: info@rudeye.com　　Tel/Fax: 020-8556 7139

SANDERS Loesje Ltd
(PMA Member)
Contact: Jo Probitts
By Post
Choreographers. Designers. Directors. Lighting Designers
Pound Square
1 North Hill, Woodbridge
Suffolk IP12 1HH
Website: www.loesjesanders.com
e-mail: loesje@loesjesanders.org.uk
Fax: 01394 388734　　Tel: 01394 385260

SANGWIN ASSOCIATES
(PMA Member)
8-30 Galena Road
Hammersmith
London W6 0LT
e-mail: info@sangwinassoc.com
Fax: 020-8741 1786　　Tel: 020-8748 8698

SARABAND ASSOCIATES
Contact: Sara Randall, Bryn Newton
265 Liverpool Road, London N1 1LX
e-mail: brynnewton@btconnect.com
Fax: 020-7609 2370　　Tel: 020-7609 5313

SASHAZE TALENT AGENCY
2 Gleannan Close
Omagh, Co. Tyrone BT79 7YA
Website: www.sashaze.com
e-mail: info@sashaze.com
Mobile: 07773 786098　　Mobile: 07968 762942

SCA MANAGEMENT
Contact: By Post
77 Oxford Street, London W1D 2ES
Website: www.sca-management.co.uk
e-mail: agency@sca-management.co.uk
Fax: 020-7659 2116　　Tel: 020-7659 2027

SCHNABL Peter
The Barn House, Cutwell, Tetbury
Gloucestershire GL8 8EB
Fax: 01666 502998　　Tel: 01666 502133

SCOTT MARSHALL PARTNERS Ltd
(See MARSHALL Scott PARTNERS Ltd)

SCOTT Tim
PO Box 61776, London SW1V 3UX
e-mail: timscott@btinternet.com　　Tel/Fax: 020-7828 3824

SCOTT-PAUL YOUNG ENTERTAINMENTS Ltd
S.P.Y. Promotions & Productions
Northern Lights House
110 Blandford Road North
Langley, Nr Windsor
Berks SL3 7TA
Website: www.spy-ents.com
e-mail: castingdirect@spy-ents.com　　Tel/Fax: 01753 693250

SCRIMGEOUR Donald ARTISTS AGENT
Dancers
49 Springcroft Avenue, London N2 9JH
Website: www.donaldscrimgeour.com
e-mail: vwest@dircon.co.uk
Fax: 020-8883 9751　　Tel: 020-8444 6248

SEARS MANAGEMENT Ltd
2 Gumping Road
Orpington
Kent BR5 1RX
e-mail: lindasears@btconnect.com
Fax: 01689 862120   Tel: 01689 861859

SECOND SKIN AGENCY
Foxgrove House
School Lane, Seer Green
Beaconsfield
Bucks HP9 2QJ
Website: www.secondskinagency.com
e-mail: jenny@secondskinagency.com
                         Tel/Fax: 01494 730166

SEDGWICK Dawn MANAGEMENT
3 Goodwins Court
Covent Garden
London WC2N 4LL
Fax: 020-7240 0415   Tel: 020-7240 0404

SHALIT GLOBAL MANAGEMENT
4th Floor
34-35 Eastcastle Street
London W1W 8DW
e-mail: rich@shalitglobal.com
Fax: 020-7462 9061   Tel: 020-7462 9060

SHAPER Susan MANAGEMENT
5 Dovedale Gardens
465 Battersea Park Road
London SW11 4LR
e-mail: shapermg@btinternet.com
Fax: 020-7350 1802   Tel: 020-7585 1023

SHEDDEN Malcolm MANAGEMENT
1 Charlotte Street
London W1T 1RD
Website: www.features.co.uk
e-mail: info@features.co.uk
Fax: 020-7636 1657   Tel: 020-7636 1876

SHEPHERD MANAGEMENT Ltd
(PMA Member)
4th Floor, 45 Maddox Street
London W1S 2PE
e-mail: info@shepherdmanagement.co.uk
Fax: 020-7499 7535   Tel: 020-7495 7813

SHEPPERD-FOX
5 Martyr Road
Guildford
Surrey GU1 4LF
Website: www.shepperd-fox.co.uk
e-mail: info@shepperd-fox.co.uk   Mobile: 07957 624601

SHOWSTOPPERS!
Events Management & Entertainment
42 Foxglove Close
Witham, Essex CM8 2XW
Website: www.showstoppers-group.com
e-mail: mail@showstoppers-group.com
Fax: 01376 510340   Tel: 01376 518486

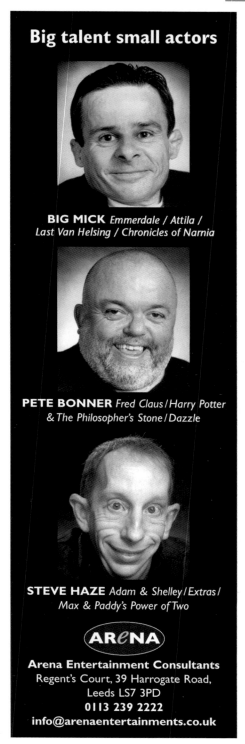

S I A MANAGEMENT
Wessex
255 Brighton Road
Lancing
West Sussex BN15 8JP
Website: www.siamanagement.co.uk
e-mail: info@siamanagement.co.uk   Tel: 01903 529882

SIBLEY Claire MANAGEMENT
15 Tweedale Wharf
Madeley, Shropshire TF7 4EW
Website: www.clairesibleymanagement.co.uk
e-mail: info@clairesibleymanagement.co.uk
Tel: 01952 588951

SIMON & HOW ASSOCIATES
90-92 Ley Street
Ilford, Essex IG1 4BX
Website: www.simon-how.com
e-mail: info@simon-how.com   Tel: 0845 0646666

SIMPSON FOX ASSOCIATES Ltd
(PMA Member)
Set, Costume and Lighting Designers. Directors
Choreographers
52 Shaftesbury Avenue, London W1D 6LP
e-mail: info@simpson-fox.com
Fax: 020-7494 2887   Tel: 020-7434 9167

SINGER Sandra ASSOCIATES
(Personal Manager)
Contact: By email
2 Agents represent 40 Performers
Children. Commercials. Dancers. Film. Television
21 Cotswold Road
Westcliff-on-Sea, Essex SS0 8AA
Website: www.sandrasinger.com
e-mail: sandrasingeruk@aol.com
Fax: 01702 339393   Tel: 01702 331616

SINGERS INC
Golden Cross House
8 Duncannon Street
The Strand, London WC2N 4JF
Website: www.internationalcollective.com
e-mail: enquiries@internationalcollective.co.uk
Fax: 020-7484 5100   Tel: 020-7484 5080

SIRR Peggy
(See ORIENTAL CASTING AGENCY Ltd)

SJ MANAGEMENT
8 Bettridge Road
London SW6 3QD
e-mail: sj@susanjames.demon.co.uk
Fax: 020-7371 0409   Tel: 020-7371 0441

SMART MANAGEMENT
Contact: Mario Renzullo
The Aberdeen Centre
22-24 Highbury Grove
London N5 2EA
e-mail: smart.management@virgin.net   Tel: 020-7354 8822

SMILE TALENT
The Studio
Units 16/17 Ickleton Riverside Barns
Frogge Street
Ickleton
Saffron Walden CB10 1SH
e-mail: info@smiletalent.com   Tel/Fax: 01799 531966

SONGTIME/CHANDLER'S MANAGEMENT
10 Wallis Mews
Leatherhead, Surrey KT22 9DQ
Website: www.songtime.co.uk
e-mail: info@songtime.co.uk
Fax: 01372 362461   Tel: 01372 372352

SOPHIE'S PEOPLE
Choreographers. Dancers
40 Mexfield Road, London SW15 2RQ
Website: www.sophiespeople.com
e-mail: sophies.people@btinternet.com
Fax: 0870 7876447   Tel: 0870 7876446

S.O.S.
85 Bannerman House
Lawn Lane, London SW8 1UA
Website: www.sportsofseb.com
e-mail: info@sportsofseb.com
Mobile: 07740 359770   Tel: 020-7735 5133

SOUL MANAGEMENT
Website: www.soulmanagement.co.uk
e-mail: info@soulmanagement.co.uk
Fax: 0871 7512661   Tel: 020-7580 1120

SPEAKERS CIRCUIT Ltd The
After Dinner Speakers
23 Tynemouth Street
Fulham, London SW6 2QS
e-mail: laura@allstarspeakers.co.uk
Fax: 01892 750089   Tel: 020-7371 7512

SPEAKERS CORNER
Facilitation & Cabaret for the Corporate Market
Presenters. Speakers
Tigana House, Catlins Lane
Pinner, Middlesex HA5 2HG
Website: www.speakerscorner.co.uk
e-mail: info@speakerscorner.co.uk
Fax: 020-8868 4409   Tel: 020-8866 8967

erin dusek

ben richards

louise dearman

steven houghton

deanne berry

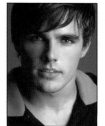
glenn ball

krysten cummings

emrhys cooper

i.n.c
INTERNATIONAL COLLECTIVE
PHOTOGRAPHIC PACKAGE
www.internationalcollective.com antoinette@internationalcollective.co.uk

Chalice
Personal Management

Sarah Harding Colin Scott
Temple Court Cathedral Road Cardiff CF11 9HA
t: 02920 786 537 **m:** 07794 051019 **f:** 02920 786666
e: agent@chalicepersonalmanagement.co.uk www.chalicepersonalmanagement.co.uk

Gemma Price
PO Box 59291 London NW3 9JW
t: 07591 503980 **e:** gemma@chalicepersonalmanagement.co.uk

Providing professional actors with dedicated quality personal management.
An Actors Agency with a difference, we really care about the quality of
service we provide to our clients. For Actors looking for placement and for
placements waiting to find actors.

Be confident...Star quality without drama

SPIRE CASTING
(Personal Manager)
Contact: By Post/email
1 Agent represents 6 Performers
PO Box 372
Chesterfield S41 0XW
Website: www.spirecasting.com
e-mail: mail@spirecasting.com
Fax: 0870 4795321   Tel: 07900 517707

SPLITTING IMAGES LOOKALIKES AGENCY
25 Clissold Court
Greenway Close, London N4 2EZ
Website: www.splitting-images.com
e-mail: info@splitting-images.com
Fax: 020-8809 6103   Tel: 020-8809 2327

SPORTABILITY Ltd
Sporting Personalities
Unit 2, 23 Green Lane
Dronfield, Derbyshire S18 2LL
e-mail: info@sportabilityuk.co.uk
Fax: 01246 290520   Tel: 01246 292010

SPORTS OF SEB Ltd
85 Bannerman House
Lawn Lane, London SW8 1UA
Website: www.sportsofseb.com
e-mail: info@sportsofseb.com
Mobile: 07740 359770   Tel: 020-7735 5133

SPORTS PROMOTIONS Ltd
Contact: By email/Telephone
300+ Performers
Commercials. Dancers. Modelling. Sports Models
PO Box 878
Crystal Palace
National Sports Centre
London SE19 2BH
e-mail: agent@sportspromotions.co.uk
Fax: 020-8776 7772   Tel: 020-8659 4561

SPYKER Paul MANAGEMENT
PO Box 48848, London WC1B 3WZ
e-mail: belinda@psmlondon.com
Fax: 020-7462 0047   Tel: 020-7462 0046

SRA PERSONAL MANAGEMENT
Lockhart Road, Cobham, Surrey KT11 2AX
e-mail: agency@susanrobertsacademy.co.uk
Tel: 01932 863194

STAFFORD Helen MANAGEMENT
Contact: Helen Stafford
By Post. Accepts Showreels/Voicereels
1 Agent represents 30 Performers
Commercials. Film. Musicals. Television
Voice Overs
14 Park Avenue, Bush Hill Park, Enfield EN1 2HP
e-mail: helen.stafford@blueyonder.co.uk
Fax: 020-8372 0611   Tel: 020-8360 6329

STAGE AND SCREEN PERSONAL MANAGEMENT
20B Kidbrooke Grove, Blackheath SE3 0LF
Website: www.stageandscreenpm.com
e-mail: info@stageandscreenpm.com
Mobile: 07958 648740   Tel: 020-7193 4994

STAGE CENTRAL CASTING AGENCY
9 Alexandra Grove
Knaresborough, N Yorkshire HG5 0PH
e-mail: darren@stagecentral.co.uk   Tel: 01423 540533

STAGE CENTRE MANAGEMENT Ltd
(Personal Manager)
(CPMA Member)
Contact: By Post. 22 Performers
41 North Road, London N7 9DP
Website: www.stagecentre.org.uk
e-mail: info@stagecentre.org.uk   Tel: 020-7607 0872

STAGEWORKS WORLDWIDE PRODUCTIONS
Contact: By email
Cirque Artistes. Corporate. Dancers. Ice-Skaters. Musicals
525 Ocean Boulevard
Blackpool FY4 1EZ
Website: www.stageworkswwp.com
e-mail: simon.george@stageworkswwp.com
Fax: 01253 343702   Tel: 01253 342426

STAR MANAGEMENT Ltd
16A Winton Drive, Glasgow G12 0QA
Website: www.starmanagement.co.uk
e-mail: star@starmanagement.co.uk   Tel: 0870 2422276

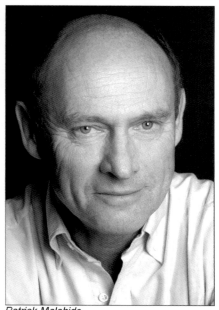

Patrick Malahide

Sarah Jayne Dunn

DAN HARWOOD-STAMPER

Tel: 07779 165777   *photographer*   www.danharwoodstamper.co.uk

STARFISH ENTERPRISES
15 Leamington Rd, Ainsdale, Southport, Merseyside PR8 3LB
Website: www.starfishents.co.uk
e-mail: info@starfishents.co.uk   Tel: 08454 754517

STEVENSON Natasha MANAGEMENT Ltd
(See NSM)

STIRLING MANAGEMENT
Contact: Glen Mortimer
By email. Accepts Showreels
3 Agents represent 15 Performers
Commercials. Film. Presenters. Stage. Television
37 Oldstead Grove, Ferncrest, Bolton, Lancs BL3 4XW
Website: www.stirlingmanagement.co.uk
e-mail: admin@stirlingmanagement.co.uk
Fax: 0844 4128689   Tel: 0845 0176500

STIVEN CHRISTIE MANAGEMENT
(Incorporating The Actors Agency of Edinburgh)
1 Glen Street
Tollcross
Edinburgh EH3 9JD
Website: www.stivenchristie.co.uk
e-mail: info@stivenchristie.co.uk
Fax: 0131-228 4645   Tel: 0131-228 4040

ST. JAMES'S MANAGEMENT
(Personal Manager)
Contact: By Post (SAE)
19 Lodge Close
Stoke D'Abernon
Cobham, Surrey KT11 2SG
Fax: 01932 863152   Tel: 01932 860666

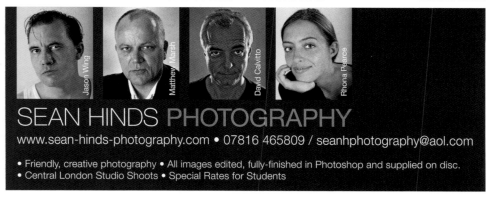

STONE Ian ASSOCIATES
Suite 262
Maddison House
226 High Street
Croydon CR9 1DF   Tel/Fax: 020-8667 1627

STONE Richard PARTNERSHIP The
(PMA Member)
2 Henrietta Street
London WC2E 8PS
Website: www.thersp.com
e-mail: all@thersp.com
Fax: 020-7497 0869   Tel: 020-7497 0849

STRAIGHT LINE MANAGEMENT
(Division of Straight Line Productions)
58 Castle Avenue
Epsom, Surrey KT17 2PH
e-mail: hilary@straightlinemanagement.co.uk
Fax: 020-8393 8079   Tel: 020-8393 4220

STRANGE John MANAGEMENT
11 Ashley Street,
Glasgow G3 6DR
Website: www.strangemanagement.co.uk
e-mail: tracy@strangemanagement.co.uk
Fax: 0141-333 9890   Tel: 0141-333 0233

SUCCESS
Room 236, 2nd Floor
Linen Hall
162-168 Regent Street
London W1B 5TB
Website: www.successagency.co.uk
e-mail: ee@successagency.co.uk
Fax: 020-7494 3787   Tel: 020-7734 3356

SUMMERS Mark MANAGEMENT
137 Freston Road
London W10 6TH
Website: www.marksummers.com
e-mail: info@marksummers.com
Fax: 020-7243 1987   Tel: 020-7229 8413

SUMMERTON Michael MANAGEMENT Ltd
Choreographers. Dancers
Mimosa House
Mimosa Street
London SW6 4DS
Website: www.michaelsummerton.com
e-mail: msminfo@btconnect.com
Fax: 020-7731 0103   Tel: 020-7731 6969

TAKE FLIGHT MANAGEMENT
Website: www.takeflightmanagement.com
                                Tel/Fax: 020-8835 8147

TALENT4 MEDIA Ltd
Studio LG16
Shepherds Building Central
Charecroft Way
London W14 0EH
Website: www.talent4media.com
e-mail: enquiries@talent4media.com
Fax: 020-7183 4331   Tel: 020-7183 4330

TALENT ARTISTS Ltd
(PMA Member)
Contact: Jane Wynn Owen
No Unsolicited Enquiries
59 Sydner Road, London N16 7UF
e-mail: talent.artists@btconnect.com
Fax: 020-7923 2009   Tel: 020-7923 1119

TAVISTOCK WOOD
(PMA Member)
45 Conduit Street
London W1S 2YN
Website: www.tavistockwood.com
Fax: 020-7434 2017   Tel: 020-7494 4767

TAYLOR Brian ASSOCIATES
(PMA Member)
50 Pembroke Road
Kensington
London W8 6NX
e-mail: briantaylor@nqassoc.freeserve.co.uk
Fax: 020-7602 6301   Tel: 020-7602 6141

TCA
(The Commercial Agency)
12 Evelyn Mansions
Carlisle Place
London SW1P 1NH
Website: www.thecommercialagency.co.uk
e-mail: mail@thecommercialagency.co.uk
Fax: 020-7233 8110   Tel: 020-7233 8100

TCG ARTIST MANAGEMENT
Contact: Kristin Tarry, Rachel Cranmer-Gordon,
Charlie Hunt
14A Goodwins Court
London WC2N 4LL
Website: www.tcgam.co.uk
e-mail: info@tcgam.co.uk
Fax: 020-7240 3606   Tel: 020-7240 3600

T.G.R. DIRECT
88 Recreation Road
Poole, Dorset BH12 2AL
e-mail: tatianaroc.tgrdirect@virgin.net
Fax: 01202 721802   Tel: 01202 721222

0870 442867
WWW.PINEWOODNET.NET
INFO@PINEWOODNET.NET

Katie Alexandra   Amy Barnes   Stephen Willis   Chloe Wicks   Katy Newell

Barbara Lanik   Jason Croot   Paul Stephen Williams   Jack Cramer   Jade Hudson

PROFESSIONAL ACTORS NETWORK

Lazarus No No

Molly Brammar

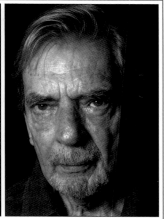
John Richards

AVA DE SOUZA
photography

020 8392 9093
www.avadesouza.co.uk
student rates

www.bossmodelmanagement.co.uk

Fashion, photographic and show models

Hair and Make Up Artists

Fashion Stylists

Still Life Stylists

Choreographers

Window Dressers

Location Finders

Member of the
Association of Model Agents

T: 0161 834 3403

F: 0161 832 5219

info@bossmodels.co.uk

Half Moon Chambers, Chapel Walks
Manchester, M2 1HN

THEATRE EXPRESS MANAGEMENT
Contact: By Post
Spindle Cottage
Allens Farm, Digby Fen
Billinghay, Lincoln LN4 4DT
e-mail: info@theatre-express.com

THOMAS & BENDA ASSOCIATES Ltd
Top Floor
15-16 Ivor Place
London NW1 6HS   Tel/Fax: 020-7723 5509

THOMPSON David ASSOCIATES
22 Montefiore Street
Battersea
London SW8 3TL
e-mail: montefioredt@aol.com
Fax: 020-7498 6548   Tel: 020-7622 6117

THOMPSON Jim
Herricks
School Lane, Arundel
West Sussex BN18 9DR
e-mail: jim@jthompson42.freeserve.co.uk
Fax: 01903 885887   Tel: 01903 885757

THOMPSON Peggy OFFICE The
(Personal Manager)
1st & 2nd Floor Offices
296 Sandycombe Road
Kew, Richmond
Surrey TW9 3NG
Fax: 020-8332 1127   Tel: 020-8332 1003

THOMSON Mia ASSOCIATES (MTA)
35 Central Avenue
Polegate
East Sussex BN26 6HA
Website: www.miathomsonassociates.co.uk
e-mail: info@miathomsonassociates.co.uk
Fax: 01323 489137   Tel: 01323 486143

THORNTON AGENCY
(Specialist Agency for Small People)
Contact: By Post/email/Telephone
50 Performers
Commercials. Corporate. Film. Stage. Television
72 Purley Downs Road
South Croydon CR2 0RB
Website: www.dwarfs4hire.com
e-mail: thorntons.leslie@tinyworld.co.uk
                              Tel/Fax: 020-8660 5588

THRELFALL Katie ASSOCIATES
2A Gladstone Road
London SW19 1QT
e-mail: info@ktthrelfall.co.uk
Fax: 020-8543 7545   Tel: 020-8543 4344

THRESH Melody MANAGEMENT ASSOCIATES Ltd (MTM)
27 Ardwick Green North
Ardwick
Manchester M12 6FZ
e-mail: melodythreshmtm@aol.com
Fax: 0161-273 5455   Tel: 0161-273 5445

TILDSLEY Janice ASSOCIATES
Contact: Kathryn Kirton
By Post
3 Agents represent 70 Performers
47 Orford Road, London E17 9NJ
Website: www.janicetildsleyassociates.co.uk
e-mail: info@janicetildsleyassociates.co.uk
Fax: 020-8521 1174   Tel: 020-8521 1888

TINKER Victoria MANAGEMENT
Technical, Non-Acting
Birchenbridge House
Brighton Road
Mannings Heath, Horsham
West Sussex RH13 6HY   Tel/Fax: 01403 210653

TOTAL VANITY Ltd
15 Walton Way
Aylesbury, Buckinghamshire HP21 7JJ
Website: www.totalvanity.com
e-mail: teresa.hellen@totalvanity.com
Mobile: 07739 381788   Mobile: 07710 780152

TOTS-TWENTIES
62 Buntingbridge Road
Newbury Park, Ilford, Essex IG1 7LR
Website: www.tots-twenties.co.uk
e-mail: sara@tots-twenties.co.uk
Fax: 020-8518 0212   Tel: 020-8518 0200

TRENDS AGENCY & MANAGEMENT Ltd
Contact: By email
Commercials. Dancers. Musicals. Singers. Stage
Sullom Lodge, Sullom Side Lane
Garstang PR3 1GH
Website: www.trendsgroup.co.uk
e-mail: info@trendsgroup.co.uk
Fax: 01253 407715   Tel: 0871 2003343

TROIKA
(PMA Member)
3rd Floor, 74 Clerkenwell Road
London EC1M 5QA
e-mail: info@troikatalent.com
Fax: 020-7490 7642   Tel: 020 7336 7868

TUCKER Tommy AGENCY
Suite 66
235 Earl's Court Road
London SW5 9FE
e-mail: TTTommytucker@aol.com   Tel: 020-7370 3911

TV MANAGEMENTS
Brink House, Avon Castle
Ringwood, Hants BH24 2BL
e-mail: etv@tvmanagements.co.uk
Fax: 01425 480123   Tel: 01425 475544

TWINS
(See PC THEATRICAL, MODEL & CASTING AGENCY)

TWITCH EVENT CHOREOGRAPHY
Contact: By Post/email/Telephone
Accepts Showreels/Voicereels
2 Agents represent 100 Performers
Corporate. Dancers. Modelling. Stage. Television
5 Breakspears Mews, Brockley SE4 1PY
Website: www.twitch.uk.com
e-mail: info@twitch.uk.com
Mobile: 07932 656358   Mobile: 07747 770816

TWO'S COMPANY
Existing Clients only
Directors. Film. Radio. Stage. Television. Writers
244 Upland Road
London SE22 0DN
e-mail: graham@2scompanytheatre.co.uk
Fax: 020-8299 3714   Tel: 020-8299 4593

UGLY MODELS
Tigris House
256 Edgware Road, London W2 1DS
Website: www.ugly.org
e-mail: info@ugly.org
Fax: 020-7402 0507   Tel: 020-7402 5564

UNITED AGENTS Ltd
(Personal Manager) (PMA Member)
12-26 Lexington Street
London W1F OLE
Website: www.unitedagents.co.uk
e-mail: info@unitedagents.co.uk   Tel: 020-3214 0800

UNITED PRODUCTIONS
Choreographers. Dancers. Stylists
6 Shaftesbury Mews
Clapham, London SW4 9BP
Website: www.unitedproductions.biz
e-mail: lyndon@unitedproductions.biz
    Tel/Fax: 020-7498 6563

UPBEAT MANAGEMENT
Theatre Touring & Events. No Actors
Larg House
Woodcote Grove
Coulsdon, Surrey CR5 2QQ
Website: www.upbeat.co.uk
e-mail: info@upbeat.co.uk
Fax: 020-8668 3922   Tel: 020-8668 3332

UPSON EDWARDS
(See REPRESENTATION UPSON EDWARDS)

URBAN HEROES
Studio One
7 Chalcot Road
Primrose Hill, London NW1 8LH
Website: www.theurbanheroes.com
e-mail: justin@theurbanheroes.com
Fax: 0870 4792458   Tel: 020-7043 1072

URBAN TALENT
Nemesis House
1 Oxford Court
Bishopsgate
Manchester M2 3WQ
Website: www.urbantalent.tv
e-mail: liz@nmsmanagement.co.uk
Fax: 0161-228 6727   Tel: 0161-228 6866

UTOPIA MODEL MANAGEMENT
348 Moorside Road
Swinton
Manchester M27 9PW
Fax: 0161-728 6600   Tel: 0161-728 6444

UVA MANAGEMENT Ltd
Contact: By email
Commercials. Film. Presenters. Stage. Television
118-120 Kenton Road
Harrow, Middlesex HA3 8AL
Website: www.uvamanagement.com
e-mail: berko@uvamanagement.com
Mobile: 07716 777885   Tel: 0845 3700883

V A MANAGEMENT
6 Barossa Road
Camberley
Surrey GU15 4JR
Website: www.viciousmanagement.com
e-mail: info@viciousmanagement.com
    Mobile: 07940 658607

VACCA Roxane MANAGEMENT
(PMA Member)
73 Beak Street, London W1F 9SR
Website: www.roxanevaccamanagement.com
Fax: 020-7734 8086   Tel: 020-7734 8085

VALLÉ ACADEMY THEATRICAL AGENCY The
The Vallé Academy Studios
Wilton House, Delamare Road
Cheshunt, Herts EN8 9SG
Website: www.valleacademy.co.uk
e-mail: agency@valleacademy.co.uk
Fax: 01992 622868   Tel: 01992 622861

VAMP JAZZ
Bands. Entertainers. Musicians. Singers
Ealing House
33 Hanger Lane
London W5 3HJ
e-mail: vampjazz@aol.com   Tel: 020-8997 3355

VIDAL-HALL Clare
(PMA Member)
Choreographers. Composers. Designers. Directors
Lighting Designers
57 Carthew Road, London W6 0DU
e-mail: info@clarevidalhall.com
Fax: 020-8741 9459   Tel: 020-8741 7647

VINE Michael ASSOCIATES
Light Entertainment
1 Stormont Road, London N6 4NS
e-mail: mpvine@aol.com
Fax: 020-8348 3277   Tel: 020-8348 5899

VisABLE PEOPLE
Artists with Disabilities only
Website: www.visablepeople.com
e-mail: louise@visablepeople.com   Tel: 01905 776631

VSA Ltd
(Formerly Vincent Shaw Associates)
(PMA Member) *Contact: Andy Charles*
186 Shaftesbury Avenue, London WC2H 8JB
Website: www.vsaltd.com
e-mail: info@vsaltd.com
Fax: 020-7240 2930
Tel: 020-7240 2927

WADE Suzann
9 Wimpole Mews, London W1G 8PG
Website: www.suzannwade.com
e-mail: info@suzannwade.com
Fax: 020-7486 5664
Tel: 020-7486 0746

WALKER Rita MANAGEMENT
34 Dovers Green Road
Reigate
Surrey RH2 8BT
e-mail: ritawalker@ntlworld.com
Mobile: 07887 884248
Tel: 01737 248313

WALMSLEY Peter ASSOCIATES
No Representation, Do Not Write
37A Crimsworth Road
London SW8 4RJ
e-mail: associates@peterwalmsley.net
Mobile: 07778 347312
Tel: 020-7787 6419

Anthony Lewis.

Laura Carter.

Alex Crosby
Photographer

www.alexcrosby.co.uk
info@alexcrosby.co.uk
07818448019

Based in Leeds.
Available throughout the north.

Head shots. Theatre. Flexible hours & short notice. Studio, location, home visits. Student discount.

WARING & McKENNA
(PMA Member)
11-12 Dover Street
Mayfair, London W1S 4LJ
Website: www.waringandmckenna.com
e-mail: dj@waringandmckenna.com
Fax: 020-7629 6466   Tel: 020-7629 6444

WELCH Janet PERSONAL MANAGEMENT
Contact: By Post
Old Orchard, The Street
Ubley, Bristol BS40 6PJ
e-mail: info@janetwelchpm.co.uk   Tel/Fax: 01761 463238

WESSON Penny
(PMA Member)
Directors
26 King Henry's Road
London NW3 3RP
e-mail: penny@pennywesson.demon.co.uk
Fax: 020-7483 2890   Tel: 020-7722 6607

WEST CENTRAL MANAGEMENT
(CPMA Member)
Co-operative of 21 Performers
Contact: By Post/email
Room 4, East Block, Panther House
38 Mount Pleasant, London WC1X 0AN
Website: www.westcentralmanagement.co.uk
e-mail: mail@westcentralmanagement.co.uk
                           Tel/Fax: 020-7833 8134

WEST END MANAGEMENT
Contact: Maureen Cairns
The Penthouse
42/17 Speirs Wharf
Glasgow G4 9TH
Website: www.west-endmgt.com
e-mail: info@west-endmgt.com   Tel: 0141-331 1340

WHATEVER ARTISTS MANAGEMENT Ltd
F24 Argo House
Kilburn Park Road
London NW6 5LF
Website: www.wamshow.biz
e-mail: info@wamshow.biz
Fax: 020-7372 5111   Tel: 020-7372 4777

WHITEHALL ARTISTS
10 Lower Common South
London SW15 1BP
e-mail: mwhitehall@msn.com
Fax: 020-8788 2340   Tel: 020-8785 3737

WILKINSON David ASSOCIATES
(PMA Member)
Existing Clients Only
115 Hazlebury Road, London SW6 2LX
e-mail: info@dwassociates.net
Fax: 020-7371 5161   Tel: 020-7371 5188

WILLIAMSON & HOLMES
9 Hop Gardens
St Martin's Lane
London WC2N 4EH
e-mail: info@williamsonandholmes.co.uk
Fax: 020-7240 0408   Tel: 020-7240 0407

WILLOW PERSONAL MANAGEMENT
Specialist Agency for Short Actors
151 Main Street, Yaxley
Peterborough
Cambs PE7 3LD
e-mail: enquiries@willowmanagement.co.uk
                           Tel/Fax: 01733 240392

WILLS Newton MANAGEMENT
(Personal Manager)
Contact: By Post/email
Accepts Showreels/Voicereels
3 Agents represent 52 Performers
Commercials. Dancers. Singers. Stage
The Studio, 29 Springvale Avenue
Brentford, Middlesex TW8 9QH
e-mail: newtoncttg@aol.com
Fax: 00 33 468 218685   Mobile: 07989 398381

WINSLETT Dave ASSOCIATES
6 Kenwood Ridge
Kenley, Surrey CR8 5JW
Website: www.davewinslett.com
e-mail: info@davewinslett.com
Fax: 020-8668 9216   Tel: 020-8668 0531

WINTERSON Niki
(See GLOBAL ARTISTS)

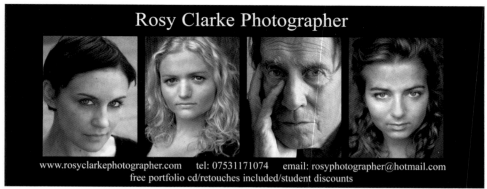

Rosy Clarke Photographer

www.rosyclarkephotographer.com   tel: 07531171074   email: rosyphotographer@hotmail.com
free portfolio cd/retouches included/student discounts

WIS CELTIC MANAGEMENT
Welsh, Irish, Scottish Performers
86 Elphinstone Road
Walthamstow
London E17 5EX
Fax: 020-8523 4523   Tel: 020-8523 4234

WISE BUDDAH TALENT
Contact: Chris North
74 Great Titchfield Street
London W1W 7QP
Website: www.wisebuddah.com
e-mail: chris.north@wisebuddah.com
Fax: 020-7307 1601   Tel: 020-7307 1600

WMG MANAGEMENT EUROPE Ltd
Sports Management Company
5th Floor
33 Soho Square
London W1D 3QU
Website: www.wwgllc.com
Fax: 020-3230 1053   Tel: 020-7009 6000

WYMAN Edward AGENCY
(English & Welsh Language)
Contact: Edward Wyman, Audrey Williams, Judith Gay
By Post. Accepts Showreels/Voicereels
3 Agents
Commercials. Corporate. Television. Voice Overs. Walk-on &
Supporting Artists
67 Llanon Road
Llanishen
Cardiff CF14 5AH
Website: www.wymancasting.co.uk
e-mail: edward.wyman@btconnect.com
Fax: 029-2075 2444   Tel: 029-2075 2351

XL MANAGEMENT
Edmund House
Rugby Road
Leamington Spa
Warwickshire CV32 6EL
Website: www.xlmanagement.co.uk
e-mail: office@xlmanagement.co.uk
Fax: 01926 811420   Tel: 01926 810449

YAT MANAGEMENT
(Young Actors Management)
70-72 Barnsbury Road, London N1 0ES
Website: www.yati.org.uk   e-mail: agent@yati.org.uk
Fax: 020-7833 9467   Tel: 020-7278 2101

YELLOW BALLOON PRODUCTIONS Ltd
Contact: Mike Smith
Freshwater House, Outdowns, Effingham, Surrey KT24 5QR
e-mail: yellowbal@aol.com
Fax: 01483 281502   Tel: 01483 281500

ZWICKLER Marlene & ASSOCIATES
1 Belgrave Crescent Lane, Edinburgh EH4 3AG
Website: www.mza-artists.com   Tel/Fax: 0131-343 3030

Cristiana Setaro
portrait photographer and stylist

www.cristianasetaro.com
info@cristianasetaro.com
07950 901492

How can my child become an actor?

If a child is interested in becoming an actor, they should try to get as much practical experience as possible. For example, joining the drama club at school, taking theatre studies as an option, reading as many plays as they can, and going to the theatre on a regular basis. They could also attend local youth theatres or drama groups. Some theatres offer evening or Saturday classes.

What are the chances of success?

As any agency or school will tell you, the entertainment industry is highly competitive and for every success story there are many children who will never be hired for paid acting work. Child artists and their parents should think very carefully before getting involved in the industry and be prepared for disappointments along the way.

What is the difference between stage schools and agencies?

Stage schools provide specialised training in acting, singing and dancing for the under 18's. They offer a variety of full and part-time courses. Please see the 'Drama Training, Schools and Coaches' section for listings. Children's and Teenagers' agencies specialise in the representation of child artists, promoting them to casting opportunities and negotiating contracts on their behalf. In return they will take commission, usually ranging from 10-15%. Some larger stage schools also have agencies attached to them. A number of agents are listed in the following pages.

Why does my child need an agent?

While many parents feel they want to retain control over their child's career, they will not have the contacts and authority an agent will have in the industry. Casting directors are more likely to look to an agent they know and trust to provide the most suitable children for a job than an independent, unrepresented child. This does not mean to say that a child will never get work without an agent to put them forward for work, but it will certainly be more difficult.

How should these listings be used?

The following pages list up-to-date contact details for agencies specialising in the representation of children and teenagers. Every company listed is done so by written request to us. Always research agencies carefully before approaching them to make sure they are suitable for your child. Many have websites you can visit, or ask around for personal recommendations. You should make a short-list of the ones you think are most appropriate rather than sending a standard letter to hundreds of agencies. Please see the main 'Agents and Personal Managers' advice section for further guidance on choosing and approaching agents.

Can Spotlight offer me advice on choosing or changing my child's Agent?

Unfortunately Spotlight is not able to advise performers on specific agents, nor is it in a position to handle any financial or contractual queries or complaints. For agent-related queries we suggest you contact The Agents' Association www.agents-uk.com or The Personal Managers' Association (PMA) www.thepma.com, or you could try one of the independent advisors on our website www.spotlight.com/artists/advice/independent.

Should I pay an agent to represent my child? Or sign a contract?

Equity does not recommend that you pay an agent an upfront fee to place your child on their client list. Before signing a contract, you should be very clear about the terms and commitments involved. For advice on both of these issues, or if you experience any problems with a current agent, we recommend that you contact Equity www.equity.org.uk.

Why do child actors need licences?

Strict regulations apply to children working in the entertainment industry. These cover areas including the maximum number of performance hours per day / week, rest times, meal times and tutoring requirements. When any child under 16 performs in a professional capacity, the production company must obtain a Child Performance Licence from the child's Local Education Authority.

Who are chaperones?

Child artists must also be accompanied by a chaperone at all times when they are working. Registered chaperones are generally used instead of parents as they have a better understanding of the employment regulations involved, and they have professional experience of dealing with production companies. Registered chaperones have been police checked and approved by their local education authority to act in loco parentis. Always contact your Local Education Authority if you have any questions or concerns.

What is the Spotlight Children and Young Performers directory?

Children who are currently represented by an agent or attend a stage school can appear in the Spotlight Children and Young Performers directory. This is a casting directory, used by production teams to source child artists for TV, film, stage or commercial work. Each child pays an annual membership fee and receives a space in the printed directory along with others represented by the same agency or stage school, as well as their own individual online CV, searchable by casting professionals. Please speak to your child's school or agency about joining Spotlight for ongoing promotion to hundreds of casting opportunities. For further information about the directory visit www.spotlight.com/join

abacus agency

LINDA DAVIES runs Abacus Agency which has been representing children and teenagers on stage and screen for over 30 years. Abacus is one of the leading independent agencies in the country and also represents adult clients under the recently launched ABA.

Entering into the world of professional acting can be a daunting, terrifying, yet exciting experience. Finding the right agent to accompany you on this roller coaster ride is important. Talk to other parents, go on to internet forums, check out websites and generally find out as much as you can about an agency before you approach them.

Look at the work their clients have done and the age groups they represent before choosing which agencies will be best for you.

Contact the agency in the first instance to find out how to apply. Most agencies will require a clear, recent photo (usually not professional at this stage) and a CV detailing all relevant acting experience, separating professional work from school plays and drama school productions. Unsolicited applications by email with large attachments are generally not welcome. Please remember that agencies receive applications on a daily basis and it may be some time before you hear back.

Once you have been taken on by an agency there will be some financial outlay initially. You will need professional headshots (your agency will have recommended photographers usually at a reduced rate) and an entry into Spotlight Children and Young Performers or similar casting book. You must also be prepared to pay out for travel to and from auditions. No agency should charge you a joining fee as they earn their money from commission taken from payment for jobs.

Agencies will expect a high level of commitment from their clients as castings are usually arranged at very short notice – often for the next day. They are usually after school (between 4pm and 6.30pm) but in reality, if you live any distance from London (or other main city where the castings take place) then you will need to leave school early in order to get to your appointment on time. It is important to have the support of your school in this respect and, if missing school is going to be a problem for you, then it would be wise not to join an agency.

So, what does an agent do? At Abacus we are approached daily by top casting directors who need children and teenagers to appear in featured roles in television programmes, films, TV commercials and West End theatre. Having studied the brief we select suitable clients from our books and submit our suggestions to the casting director (usually via Spotlight). They will then contact us if they want to see any of our clients. Thereafter may follow a number of castings, recalls and sometimes screen tests before the part is offered. We will negotiate the best deal we can, organise a licence for children under school-leaving age, and oversee all the arrangements regarding venues, travel and accommodation where needed. We always have the best interests of our clients at heart and have been known to withdraw clients from jobs if we are not happy. The well-being of the child is paramount and we work closely with the production companies and local councils (who issue the licences) to ensure that every provision has been made.

Finally, it is important that the whole experience is a positive one. Approach it like a hobby, enjoy your castings as much as you can, be prepared for disappointment and relish every opportunity you are given. Above all, be realistic and keep your feet on the ground. Don't expect to be the next Keira Knightley – although she did start her career with Abacus!

Please visit www.abacusagency.co.uk for further information.

Artist Management
adults children

byron's Management

Byron's Management
Tel: 020 8444 4445
Fax: 020 8444 4040
byronsmanagement@aol.com
www.byronsmanagement.co.uk

A & J MANAGEMENT ✆
242A The Ridgeway
Botany Bay, Enfield EN2 8AP
Website: www.ajmanagement.co.uk
e-mail: info@ajmanagement.co.uk
Fax: 020-8342 0842   Tel: 020-8342 0542

ABACUS AGENCY ✆
The Studio, 4 Bailey Road
Westcott
Dorking, Surrey RH4 3QS
Website: www.abacusagency.co.uk
e-mail: admin@abacusagency.co.uk
Fax: 01306 877813   Tel: 01306 877144

ACT OUT AGENCY ✗
(Children, Teenagers & New Graduates)
22 Greek Street
Stockport, Cheshire SK3 8AB
e-mail: ab22actout@aol.com   Tel/Fax: 0161-429 7413

ADAMS Juliet CHILD MODEL & TALENT AGENCY
19 Gwynne House
Challice Way, London SW2 3RB
Website: www.julietadams.co.uk
e-mail: bookingdesk@julietadams.co.uk
Fax: 020-8671 9314   Tel: 020-8671 7673

ALLSORTS AGENCY ✗
Suite 1 & 2 Marlborough Business Centre
96 George Lane
London E18 1AD
Website: www.allsortsagency.com
e-mail: bookings@allsortsagency.com
Fax: 020-8989 5600   Tel: 020-8989 0500

ALLSORTS DRAMA FOR CHILDREN
(In Association with Sasha Leslie Management)
34 Pember Road
London NW10 5LS
e-mail: sasha@allsortsdrama.com
Fax: 020-8969 3196   Tel: 020-8969 3249

ALLSTARS CASTING
Apt 4, 66 Hope Street
Liverpool L1 9BZ
Website: www.allstarsweb.co.uk
e-mail: allstarsweb@hotmail.co.uk
Mobile: 07739 359737   Tel/Fax: 0151-707 2100

ALPHABET KIDZ TALENT & VOICE-OVER AGENCY
189 Southampton Way
London SE5 7EJ
Website: www.alphabetkidz.co.uk
e-mail: contact@alphabetkidz.co.uk
Fax: 020-7252 4341   Tel: 020-7252 4343

ANNA'S MANAGEMENT
(Formerly of ALADDIN'S CAVE)
25 Tintagel Drive
Stanmore
Middlesex HA7 4SR
e-mail: annasmanage@aol.com
Fax: 020-8238 2899   Tel: 020-8958 7636

AQUITAINE PERSONAL MANAGEMENT
PO Box 1896
Stanford-Le-Hope
Essex SS17 0WR
Website: www.aquitainepersonalmanagement.co.uk
e-mail: apm@aquitaine.org.uk   Tel: 01375 361888

ARAENA/COLLECTIVE
10 Bramshaw Gardens
South Oxhey
Herts WD19 6XP   Tel/Fax: 020-8428 0037

ARTS ACADEMY (T.A.A.) The
15 Lexham Mews, London W8 6JW
e-mail: jill@galloways.ltd.uk
Fax: 020-7376 2416   Tel: 020-7376 0267

ASHCROFT ACADEMY OF DRAMATIC ART & AGENCY
Malcolm Primary School
Malcolm Road
Penge, London SE20 8RH
Website: www.ashcroftacademy.com
e-mail: geraldi.gillma@btconnect.com
Mobile: 07799 791586   Tel/Fax: 0844 8005328

AWA - ANDREA WILDER AGENCY
23 Cambrian Drive
Colwyn Bay, Conwy LL28 4SL
Website: www.awagency.co.uk
e-mail: casting@awagency.co.uk
Fax: 07092 249314   Mobile: 07919 202401

BABY BODENS
Bodens Studios & Agency
99 East Barnet Road
New Barnet
Herts EN4 8RF
Website: www.bodensagency.com
e-mail: info@bodensagency.com
Fax: 020-8449 5212   Tel: 020-8447 1035

BABYSHAK
Bizzy House
73A Mayplace Road West
Bexleyheath, Kent DA7 4JL
Website: www.babyshak.com
e-mail: bookings@babyshak.com   Tel/Fax: 020-8304 5439

BANANAFISH MANAGEMENT
85-89 Duke Street
Liverpool L1 5AP
Website: www.bananafish.co.uk
e-mail: info@bananafish.co.uk
Mobile: 07974 206622   Tel: 0151-324 2222

BARDSLEY'S Pamela UNIQUE AGENCY
93 Bispham Road
Churchtown
Southport PR9 7DF
Website: www.pamelabardsleyschool.co.uk
e-mail: pamela_bardsley@hotmail.com
Mobile: 07969 774506   Tel: 01704 231101

BELCANTO LONDON ACADEMY
(Stage School & Agency)
Performance House
20 Passey Place
Eltham, London SE9 5DQ
e-mail: agent@belcantolondonacademy.com
Fax: 020-8850 9944   Tel: 020-8850 9888

BIZZYKIDZ
Bizzy House
73A Mayplace Road West
Bexleyheath
Kent DA7 4JL
Website: www.bizzykidz.com
e-mail: bookings@bizzykidz.com
Fax: 020-8303 2730   Tel: 020-8303 2627

BODENS AGENCY
99 East Barnet Road
New Barnet
Herts EN4 8RF
Website: www.bodensagency.com
e-mail: info@bodensagency.com
Fax: 020-8449 5212   Tel: 020-8447 1226

BOURNE Michelle ACADEMY & AGENCY The
Studio 1, 22 Dorman Walk
Garden Way
London NW10 0PF
Website: www.michellebourneacademy.co.uk
e-mail: info@michellebourneacademy.co.uk
Mobile: 07852 932473   Tel/Fax: 020-8451 8808

BRUCE & BROWN
203 Canalot Studios
222 Kensal Road, London W10 5BN   *modelling*
Website: www.bruceandbrown.com
e-mail: info@bruceandbrown.com
Fax: 020-8964 0457   Tel: 020-8968 5585

BUBBLEGUM
Pinewood Studios   *me del*
Pinewood Road
Iver Heath, Bucks SL0 0NH
Website: www.bubblegummodels.com
e-mail: info@bubblegummodels.com
Fax: 01753 652521   Tel: 01753 632867

BYRON'S MANAGEMENT
(Children & Adults)
76 St James Lane
Muswell Hill, London N10 3DF
Website: www.byronsmanagement.co.uk
e-mail: byronsmanagement@aol.com
Fax: 020-8444 4040   Tel: 020-8444 4445

CAROUSEL KIDZ
1 Dukes Court
250 Croydon Road
Beckenham
Kent BR3 4DA
Website: www.carouselkidz.co.uk
e-mail: info@carouselkidz.co.uk   Tel/Fax: 020-8249 3597

CARR Norrie AGENCY
(Babies, Children & Adults)
Holborn Studios   X
49-50 Eagle Wharf Road
London N1 7ED
Website: www.norriecarr.com
e-mail: info@norriecarr.com
Fax: 020-7253 1772   Tel: 020-7253 1771

CAVAT SCHOOL OF THEATRE ARTS & AGENCY
16A Hook Hill, South Croydon, Surrey CR2 0LA
Website: www.cavattheatrearts.co.uk
e-mail: enquiries@cavattheatrearts.co.uk
                                           Tel: 020-8651 1099

CHADWICK Jacqueline ACADEMY The
Oakdene Studios
Brewery Lane, Leigh WN7 2RJ
Website: www.jacquelinechadwickacademy.co.uk
e-mail: chadwickacademy@btconnect.com
Fax: 01942 609690   Tel: 01942 675747

CHILDSPLAY MODELS LLP
114 Avenue Road
Beckenham, Kent BR3 4SA
Website: www.childsplaymodels.co.uk
e-mail: info@childsplaymodels.co.uk
Fax: 020-8778 2672   Tel: 020-8659 9860

CHILLI KIDS
1 Badhan Court
Castle Street, Telford TF1 5QX
Website: www.chillimodels.com
e-mail: kids@chillimodels.com   Tel: 01952 320280

CHRYSTEL ARTS AGENCY
6 Eunice Grove
Chesham, Bucks HP5 1RL
e-mail: chrystelarts@waitrose.com
Mobile: 07799 605489   Tel/Fax: 01494 773336

CIRCUS MANIACS AGENCY
(Circus, Theatre, Dance, Extreme Sports)
Office 8A, The Kingswood Foundation
Britannia Road, Kingswood
Bristol BS15 8DB
Website: www.circusmaniacsagency.com
e-mail: agency@circusmaniacs.com
Mobile: 07977 247287   Tel/Fax: 0117-947 7042

COLIN'S PERFORMING ARTS AGENCY
(Colin's Performing Arts Ltd)
The Studios
219B North Street
Romford, Essex RM1 4QA
Website: www.colinsperformingarts.co.uk
e-mail: agency@colinsperformingarts.co.uk
Fax: 01708 766077   Tel: 01708 766444

CONTI Italia AGENCY Ltd
23 Goswell Road
London EC1M 7AJ
e-mail: agency@italiaconti.co.uk
Fax: 020-7253 1430   Tel: 020-7608 7500

CS MANAGEMENT
(Children & Young Adults)
The Croft
7 Cannon Road
Southgate, London N14 7HE
Website: www.csmanagementuk.com
e-mail: carole@csmanagementuk.com
Fax: 020-8886 7555   Tel: 020-8886 4264

D & B MANAGEMENT & THEATRE SCHOOL
470 Bromley Road
Bromley
Kent BR1 4PN
Website: www.dandbperformingarts.co.uk
e-mail: bonnie@dandbmanagement.com
Fax: 020-8697 8100   Tel: 020-8698 8880

DD'S CHILDREN'S AGENCY
6 Acle Close
Hainault, Essex IG6 2GQ
Website: www.debdaystudio.com
e-mail: ddsagency@yahoo.co.uk
Mobile: 07957 398501   Tel: 020-8502 6866

DEBUT KIDS
25 Crossways
Shenfield
Essex CM15 8QX
Website: www.debutkids.co.uk
e-mail: team@debutkids.co.uk   Mobile: 07946 618328

DIMPLES MODEL & CASTING ACADEMY
(Children, Teenagers & Adults)
84 Kirk Hall Lane
Leigh
Lancs WN7 5QQ
e-mail: info@dimplesacademy.com
Fax: 01942 262232   Tel: 01942 262012

DMS AGENCY
30 Lakedale Road
Plumstead
London SE18 1PP   Tel/Fax: 020-8317 6622

DRAGON DRAMA
(Drama for Children)
347 Hanworth Road TW12 3EJ
Website: www.dragondrama.co.uk
e-mail: info@dragondrama.co.uk   Tel/Fax: 020-8255 8356

DRAMA STUDIO EDINBURGH The
19 Belmont Road
Edinburgh EH14 5DZ
Website: www.thedramastudio.com
e-mail: info@thedramastudio.com
Fax: 0131-453 3108   Tel: 0131-453 3284

EARNSHAW Susi MANAGEMENT
68 High Street
Barnet, Herts EN5 5SJ
Website: www.susiearnshaw.co.uk
e-mail: casting@susiearnshaw.co.uk
Fax: 020-8364 9618   Tel: 020-8441 5010

Mark Jermin
 Management

8 Heathfield, Swansea, SA1 6EJ
Phone: 01792 458855 Fax: 01792 458844
E mail: info@markjermin.co.uk

Children and young adults from all over the UK.

Audition workshops and classes in London, Manchester, Bristol and Wales.

Children with open performance licences, guaranteed to be licensed for any production and at very short notice.

www.markjermin.co.uk

ENGLISH Doreen '95
(Gerry Kinner)
4 Selsey Avenue
Aldwick, Bognor Regis
West Sussex PO21 2QZ   Tel/Fax: 01243 825968

EUROKIDS CASTING & MODEL AGENCY
The Warehouse Studios, Glaziers Lane
Culcheth Warrington, Cheshire WA3 4AQ
Website: www.eka-agency.com
e-mail: castings@eka-agency.com
Fax: 01925 767563   Tel: 01925 761088

EXPRESSIONS CASTING AGENCY
3 Newgate Lane
Mansfield
Nottingham NG18 2LB
Website: www.expressionsperformingarts.co.uk
e-mail: expressions-uk@btconnect.com
Fax: 01623 647337   Tel: 01623 424334

FBI AGENCY Ltd The
PO Box 250, Leeds LS1 2AZ
Website: www.fbi-agency.co.uk
e-mail: casting@fbi-agency.co.uk   Tel/Fax: 07050 222747

FEA MANAGEMENT
(Ferris Entertainment)
Number 8
132 Charing Cross Road
London WC2H 0LA
Website: www.ferrisentertainment.com
e-mail: info@ferrisentertainment.com   Mobile: 07801 493133

FIORENTINI Anna AGENCY
Islington Business Design Centre
Unit 10/i, 52 Upper Street
London N1 0QH
Website: www.annafiorentini.co.uk
e-mail: info@annafiorentini.co.uk
Mobile: 07904 962779   Tel/Fax: 020-7682 1403

FOOTSTEPS THEATRE SCHOOL CASTING AGENCY
55 Pullan Avenue
Eccleshill
Bradford BD2 3RP
e-mail: helen@footsteps.fslife.co.uk
Tel/Fax: 01274 637429   Tel: 01274 636036

FOX Betty AGENCY
Slade Road
Erdington
Birmingham B23 7PX
e-mail: bettyfox.school@virgin.net
Mobile: 07703 436045   Tel/Fax: 0121-327 1020

GENESIS THEATRE SCHOOL & AGENCY
88 Hempland Close
Great Oakley, Corby
Northants NN18 8LT
e-mail: info@saracharles.com   Tel: 01536 460928

GLYNNE Frances THEATRE STUDENTS & MANAGEMENT
Flat 9, Elmwood, 6 The Avenue
Hatch End
Middlesex HA5 4EP
e-mail: franandmo@googlemail.com   Mobile: 07950 918355

Do you need a Model Child?
EXTRAS • WALK ONS • CROWD ARTISTS
Modelling/Casting for children aged 0 to 21 years
Please call today on Tel: 01625 442 742

some of our clients:

www.modelchild.co.uk

GO FOR IT CHILDREN'S AGENCY
(Children & Teenagers)
47 North Lane
Teddington
Middlesex TW11 0HU
Website: www.goforitts.com
e-mail: agency@goforitts.com
Tel: 020-8943 1120

GOBSTOPPERS MANAGEMENT
37 St Nicholas Mount
Hemel Hempstead, Herts HP1 2BB
e-mail: chrisgobstoppers@btinternet.com
Mobile: 07961 372319
Tel: 01442 269543

GP ASSOCIATES
4 Gallus Close
Winchmore Hill
London N21 1JR
Website: www.greasepaintanonymous.co.uk
e-mail: info@gpassociates.co.uk
Fax: 020-8882 9189
Tel: 020-8886 2263

GRAYSTONS
843-845 Green Lanes
Winchmore Hill, London N21 2RX
e-mail: graystons@btinternet.com
Fax: 020-8364 2009
Tel: 020-8360 5700

GREVILLE Jeannine THEATRICAL AGENCY
Melody House
Gillotts Corner
Henley-on-Thames
Oxon RG9 1QU
e-mail: jeannines.dance@ukonline.co.uk
Fax: 01491 411533
Tel: 01491 572000

HARLEQUIN STUDIOS AGENCY FOR CHILDREN
122A Phyllis Avenue
Peacehaven
East Sussex BN10 7RQ
Tel: 01273 581742

HARRIS AGENCY Ltd The
PO Box 308
Northwood, Middlesex HA6 9DT
e-mail: theharrisagency@btconnect.com
Fax: 01923 822253
Tel: 01923 822744

HOBSON'S KIDS
62 Chiswick High Road, London W4 1SY
Website: www.hobsons-international.com
e-mail: kids@hobsons-international.com
Fax: 020-8996 5350
Tel: 020-8995 3628

HOWE Janet CHILDREN'S CASTING & MODELLING AGENCY
58A High Street
Newcastle-under-Lyme
Staffordshire ST5 1QE
e-mail: info@janethowe.com
Tel/Fax: 01782 661777

The Pie Factory
101 Broadway, Salford Quays
Manchester M60 2EQ
Tel/Fax: 0161-263 0633

Works Media Centre
36 White House Street
Hunslet
Leeds LS10 1AD
Tel/Fax: 0113-242 5225

INTER-CITY KIDS
Portland Tower
Portland Street, Manchester M1 3LF
Website: www.iccast.co.uk
e-mail: intercitycasting@btconnect.com
Tel/Fax: 0161-238 4950

JABBERWOCKY AGENCY
(Children & Teenagers)
Glassenbury Hill Farm
Glassenbury Road
Cranbrook, Kent TN17 2QF
Website: www.jabberwockyagency.com
e-mail: info@jabberwockyagency.com
Fax: 01580 714346
Tel: 01580 714306

JB ASSOCIATES
(Children & Teenagers 10-18 Years)
4th Floor, Manchester House
84-86 Princess Street
Manchester M1 6NG
Website: www.j-b-a.net
e-mail: info@j-b-a.net
Fax: 0161-237 1809
Tel: 0161-237 1808

JERMIN Mark MANAGEMENT
8 Heathfield
Swansea SA1 6EJ
Website: www.markjermin.co.uk
e-mail: info@markjermin.co.uk
Fax: 01792 458844
Tel: 01792 458855

STOMP! MANAGEMENT *Representing:*
• CHILDREN & TEENAGERS 6-19 Yrs
• CONFIDENT, TRAINED, NATURAL. MANY BOY ACTORS.
• COMPLIMENTARY CASTING FACILITIES.
T: 020 8959 5353
www.stompmanagement.com

JIGSAW ARTS MANAGEMENT
(Representing Children & Young People from Jigsaw
Performing Arts Schools)
64-66 High Street
Barnet
Herts EN5 5SJ
Website: www.jigsaw-arts.co.uk/agency
Tel: 020-8447 4534

JMB MANAGEMENT
Buttercup Cottage
Down End, Hook Norton
Oxfordshire OX15 5LL
e-mail: managementjmb@yahoo.com
Mobile: 07814 768862
Tel: 01608 737979

JOHNSTON & MATHERS ASSOCIATES Ltd
PO Box 3167, Barnet
Herts EN5 2WA
Website: www.johnstonandmathers.com
e-mail: johnstonmathers@aol.com
Fax: 020-8449 2386
Tel: 020-8449 4968

KELLY MANAGEMENT Ltd
3rd Floor
50 South Molton Street
Mayfair
London W1K 5SB
Website: www.kelly-manangement.com
e-mail: assistant@kelly-management.com
Fax: 020-7495 5212
Tel: 020-7495 5211

KENT Tim & FOX Julie CHILD TALENT
Pinewood Studios, Pinewood Road
Iver Heath, Bucks SL0 0NH
e-mail: childtalent@tkassociates.co.uk
Fax: 01753 655622   Tel: 01753 655517

KENT YOUTH THEATRE AGENCY
Mulberry Croft
Mulberry Hill, Chilham CT4 8AJ
Website: www.kentyouththeatre.co.uk
e-mail: richard@kyt.org.uk   Tel/Fax: 01227 730177

KIDS LONDON
67 Dulwich Road
London SE24 0NJ
Website: www.kidslondonltd.com
e-mail: sue@kidslondonltd.com
Fax: 020-7924 9766   Tel: 020-7924 9595

KIDS PLUS
Malcolm House
Malcolm Primary School
Penge
London SE20 8RH
Website: www.kidsplusagency.co.uk
e-mail: geraldi.gillma@btinternet.com
Mobile: 07799 791586   Tel: 0844 8005328

KIDZ Ltd
Beckinsdale
Ingol Lane
Hambleton SY6 9BJ
Website: www.kidzltd.com
e-mail: info@kidzltd.com
Tel/Fax: 0870 2416260   Tel: 0870 2414418

KMC AGENCIES
PO Box 122
48 Great Ancoats Street
Manchester M4 5AB
e-mail: casting@kmcagencies.co.uk
Fax: 0161-237 9812   Tel: 0161-237 3009

KRACKERS KIDS THEATRICAL AGENCY
6-7 Electric Parade
Seven Kings Road
Ilford
Essex IG3 8BY
Website: www.krackerskids.co.uk
e-mail: krackerskids@hotmail.com   Tel/Fax: 01708 502046

EXPRESSIONS

Academy of Performing Arts and Casting Agency

Children & Graduates
Theatre TV Film Commercials
Representation from London & all over the UK

www.expressionsperformingarts.co.uk

3 Newgate Lane, Mansfield
Nottinghamshire NG18 2LB
Phone: 01623 424334 Fax: 01623 647337
e-mail: expressions-uk@btconnect.com

LAMONT CASTING AGENCY
2 Harewood Avenue
Ainsdale
Merseyside PR8 2PH
Website: www.lamontcasting.co.uk
e-mail: diane@lamontcasting.co.uk   Mobile: 07736 387543

LESLIE Sasha MANAGEMENT
(In Association with Allsorts Drama for Children)
34 Pember Road
London NW10 5LS
e-mail: sasha@allsortsdrama.com   Tel/Fax: 020-8969 3249

LIFE AND SOUL THEATRE AGENCY
Boxmoor Hall
St Johns Road
Hemel Hempstead
Herts HP1 1JR
Website: www.lifeandsoultheatreacademy.co.uk
e-mail: lifeandsoulta@hotmail.com   Tel/Fax: 01442 233050

LIL DEVILS AGENCY
1st Floor, 76 School Road
Tilehurst, Reading
Berks RG31 5AW
Website: www.lildevils.co.uk
e-mail: kids@lildevils.co.uk
Fax: 0118-941 7273   Tel: 0118-943 3057

LINTON MANAGEMENT
3 The Rock, Bury BL9 0JP
e-mail: carol@linton.tv
Fax: 0161-761 1999   Tel: 0161-761 2020

LITTLE ADULTS ACADEMY & MODELLING AGENCY Ltd
Studio 1
Essex House
375-377 High Street
Stratford, London E15 4QZ
Website: www.littleadultsagency.co.uk
e-mail: info@littleadults.demon.co.uk
Fax: 020-8519 9797   Tel: 020-8519 9755

LIVE & LOUD AGENCY
The Penthouse
42/17 Speirs Wharf
Glasgow G4 9TH
e-mail: info@liveandloudagency.com   Tel: 0141-331 1340

MODEL CHILD AGENCY
York Chambers, Dukes Court
Macclesfield
Cheshire SK11 6NN
Website: www.modelchild.co.uk
e-mail: sam@modelchild.co.uk
Fax: 01625 442745   Tel: 01625 442742

MONDI ASSOCIATES Ltd
Unit 3 0, Cooper House
2 Michael Road
London SW6 2AD
Website: www.mondiassociates.com
e-mail: info@mondiassociates.com   Mobile: 07817 133349

MRS WORTHINGTON'S
(6-16 Years)
16 Ouseley Road
London SW12 8EF   Tel/Fax: 020-8767 6944

The Stagecoach Agency (UK)

The UK's largest children and young performers agency.

We represent over 2,200 children and young performers aged between 4 and 20 all of whom attend one of our 620 schools throughout the whole of the U.K. We have members appearing in films, television, commercials, West End shows, regional theatre, voice-overs, radio drama, corporate video, photo-shoots, promotions, modelling and as background artists. The Stagecoach Agency can arrange and organize casting workshops and auditions throughout the UK. We have a large team of licensed chaperones and tutors. Our experienced staff will be pleased to offer you advice, or to help you with any enquiry.

Call us on: 0845 408 2468 (local rate)
Or email: tarquin@stagecoachagency.co.uk

The Stagecoach Agency (UK), P.O. box 127, Ross-on Wye, HR9 6WZ
www.stagecoachagency.co.uk

NFD - THE FILM AND TV AGENCY
PO Box 76
Leeds LS25 9AG
Website: www.film-tv-agency.com
e-mail: info@film-tv-agency.com   Tel/Fax: 01977 681949

O'FARRELL STAGE & THEATRE SCHOOL
(Babies, Children, Teenagers & Young Adults)
36 Shirley Street
Canning Town
London E16 1HU
Mobile: 07956 941497   Tel: 020-7511 9444

ORR MANAGEMENT AGENCY
(Children, Teenagers & Adults)
1st Floor, 147-149 Market Street
Farnworth BL4 8EX
Website: www.orrmanagement.co.uk
e-mail: barbara@orrmanagement.co.uk
Mobile: 07773 227784   Tel: 01204 579842

PALMER Jackie AGENCY
30 Daws Hill Lane
High Wycombe, Bucks HP11 1PW
Website: www.jackiepalmer.co.uk
e-mail: jackie.palmer@btinternet.com
Fax: 01494 510479   Tel: 01494 520978

PAUL'S THEATRE AGENCY
Ardleigh House
42 Ardleigh Green Road
Hornchurch, Essex RM11 2LG
Website: www.paulstheatreschool.co.uk
e-mail: penny@paulstheatreschoolagency.co.uk
    Tel: 01708 446167

PC THEATRICAL, MODEL & CASTING AGENCY
12 Carlisle Road
Colindale NW9 0HL
Website: www.twinagency.com
e-mail: twinagy@aol.com
Fax: 020-8933 3418   Tel: 020-8381 2229

PERFORMERS AGENCY Ltd
Southend Road
Corringham
Essex SS17 8JT
Website: www.performersagency.biz
e-mail: mandy@performersagency.biz
Fax: 01375 672353   Tel: 01375 672053

PHA YOUTH
Tanzaro House
Ardwick Green North
Manchester M12 6FZ
Website: www.pha-agency.co.uk
e-mail: youth@pha-agency.co.uk
Fax: 0161-273 4567   Tel: 0161-273 4444

PLATFORM TALENT MANAGEMENT
16 Shelbourne Rise
Camberley
Surrey GU15 2EJ
Website: www.kidsagency.tv
e-mail: castings@kidsagency.tv   Tel: 01276 23256

POLLYANNA MANAGEMENT Ltd
1 Knighten Street
Wapping
London E1W 1PH
Website: www.pollyannatheatre.com
e-mail: aliceharwood@talktalk.net
Fax: 020-7480 6761   Tel: 020-7481 1911

POWER MODEL MANAGEMENT CASTING AGENCY
PO Box 1198
Salhouse
Norwich NR13 6WD
Website: www.powermodel.co.uk
e-mail: info@powermodel.co.uk   Tel: 01603 777190

RAMA YOUNG ACTORS AGENCY
Huntingdon House
278-290 Huntingdon Street
Nottingham NG1 3LY
Website: www.ramayoungactors.co.uk
e-mail: martin@rama-global.co.uk
Fax: 0115-948 3696   Tel: 0845 0540255

RASCALS MODEL AGENCY
13 Jubilee Parade
Snakes Lane East
Woodford Green
Essex IG8 7QG
Website: www.rascals.co.uk
e-mail: kids@rascals.co.uk
Fax: 020-8559 1035   Tel: 020-8504 1111

RAVENSCOURT MANAGEMENT
8-30 Galena Road
Hammersmith
London W6 0LT
e-mail: info@ravenscourt.net
Fax: 020-8741 1786   Tel: 020-8741 0707

**REBEL SCHOOL OF THEATRE ARTS AND CASTING
AGENCY Ltd**
(Based in Leeds)
PO Box 169
Huddersfield HD8 1BE
e-mail: suerebeltheatre@aol.com
Mobile: 07808 803637   Tel: 0113-305 3796

REDROOFS THEATRE SCHOOL AGENCY
Redroofs
Littlewick Green
Maidenhead, Berks SL6 3QY
Fax: 01628 822461   Tel: 01628 822982 Ext 1

REFLECTIONS AGENCY
9 Weavers Terrace
Fulham
London SW6 1QE
Website: www.reflectionsperfarts.tripod.com
e-mail: c.johnson717@ntlworld.com
Mobile: 07709 429354   Tel/Fax: 01322 410003

RHODES AGENCY
5 Dymoke Road
Hornchurch, Essex RM11 1AA
e-mail: rhodesarts@hotmail.com
Fax: 01708 730431   Tel: 01708 747013

RIDGEWAY MANAGEMENT
Fairley House
Andrews Lane
Cheshunt
Herts EN7 6LB
Website: www.ridgewaystudios.co.uk
e-mail: info@ridgewaystudios.co.uk
Fax: 01992 633844   Tel: 01992 633775

ROSS David ACTING Ltd
83 The Avenue
Sale
Cheshire M33 4YA
Website: www.davidrossacting.com
e-mail: info@davidrossacting.com
Mobile: 07957 862317   Tel: 0161-718 5835

SCALA KIDS CASTING
42 Rufford Avenue
Yeadon, Leeds LS19 7QR
Website: www.scalakids.com
e-mail: office@scalakids.com
Fax: 0113-250 8806   Tel: 0113-250 6823

SCALLYWAGS AGENCY Ltd
90-92 Ley Street
Ilford
Essex IG1 4BX
Website: www.scallywags.co.uk
e-mail: info@scallywags.co.uk
Fax: 020-8553 4849   Tel: 020-8553 9999

SCREAM MANAGEMENT
The Pie Factory
101 Broadway
Media City
Manchester M50 2EQ
Website: www.screammanagement.com
e-mail: info@screammanagement.com   Tel: 0161-660 3652

Tuesdays Child Agency

Established 1976

Babies, Children and Adults (0-80+)
North and South UK

Tel: 01625 501765

info@tuesdayschildagency.co.uk
www.tuesdayschildagency.co.uk

SEQUINS THEATRICAL AGENCY
8 Bideford Gardens
Bush Hill Park, Enfield
Middlesex EN1 2RP
Tel: 020-8360 6601

SINGER Sandra ASSOCIATES
21 Cotswold Road
Westcliff-on-Sea
Essex SS0 8AA
Website: www.sandrasinger.com
e-mail: sandrasingeruk@aol.com
Fax: 01702 339393
Tel: 01702 331616

SMITH Elisabeth Ltd
20 Chenies
Rickmansworth,, Herts WD3 6ET
Website: www.elisabethsmith.com
e-mail: models@elisabethsmith.com
Fax: 0845 8721332
Tel: 0845 8721331

SPEAKE Barbara AGENCY
East Acton Lane, London W3 7EG
e-mail: speakekids2@aol.com
Fax: 020-8740 6542
Tel: 020-8743 6096

SRA AGENCY
Lockhart Road, Cobham
Surrey KT11 2AX
e-mail: agency@susanrobertsacademy.co.uk
Tel: 01932 863194

STAGE 84 YORKSHIRE SCHOOL OF PERFORMING ARTS
Old Bell Chapel
Town Lane
Idle, Bradford
West Yorks BD10 8PR
e-mail: valeriejackson@stage84.com
Mobile: 07785 244984
Tel: 01274 569197

STAGE CENTRAL CASTING AGENCY
9 Alexandra Grove
Knaresborough
North Yorkshire HG5 0PH
Website: www.stagecentral.co.uk
e-mail: darren@stagecentral.co.uk
Tel: 01423 540533

STAGE KIDS AGENCY
(Children & Teenagers)
1 Greenfield
Welwyn Garden City
Herts AL8 7HW
Website: www.stagekids.co.uk
Tel: 01707 328359

STAGECOACH AGENCY (UK) The
PO Box 127
Ross-on-Wye HR9 6WZ
Website: www.stagecoachagency.co.uk
e-mail: tarquin@stagecoachagency.co.uk
Fax: 0845 4082464
Tel: 0845 4082468

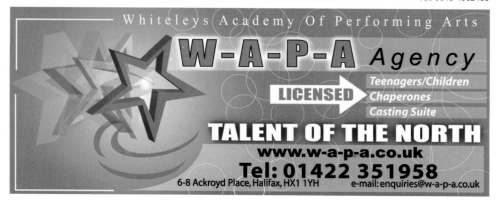

SSTARDOM CASTING AGENCY & THEATRE SCHOOL
16 Pinebury Drive
Queensbury
Bradford BD13 2TA
e-mail: liz.stardom@btinternet.com
Mobile: 07740 091019   Tel/Fax: 01274 818051

STARSTRUCK MANAGEMENT
85 Hewson Road
Lincoln, Lincolnshire LN1 1RZ
e-mail: starstruckacademy@hotmail.com   Tel: 01522 887894

STOMP! MANAGEMENT
Suite 5, Lyndhurst House
120 Bunns Lane, London NW7 2AR
Website: www.stompmanagement.com
e-mail: stompmanagement@aol.com
                                    Tel/Fax: 020-8959 5353

TALENTED KIDS PERFORMING ARTS SCHOOL & AGENCY
23 Burrow Manor
Calverstown
Kilcullen, Co. Kildare, Ireland
Website: www.talentedkidsireland.com
e-mail: talentedkids@hotmail.com
Mobile: 00 353 87 2480348   Tel/Fax: 00 353 45 485464

TANWOOD
72 Nyland Road, Nythe
Swindon, Wilts SN3 3RJ
Website: www.tanwood.co.uk
e-mail: tanwood.agency2@ntlworld.com
                                    Mobile: 07774 517469

TELEVISION WORKSHOP The
(Birmingham Group)
ITV Central
Gas Street
Birmingham B1 2JT
e-mail: colin.edwards@itv.com
Fax: 0121-634 4835   Tel: 0844 8814000

TELEVISION WORKSHOP The
(Nottingham Group)
30 Main Street
Calverton, Notts NG14 6FQ
e-mail: ian@thetelevisionworkshop.co.uk
                                    Tel: 0115-845 0764

THAMES VALLEY THEATRICAL AGENCY
Mobile: 07956 256189   Tel/Fax: 01865 340333

TOP TALENT AGENCY Ltd
(Children & Teenagers)
PO Box 860
St Albans, Herts AL1 9BR
Website: www.toptalentagency.co.uk
e-mail: admin@tophatstageschool.co.uk
                                    Tel/Fax: 01727 812666

TOTS-TWENTIES AGENCY
62 Buntingbridge Road
Newbury Park
Ilford
Essex IG2 7LR
Website: www.tots-twenties.co.uk
e-mail: sara@tots-twenties.co.uk
Fax: 020-8518 0212   Tel: 020-8518 0200

TRULY SCRUMPTIOUS Ltd
66 Bidwell Gardens
London N11 2AU
Website: www.trulyscrumptious.co.uk
e-mail: bookings@trulyscrumptious.co.uk
Fax: 020-8888 4584   Tel: 020-8888 4204

TUESDAYS CHILD
(Children, Teenagers & Adults)
Oakfield House
Springwood Way
Macclesfield SK10 2XA
Website: www.tuesdayschildagency.co.uk
e-mail: info@tuesdayschildagency.co.uk
                                    Tel/Fax: 01625 501765

TWINS
(See PC THEATRICAL, MODEL & CASTING AGENCY)

URBAN ANGELS
PO Box 45453
London SE26 6UZ
e-mail: info@urbanangelsagency.com
Fax: 0870 8710046   Tel: 0870 8710045

VALLÉ ACADEMY THEATRICAL AGENCY
The Vallé Academy Studios
Wilton House
Delamare Road
Cheshunt
Herts EN8 9SG
Website: www.valleacademy.co.uk
e-mail: agency@valleacademy.co.uk
Fax: 01992 622868   Tel: 01992 622861

W-A-P-A CASTING AGENCY
6-8 Akroyd Place
Halifax
West Yorkshire HX1 1YH
Website: www.w-a-p-a.co.uk
e-mail: enquiries@w-a-p-a.co.uk
Fax: 01422 360958   Tel: 01422 351958

WHITEHALL PERFORMING ARTS CENTRE
Rayleigh Road
Leigh-on-Sea
Essex SS9 5UU   Tel/Fax: 01702 529290

WILLIAMSON & HOLMES
9 Hop Gardens, St Martin's Lane
London WC2N 4EH
e-mail: info@williamsonandholmes.co.uk
Fax: 020-7240 0408   Tel: 020-7240 0407

WINGS AGENCY
(Affiliated to Angels Theatre School)
49 Midhurst Road
Fernhurst, Haslemere GU27 3EN
Website: www.angelstheatreschool.co.uk
e-mail: wingsagency@btconnect.com
Fax: 01428 658990   Tel: 01428 658990

WYSE AGENCY
Hill House, 1 Hill Farm Road
Whittlesford, Cambs CB22 4NB
e-mail: frances.wyse@btinternet.com   Tel: 01223 832288

YAT MANAGEMENT
(Young Actors Theatre)
70-72 Barnsbury Road, London N1 0ES
Website: www.yati.org.uk
e-mail: agent@yati.org.uk
Fax: 020-7833 9467   Tel: 020-7278 2101

YOUNG ACTORS COMPANY Ltd The
3 Marshall Road, Cambridge CB1 7TY
Website: www.theyoungactorscompany.com
e-mail: info@theyoungactorscompany.com
Fax: 01223 416511   Tel: 01223 416474

YOUNG ACTORS FILE The
31 Nursery Road, Angmering
West Sussex BN16 4GQ
e-mail: young.actorsfile@btinternet.com
Mobile: 07789 888575   Tel: 01903 782354

YOUNGBLOOD
BWH Agency
Barley Mow Centre
10 Barley Mow Passage
Chiswick, London W4 4PH
Website: www.thebwhagency.co.uk
e-mail: rep@thebwhagency.co.uk
Fax: 020-8996 1662   Tel: 020-8996 1661

YOUNGSTARS
(Coralyn Canfor-Dumas)
4 Haydon Dell
Bushey
Herts WD23 1DD
e-mail: coralyncd@gmail.com
Fax: 020-8950 5701   Mobile: 07966 176756

YOUNG 'UNS AGENCY
Sylvia Young Theatre School
Rossmore Road
Marylebone
London NW1 6NJ
e-mail: enquiries@youngunsagency.co.uk
Fax: 020-7723 1040   Tel: 020-7723 0037

ACORN ENTERTAINMENTS Ltd
PO Box 64, Cirencester, Glos GL7 5YD
Website: www.acornents.co.uk
e-mail: info@acornents.co.uk
Fax: 01285 642291 Tel: 01285 644622

ASKONAS HOLT Ltd
(Classical Music)
Lincoln House
300 High Holborn, London WC1V 7JH
Website: www.askonasholt.co.uk
e-mail: info@askonasholt.co.uk
Fax: 020-7400 1799 Tel: 020-7400 1700

AVALON PROMOTIONS Ltd
4A Exmoor Street, London W10 6BD
Fax: 020-7598 7334 Tel: 020-7598 7333

BARRUCCI LEISURE ENTERPRISES Ltd
(Promoters)
45-47 Cheval Place
London SW7 1EW
e-mail: barrucci@barrucci.com
Fax: 020-7581 2509 Tel: 020-7225 2255

BLOCK Derek ARTISTES AGENCY
70-76 Bell Street
Marylebone, London NW1 6SP
e-mail: derekblock@derekblock.co.uk
Fax: 020-7724 2102 Tel: 020-7724 2101

CITY CONCERT ORGANISATION Ltd The
PO Box 3145
Lichfield WS13 6YN
Website: www.cityconcert.com
e-mail: admin@cityconcert.com Tel/Fax: 01543 262286

FLYING MUSIC
FM House
110 Clarendon Road, London W11 2HR
Website: www.flyingmusic.com
e-mail: reception@flyingmusic.com
Fax: 020-7221 5016 Tel: 020-7221 7799

GOLDSMITH Harvey PRODUCTIONS Ltd
(Concert Promotion)
13-14 Margaret Street
London W1W 8RN
Website: www.harveygoldsmith.com
e-mail: mail@harveygoldsmith.com
Fax: 020-7224 0111 Tel: 020-7224 1992

GUBBAY Raymond Ltd
Dickens House
15 Tooks Court
London EC4A 1QH
Website: www.raymondgubbay.co.uk
e-mail: info@raymondgubbay.co.uk
Fax: 020-7025 3751 Tel: 020-7025 3750

HOBBS Liz CONCERTS & EVENTS Ltd
65 London Road
Newark
Nottinghamshire NG24 1RZ
Website: www.lizhobbsgroup.com
e-mail: events@lizhobbsgroup.com
Fax: 0870 3337009 Tel: 0870 0702702

HOCHHAUSER Victor
4 Oak Hill Way
London NW3 7LR
e-mail: admin@victorhochhauser.co.uk
Fax: 020-7431 2531 Tel: 020-7794 0987

IMG ARTS & ENTERTAINMENT
Pier House
Strand on the Green
Chiswick, London W4 3NN
Fax: 020-8233 5001 Tel: 020-8233 5000

McINTYRE Phil ENTERTAINMENT
2nd Floor
35 Soho Square
London W1D 3QX
e-mail: info@mcintyre-ents.com
Fax: 020-7439 2280 Tel: 020-7439 2270

MEADOW Jeremy Ltd
73 Great Titchfield Street
London W1W 6RD
Website: www.jeremymeadow.com
e-mail: info@jeremymeadow.com
Fax: 0870 7627882 Tel: 020-7436 2244

RBM
(Comedy)
3rd Floor
168 Victoria Street
London SW1E 5LB
Website: www.rbmcomedy.com
e-mail: info@rbmcomedy.com
Fax: 020-7630 6549 Tel: 020-7630 7733

Why do I need a dance agent?

As with any other agent, a dance agent will submit their clients for jobs, negotiate contracts, handle paperwork and offer advice. In return for these services they will charge commission ranging from 10-15%. The agents listed on the following pages specialise in representing and promoting dancers. They will possess the relevant contacts in the industry that you need to get auditions and jobs.

How should I use these listings?

If you are a dancer getting started in the industry, looking to change your existing agent, or wishing to take on an additional agent that represents you for dance alongside your main acting agent, the following pages will supply you with up-to-date contact details for dance agencies. Every company listed is done so by written request to us. Please see the main 'Agents and Personal Managers' advice section for further guidance on choosing and approaching agents.

Should I pay an agent to join their books?
Or sign a contract?

Equity (the actors' trade union) does not recommend that artists pay an agent to join their client list. Before signing a contract, you should be very clear about the terms and commitments involved. For advice on both of these issues, or if you experience any problems with a current agent, we recommend that you contact Equity www.equity.org.uk. They also publish the booklet 'You and your Agent' which is free to all Equity members.

What is Spotlight Dancers?

Spotlight Dancers is a new specialist directory published annually by Spotlight. Members receive a page in the directory containing a headshot and body shot, agency contact details and selected credits as well as an online CV. These are used by dance employers throughout the UK to locate dancers and send out casting or audition information. Dancers wishing to promote themselves for job opportunities in commercial theatre, musicals, opera, film, television, live music and video, corporate events and many other areas of the industry should consider joining: see www.spotlight.com/join for more information.

Should I join Spotlight's Actors/Actresses
directory or the Dancers directory?

Depending on your skills, training and experience, you may be eligible for both directories if you are interested in promoting yourself both as an actor and as a dancer. If you join both, you would receive an entry into each directory and two separate online CVs. You would also qualify for a 25% discount off the Dancers entry fee. If you only want to join one or the other, then you will need to consider which area of the industry you want to focus on in your career. Musical theatre experience can qualify you for either directory, depending on whether your role involved mainly dancing or acting. This is something you will need to think about, and something you should discuss with your agent if you sign with one.

Where can I find more information?

Please refer to the guest article overleaf and the advice articles preceding the 'Dance Companies' listings for further information about the dance industry.

Re|animator

Piers Gielgud trained at the Rambert School and, after a long career as a dancer, founded Re|animator (originally a small dance company) in 1992. In 1997 Piers and his wife Suzanne founded Re|animator Management which has since earned a reputation for supplying some of the very best dancers and musical theatre performers to the profession. Piers is also a successful feature film choreographer, working with, amongst others, Robert de Niro and Oliver Stone. Visit www.reanimator.co.uk for more information.

At the time of writing, we have just finished our annual agency auditions. Over the past year we received over 1000 CVs, out of which we selected 150 to audition. We have 10 places to fill. Here's how to beat the competition and find an agent...

Finding the Right Agent For You:
The Personal Managers' Association (PMA) or the Agents' Association ensure that their members are fully accountable and law-abiding and can advise you on choosing the right agent. Make sure the agent actually covers the area of the profession you have trained to work in. I still get applications from drama school graduates who want to join the RSC! If you only want to dance, you only need to join a commercial agency. It's a relatively impersonal relationship because they tend to have hundreds of clients, but you can sign with several and be submitted for a huge variety of work. Find out who the most successful commercial dancers are and who represents them.

Doing Your Research:
If the agency has specific criteria for joining or auditioning, follow this carefully. If they want you to post a CV with a headshot, don't email them body shots and your Spotlight number. Nobody likes to be addressed as 'Dear Sir or Madam' or 'Hiya'. Worst of all is the email simultaneously sent to hundreds of agents. We all like to feel special and exclusive, so if you address me by name and tell me that out of all the agents in the world I'm the one you want to sign with and why, your CV is more likely to receive consideration and not get thrown in the bin.

Sending Your CV:
Don't lie about your credits, age or ability. Try to keep everything on one page and prioritise your best credits. Provide a simple email address with your name in it, not something weird. Always have your voicemail activated and record a message so that we can be certain it's you we are calling.

Sending Photos and Showreels:
A good headshot is really all we need unless you have a great commercial photo. Don't send us your whole portfolio. Make sure the photo shows how you look right now, not two years ago with different coloured hair. Don't send a showreel without checking it's OK to do so.

The Audition:
Be on time. Be dressed the way you have been asked to, so if they say tight clothing and hair up, don't turn up in baggies with hair in your face. Be prepared: if you are not sure which shoes to take bring them all. Likewise if you're not sure of the best song to sing take a selection, but always have the sheet music. If you are cut, please don't argue. Reputation is everything in this business so get yourself a good one and guard it with your life.

The Interview:
There may be several agents you are considering signing with. Make this clear when you are invited to interview: honesty is always appreciated. Ideally you will end up with a personal manager for entertainment and several commercial agents. If you have done your research properly you will know whom you are meeting. Make a list of relevant questions to ask. Remember that personalities are important. A person might be the finest agent in the world, but if it's clear you don't like or get on with them, it would be crazy to sign with them. Go with your instincts. If you have any concerns about an agent, ask their governing body. Client recommendations are useful too.

One of the pleasures of this year's auditions was seeing people from last year that have worked hard and really improved. I can now offer them representation. This goes to show that if you are not at first successful in signing with the agent of your choice, it doesn't mean that you won't ever be. We are all in this profession because we know those infrequent highs far outweigh the regular lows and I hope in some small way my advice can help you all enjoy a great career.

DANCERS
CHOREOGRAPHERS
ACTORS

HEADNOD TALENT AGENCY
www.headnodagency.com 020 7502 9478 info@headnodagency.com

MODELS
MUSICIANS
TALENTS!

A@B (AGENCY AT BODYWORK)
25-29 Glisson Road
Cambridge CB1 2HA
e-mail: agency@bodyworkds.co.uk
Fax: 01223 568231   Tel: 01223 309990

ACCELERATE PRODUCTIONS Ltd
73 St Johns Sreet, London EC1M 4NJ
Website: www.accelerate-productions.co.uk
e-mail: info@accelerate-productions.co.uk
                                     Tel: 020-7490 2772

BLACKFISH PRODUCTIONS
4 Knox Road, London E7 9HW
Website: www.blackfishproductions.co.uk
e-mail: team@blackfishproductions.co.uk
Fax: 0845 8679307   Tel: 0845 4650735

DANCERS
1 Charlotte Street, London W1T 1RD
Website: www.features.co.uk
e-mail: info@features.co.uk
Fax: 020-7636 1657   Tel: 020-7636 1473

DANCERS INC. INTERNATIONAL COLLECTIVE
Golden Cross House
8 Duncannon Street
The Strand, London WC2N 4JF
Website: www.internationalcollective.com
e-mail: enquiries@internationalcollective.co.uk
Fax: 020-7484 5100   Tel: 020-7484 5080

ELLITE MANAGEMENT
The Dancer
8 Peterson Road, Wakefield WF1 4EB
Website: www.elliteproductions.co.uk
e-mail: enquiries@ellitemanagement.co.uk
Mobile: 07957 631510   Tel: 0845 6525361

FEATURES
1 Charlotte Street, London W1T 1RD
Website: www.features.co.uk
e-mail: info@features.co.uk
Fax: 020-7636 1657   Tel: 020-7637 1487

HEADNOD TALENT AGENCY
2nd Floor Office (Unit 4)
18 Kingsland Road
Shoreditch, London E2 8DA
Website: www.headnodagency.com
e-mail: info@headnodagency.com   Tel/Fax: 020-7502 9478

JK DANCE PRODUCTIONS
South Manchester Film & Television Studios
Battersea Road
Stockport SK4 3EA
Website: www.jkdance.co.uk
e-mail: info@jkdance.co.uk   Tel: 0161-432 5222

K TALENT
1st Floor
28 Grays Inn Road, London WC1X 8HR
Website: www.ktalent.co.uk
e-mail: mail@ktalent.co.uk   Tel: 0844 5672470

KEW PERSONAL MANAGEMENT
PO Box 53974
London SW15 2SQ
Website: www.kewpersonalmanagement.com
e-mail: info@kewpersonalmanagement.com
                                     Tel: 020-8871 3697

KMC AGENCIES
Garden Studios
11-15 Betterton Street
London WC2H 9BP
e-mail: london@kmcagencies.co.uk
Fax: 0870 4421780   Tel: 0870 4604868

PO Box 122
48 Great Ancoats Street
Manchester M4 5AB
e-mail: casting@kmcagencies.co.uk
Fax: 0161-237 9812   Tel: 0161-237 3009

LONGRUN ARTISTES
(Gina Long)
3 Chelsworth Drive
Plumstead Common, London SE18 2RB
Website: www.longrunartistes.co.uk
e-mail: gina@longrunartistes.co.uk
Fax: 0871 5227926   Mobile: 07748 723228

MBK DANCE & ENTERTAINEMENT
10 St Julians Close
London SW16 2RY
Website: www.mbkonline.co.uk
e-mail: mbkdance@msn.com
Fax: 020-8488 9121   Tel: 020-8664 6676

MITCHELL MAAS McLENNAN
MD2000 Offices
Island Business Centre
Thomas Street, Woolwich, London SE18 6PF
Website: www.mmm2000.co.uk
e-mail: agency@mmm2000.co.uk   Tel/Fax: 01767 650020

PINEAPPLE AGENCY
Montgomery House
159-161 Balls Pond Road
Islington, London N1 4BG
Website: www.pineappleagency.com
e-mail: pineapple.agency@btconnect.com
Fax: 020-7241 3006   Tel: 020-7241 6601

RAZZAMATAZZ MANAGEMENT
Mulberry Cottage, Park Farm
Haxted Road
Lingfield RH7 6DE
e-mail: razzamatazzmanagement@btconnect.com
                          Tel/Fax: 01342 835359

RE.ANIMATOR
3rd Floor, The Priory
Syresham Gardens
West Sussex RH16 3LB
Website: www.reanimator.co.uk
e-mail: re.animator@gmail.com
Fax: 01444 447030   Tel: 01444 447020

RED & BLACK
Website: www.red-black.co.uk
e-mail: info@red-black.co.uk   Mobile: 07722 887277

RUDEYE DANCE AGENCY
PO Box 38743, London E10 5WN
Website: www.rudeye.com
e-mail: info@rudeye.com   Tel/Fax: 020-8556 7139

SCRIMGEOUR Donald ARTISTS AGENT
49 Springcroft Avenue, London N2 9JH
e-mail: vwest@dircon.co.uk
Fax: 020-8883 9751   Tel: 020-8444 6248

SHOW TEAM PRODUCTIONS The
(Dancers & Choreographers)
9 Church Street, Brighton BN1 1US
Website: www.theshowteam.co.uk
e-mail: info@theshowteam.co.uk   Tel: 0845 4671010

SINGER Sandra ASSOCIATES
21 Cotswold Road
Westcliff-on-Sea, Essex SS0 8AA
Website: www.sandrasinger.com
e-mail: sandrasingeruk@aol.com
Fax: 01702 339393   Tel: 01702 331616

S.O.S.
85 Bannerman House
Lawn Lane, London SW8 1UA
Website: www.sportsofseb.com
e-mail: info@sportsofseb.com
Mobile: 07740 359770   Tel: 020-7735 5133

SUCCESS
Room 236, 2nd Floor
Linen Hall, 162-168 Regent Street
London W1B 5TB
Website: www.successagency.co.uk
e-mail: ee@successagency.co.uk
Fax: 020-7494 3787   Tel: 020-7734 3356

TUCKER Tommy AGENCY
Suite 66, 235 Earls Court Road
London SW5 9FE
e-mail: TTTommytucker@aol.com   Tel: 020-7370 3911

TWITCH EVENT CHOREOGRAPHY
5 Breakspears Mews, Brockley SE4 1PY
Website: www.twitch.uk.com
e-mail: info@twitch.uk.com
Mobile: 07932 656358   Mobile: 07747 770816

Culverhouse and James limited Literary Agents

Suite 2, Galleon Buildings, 16-18 Stanley Street, Southport PR9 0BY
t: 01704 542965　**f:** 01704 541144　**e:** enquiries@culverhousejames.co.uk

Shepperton Studios, Shepperton, Middx TW17 0QD
t: 01932 592546　**f:** 01932 592233　www.culverhousejames.co.uk

A & B PERSONAL MANAGEMENT Ltd
(PMA Member)
Suite 330, Linen Hall
162-168 Regent Street, London W1B 5TD
e-mail: billellis@aandb.co.uk
Fax: 020-7038 3699　　　　　　　Tel: 020-7434 4262

ABNER STEIN
10 Roland Gardens, London SW7 3PH
e-mail: abner@abnerstein.co.uk
Fax: 020-7370 6316　　　　　　　Tel: 020-7373 0456

AGENCY (LONDON) Ltd The
(PMA Member)
24 Pottery Lane, Holland Park, London W11 4LZ
Website: www.theagency.co.uk
e-mail: info@theagency.co.uk
Fax: 020-7727 9037　　　　　　　Tel: 020-7727 1346

A J ASSOCIATES LITERARY AGENTS
Higher Healey House, Higher House Lane
White Coppice, Chorley PR6 9BT
e-mail: info@ajassociates.net　　　Tel/Fax: 01257 273148

A M HEATH & Co Ltd
(Fiction & Non-Fiction only)
6 Warwick Court, London WC1R 5DJ
e-mail: enquiries@amheath.com
Fax: 020-7242 2711　　　　　　　Tel: 020-7242 2811

A R G (ARTISTS RIGHTS GROUP Ltd)
(PMA Member)
4 Great Portland Street, London W1W 8PA
e-mail: argall@argtalent.com
Fax: 020-7436 6700　　　　　　　Tel: 020-7436 6400

ASPER Pauline MANAGEMENT
(PMA Member)
Jacobs Cottage, Reservoir Lane
Sedlescombe, East Sussex TN33 0PJ
e-mail: pauline.asper@virgin.net　　Tel/Fax: 01424 870412

BERLIN ASSOCIATES
(PMA Member)
14 Floral Street, London WC2E 9DH
Website: www.berlinassociates.com
e-mail: agents@berlinassociates.com
Fax: 020-7632 5296　　　　　　　Tel: 020-7836 1112

BLAKE FRIEDMANN
(Novels, Non-Fiction & TV/Film Scripts)
122 Arlington Road, London NW1 7HP
Website: www.blakefriedmann.co.uk
e-mail: julian@blakefriedmann.co.uk
Fax: 020-7284 0442　　　　　　　Tel: 020-7284 0408

BRITTEN Nigel MANAGEMENT
(PMA Member)
Riverbank House
1 Putney Bridge Approach, London SW6 3JD
e-mail: office@nbmanagement.com
Fax: 020-7384 3862　　　　　　　Tel: 020-7384 3842

BRODIE Alan REPRESENTATION Ltd
(PMA Member)
6th Floor, Fairgate House
78 New Oxford Street, London WC1A 1HB
Website: www.alanbrodie.com
e-mail: abr@alanbrodie.com
Fax: 020-7079 7999　　　　　　　Tel: 020-7079 7990

CANN Alexandra REPRESENTATION
(PMA Member)
2 St Thomas Square,
Newport, Isle of Wight PO30 1SN
e-mail: alex@alexandracann.co.uk　Tel: 01983 556866

CASAROTTO RAMSAY & ASSOCIATES Ltd
(PMA Member)
Waverley House
7-12 Noel Street, London W1F 8GQ
Website: www.casarotto.co.uk
e-mail: agents@casarotto.co.uk
Fax: 020-7287 9128　　　　　　　Tel: 020-7287 4450

CLOWES Jonathan Ltd
(PMA Member)
10 Iron Bridge House, Bridge Approach, London NW1 8BD
Fax: 020-7722 7677　　　　　　　Tel: 020-7722 7674

COCHRANE Elspeth PERSONAL MANAGEMENT
(PMA Member)
16 Trinity Close
The Pavement, London SW4 0JD
e-mail: elspethcochrane@talktalk.net　Tel: 020-7622 3566

CULVERHOUSE & JAMES Ltd
Suite 2, Galleon Buildings
16-18 Stanley Street, Southport PR9 0BY
Website: www.culverhousejames.co.uk
e-mail: enquiries@culverhousejames.co.uk
Fax: 01704 541144　　　　　　　Tel: 01704 542965

Shepperton Studios
Shepperton, Middlesex TW17 0QD
Fax: 01932 592233　　　　　　　Tel: 01932 592546

CURTIS BROWN GROUP Ltd
(PMA Member)
5th Floor, Haymarket House
28-29 Haymarket, London SW1Y 4SP
e-mail: cb@curtisbrown.co.uk
Fax: 020-7393 4401　　　　　　　Tel: 020-7393 4400

DAISH Judy ASSOCIATES Ltd
(PMA Member)
2 St Charles Place, London W10 6EG
e-mail: judy@judydaish.com
Fax: 020-8964 8966　　　　　　　Tel: 020-8964 8811

DENCH ARNOLD AGENCY The
(PMA Member)
10 Newburgh Street, London W1F 7RN
e-mail: contact@dencharnold.com
Fax: 020-7439 1355　　　　　　　Tel: 020-7437 4551

A

de WOLFE Felix
(PMA Member)
Kingsway House, 103 Kingsway, London WC2B 6QX
e-mail: info@felixdewolfe.com
Fax: 020-7242 8119   Tel: 020-7242 5066

DREW Bryan Ltd
Mezzanine, Quadrant House
80-82 Regent Street, London W1B 5AU
e-mail: bryan@bryandrewltd.com
Fax: 020-7437 0561   Tel: 020-7437 2293

FARNES Norma MANAGEMENT
9 Orme Court, London W2 4RL
Fax: 020-7792 2110   Tel: 020-7727 1544

FILLINGHAM Janet ASSOCIATES
(PMA Member)
52 Lowther Road, London SW13 9NU
Website: www.janetfillingham.com
e-mail: info@jfillassoc.co.uk
Fax: 020-8748 7374   Tel: 020-8748 5594

FILM RIGHTS Ltd
Mezzanine, Quadrant House
80-82 Regent Street, London W1B 5AU
Website: www.filmrights.ltd.uk
e-mail: information@filmrights.ltd.uk
Fax: 020-7734 0044   Tel: 020-7734 9911

FITCH Laurence Ltd
Mezzanine, Quadrant House
80-82 Regent Street, London W1B 5AU
Fax: 020-7734 0044   Tel: 020-7734 9911

FOSTER Jill Ltd
(PMA Member)
9 Barb Mews, London W6 7PA
Website: www.jflagency.com
e-mail: agents@jflagency.com
Fax: 020-7602 9336   Tel: 020-7602 1263

FRENCH Samuel Ltd
(PMA Member)
52 Fitzroy Street, Fitzrovia, London W1T 5JR
Website: www.samuelfrench-london.co.uk
e-mail: theatre@samuelfrench-london.co.uk
Fax: 020-7387 2161   Tel: 020-7387 9373

FUTERMAN, ROSE & ASSOCIATES
(PMA Member) (TV/Film, Showbiz & Music Biographies)
91 St Leonards Road, London SW14 7BL
Website: www.futermanrose.co.uk
e-mail: guy@futermanrose.co.uk
Fax: 020-8286 4860   Tel: 020-8255 7755

GILLIS Pamela MANAGEMENT
46 Sheldon Avenue, London N6 4JR
Fax: 020-8341 5564   Tel: 020-8340 7868

GLASS Eric Ltd
25 Ladbroke Crescent, Notting Hill, London W11 1PS
e-mail: eglassltd@aol.com
Fax: 020-7229 6220   Tel: 020-7229 9500

HALL Rod AGENCY Ltd The
(PMA Member)
6th Floor, Fairgate House
78 New Oxford Street, London WC1A 1HB
Website: www.rodhallagency.com
e-mail: office@rodhallagency.com
Fax: 0845 6384094   Tel: 020-7079 7987

HANCOCK Roger Ltd
(PMA Member)
4 Water Lane, London NW1 8NZ
e-mail: info@rogerhancock.com
Fax: 020-7267 0705   Tel: 020-7267 4418

HIGHAM David ASSOCIATES Ltd
(PMA Member)
5-8 Lower John Street, Golden Square, London W1F 9HA
e-mail: dha@davidhigham.co.uk
Fax: 020-7437 1072   Tel: 020-7434 5900

HOSKINS Valerie ASSOCIATES Ltd
(PMA Member)
20 Charlotte Street, London W1T 2NA
e-mail: vha@vhassociates.co.uk
Fax: 020-7637 4493   Tel: 020-7637 4490

HOWARD Amanda ASSOCIATES Ltd
(PMA Member)
21 Berwick Street, London W1F 0PZ
Website: www.amandahowardassociates.co.uk
e-mail: mail@amandahowardassociates.co.uk
Fax: 020-7287 7785   Tel: 020-7287 9277

HURLEY LOWE MANAGEMENT
(PMA Member)
27 Rosenau Crescent, London SW11 4RY
e-mail: kate@hurleylowemanagement.com
                                      Tel: 020-7978 7325

INDEPENDENT TALENT GROUP Ltd
(PMA Member) (Formerly ICM, London)
Oxford House, 76 Oxford Street, London W1D 1BS
Website: www.independenttalent.com
Fax: 020-7323 0101   Tel: 020-7636 6565

KASS Michelle ASSOCIATES
(PMA Member)
85 Charing Cross Road, London WC2H 0AA
e-mail: office@michellekass.co.uk
Fax: 020-7734 3394   Tel: 020-7439 1624

KENIS Steve & Co
(PMA Member)
Royalty House
72-74 Dean Street, London W1D 3SG
e-mail: sk@sknco.com
Fax: 020-7287 6328   Tel: 020-7434 9055

MACFARLANE CHARD ASSOCIATES Ltd
(PMA Member)
33 Percy Street, London W1T 2DF
Website: www.macfarlane-chard.co.uk
e-mail: louise@macfarlane-chard.co.uk
Fax: 020-7636 7751   Tel: 020-7636 7750

MACNAUGHTON LORD REPRESENTATION
(PMA Member)
Unit 10, The Broomhouse Studios
50 Sulivan Road, London SW6 3DX
Website: www.mlrep.com
e-mail: info@mlrep.com
Fax: 020-7371 7563   Tel: 020-7384 9517

MANN Andrew Ltd
(PMA Member)
1 Old Compton Street, London W1D 5JA
e-mail: info@andrewmann.co.uk
Fax: 020-7287 9264   Tel: 020-7734 4751

MANS Johnny PRODUCTIONS Ltd
PO Box 196, Hoddesdon, Herts EN10 7WQ
Website: www.johnnymansproductions.co.uk
e-mail: johnnymansagent@aol.com
Fax: 01992 470516   Tel: 01992 470907

MARJACQ SCRIPTS Ltd
34 Devonshire Place, London W1G 6JW
Website: www.marjacq.com
e-mail: enquiries@marjacq.com
Fax: 020-7935 9115   Tel: 020-7935 9499

Publishers of Plays • Agents for the Collection of Royalties
Specialist Booksellers
52 Fitzroy Street London W1T 5JR
Tel 020 7255 4300 (Bookshop) 020 7387 9373 (Enquiries)
Fax 020 7387 2161 www.samuelfrench-london.co.uk
e-mail: theatre@samuelfrench-london.co.uk

SAMUEL FRENCH LTD

MARVIN Blanche
(PMA Member)
21A St Johns Wood High Street, London NW8 7NG
e-mail: blanchemarvin17@hotmail.com
Tel/Fax: 020-7722 2313

M.B.A. LITERARY AGENTS Ltd
(PMA Member)
62 Grafton Way, London W1T 5DW
Website: www.mbalit.co.uk
e-mail: agent@mbalit.co.uk
Fax: 020-7387 2042   Tel: 020-7387 2076

McLEAN Bill PERSONAL MANAGEMENT
23B Deodar Road, London SW15 2NP   Tel: 020-8789 8191

MLR
(See MACNAUGHTON LORD REPRESENTATION)

MORRIS William AGENCY (UK) Ltd
(PMA Member)
Centre Point, 103 New Oxford Street, London WC1A 1DD
Fax: 020-7534 6900   Tel: 020-7534 6800

NARROW ROAD COMPANY The
(PMA Member)
182 Brighton Road
Coulsdon, Surrey CR5 2NF
e-mail: richardireson@narrowroad.co.uk
Fax: 020-8763 2558   Tel: 020-8763 9895

PFD
(PMA Member)
Drury House, 34-43 Russell Street, London WC2B 5HA
Website: www.pfd.co.uk
e-mail: postmaster@pfd.co.uk
Fax: 020-7836 9539   Tel: 020-7344 1000

POLLINGER Ltd
9 Staple Inn, Holborn, London WC1V 7QH
Website: www.pollingerltd.com
e-mail: info@pollingerltd.com
Fax: 020-7242 5737   Tel: 020-7404 0342

ROSICA COLIN Ltd
1 Clareville Grove Mews, London SW7 5AH
Fax: 020-7244 6441   Tel: 020-7370 1080

SAYLE SCREEN Ltd
(PMA Member) (Screenwriters & Directors for Film & TV)
11 Jubilee Place, London SW3 3TD
Fax: 020-7823 3363   Tel: 020-7823 3883

SEIFERT Linda MANAGEMENT
(PMA Member)
22 Poland Street, London W1F 8QQ
e-mail: contact@lindaseifert.com
Fax: 020-7292 7391   Tel: 020-7292 7390

SHARLAND ORGANISATION Ltd
(PMA Member)
The Manor Hse, Manor Street, Raunds, Northants NN9 6JW
e-mail: tso@btconnect.com   Tel: 01933 626600

SHEIL LAND ASSOCIATES Ltd
(PMA Member) (Literary, Theatre & Film)
52 Doughty Street, London WC1N 2LS
e-mail: info@sheilland.co.uk
Fax: 020-7831 2127   Tel: 020-7405 9351

STAGESCRIPTS Ltd
Lantern House
84 Littlehaven Lane
Horsham, West Sussex RH12 4JB
Website: www.stagescripts.com
e-mail: sales@stagescripts.com
Fax: 0700 5810582   Tel: 0700 5810581

STEEL Elaine
(PMA Member) (Writers' Agent)
110 Gloucester Avenue, London NW1 8HX
e-mail: ecmsteel@aol.com
Fax: 01273 772400   Tel: 01273 739022

STEINBERG Micheline ASSOCIATES
(PMA Member)
104 Great Portland Street
London W1W 6PE
Website: www.steinplays.com
e-mail: info@steinplays.com   Tel: 020-7631 1310

STEVENS Rochelle & Co
(PMA Member)
2 Terretts Place
Upper Street, London N1 1QZ
e-mail: info@rochellestevens.com
Fax: 020-7354 5729   Tel: 020-7359 3900

TENNYSON AGENCY The
10 Cleveland Avenue
Merton Park, London SW20 9EW
Website: www.tenagy.co.uk
e-mail: agency@tennysonagency.co.uk
Tel: 020-8543 5939

THEATRE OF LITERATURE
(c/o Calder Publications)
51 The Cut, London SE1 8LF
e-mail: info@calderbookshop.com
Fax: 020-7928 5930   Tel: 020-7633 0599

THURLEY J M MANAGEMENT
Archery House
33 Archery Square, Walmer, Deal CT14 7AY
e-mail: jmthurley@aol.com
Fax: 01304 371416   Tel: 01304 371721

TYRRELL Julia MANAGEMENT
(PMA Member)
57 Greenham Road, London N10 1LN
Website: www.jtmanagement.co.uk
e-mail: julia@jtmanagement.co.uk
Fax: 020-8374 5580   Tel: 020-8374 0575

WARE Cecily LITERARY AGENTS
(PMA Member)
19C John Spencer Square, London N1 2LZ
Website: www.cecilyware.com
e-mail: info@cecilyware.com
Fax: 020-7226 9828   Tel: 020-7359 3787

WEINBERGER Josef Ltd
(PMA Member)
12-14 Mortimer Street, London W1T 3JJ
Website: www.josef-weinberger.com
e-mail: general.info@jwmail.co.uk
Fax: 020-7436 9616   Tel: 020-7580 2827

ALEXANDER PERSONAL MANAGEMENT Ltd
Pinewood Studios, Pinewood Road
Iver Heath, Bucks SL0 0NH
Website: www.apmassociates.net
e-mail: lindafrench@apmassociates.net
Fax: 01753 639205   Tel: 01753 639204

A.P.M. (Linda French)
(See ALEXANDER PERSONAL MANAGEMENT Ltd)

ARLINGTON ENTERPRISES Ltd
1-3 Charlotte Street, London W1T 1RD
Website: www.arlingtonenterprises.co.uk
e-mail: info@arlington-enterprises.co.uk
Fax: 020-7580 4994   Tel: 020-7580 0702

BLACKBURN SACHS ASSOCIATES
Argyll House, All Saints Passage
London SW18 1EP
Website: www.blackburnsachsassociates.com
e-mail: presenters@blackburnsachsassociates.com
Fax: 020-8875 8301   Tel: 020-7292 7555

CAMERON Sara MANAGEMENT
(See TAKE THREE MANAGEMENT)

CHASE PERSONAL MANAGEMENT
Celebrity Division of Modelplan
1st Floor, 18-22 Lloyd Street, Manchester M2 5WA
Website: www.chasepersonalmanagement.co.uk
e-mail: sue@chasemanagement.co.uk
Mobile: 07775 683955   Tel: 0161-819 1162

CINEL GABRAN MANAGEMENT
PO Box 5163, Cardiff CF5 9BJ
Website: www.cinelgabran.co.uk
e-mail: info@cinelgabran.co.uk
Fax: 0845 0666601   Tel: 0845 0666605

PO Box 101, Newholm, Whitby
North Yorkshire YO21 3WT

CRAWFORDS
PO Box 44394, London SW20 0YP
Website: www.crawfords.tv
e-mail: cr@wfords.com
Fax: 020-3258 5037   Tel: 020-8947 9999

CURTIS BROWN GROUP Ltd
Haymarket House, 28-29 Haymarket, London SW1Y 4SP
e-mail: presenters@curtisbrown.co.uk
Fax: 020-7393 4401   Tel: 020-7393 4460

DAVID ANTHONY PROMOTIONS
PO Box 286, Warrington, Cheshire WA2 8GA
Website: www.davewarwick.co.uk
e-mail: dave@davewarwick.co.uk
Fax: 01925 416589   Tel: 01925 632496

DOWNES PRESENTERS AGENCY
96 Broadway, Bexleyheath, Kent DA6 7DE
Website: www.presentersagency.com
e-mail: downes@presentersagency.com Tel: 020-8304 0541

EVANS Jacque MANAGEMENT Ltd
Top Floor Suite
14 Holmesley Road, London SE23 1PJ
e-mail: jacque@jacqueevans.com
Fax: 020-8699 5192   Tel: 020-8699 1202

EXCELLENT TALENT COMPANY The
118-120 Great Titchfield Street, London W1W 6SS
Website: www.excellentvoice.co.uk
e-mail: viv@excellentvoice.co.uk
Fax: 020-7637 4091   Tel: 08452 100111

FBI AGENCY Ltd The
PO Box 250, Leeds LS1 2AZ
Website: www.fbi-agency.co.uk
e-mail: casting@fbi-agency.co.uk   Tel/Fax: 07050 222747

FIRST ARTIST ENTERTAINMENT Ltd
3 Tenterden Street, Hanover Square, London W1S 1TD
Website: www.firstartist.co.uk
e-mail: info@firstartist.co.uk
Fax: 020-3205 2140   Tel: 020-7096 9999

FLETCHER ASSOCIATES
(Broadcast & Media)
25 Parkway, London N20 0XN
Fax: 020-8361 8866   Tel: 020-8361 8061

FORD-CRUSH June PERSONAL MANAGEMENT & REPRESENTATION
PO Box 57948, London W4 2UJ
Website: www.junefordcrush.com
e-mail: june@junefordcrush.com
Mobile: 07711 764160   Tel/Fax: 020-8742 7724

GAY Noel
19 Denmark Street, London WC2H 8NA
Website: www.noelgay.com
Fax: 020-7287 1816   Tel: 020-7836 3941

GLORIOUS TALENT
Lower Ground Floor
79 Noel Road, London N1 8HE
e-mail: lisa@glorioustalent.co.uk   Tel: 020-7704 6555

GRANT James MANAGEMENT
94 Strand on The Green, London W4 3NN
Website: www.jamesgrant.co.uk
e-mail: info@jamesgrant.co.uk
Fax: 020-8742 4951   Tel: 020-8742 4950

GURNETT J. PERSONAL MANAGEMENT Ltd
12 Newburgh Street, London W1F 7RP
Website: www.jgpm.co.uk
e-mail: mail@jgpm.co.uk
Fax: 020-7287 9642   Tel: 020-7440 1850

HICKS Jeremy ASSOCIATES
114-115 Tottenham Court Road, London W1T 5AH
Website: www.jeremyhicks.com
e-mail: info@jeremyhicks.com
Fax: 020-7383 2777   Tel: 020-7383 2000

How do I become a presenter?

There is no easy answer to this question. Some presenters start out as actors and move into presenting work, others may be 'experts' such as chefs, designers or sports people who are taken on in a presenting capacity. Others may have a background in stand-up comedy. All newsreaders are professional journalists with specialist training and experience. Often presenters work their way up through the production side of broadcasting, starting by working as a runner or researcher and then moving to appear in front of the camera. To get this kind of production work you could contact TV and Film Production companies, many of whom are listed in this book. A number of Performing Arts Schools, Colleges and Academies also offer useful part-time training courses for presenters. See the 'Drama Training, Schools and Coaches' section of this book for college / school listings.

Why do I need a presenting agent?

As with any other agent, a presenting agent will promote their clients to job opportunities, negotiate contracts on their behalf, handle paperwork and offer advice. In return for these services they take commission ranging from 10-15%. The following pages contain contact details for the UK's leading presenter agencies. They will possess the relevant contacts in the industry that you need to get auditions and jobs.

How should I use these listings?

Before you approach any agency looking for representation, do some research into their current client list and the areas in which they specialise. Many have websites you can visit. Once you have made a short-list of the ones you think are most appropriate, you should send them your CV with a covering letter and a good quality, recent photograph which is a genuine likeness of you. Showreels can also be a good way of showcasing your talents, but only send these if you have checked with the agency first. Enclosing a stamped-addressed envelope with sufficient postage (SAE) will also give you a better chance of a reply. Please see the main 'Agents and Personal Managers' advice section for further guidance on choosing and approaching agents.

Should I pay a presenter's agent to join their books?
Or sign a contract?

As with other types of agencies, Equity does not generally recommend that artists pay an agent to join their client list. Before signing any contract, you should be clear about the terms and commitments involved. Always speak to Equity www.equity.org.uk if you have any concerns or queries.

What is Spotlight Presenters?

Spotlight Presenters is a specialist directory published annually. It contains photographs and contact details for over seven hundred professional TV and radio presenters and is a great way of promoting yourself for work. It is used by production companies, casting directors, TV and radio stations, advertising agencies and publicists to browse and locate talent for future productions. Entry is available to any presenter with proven professional broadcast experience. Please see www.spotlight.com/join for more information.

Should I join the Spotlight Actors/Actresses directory or the Presenters directory?

Depending on your skills, training and experience, you may be eligible for both directories if you are interested in promoting yourself as an actor and as a presenter. You would receive an entry into each directory and two separate online CVs. You would also qualify for a 25% discount off the Presenters entry fee. You will however have to prove that you already have professional experience and/or relevant training.

Craig Latto is an agent at RDF Management and has been an agent for 14 years. RDF Management represents presenters, actors and comedians including Liza Tarbuck, Bradley Walsh, Tim Lovejoy, Rav Wilding, Toyah Willcox, and Sherrie Hewson amongst others.

Presenting can be great fun, very exciting and a hugely rewarding career in many ways. However it's not as easy or as glamorous as you may think. It involves a lot of hard work, disappointments and frustration so you need to be prepared to roll with it and get stuck in!

Having a good agent is very important. Your agent will have years of experience and lots of contacts to utilise to find you work and negotiate the deals as well as handle day-to-day arrangements such as travel, wardrobe and invoicing. However you will need to work just as hard as your agent both off screen and on. Sometimes it can be easier to get your foot on the ladder in this industry because people are always looking for the next 'new' face but it's even harder to move upwards. Once you are no longer the new face you need to work even harder to sustain your career. This is where an agent can help, however it's a symbiotic relationship; an agent can only do so much and then it's up to you.

Getting an agent can be difficult but you need to be persistent and business-like. Get together a showreel, photograph and CV to send in to the relevant person. Find out who that is first and keep your reel short. Remember it doesn't need to be fancy, it just needs to give an idea of who you are and how you come across on camera. The first 30 seconds are the most important (and often the only bit that will be watched). Don't pester agents; they do get inundated with requests for representation, so you won't necessarily get a response straight away or when you want one. Allow at least a month before you should expect to hear back from them.

Nowadays production companies are looking for as many 'experts' to front shows as they are looking for presenters. It could be anything from doctors or vets to interior designers, cake makers or psychologists. So have a think about what previous experience you may have that could prove useful. Strong journalistic skills or experience can always be helpful so think about what skills or experience might make you more interesting when writing the covering letter.

It's important to be liked in the industry so behaving well is essential as people have very long memories. They will always remember a presenter who works hard, is professional and gets on well with everyone. They will also remember the presenter who showed up late or unprepared for a shoot, or who was rude to them whilst they were a runner. That runner today could be the channel commissioner in a couple of years' time and could make the decision about whether you get a job!

You need to be thick-skinned in this industry too. Be prepared to take constructive criticism from your agent; it might not be what you want to hear, but will be given for a reason. It's also important to listen to what producers, directors and other industry people have to say. Keep your eyes and ears open for other opportunities yourself – in this industry who you have worked with and who you know can stand you in good stead, so make sure you network and keep in contact with people you have enjoyed working with. It sounds obvious but it's also vital that you watch television and have a broad knowledge of the kind of shows that are currently being made and who makes them.

Be realistic when you start out. You may need to do work that's not well paid or even possibly unpaid, but think about the experience you may get, the important contacts you may make and the footage you may obtain for your showreel. Always think long term when you are considering work; don't just think of the financial gain because you can do serious harm to your career with any wrong choices. Think about what benefit it will have to your future career.

Please visit www.rdfmanagement.com for further information.

RED24 MANAGEMENT

Presenters and Specialists
for all areas of television
and the media

www.red24management.com | Office 020 7559 3611
Crown House | 72 Hammersmith Rd | Kensington Olympia | W14 8TH

HOBBS Liz GROUP Ltd
65 London Road, Newark, Notts NG24 1RZ
Website: www.lizhobbsgroup.com
e-mail: casting@lizhobbsgroup.com
Fax: 0870 3337009   Tel: 08700 702702

INTERNATIONAL ARTISTES Ltd
4th Floor, Holborn Hall
193-197 High Holborn, London WC1V 7BD
e-mail: reception@internationalartistes.com
Fax: 020-7404 9865   Tel: 020-7025 0600

JLA (Jeremy Lee Associates Ltd)
(Supplies celebrities and after dinner speakers)
80 Great Portland Street, London W1W 7NW
e-mail: talk@jla.co.uk
Fax: 020-7907 2801   Tel: 020-7907 2800

KBJ MANAGEMENT Ltd
(TV Presenters)
7 Soho Street, London W1D 3DQ
e-mail: general@kbjmgt.co.uk
Fax: 020-7287 1191   Tel: 020-7434 6767

KNIGHT AYTON MANAGEMENT
114 St Martin's Lane, London WC2N 4BE
Website: www.knightayton.co.uk
e-mail: info@knightayton.co.uk
Fax: 020-7836 8333   Tel: 020-7836 5333

KNIGHT Hilary MANAGEMENT Ltd
Grange Farm, Church Lane, Old, Northampton NN6 9QZ
Website: www.hkmanagement.co.uk
e-mail: hilary@hkmanagement.co.uk   Tel: 01604 781818

LEIGH Mike ASSOCIATES
37 Marylebone Lane, London W1U 2NW
Website: www.mikeleighassoc.com
Fax: 020-7486 5886   Tel: 020-7935 5500

LYTE Seamus MANAGEMENT Ltd
Apartment 5, Oswald Building, Chelsea Bridge Wharf
374 Queenstown Road, London SW8 4NU
e-mail: seamus@seamuslyte.com   Mobile: 07930 391401

MACFARLANE CHARD ASSOCIATES Ltd
33 Percy Street, London W1T 2DF
Website: www.macfarlane-chard.co.uk
e-mail: enquiries@macfarlane-chard.co.uk
Fax: 020-7636 7751   Tel: 020-7636 7750

MARKS PRODUCTIONS Ltd
2 Gloucester Gate Mews, London NW1 4AD
Fax: 020-7486 2165   Tel: 020-7486 2001

MARSH Billy ASSOCIATES Ltd
76A Grove End Road, St Johns Wood, London NW8 9ND
Website: www.billymarsh.co.uk
e-mail: talent@billymarsh.co.uk
Fax: 020-7449 6933   Tel: 020-7449 6930

MEDIA PEOPLE
(The Celebrity Group Ltd)
13 Montagu Mews South, London W1H 7ER
Website: www.celebrity.co.uk
e-mail: info@celebrity.co.uk   Tel: 0871 2501234

MILES John ORGANISATION
Cadbury Camp Lane, Clapton-in-Gordano, Bristol BS20 7SB
e-mail: john@johnmiles.org.uk
Fax: 01275 810186   Tel: 01275 854675

MONDI ASSOCIATES Ltd
Unit 3 0, Cooper House, 2 Michael Road, London SW6 2AD
Website: www.mondiassociates.com
e-mail: michelle@mondiassociates.com
                                     Mobile: 07817 133349

MPC ENTERTAINMENT
MPC House, 15-16 Maple Mews, London NW6 5UZ
Website: www.mpce.com
e-mail: mpc@mpce.com
Fax: 020-7624 4220   Tel: 020-7624 1184

MTC (UK) Ltd
20 York Street, London W1U 6PU
Website: www.mtc-uk.com
e-mail: kirsty@mtc-uk.com
Fax: 020-7935 8066   Tel: 020-7935 8000

NOEL John MANAGEMENT
Block B, Imperial Works
Perren Street, London NW5 3ED
Website: www.johnnoel.com
e-mail: john@johnnoel.com
Fax: 020-7428 8401   Tel: 020-7428 8400

OFF THE KERB PRODUCTIONS
(Comedy Presenters & Comedians)
3rd Floor, Hammer House
113-117 Wardour Street, London W1F 0UN
Website: www.offthekerb.co.uk
e-mail: westend@offthekerb.co.uk
Fax: 020-7437 0647   Tel: 020-7437 0607

PANMEDIA UK Ltd
18 Montrose Crescent
London N12 0ED
e-mail: v.panagi@btinternet.com   Tel: 020-8446 9662

PHA MANAGEMENT
Tanzaro House
Ardwick Green North
Manchester M12 6FZ
Website: www.pha-agency.co.uk
e-mail: casting@pha-agency.co.uk
Fax: 0161-273 4567   Tel: 0161-273 4444

PVA MANAGEMENT Ltd
Hallow Park, Hallow, Worcester WR2 6PG
e-mail: clients@pva.co.uk
Fax: 01905 641842   Tel: 01905 640663

RAZZAMATAZZ MANAGEMENT
Mulberry Cottage, Park Farm
Haxted Road, Lingfield RH7 6DE
e-mail: razzamatazzmanagement@btconnect.com
                    Tel/Fax: 01342 835359

RDF MANAGEMENT
3-6 Kenrick Place, London W1U 6HD
e-mail: debi.allen@rdfmanagement.com
Fax: 020-7317 2245   Tel: 020-7317 2251

RED 24 MANAGEMENT
Crown House
72 Hammersmith Road, London W14 8TH
Website: www.red24management.com
e-mail: info@red24management.com   Tel: 020-7559 3611

RED CANYON MANAGEMENT
Website: www.redcanyon.co.uk
e-mail: showkins@redcanyon.co.uk
Mobile: 07939 365578   Mobile: 07931 381696

RHINO PERSONAL MANAGEMENT
Studio House, Delamare Road
Cheshunt, Hertfordshire EN8 9SH
Website: www.rhino-management.co.uk
e-mail: rhinomanagement@hotmail.co.uk
Fax: 0845 3625457   Tel: 0845 3625456

ROSEMAN ORGANISATION The
51 Queen Anne Street, London W1G 9HS
Website: www.therosemanorganisation.co.uk
e-mail: info@therosemanorganisation.co.uk
Fax: 020-7486 4600   Tel: 020-7486 4500

SINGER Sandra ASSOCIATES
21 Cotswold Road, Westcliff-on-Sea, Essex SS0 8AA
Website: www.sandrasinger.com
e-mail: sandrasingeruk@aol.com
Fax: 01702 339393   Tel: 01702 331616

SOMETHIN' ELSE
20-26 Brunswick Place
London N1 6DZ
Website: www.somethinelse.com
e-mail: info@somethinelse.com
Fax: 020-7250 0937   Tel: 020-7250 5500

SPEAK-EASY Ltd
PO Box 648, Harrington
Northampton, NN6 9XT
Website: www.speak-easy.co.uk
e-mail: enquiries@speak-easy.co.uk
Tel: 01536 418526   Tel: 0870 0135126

STAR MANAGEMENT Ltd
16A Winton Drive
Glasgow G12 0QA
Website: www.starmanagement.co.uk
e-mail: star@starmanagement.co.uk   Tel: 0870 2422276

TAKE THREE MANAGEMENT
110 Gloucester Avenue
Primrose Hill, London NW1 8HX
Website: www.take3management.co.uk
e-mail: info@take3management.com
Fax: 020-7209 3770   Tel: 020-7209 3777

TALENT4 MEDIA Ltd
Studio LG16
Shepherds Building Central
Charecroft Way, London W14 0EH
Website: www.talent4media.com
e-mail: enquiries@talent4media.com
Fax: 020-7183 4331   Tel: 020-7183 4330

TROIKA
3rd Floor
74 Clerkenwell Road, London EC1M 5QA
e-mail: info@troikatalent.com
Fax: 020-7490 7642   Tel: 020-7336 7868

WANDER Jo MANAGEMENT
110 Gloucester Avenue
London NW1 8HX
Website: www.jowandermanagement.com
e-mail: jo@jowandermanagement.com   Tel: 020-7209 3777

WILLCOCKS John MEDIA AGENCY Ltd
34 Carisbrook Close
Enfield, Middlesex EN1 3NB
e-mail: john.willcocks@blueyonder.co.uk
                    Tel/Fax: 020-8364 4556

WISE BUDDAH TALENT
74 Great Titchfield Street
London W1W 7QP
Website: www.wisebuddah.com
e-mail: talent@wisebuddah.com
Fax: 020-7307 1601   Tel: 020-7307 1600

WWW.PEOPLEMATTER.TV
(Tony Fitzpatrick)
40 Bowling Green Lane
Clerkenwell, London EC1R 0NE
Website: www.peoplematter.tv
e-mail: tony@peoplematter.tv
Fax: 020-7415 7074   Tel: 07000 300707

ZWICKLER Marlene & ASSOCIATES
1 Belgrave Crescent Lane
Edinburgh EH4 3AG
Website: www.mza-artists.com   Tel/Fax: 0131-343 3030

How do I become a voice-over artist?

The voice-over business has opened up a lot more to newcomers in recent years; you don't have to already be a celebrity to be booked for a job. However, it is a competitive industry, and it is important to bear in mind that only a select few are able to earn a living from voice-over work. It is more likely that voice-over work could become a supplement to your regular income.

In order to get work you have to have a great voice and be able to put it to good use. Being able to act does not necessarily mean that you will also be able to do voice-overs. Whether your particular voice will get you the job or not will ultimately depend on the client's personal choice, so your technical ability to do voice-over work initially comes second in this industry. Once the client has chosen you, however, then you must be able to consistently demonstrate that you can take direction well, you don't need numerous takes to get the job finished, you have a positive attitude and you don't complain if recording goes a little over schedule.

Before you get to this stage, however, you will need a professional-sounding voicereel and, in the majority of cases, an agent.

How do I produce a voicereel?

Please see the 'Promotional Services' section for advice on creating your voicereel.

Why do I need a voice-over agent?

As with any other agent, a voice-over agent will promote their clients to job opportunities, negotiate contracts on their behalf, handle paperwork and offer advice. In return for these services they take commission ranging from 10-15%. The agents listed on the following pages specialise in representing and promoting voice-over artists, mostly in the commercial and corporate sectors, but also areas such as radio and animation. They will possess the relevant contacts in the industry that you need to get auditions and jobs. In this industry in particular, time is money, and clients are often more likely to trust that an agent can provide someone who can get the job done in the least amount of takes but still sounds good in every project, rather than taking on an unknown newcomer.

How do I find work in radio?

Please see the 'Radio' section of Contacts for further information on this specific area of voice work.

How should I use these listings?

Whether you are completely new to the industry, looking to change your existing agent, or wishing to take on an additional agent that represents you for voice-overs alongside your main acting or presenting agent, the following pages will supply you with up-to-date contact details for voice-over agencies. Every company listed is done so by written request to us. Please see the main 'Agents and Personal Managers' advice section for further guidance on choosing and approaching agents.

Should I pay an agent to join their books?
Or sign a contract?

Equity (the actors' trade union) does not recommend that artists pay an agent to join their client list. Before signing a contract, you should be very clear about the terms and commitments involved. For advice on both of these issues, or if you experience any problems with a current agent, we recommend that you contact Equity www.equity.org.uk. They also publish the booklet 'You and your Agent' which is free to all Equity members.

Nicola Sandon has been an agent for 12 years. She started her career at Polygram Television and A&M Records before moving over to Hobsons where she became a voiceover agent. She then moved over to International Artistes to set up a voiceover agency in-house before moving to Markham & Froggatt. She is currently an agent at Calypso Voices.

To get anywhere in the voiceover world as a voiceover artist you need to have a professional voicereel and an agent to promote your voice and what you can do with it. My best piece of advice, initially, would be to listen to established artists' voicereels on various voiceover agency websites (listed in Contacts) to listen to the competition. It will also give you a very good idea of what is needed to be a contender in this field. You need to find a suitable studio with an engineer / director who can supply scripts, if necessary, to record your voicereel. So many times I have heard voicereels which are much too busy so stick to what you can do best. If your natural voice is your selling point, stick to natural reads. If you are versatile and can sustain characters and accents add these on too. Don't try comedy unless you have great timing and can sound funny. That may sound obvious but you would be surprised. Many voiceovers are used on commercial radio and if you think of your ears as your eyes, you realise how good they have to be to sell a product or bring it to life.

Most voiceover agencies represent artists across the board for animation, TV and radio commercials, corporate, audiobooks and computer games. The client will call an agency with a specific brief for their campaign and the agent will then suggest who they feel is suitable, nine times out of ten via email with mp3s (hence the importance of having your own voicereel). As there is now so much more interest in voiceovers, well-known artists are often approached to become the exclusive voice of a product. It is incredibly big business now and everyone has caught on to how lucrative it can be. It is a fast turnaround. One hour and the job is over, whereas acting can take you away for six months at a time.

Your next step is to find an agent. There is no set route to obtaining an agent. It is a tough world out there and luck always goes hand in hand with talent. So, you are armed with your new voicereel and it is now time to plug yourself. With a copy of Contacts, call the relevant agents, send in your voicereel with an SAE and keep your fingers crossed. It is best not to keep calling to see what they think of your voicereel as they may not have had a chance to listen to it yet, it may not be the right time to take anyone new on, or you may clash with an existing artist. If and when the time is right, they will contact you.

Whenever I have taken on an artist, I have always thought it is so important that you genuinely both get on and have a rapport with each other and that you are both in agreement as to how our professional world operates. Remember a good agent knows what they are talking about and is on your side. It is important to have a contract or letter of agreement between artist and agent so that you can start off on the same page: understanding how much commission you are being charged, for example.

Hearing a voice selling or promoting a product is totally different to watching an actor in vision. There you are watching the whole package; with a voice, that is it. Consequently this is what makes voiceovers an art form, requiring confidence, timing, being able to take direction and, if you want to learn anything, listening and observing what is going on around you. There will always be artists you are working with who have been doing it a lot longer than you and making a success of it. Show interest in the script but do not suggest how you think something can be changed for the better, only offer your opinion if it is asked for. Oh, and turn up five minutes early!

You have chosen a very tough, competitive and ultimately rewarding industry.
Go for it and good luck!

Please visit www.calypsovoices.com for more information.

The voice agency of Amanda Howard Associates

www.meetthejoneses.co.uk +44 (0)20 7287 9666

ACCENT BANK
420 Falcon Wharf, 34 Lombard Road, London SW11 3RF
Website: www.accentbank.co.uk
e-mail: info@accentbank.co.uk   Tel: 020-7223 5160

AD VOICE
Oxford House, 76 Oxford Street, London W1D 1BS
Website: www.advoice.co.uk
e-mail: info@advoice.co.uk
Fax: 020-7323 0101   Tel: 020-7323 2345

ALPHABET KIDZ TALENT & VOICE-OVER AGENCY
189 Southampton Way, London SE5 7EJ
Website: www.alphabetkidz.co.uk
e-mail: contact@alphabetkidz.co.uk
Fax: 020-7252 4341   Tel: 020-7252 4343

AMERICAN AGENCY VOICES The
14 Bonny Street, London NW1 9PG
Website: www.americanagency.tv
e-mail: americanagency@btconnect.com
Fax: 020-7482 4666   Tel: 020-7485 8883

ANOTHER TONGUE VOICES Ltd
The Basement, 10-11 D'Arblay Street, London W1F 8DS
Website: www.anothertongue.com
e-mail: john@anothertongue.com
Fax: 020-7494 7080   Tel: 020-7494 0300

ASQUITH & HORNER
Contact: By Post (SAE)
The Studio, 14 College Road, Bromley, Kent BR1 3NS
Fax: 020-8313 0443   Tel: 020-8466 5580

CALYPSO VOICES
25-26 Poland Street, London W1F 8QN
Website: www.calypsovoices.com
e-mail: calypso@calypsovoices.com
Fax: 020-7437 0410   Tel: 020-7734 6415

CASTAWAY
Suite 3, 15 Broad Court, London WC2B 5QN
Website: www.castaway.org.uk
e-mail: info@castaway.org.uk
Fax: 020-7240 2772   Tel: 020-7240 2345

CINEL GABRAN MANAGEMENT
PO Box 5163, Cardiff CF5 9BJ
Website: www.cinelgabran.co.uk
e-mail: info@cinelgabran.co.uk
Fax: 0845 0666601   Tel: 0845 0666605

PO Box 101, Newholm, Whitby, North Yorkshire YO21 3WT

COLE KITCHENN
212 Strand, London WC2R 1AP
Website: www.colekitchenn.com
Fax: 020-7353 9639   Tel: 020-7427 5681

CONWAY VAN GELDER GRANT Ltd
3rd Floor, 18-21 Jermyn Street, London SW1Y 6HP
Website: www.conwayvangelder.com
e-mail: kate@conwayvg.co.uk
Fax: 020-7287 1940   Tel: 020-7287 1070

CUT GLASS VOICES
Studio 185
181-187 Queens Crescent
Camden, London NW5 4DS
Website: www.cutglassproductions.com
e-mail: info@cutglassproductions.com   Tel: 020-7267 2339

DIAMOND MANAGEMENT
31 Percy Street, London W1T 2DD
e-mail: hj@diman.co.uk
Fax: 020-7631 0500   Tel: 020-7631 0400

fŏ'reignversions

Voice Overs
Translations
Script Adaptation
Foreign Copywriting
Studio Production

Contact: Margaret Davies, Annie Geary
or Bérangère Capelle

On 020 7935 0993

Foreign Versions Ltd
60 Blandford Street
London W1U 7JD

e-mail: info@foreignversions.co.uk
www.foreignversions.com

DREW Bryan Ltd
Mezzanine, Quadrant House
80-82 Regent Street, London W1B 5AU
e-mail: bryan@bryandrewltd.com
Fax: 020-7437 0561   Tel: 020-7437 2293

EARACHE VOICES
177 Wardour Street, London W1F 8WX
Website: www.earachevoices.com
e-mail: alex@earachevoices.com
Fax: 020-7287 2288   Tel: 020-7287 2291

EVANS O'BRIEN
2 Lammpead Road, London SE12 8QL
Website: www.evansobrien.co.uk
e-mail: info@evansobrien.co.uk   Tel: 020-8318 9058

EXCELLENT VOICE COMPANY
118-120 Great Titchfield Street, London W1W 6SS
Website: www.excellentvoice.co.uk
e-mail: info@excellentvoice.co.uk
Fax: 020-7637 4091   Tel: 08452 100111

FERRIS ENTERTAINMENT VOICES
Number 8, 132 Charing Cross Road, London WC2H 0LA
Website: www.ferrisentertainment.com
e-mail: info@ferrisentertainment.com   Mobile: 07801 493133

FIRST VOICE AGENCY
Foxgrove House, School Lane, Seer Green HP9 2QJ
Website: www.firstvoiceagency.com
e-mail: jenny@firstvoiceagency.com
Fax: 01494 730166   Tel: 01494 678277

FOREIGN LEGION
1 Kendal Road, London NW10 1JH
Website: www.foreignlegion.co.uk
e-mail: voices@foreignlegion.co.uk   Tel: 020-8450 4451

FOREIGN VERSIONS Ltd
(Translation)
60 Blandford Street, London W1U 7JD
Website: www.foreignversions.com
e-mail: info@foreignversions.co.uk
Fax: 020-7935 0507   Tel: 020-7935 0993

GAY Noel VOICES
19 Denmark Street, London WC2H 8NA
Website: www.noelgay.com
Fax: 020-7287 1816   Tel: 020-7836 3941

GORDON & FRENCH
Contact: By post
12-13 Poland Street, London W1F 8QB
Website: www.gordonandfrench.net
e-mail: voices@gordonandfrench.net
Fax: 020-7734 4832   Tel: 020-7734 4818

HAMILTON HODELL Ltd
Contact: Louise Donald
5th Floor, 66-68 Margaret Street
London W1W 8SR
Website: www.hamiltonhodell.co.uk
e-mail: louise@hamiltonhodell.co.uk
Fax: 020-7636 1226   Tel: 020-7636 1221

HARVEY VOICES
(No unsolicited correspondence)
52-53 Margaret Street, London W1W 8SQ
Website: www.harveyvoices.co.uk
e-mail: info@harveyvoices.co.uk   Tel: 020-7952 4361

HOBSON'S SINGERS
62 Chiswick High Road, London W4 1SY
Website: www.hobsons-international.com
e-mail: singers@hobsons-international.com
Fax: 020-8996 5350   Tel: 020-8995 3628

HOBSON'S VOICES
62 Chiswick High Road, London W4 1SY
Website: www.hobsons-international.com
e-mail: voices@hobsons-international.com
Fax: 020-8996 5350   Tel: 020-8995 3628

HOPE Sally ASSOCIATES
108 Leonard Street, London EC2A 4XS
Website: www.sallyhope.biz
e-mail: casting@sallyhope.biz
Fax: 020-7613 4848   Tel: 020-7613 5353

HOWARD Amanda ASSOCIATES
(See JONESES The)

J H A VOICE
114-115 Tottenham Court Road
London W1T 5AH
Website: www.jeremyhicks.com
e-mail: info@jeremyhicks.com
Fax: 020-7383 2777   Tel: 020-7383 2000

Silver~Tongued Productions

Specialising in the recording and production of voice reels & production tracks

020 8309 0659
www.silver~tongued.co.uk
contactus@silver~tongued.co.uk

We will guide you through the whole process of recording your voice reel. From choosing your scripts to directing you during the recording session, making it as simple and as easy as possible.

Call us for a brochure and our free sample CD.

High Quality Voice Reels at a Competitive Price!

JONESES The
21 Berwick Street, London W1F 0PZ
Website: www.meetthejoneses.co.uk
e-mail: mail@meetthejoneses.co.uk
Fax: 020-7287 7785   Tel: 020-7287 9666

JUST VOICES AGENCY The
140 Buckingham Palace Road, London SW1W 9SA
Website: www.justvoicesagency.com
e-mail: info@justvoicesagency.com
Fax: 020-7881 2501   Tel: 020-7881 2567

KIDZTALK Ltd
(Children's Voices, 4-24 yrs)
Website: www.kidztalk.com
e-mail: studio@kidztalk.com
Fax: 01737 352456   Tel: 01737 350808

LIP SERVICE CASTING Ltd
60-66 Wardour Street, London W1F 0TA
Website: www.lipservice.co.uk
e-mail: bookings@lipservice.co.uk
Fax: 020-7734 3373   Tel: 020-7734 3393

MANSON Andrew
(Genuine Americans only)
288 Munster Road, London SW6 6BQ
Website: www.andrewmanson.com
e-mail: post@andrewmanson.com
Fax: 020-7381 8874   Tel: 020-7386 9158

MARCUS & McCRIMMON VOICES
1 Heathgate Place, 75 Agincourt Road
Hampstead, London NW3 2NU
Website: www.marcusandmccrimmon.com
e-mail: voices@marcusandmccrimmon.com
Fax: 020-7485 5030   Tel: 020-7485 4040

MARKHAM & FROGGATT Ltd
4 Windmill Street
London W1T 2HZ
Website: www.markhamfroggatt.com
e-mail: millie@markhamfroggatt.co.uk
Fax: 020-7637 5233   Tel: 020-7636 4412

MBA
2 Futura House
169 Grange Road, London SE1 3BN
e-mail: info@braidman.com
Fax: 020-7231 4634   Tel: 020-7237 3523

McREDDIE Ken ASSOCIATES Ltd
Contact: Jan Thornton
36-40 Glasshouse Street
London W1B 5DL
e-mail: jan@kenmcreddie.com
Fax: 020-7734 6530   Tel: 020-7439 1456

NOEL John MANAGEMENT
Block B, Imperial Works
Perren Street, London NW5 3ED
Website: www.johnnoel.com
e-mail: john@johnnoel.com
Fax: 020-7428 8401   Tel: 020-7428 8400

PEMBERTON VOICES
193 Wardour Street
London W1F 8ZF
Website: www.pembertonassociates.com
e-mail: general@pembertonassociates.com
Fax: 020-7734 2522   Tel: 020-7734 4144

Express Networks, 1 George Leigh Street
Manchester M4 5DL
Fax: 0161-235 8442   Tel: 0161-235 8440

The very best in voice over talent for advertising, animation, audio books, corporate videos, documentaries and television programmes

www.red24voices.com | Office 020 7559 3611

Crown House | 72 Hammersmith Rd | Kensington Olympia | W14 8TH

PFD
Drury House, 34-43 Russell Street
London WC2B 5HA
Website: www.pfd.co.uk
e-mail: postmaster@pfd.co.uk
Fax: 020-7836 9539
Tel: 020-7344 1010

QVOICE
4th Floor, Holborn Hall
193-197 High Holborn, London WC1V 7BD
Website: www.qvoice.co.uk
e-mail: info@qvoice.co.uk
Fax: 020-7025 0659
Tel: 020-7025 0660

RABBIT VOCAL MANAGEMENT
2nd Floor, 18 Broadwick Street, London W1F 8HS
Website: www.rabbit.uk.net
e-mail: info@rabbit.uk.net
Fax: 020-7287 6566
Tel: 020-7287 6466

RED 24 VOICES
Crown House, 72 Hammersmith Road
London W14 8TH
Website: www.red24voices.com
e-mail: paul@red24voices.com
Tel: 020-7559 3611

RED CANYON MANAGEMENT
Website: www.redcanyon.co.uk
e-mail: showkins@redcanyon.co.uk
Mobile: 07939 365578
Mobile: 07931 381696

RHINO PERSONAL MANAGEMENT
Studio House, Delamare Road
Cheshunt, Hertfordshire EN8 9SH
Website: www.rhino-management.co.uk
e-mail: rhinomanagement@hotmail.co.uk
Fax: 0845 3625457
Tel: 0845 3625456

RHUBARB VOICES
1st Floor, 1A Devonshire Road, London W4 2EU
Website: www.rhubarbvoices.co.uk
e-mail: enquiries@rhubarbvoices.co.uk
Fax: 020-8742 8693
Tel: 020-8742 8683

RICHARD STONE PARTNERSHIP
(See STONE Richard PARTNERSHIP The)

SHINING MANAGEMENT Ltd
12 D'Arblay Street, London W1F 8DU
Website: www.shiningvoices.com
e-mail: info@shiningvoices.com
Fax: 020-7734 2528
Tel: 020-7734 1981

SPEAK-EASY Ltd
PO Box 648, Harrington, Northampton NN6 9XT
Website: www.speak-easy.co.uk
e-mail: enquiries@speak-easy.co.uk
Tel: 01536 418526
Tel: 0870 0135126

STONE Richard PARTNERSHIP The
2 Henrietta Street, London WC2E 8PS
Website: www.thersp.com
e-mail: all@thersp.com
Fax: 020-7497 0869
Tel: 020-7497 0849

TALKING HEADS
Argyll House, All Saints Passage, London SW18 1EP
Website: www.talkingheadsvoices.com
e-mail: voices@talkingheadsvoices.com
Fax: 020-7292 7576
Tel: 020-7292 7575

TERRY Sue VOICES Ltd
3rd Floor, 18 Broadwick Street, London W1F 8HS
Website: www.sueterryvoices.co.uk
e-mail: sue@sueterryvoices.co.uk
Fax: 020-7434 2042
Tel: 020-7434 2040

TONGUE & GROOVE
4th Floor, Manchester House
84-86 Princess Street, Manchester M1 6NG
Website: www.tongueandgroove.co.uk
e-mail: info@tongueandgroove.co.uk
Fax: 0161-237 1809   Tel: 0161-228 2469

VOCAL POINT
25 Denmark Street, London WC2H 8NJ
Website: www.vocalpoint.net
e-mail: enquiries@vocalpoint.net
Fax: 020-7419 0699   Tel: 020-7419 0700

VOICE BANK Ltd
1st Floor, 100 Talbot Road
Old Trafford, Manchester M16 0PG
Website: www.voicebankltd.co.uk
Fax: 0161-888 2242   Tel: 0161-874 5741

VOICE MASTER STUDIO
(Specialising in Foreign Language Voice-Overs)
88 Erskine Hill, London NW11 6HR
Website: www.voicemaster.co.uk
e-mail: stevehudson@voicemaster.co.uk   Tel: 020-8455 2211

VOICE SHOP
First Floor, Thomas Place
1A Devonshire Road, London W4 2EU
Website: www.voice-shop.co.uk
e-mail: info@voice-shop.co.uk
Fax: 020-8742 7011   Tel: 020-8742 7077

VOICE SQUAD
1 Kendal Road, London NW10 1JH
Website: www.voicesquad.com
e-mail: voices@voicesquad.com   Tel: 020-8450 4451

VOICEBANK, THE IRISH VOICE-OVER AGENCY
The Barracks, 76 Irishtown Road, Dublin 4, Ireland
Website: www.voicebank.ie
e-mail: voicebank@voicebank.ie
Fax: 00 353 1 6607850   Tel: 00 353 1 6687234

VOICECALL
67A Gondar Gardens, London NW6 1EP
e-mail: voices@voicecall-online.co.uk   Tel: 020-7209 1064

VOICEOVER GALLERY The
Paragon House, 3rd Floor
48 Seymour Grove
Old Trafford, Manchester M16 0LN
Website: www.thevoiceovergallery.co.uk
e-mail: manchester@thevoiceovergallery.co.uk
    Tel: 0161-881 8844

24 Hawgood Street
London E3 3RU
e-mail: london@thevoiceovergallery.co.uk
    Tel: 020-7987 0951

VOICEOVERS.CO.UK
PO Box 326
Plymouth, Devon PL4 9YQ
Website: www.voiceovers.co.uk
e-mail: info@voiceovers.co.uk   Tel: 01752 207313

VSI - VOICE & SCRIPT INTERNATIONAL
(Foreign Language Specialists)
132 Cleveland Street, London W1T 6AB
Website: www.vsi.tv
e-mail: info@vsi.tv
Fax: 020-7692 7711   Tel: 020-7692 7700

WAM VOICES
(The Voice Agency of Waring & McKenna)
11-12 Dover Street
Mayfair, London W1S 4LJ
Website: www.wamvoices.com
e-mail: info@wamvoices.com
Fax: 020-7629 6466   Tel: 020-7495 6665

WOOTTON Suzy VOICES
72 Towcester Road
Far Cotton, Northampton NN4 8LQ
Website: www.suzywoottonvoices.com
e-mail: suzy@suzywoottonvoices.com
Fax: 0870 7659668   Tel: 0870 7659660

YAKETY YAK
7A Bloomsbury Square, London WC1A 2LP
Website: www.yaketyyak.co.uk
e-mail: info@yaketyyak.co.uk
Fax: 020-7404 6109   Tel: 020-7430 2600

Who are Walk-on and Supporting Artists?

Sometimes known as 'Extras', walk-on and supporting artists appear in the background of TV and film scenes in order to add a sense of realism, character or atmosphere. They do not have individual speaking roles, unless required to make background / ambient noise. Working as a walk-on or supporting artist does not require any specific 'look', training or experience as such; however it does involve more effort than people think. Artists are often required to start very early in the morning (6am is not uncommon), and days can be long with lots of waiting around, sometimes in tough conditions on location. It is certainly not glamorous, nor is it a way to become a TV or film star! Artists must be reliable and available at very short notice, which can make it difficult to juggle with other work or family commitments. Requirements vary from production to production and, as with mainstream acting work, there are no guarantees that you will get regular work, let alone be able to earn a living as a walk-on.

How should I use these listings?

If you are serious about working as a walk-on artist, you will need to register with an agency in order to be put forward for jobs. In return for finding you work, you can expect an agency to take between 10-15% in commission. The following pages contain contact details of many walk-on and supporting artist agencies. Some will specialise in certain areas, so make sure you research the different companies carefully to see if they are appropriate for you. Many have websites you can visit. It is also worth asking questions about how long an agency has existed, and about their recent production credits. When approaching an agency for representation, you should send them your CV with a covering letter and a recent photograph which is a genuine, natural likeness of you. Enclosing a stamped-addressed envelope with sufficient postage (SAE) will give you a better chance of a reply.

Should I pay a Walk-on Agent to join their books? Or sign a contract?

As with other types of agencies, Equity does not generally recommend that artists pay an agent to join their client list. Before signing any contract, you should be clear about the terms and commitments involved. Always speak to Equity www.equity.org.uk or BECTU www.bectu.org.uk if you have any concerns or queries.

Where can I find more information?

You may find it useful to contact the Film Artists Association, part of BECTU www.bectu.org.uk, or the National Association of Supporting Artistes Agents www.nasaa.org.uk. NASAA members listed in the following pages have indicated their status under their agency name.

Ray Knight Casting was founded in 1988 and is an Agency specialising in the supply of walk-on and supporting artists for Film, Television and Commercials. They have a main workforce of approximately 1800 artists on their books. Ray Knight offers the following advice to budding supporting artists:

Supporting artist work is not for everybody. You need to have endless patience, a very compliant and tolerant attitude, and the ability to get on with other people in close and often awkward circumstances. The vast majority of employment is handled by agencies specialising in this field of work. I have been such an agent since 1988 and like to think I have done a good job for both artist and client, building a reputation for fairness and reliability.

When seeking an agent to represent you, please bear the following useful pointers in mind. There are unfortunately some real cowboys in the field. Do not part with any money in advance of receiving any viable work, whatever the explanation you are given. Be it for registration, photographs, advertising or promotional material or for any other reason, do not pay *anything* 'up-front'. Honest agencies will make a nominal charge for promotional material they produce on behalf of their artists, but this will always be taken from fees earned from work supplied. It will be a one-off annual charge and by law, only based on an estimate of cost basis.

A good agent will want to see you before he or she will offer to put you forward for employment, be keen to make an appointment. This will give you an opportunity to check that the agent has proper premises and is operating in a viable fashion. Get to know as much as you can about your agent, both before and after you join. Check to see if they are members of the trade association NASAA www.nasaa.org.uk

Supporting artist work does not lead to stardom. If you want to be an actor, go to drama school. It is essentially a part-time occupation for those who have a good level of availability, often at short notice, and find it both rewarding and interesting. Much depends on types and age groups. Over the years it has been my perception that 60% of work goes to men and 40% to women, with the greatest demand being for men aged between 25 and 45, and women between 20 and 40. This does not mean that there is no work for those outside those rough parameters, but just that it is likely to be more erratic than for those in the categories for which there is a concentration of demand. It also helps to be of average size and measurements.

Please remember that leading artists are carrying the burden of scripted lines, close up action and focusing on their work. They may not welcome chatting to the supporting artists, even though at other times they would be very approachable. Do not bother them unless they invite you to socialise with them, give them space and respect their need for concentration.

The best supporting artists are the ones who turn up on time, wearing the right clothes where appropriate, only need telling once, are quick to re-position, and are amenable to all they work with be it fellow artist or crew. Do not adopt a high profile - people who try to get noticed are only seen as irritating. There is enough ego on a film set already, it is not a good idea for supporting artists to add to it.

Having said all of this, supporting artists can have an interesting, rewarding and enjoyable time with the right attitude and approach. I have been fortunate to represent some lovely people whom I have very much enjoyed having on my books. I hope they have thought as well of me as I of them.

Please visit www.rayknight.co.uk for more information.

10 TWENTYTWO CASTING
(NASAA Member)
PO Box 1022, Liverpool L69 5WZ
Website: www.10twentytwo.com
e-mail: contact@10twentytwo.com
Fax: 0151-207 4230   Tel: 0871 7891022

2020 CASTING Ltd
(NASAA Member)
2020 Hopgood Street, London W12 7JU
Website: www.2020casting.com
e-mail: info@2020casting.com
Fax: 020-8735 2727   Tel: 020-8746 2020

ALLSORTS AGENCY
(Modelling)
Suite 1 & 2 Marlborough Business Centre
96 George Lane, London E18 1AD
Website: www.allsortsagency.com
e-mail: bookings@allsortsagency.com
Fax: 020-8989 5600   Tel: 020-8989 0500

ARTIST MANAGEMENT UK Ltd
PO Box 96, Liverpool L9 8WY
Website: www.artistmanagementuk.com
e-mail: chris@artistmanagementuk.com Tel: 0151-523 6222

AVENUE ARTISTES Ltd
PO Box 1573, Southampton SO16 3XS
Website: www.avenueartistes.com
e-mail: info@avenueartistes.com   Tel: 023-8076 0930

AWA - ANDREA WILDER AGENCY
23 Cambrian Drive, Colwyn Bay, Conwy LL28 4SL
Website: www.awagency.co.uk
e-mail: casting@awagency.co.uk
Fax: 07092 249314   Mobile: 07919 202401

BIRMINGHAM CENTRAL CASTING
PO Box 145, Inkberrow
Worcestershire WR7 4EL
Website: www.bccasting.co.uk
e-mail: keith@bccasting.co.uk
Mobile: 07950 024561   Tel: 01527 450188

BLUE WAND MANAGEMENT
2nd Floor, 12 Weljte Road
Hammersmith, London W6 9TG
e-mail: bluewand@btinternet.com   Tel: 020-8741 2038

BODENS ADVANCED
Bodens Studios & Agency
99 East Barnet Road
New Barnet, Herts EN4 8RF
Website: www.bodensagency.com
e-mail: info@bodensagency.com
Fax: 020-8449 5212   Tel: 020-8447 1226

BROADCASTING AGENCY
Unit 36, Pall Mall Deposit
124-128 Barlby Road, London W10 6BL
Website: www.broadcastingagency.co.uk
e-mail: info@broadcastingagency.co.uk Tel: 020-8960 5020

BROOK Dolly CASTING AGENCY
PO Box 5436
Dunmow CM6 1WW
e-mail: dollybrookcasting@btinternet.com
Fax: 01371 875996   Tel: 01371 875767

CAIRNS AGENCY The
Contact: Maureen Cairns
The Penthouse, 42/17 Speirs Wharf
Glasgow G4 9TH
Website: www.thecairnsagency.com   Tel: 0141-331 1340

CAMCAST
(NASAA Member)
Laragain, Upper Banavie
Fort William
Inverness-shire PH33 7PB
Website: www.camcast.co.uk
e-mail: anne@camcast.co.uk
Fax: 01397 772456   Tel: 01397 772523

CASTING COLLECTIVE Ltd The
(NASAA Member)
Olympic House
317-321 Latimer Road, London W10 6RA
Website: www.castingcollective.co.uk
e-mail: enquiries@castingcollective.co.uk
Fax: 020-8962 0333   Tel: 020-8962 0099

CASTING NETWORK Ltd The
(NASAA Member)
4 Vidler Close
Chessington, Surrey KT9 2GL
Website: www.thecastingnetwork.co.uk
e-mail: casting-network@talk21.com
Fax: 020-8391 5119   Tel: 020-8391 2979

CASTING STUDIO The
PO Box 167, Middleton
Manchester M24 5WY
Website: www.thecastingstudio.co.uk
e-mail: info@thecastingstudio.co.uk   Tel/Fax: 0161-643 6266

CELEX CASTING Ltd
(NASAA Member) (Children available)
PO Box 7317, Derby DE1 0GS
e-mail: anne@celex.co.uk
Fax: 01332 232115   Tel: 01332 232445

CENTRAL CASTING Ltd
(See also KNIGHT Ray CASTING)
21A Lambolle Place, Belsize Park, London NW3 4PG
Website: www.rayknight.co.uk
e-mail: casting@rayknight.co.uk
Fax: 020-7722 2322   Tel: 020-7722 1551

DAVID AGENCY The
(NASAA Member)
26-28 Hammersmith Grove
London W6 7BA
Website: www.davidagency.net
e-mail: casting@davidagency.net   Tel: 020-7967 7001

DOE John ASSOCIATES
26 Noko, 3-6 Banister Road
London W10 4AR
Website: www.johndoeassociates.com
e-mail: johndoemgt@yahoo.co.uk
Mobile: 07957 114175   Tel: 020-8960 2848

ELLIOTT AGENCY Ltd The
(NASAA Member)
10 High Street
Shoreham-by-Sea BN43 5DA
Website: www.elliottagency.co.uk
e-mail: elliottagency@btconnect.com   Tel: 01273 454111

ETHNIKA CASTING
14 Bowmont Gardens
Glasgow G12 9LR
Website: www.ethnikacasting.co.uk
e-mail: ethnikacasting@yahoo.co.uk
Mobile: 07778 296002   Tel/Fax: 0141-334 6246

EUROKIDS & EUROXTRAS CASTING AGENCY
The Warehouse Studios
Glaziers Lane
Culcheth, Warrington, Cheshire WA3 4AQ
Website: www.eka-agency.com
e-mail: castings@eka-agency.com
Fax: 01925 767563   Tel: 01925 761088

EXTRASPECIAL Ltd
4th Floor, 20 Bedford St
Covent Garden, London WC2E 9HP
e-mail: info@extraspecialartists.com
Fax: 020-7240 4879   Tel: 020-7240 9240

FACE MUSIC
(Musician's Agency)
13 Elvendon Road, London N13 4SJ
e-mail: facemusic@btinternet.com   Tel: 020-8889 3969

FBI AGENCY The
(NASAA Member)
PO Box 250, Leeds LS1 2AZ
Website: www.fbi-agency.co.uk
e-mail: casting@fbi-agency.co.uk   Mobile: 07050 222747

FRESH AGENTS Ltd
Suite 5, Saks House, 19 Ship Street, Brighton BN1 1AD
Website: www.freshagents.co.uk
e-mail: info@freshagents.co.uk
Tel: 0845 4080998   Tel: 01273 711777

FTS CASTING AGENCY
55 Pullan Avenue
Eccleshill, Bradford BD2 3RP
e-mail: helen@footsteps.fslife.co.uk
Fax: 01274 637429   Tel: 01274 636036

GUYS & DOLLS CASTING
(NASAA Member)
Trafalgar House
Grenville Place
Mill Hill, London NW7 3SA
Website: www.guysanddollscasting.com
e-mail: info@guysanddollscasting.com
Mobile: 07890 774454   Tel: 020-8906 4144

HOWE Janet CASTING AGENCY
The Pie Factory
101 Broadway
Salford Quays
Manchester M50 2EQ
e-mail: info@janethowe.com
Mobile: 07801 942178   Tel/Fax: 0161-263 0633

The Works Media Centre
36 White House Street
Hunslet, Leeds LS10 1AD
Mobile: 07801 942178   Tel/Fax: 0113-242 5225

58 High Street, Newcastle-under-Lyme
Staffordshire ST5 1PE
e-mail: janet@janethowe.com
                                       Tel: 01782 661777

INDUSTRY CASTING
Suite 332, Royal Exchange
Manchester M2 7BR
Website: www.industrycasting.co.uk
e-mail: mark@industrypeople.co.uk
Fax: 0161-839 1661   Tel: 0161-839 1551

JACLYN AGENCY
(NASAA Member)
52 Bessemer Road
Norwich, Norfolk NR4 6DQ
Website: www.jaclyncastingagency.co.uk
e-mail: info@jaclynagency.co.uk
Fax: 01603 612532   Tel: 01603 622027

JB AGENCY ONLINE Ltd
(NASAA Member)
Chelsea Business Centre
73-77 Brittania Road, London SW6 2JR
Website: www.jb-agency.com
e-mail: info@jb-agency.com   Mobile: 07962 434111

JPM EXTRAS
(A Division of Janet Plater Management Ltd)
D Floor, Milburn House
Dean Street, Newcastle upon Tyne NE1 1LF
Website: www.janetplatermanagement.co.uk
e-mail: extras@tynebridge.demon.co.uk
Fax: 0191-233 1709   Tel: 0191-221 2491

KNIGHT Ray CASTING
(NASAA Member)
21A Lambolle Place
Belsize Park, London NW3 4PG
Website: www.rayknight.co.uk
e-mail: casting@rayknight.co.uk
Fax: 020-7722 2322   Tel: 020-7722 4111

KREATE PRODUCTIONS
Unit 232, 30 Great Guildford Street
London SE1 0HS
Website: www.kreatepromotions.co.uk
e-mail: enquiries@kreatepromotions.co.uk
Fax: 020-7401 3003   Tel: 020-7401 9007

LEMON CASTING Ltd
The Pie Factory, 101 Broadway
Salford Quays, Manchester M50 2EQ
e-mail: lemon.tv@btconnect.com
Mobile: 07723 317489   Tel: 0161-876 0088

LINTON MANAGEMENT
3 The Rock, Bury BL9 0JP
e-mail: carol@linton.tv
Fax: 0161-761 1999   Tel: 0161-761 2020

MAD DOG CASTING Ltd
(NASAA Member)
Third Floor, 15 Leighton Place
London NW5 2QL
e-mail: info@maddogcasting.com
Fax: 020-7284 2689   Tel: 020-7482 4703

M.E.P. MANAGEMENT
1 Malvern Avenue
Highams Park, London E4 9NP
Website: www.mepmanagement.com
e-mail: mep@btclick.com   Tel/Fax: 020-8523 3540

MODEL CHILD AGENCY
York Chambers, Dukes Court
Macclesfield
Cheshire SK11 6NN
Website: www.modelchild.co.uk
e-mail: sam@modelchild.co.uk
Fax: 01625 442745   Tel: 01625 442742

NE REPRESENTATION
(Models, Photographers, Hair & make-up artists, Stylists
and Film Extras)
3-5 Bakehouse Hill
Darlington
Co. Durham DL1 5QA
Website: www.nerepresentation.co.uk
e-mail: info@nerepresentation.co.uk
Fax: 01325 488390   Tel: 01325 488385

NEMESIS AGENCY Ltd
Nemesis House
1 Oxford Court
Bishopsgate, Manchester M2 3WQ
Website: www.nemesisagency.co.uk
e-mail: laura@nmsmanagement.co.uk
Fax: 0161-228 6727   Tel: 0161-228 6404

NICHE CASTING AGENCY
The Malvern Suite
Borough Hill, Neild Street
Oldham
Manchester OL8 1QG
Website: www.nichecasting.co.uk
e-mail: shenaz@nichecasting.co.uk
Mobile: 07809 748713   Tel: 0161-622 2932

NIDGES CASTING AGENCY
Half Moon Chambers
Chapel Walks, Manchester M2 1HN
e-mail: kirstie@nidgescasting.co.uk
Fax: 0161-832 5219   Tel: 0161-832 8259

Bill Gerard

Licence No. L1299.....

Casting - Supporting/Principal Artistes
Action Safety Consultant
Diving support teams - Boat Hire - Diving Equipment Hire
Office: 0191 257 8635 Mob: 07860 186978 Fax: 0191 296 3243
21 Cresswell Avenue, North Shields, Near Tyne & Wear NE29 9BQ
www.northernprocasting.co.uk

NORTHERN PROFESSIONALS CASTING COMPANY
21 Cresswell Avenue
North Shields
Tyne & Wear NE29 9BQ
Website: www.northernprocasting.co.uk
e-mail: bill@northernprocasting.co.uk
Fax: 0191-296 3243   Tel: 0191-257 8635

ORIENTAL CASTING AGENCY Ltd (Peggy Sirr)
(NASAA Member) (Afro/Asian Artists)
1 Wyatt Park Road
Streatham Hill
London SW2 3TN
Website: www.orientalcasting.com
e-mail: peggy.sirr@btconnect.com
Fax: 020-8674 9303   Tel: 020-8671 8538

PAN ARTISTS AGENCY Ltd
Cornerways, 34 Woodhouse Lane
Sale, Cheshire M33 4JX
Website: www.panartists.co.uk
e-mail: panartists@btconnect.com
Mobile: 07890 715115   Tel: 0800 6349147

PC THEATRICAL MODEL & CASTING AGENCY
12 Carlisle Road, Colindale
London NW9 0HL
Website: www.twinagency.com
e-mail: twinagy@aol.com
Fax: 020-8933 3418   Tel: 020-8381 2229

PERFORMERS LEAGUE AGENCY Ltd The
21 Clothworkers Road, Plumstead, London SE18 2PD
Website: www.tpla.co.uk
e-mail: info@tpla.co.uk
Mobile: 07886 319807   Tel: 020-8854 4576

PHA CASTING
Tanzaro House, Ardwick Green North
Manchester M12 6FZ
Website: www.pha-agency.co.uk
e-mail: casting@pha-agency.co.uk
Fax: 0161-273 4567   Tel: 0161-273 4444

PHOENIX CASTING AGENCY
(NASAA Member)
PO Box 387, Bristol BS99 3JZ
Website: www.phoenixagency.biz
e-mail: info@phoenixagency.biz
Fax: 0117-973 4160   Tel: 0117-973 1100

POLEASE
1 Noake Road, Hucclecote
Gloucester GL3 3PE
Website: www.polease.co.uk
e-mail: info@polease.co.uk
Mobile: 07811 504079   Tel: 05600 650524

POLICE ACTION
39 Gregson Close, Borehamwood WD6 5RW
e-mail: police-action@hotmail.co.uk
Mobile: 07899 651280   Tel: 020-8953 0166

POWER MODEL MANAGEMENT CASTING AGENCY
PO Box 1198, Salhouse
Norwich NR13 6WD
Website: www.powermodel.co.uk
e-mail: info@powermodel.co.uk   Tel: 01603 777190

PRAETORIAN ASSOCIATES
(Specialist Action Extras)
Room 501, 2 Old Brompton Road
London SW7 3DG
Website: www.praetorianasc.com
e-mail: info@praetorianasc.com   Tel/Fax: 020-7096 1827

RAPID TALENT Ltd
(NASAA Member)
10 Cornfield Lane
Eastbourne
East Sussex BN21 4NE
Website: www.rapidtalent.co.uk
e-mail: enquiries@rapidtalent.co.uk
Fax: 01323 720342   Tel: 020-7734 5775

RAY'S NORTHERN CASTING AGENCY
7 Wince Close
Alkrington, Middleton
Manchester M24 1UJ
e-mail: rayscasting@yahoo.co.uk   Tel/Fax: 0161-643 6745

REGENCY AGENCY
25 Carr Road, Calverley, Pudsey
West Yorks LS28 5NE   Tel: 0113-255 8980

REYNOLDS Sandra AGENCY
Shakespeare House
168 Lavender Hill, London SW11 5TF
Website: www.sandrareynolds.co.uk
e-mail: info@sandrareynolds.co.uk
Fax: 020-7387 5848   Tel: 020-7387 5858

Bacon House
35 St Georges Street, Norwich NR3 1DA
Fax: 01603 219825   Tel: 01603 623842

RHODES AGENCY
5 Dymoke Road
Hornchurch, Essex RM11 1AA
e-mail: rhodesarts@hotmail.com
Fax: 01708 730431   Tel: 01708 747013

SA19 - THE UNIFORMED ARTISTE AGENCY
(NASAA Member)
2020 Hopgood Street
Shepherds Bush, London W12 7JU
Website: www.sa19.co.uk
e-mail: info@sa19.co.uk
Fax: 020-8735 2727   Tel: 020-8746 2523

SAPPHIRES MODEL MANAGEMENT
The Makers Dozen, Studio 11
8 Wulfruna Street
Wolverhampton WV1 1LW
Website: www.sapphiresmodel.com
e-mail: contact@sapphiresmodel.com
Fax: 0870 9127563   Tel: 0844 8845404

SCREAM MANAGEMENT
The Pie Factory
101 Broadway
Media City, Manchester M50 2EQ
Website: www.screammanagement.com
e-mail: info@screammanagement.com
Fax: 01253 309069   Tel: 0161-660 3653

SCREENLITE AGENCY
(NASAA Member)
Room 646/PB, Pinewood Studios
Pinewood Road
Iver Heath, Bucks SL0 0NH
Website: www.screenliteagency.co.uk
e-mail: kerry@screenliteagency.co.uk   Tel: 01753 785372

SOLOMON ARTISTES
30 Clarence Street
Southend-on-Sea, Essex SS1 1BD
Website: www.solomon-artistes.co.uk
e-mail: info@solomon-artistes.co.uk
Tel: 01702 437118   Tel: 020-7748 4409

SUMMERS Mark MANAGEMENT
(Formerly Extras Unlimited)
137 Freston Road, London W10 6TH
Website: www.marksummers.com
e-mail: info@marksummers.com
Fax: 020-7243 1987   Tel: 020-7229 8413

TO BE SEEN Ltd
50 Frith Street, Soho, London W1D 4SQ
Website: www.tobeseen.co.uk
e-mail: info@tobeseen.co.uk   Tel: 020-7434 1615

TUESDAYS CHILD Ltd
(Children & Adults)
Oakfield House
Springwood Way, Macclesfield SK10 2XA
Website: www.tuesdayschildagency.co.uk
e-mail: info@tuesdayschildagency.co.uk
Tel/Fax: 01625 501765

UNI-VERSAL EXTRAS
118-120 Kenton Road
Harrow HA3 8AL
Website: www.universalextrascasting.co.uk
e-mail: wayne.berko@universalextras.co.uk
Tel: 0845 0090344

A-Z ANIMALS Ltd
The Bell House, Bell Lane, Fetcham, Surrey KT22 9ND
Website: www.a-zanimals.com
e-mail: info@a-zanimals.com
Fax: 01372 377666   Tel: 01372 377111

A1 ANIMALS
(Farm, Domestic & Exotic Animals)
9 The Drive, Enstone, Oxon OX7 4NQ
Website: www.a1animals.co.uk
e-mail: info@a1animals.freeserve.co.uk
                                   Tel/Fax: 01608 677348

ACTION STUNT DOGS
3 The Chestnuts, Clifton, Deddington, Oxon OX15 0PE
e-mail: gill@stuntdogs.net   Tel/Fax: 01869 338546

ALTERNATIVE ANIMALS
(Animatronics/Taxidermy)
19 Greaves Road, High Wycombe, Bucks HP13 7JU
Website: www.animalworld.org.uk
e-mail: animalswork1@yahoo.co.uk
Fax: 01494 441385   Tel: 01494 442750

ANIMAL ACTING
(Animals, Stunts, Prop, Horse-Drawn Vehicles)
7 Dovedale Court, Windermere Road
Middleton, Manchester M24 5QT
Website: www.animalacting.com
e-mail: information@animalacting.com
Mobile: 07831 800567   Tel: 0161-655 3700

ANIMAL ACTORS
(Animals, Birds, Reptiles)
95 Ditchling Road, Brighton
Sussex BN1 4ST   Tel: 020-8654 0450

ANIMAL AMBASSADORS
Old Forest, Hampstead Norreys Road
Hermitage, Berks RG18 9SA
Website: www.animalambassadors.co.uk
e-mail: kayweston@tiscali.co.uk
Mobile: 07831 558594   Tel/Fax: 01635 200900

ANIMAL ARRANGERS
(Animal Suppliers & Co-ordinators)
28 Greaves Road, High Wycombe, Bucks HP13 7JU
Website: www.animalworld.org.uk
e-mail: animalwork1@yahoo.co.uk
Mobile: 07956 564715   Tel: 01494 442750

ANIMAL CASTING
119 Magdalen Road, London SW18 3ES
e-mail: silcresta@aol.com
Mobile: 07956 246450   Tel: 020-8874 9530

ANIMAL WORK
19 Greaves Road
High Wycombe, Bucks HP13 7JU
Website: www.animalworld.org.uk
e-mail: animalswork1@yahoo.co.uk
Fax: 01494 441385   Tel: 01494 442750

ANIMALS GALORE Ltd
208 Smallfield Road, Horley, Surrey RH6 9LS
Website: www.animals-galore.co.uk
Fax: 01342 841546   Tel: 01342 842400

ANIMALS O KAY
16 Queen Street, Chipperfield
Kings Langley, Herts WD4 9BT
Website: www.animalsokay.com
e-mail: kay@animalsokay.com
Fax: 01923 269076   Tel: 01923 291277

ANIMAL WELFARE FILMING FEDERATION
28 Greaves Road
High Wycombe, Bucks HP13 7JU
Website: www.animalworld.org.uk
e-mail: animalswork1@yahoo.co.uk
Fax: 01494 441385   Mobile: 07770 666088

CANINE FILM ACADEMY The
57C Cheapside Road, Ascot, Berks SL5 7QR
Website: www.thecaninefilmacademy.com
e-mail: katie.cfa@virgin.net
Mobile: 07767 341424   Tel: 01344 291465

CHEESEMAN Virginia
21 Willow Close, Flackwell Heath
High Wycombe, Bucks HP10 9LH
Website: www.virginiacheeseman.co.uk
e-mail: virginia@virginiacheeseman.co.uk
Mobile: 07971 838724   Tel: 01628 522632

COTSWOLD FARM PARK
(Rare Breed Farm Animals)
Guiting Power, Cheltenham, Gloucestershire GL54 5UG
e-mail: info@cotswoldfarmpark.co.uk
Fax: 01451 850423   Tel: 01451 850307

CREATURE FEATURE
(Animal Agent)
Gubhill Farm, Ae, Dumfries, Scotland DG1 1RL
Website: www.creaturefeature.co.uk
e-mail: david@creaturefeature.co.uk
Mobile: 07770 774866   Tel/Fax: 01387 860648

DOG EXTRAS
11 Colster Way, Colsterworth
Grantham, Lincs NG33 5JT
Website: www.dog-extras.co.uk
e-mail: info@dog-extras.co.uk
Mobile: 07956 369890   Tel/Fax: 01476 862028

DOLBADARN FILM HORSES
Dolbadarn Hotel, High Street
Llanberis, Gwynedd, North Wales LL55 4SU
Website: www.filmhorses.co.uk
e-mail: info@filmhorses.co.uk
Mobile: 07710 461341   Tel/Fax: 01286 870277

DUDLEY Yvonne LRPS
(Glamour Dogs)
55 Cambridge Park, Wanstead
London E11 2PR   Tel: 020-8989 1528

FILM HORSES
(Horses, Saddlery, Equestrian Centre)
Free Range Farm, Oakleigh Green Road
Windsor, Berks SL4 4GW
Website: www.filmhorses.com
e-mail: filmhorses@yahoo.co.uk
Mobile: 07831 629662   Tel/Fax: 01628 675105

FREE ANIMAL CONSULTANT SERVICES
28 Greaves Road, High Wycombe, Bucks HP13 7JU
Website: www.animalworld.org.uk
e-mail: animalswork1@yahoo.co.uk
Fax: 01494 441385   Tel: 08000 749383

GET STUFFED
(Taxidermy)
105 Essex Road, London N1 2SL
Website: www.thegetstuffed.co.uk
e-mail: taxidermy@thegetstuffed.co.uk
Fax: 020-7359 8253   Tel: 020-7226 1364

GRAY Robin COMMENTARIES
(Equestrian Equipment, Horse Race Commentaries,
Voice Overs)
Comptons, Isington, Alton, Hants GU34 4PL
e-mail: gray@isington.fsnet.co.uk
Mobile: 07831 828424   Tel: 01420 23347

HILTON HORSES
(Samantha Jones)
478 London Road, Ashford, Middlesex TW15 3AD
Website: www.hilton-horses.com
e-mail: samantha@hilton-horses.com Mobile: 07958 292222

KNIGHTS OF ARKLEY The
Glyn Sylen Farm, Five Roads, Llanelli SA15 5BJ
Website: www.knightsofarkley.com
e-mail: penny@knightsofarkley.fsnet.co.uk
                                     Tel/Fax: 01269 861001

MILLENNIUM BUGS
(Live Insects)
28 Greaves Road
High Wycombe, Bucks HP13 7JU
Website: www.animalworld.org.uk
e-mail: animalswork1@yahoo.co.uk
Fax: 01494 441385   Tel: 01494 442750

MORTON Geoff
(Shire Horse & Equipment)
Hasholme Carr Farm
Holme on Spalding Moor
York YO43 4BD   Tel: 01430 860393

NOLTON STABLES
Nolton, Nr Newgale, Haverfordwest
Pembrokeshire SA62 3NW
Website: www.noltonstables.com
e-mail: noltonstables@aol.com
Fax: 01437 710967   Tel: 01437 710360

OTTERS
Contact: Daphne & Martin Neville. Tame Otters
Baker's Mill, Frampton Mansell
Stroud, Glos GL6 8JH
e-mail: martin_neville.bakers_mill@yahoo.co.uk
                                     Tel: 01285 760234

PETMUNCH
114 Mill Lane, West Hampstead
London NW6 1NF
e-mail: info@petmunch.com   Tel/Fax: 020-7813 2644

PROP FARM Ltd
(Pat Ward)
Grange Farm, Elmton
Nr Creswell, North Derbyshire S80 4LX
e-mail: pat/les@propfarm.co.uk
Fax: 01909 721465   Tel: 01909 723100

ROCKWOOD ANIMALS ON FILM
Lewis Terrace, Llanbradach, Caerphilly CF83 3JZ
Website: www.rockwoodanimals.com
e-mail: martin@rockwoodanimals.com
Mobile: 07973 930983   Tel: 029-2088 5420

SCHOOL OF NATIONAL EQUITATION Ltd
Contact: Sam Humphrey
Bunny Hill Top, Costock
Loughborough, Leicestershire LE12 6XE
Website: www.bunnyhill.co.uk
e-mail: sam@bunnyhill.co.uk
Fax: 01509 856067   Tel: 01509 852366

TATE Olive
(Trained Dogs & Cats)
49 Upton Road, Bexleyheath, Kent DA6 8LW
Mobile: 07504 113298   Tel/Fax: 020-8303 0683

THORNE'S OF WINDSOR
(Beekeeping & Other Insect Suppliers)
Oakley Green Farm, Oakley Green
Windsor, Berks SL4 4PZ   Tel: 01753 830256

WHITE DOVES COMPANY Ltd The
(Provision of up to 150 Doves for Release)
Suite 210 Sterling House
Langston Road, Loughton, Essex IG10 3TS
Website: www.thewhitedovecompany.co.uk
e-mail: thewhitedovecompany@yahoo.co.uk
Fax: 020-8502 2461   Tel: 020-8508 1414

WOLF SPECIALISTS The
The UK Wolf Conservation Trust
UK Wolf Centre, Butlers Farm
Beenham, Berks RG7 5NT
Website: www.ukwolf.org
e-mail: ukwct@ukwolf.org   Tel: 0118-971 3330

WOODS Sue
(Animal Promotions, Specialising in Dogs, Domestic Cats,
Rodents, Poultry & Farm Stock)
White Rocks Farm
Underriver, Sevenoaks, Kent TN15 0SL
Website: www.animalpromotions.co.uk
e-mail: happyhoundschool@yahoo.co.uk
Fax: 01732 763767   Tel: 01732 762913

ALDERSHOT
West End Centre
Queens Road, Aldershot, Hants GU11 3JD
Website: www.westendcentre.co.uk
BO: 01252 330040   Admin: 01252 408040

BILLERICAY
Billericay Arts Association
The Fold, 72 Laindon Road
Billericay, Essex CM12 9LD
Secretary: Edmond Philpott   Tel: 01277 659286

BINGLEY
Bingley Arts Centre
Main Street, Bingley
West Yorkshire BD16 2LZ   Tel: 01274 431576

BIRMINGHAM
The Custard Factory
Gibb Street, Digbeth, Birmingham B9 4AA
Website: www.custardfactory.co.uk
e-mail: info@custardfactory.co.uk
Fax: 0121-604 8888   Tel: 0121-693 7777

BOSTON
Blackfriars Arts Centre
Spain Lane, Boston, Lincolnshire PE21 6HP
Website: www.blackfriars.uk.com
e-mail: director@blackfriars.uk.com
Contact: Tony Hill
Fax: 01205 358855   Tel: 01205 363108

BRACKNELL
South Hill Park Arts Centre
Ringmead, Bracknell, Berkshire RG12 7PA
Chief Executive: Ron McAllister
Fax: 01344 411427
BO: 01344 484123   Admin: 01344 484858

BRADFORD
Theatre in The Mill
University of Bradford
Shearbridge Road
Bradford, West Yorkshire BD7 1DP
e-mail: theatre@bradford.ac.uk
BO: 01274 233200   Tel: 01274 233185

BRAINTREE
The Town Hall Centre
Market Square, Braintree, Essex CM7 3YG
Tourism Manager: Marie Orpe   Tel: 01376 557776

BRENTFORD
Watermans
40 High Street, Brentford TW8 0DS
Fax: 020-8232 1030
BO: 020-8232 1010   Admin: 020-8232 1020

BRIDGWATER
Bridgwater Arts Centre
11-13 Castle Street
Bridgwater, Somerset TA6 3DD
Website: www.bridgwaterartscentre.co.uk
e-mail: info@bridgwaterartscentre.co.uk
                                    Tel: 01278 422700

BRISTOL
Arnolfini, 16 Narrow Quay, Bristol BS1 4QA
e-mail: boxoffice@arnolfini.org.uk
Fax: 0117-917 2303   Tel: 0117-917 2300

BUILTH WELLS
Wyeside Arts Centre
Castle Street, Builth Wells, Powys LD2 3BN
Fax: 01982 553995   Tel: 01982 553668

BURY
The Met, Market Street, Bury, Lancs BL9 0BW
e-mail: post@themet.biz
Director: David Agnew
Fax: 0870 0520297
BO: 0161-761 2216   Admin: 0161-761 7107

CANNOCK
Prince of Wales Centre
Church Sreet, Cannock, Staffs WS11 1DE
e-mail: princeofwales@cannockchasedc.gov.uk
General Manager: Richard Kay
Fax: 01543 574439BO: 01543 578672   Tel: 01543 466453

CARDIFF
Chapter Arts Centre
Market Road, Canton, Cardiff CF5 1QE
Theatre Programmer: James Tyson
BO: 029-2030 4400   Admin: 029-2031 1050

CHIPPING NORTON
The Theatre, 2 Spring Street
Chipping Norton, Oxon OX7 5NL
Website: www.chippingnortontheatre.com
e-mail: admin@chippingnortontheatre.com
Director: John Terry
General Manager: Chris Durham
Fax: 01608 642324
BO: 01608 642350   Admin: 01608 642349

CHRISTCHURCH
The Regent Centre, 51 High Street
Christchurch, Dorset BH23 1AS
Website: www.regentcentre.co.uk
e-mail: info@regentcentre.co.uk
General Manager: Keith Lancing   Admin: 01202 499199

CIRENCESTER
New Brewery Arts
Brewery Court, Cirencester, Glos GL7 1JH
Website: www.newbreweryarts.org.uk
e-mail: admin@newbreweryarts.org.uk
Fax: 01285 644060   Admin: 01285 657181

COLCHESTER
Colchester Arts Centre
Church Street, Colchester, Essex CO1 1NF
Website: www.colchesterartscentre.com
e-mail: info@colchesterartscentre.com
Director: Anthony Roberts   Tel: 01206 500900

COVENTRY
Warwick Arts Centre
University of Warwick, Coventry CV4 7AL
Website: www.warwickartscentre.co.uk
e-mail: arts.centre@warwick.ac.uk
Director: Alan Rivett
BO: 024-7652 4524   Admin: 024-7652 3734

CUMBERNAULD
Cumbernauld Theatre, Kildrum, Cumbernauld G67 2BN
Artistic Director: Ed Robson
Fax: 01236 738408
BO: 01236 732887   Admin: 01236 737235

DARLINGTON
Darlington Arts Centre
Vane Terrace, Darlington, County Durham DL3 7AX
Website: www.darlingtonarts.co.uk
BO: 01325 486555   Admin: 01325 348843

DORSET
The Coade Hall Theatre
Blandford Forum, Dorset DT11 0PX
e-mail: clt@bryanston.co.uk
Administrator: Claire Topping
Artistic Director: Jane Quan
Fax: 01258 484506   Tel: 01258 484623

EDINBURGH
Scottish Storytelling Centre
The Netherbow, 43-45 High Street
Edinburgh EH1 1SR
Website: www.scottishstorytellingcentre.co.uk
e-mail: reception@scottishstorytellingcentre.com
Director: Dr Donald Smith   Tel: 0131-556 9579

EDINBURGH
Theatre Workshop, 34 Hamilton Place
Edinburgh EH3 5AX
Website: www.theatre-workshop.com
Director: Robert Rae
Fax: 0131-220 0112   Tel: 0131-225 7942

EPSOM
Playhouse, Ashley Avenue
Epsom, Surrey KT18 5AL
Website: www.epsomplayhouse.co.uk
e-mail: tmitchell@epsom-ewell.gov.uk
General Manager/Artistic Director: Trevor Mitchell
Fax: 01372 726228
BO: 01372 742555   Admin: 01372 742226

EXETER
Exeter Phoenix
Bradninch Place, Gandy Street
Exeter, Devon EX4 3LS
Website: www.exeterphoenix.org.uk
e-mail: admin@exeterphoenix.org.uk
Director: Patrick Cunningham
Fax: 01392 667599
BO: 01392 667080   Admin: 01392 667060

FAREHAM
Ashcroft Arts Centre
Osborn Road
Fareham, Hants PO16 7DX
Website: www.ashcroft.org.uk
e-mail: info@ashcroft.org.uk
Director/Programmer: Annabel Cook
Fax: 01329 825661
BO: 01329 223100   Tel: 01329 235161

FROME
Merlin Theatre, Bath Road
Frome, Somerset BA11 2HG
Website: www.merlintheatre.co.uk
BO: 01373 465949   Admin: 01373 461360

GAINSBOROUGH
Trinity Arts Centre
Trinity Street, Gainsborough
Lincolnshire DN21 2AL
Fax: 01427 811198   BO/Admin: 01427 676655

GREAT TORRINGTON
The Plough Arts Centre
9-11 Fore Street, Great Torrington, Devon EX38 8HQ
Website: www.plough-arts.org
BO: 01805 624624   Admin: 01805 622552

HARLECH
Theatr Harlech, Harlech, Gwynedd LL46 2PU
Theatre Director: Clare Williams   BO: 01766 780667

HAVANT
Havant Arts Centre
East Street, Havant, Hants PO9 1BS
Website: www.havantartscentre.co.uk
e-mail: info@havantartsactive.co.uk
Director: Amanda O'Reilly   BO: 023-9247 2700

HELMSLEY
Helmsley Arts Centre
Meeting House Court, Helmsley, York YO62 5DW
Website: www.helmsleyarts.co.uk
e-mail: clairehelmsleyarts@yahoo.co.uk
Marketing & Theatre Manager: Claire Lishman
BO: 01439 771700   Tel: 01439 772112

HEMEL HEMPSTEAD
Old Town Hall Arts Centre
High Street, Hemel Hempstead, Herts HP1 3AE
Website: www.oldtownhall.co.uk
e-mail: othadmin@dacorum.gov.uk
Art & Entertainment Manager: Sara Railson
BO: 01442 228091   Admin: 01442 228095

HEXHAM
Queens Hall Arts, Beaumont Street, Hexham
Northumberland NE46 3LS
Website: www.queenshall.co.uk
e-mail: boxoffice@queenshall.co.uk
Artistic Director: Geof Keys
Fax: 01434 652478
BO: 01434 652477   Admin: 01434 652476

HORSHAM
The Capitol
North Street, Horsham, West Sussex RH12 1RG
Website: www.thecapitolhorsham.com
General Manager: Michael Gattrell
Fax: 01403 756092   Tel: 01403 756080

HUDDERSFIELD
Kirklees (various venues)
Kirklees Culture & Leisure Services
Red Doles Lane, Huddersfield HD2 1YF
BO: 01484 223200   Admin: 01484 226300

INVERNESS
Eden Court, Bishop's Road, Inverness IV3 5SA
e-mail: admin@eden-court.co.uk
Director: Colin Marr
BO: 01463 234234   Admin: 01463 239841

JERSEY
Jersey Arts Centre
Phillips Street, St Helier, Jersey JE2 4SW
Website: www.artscentre.je
Director: Daniel Austin
Deputy Directors: Steven Edwards, Graeme Humphries
Fax: 01534 726788
BO: 01534 700444   Admin: 01534 700400

KENDAL
Brewery Arts Centre
Highgate, Kendal, Cumbria LA9 4HE
Website: www.breweryarts.co.uk
e-mail: admin@breweryarts.co.uk
Chief Executive: Sam Mason
BO: 01539 725133   Admin: 01539 722833

KING'S LYNN
King's Lynn Arts Centre
29 King Street
King's Lynn, Norfolk PE30 1HA
Website: www.kingslynnarts.co.uk
Fax: 01553 762141
BO: 01553 764864   Tel: 01553 765565

LEICESTER
Phoenix Arts Centre
21 Upper Brown Street
Leicester LE1 5TE
e-mail: admin@phoenix.org.uk
BO: 0116-255 4854   Admin: 0116-224 7700

LICHFIELD
Lichfield District Arts Association
Donegal House
Bore Street, Lichfield WS13 6LU
Website: www.lichfieldarts.org.uk
e-mail: info@lichfieldarts.org.uk
Director: Brian Pretty
Fax: 01543 308211   Tel: 01543 262223

LISKEARD
Sterts Theatre & Arts Centre
Upton Cross
Liskeard, Cornwall PL14 5AZ
Website: www.sterts.co.uk
Tel/Fax: 01579 362382   Tel/Fax: 01579 362962

LONDON
Artsdepot
5 Nether Street, Tally Ho Corner
North Finchley
London N12 0GA
Website: www.artsdepot.co.uk
e-mail: info@artsdepot.co.uk   BO: 020-8369 5454

LONDON
BAC
Lavender Hill, Battersea, London SW11 5TN
Website: www.bac.org.uk
e-mail: mailbox@bac.org.uk
Fax: 020-7978 5207
BO: 020-7223 2223   Admin: 020-7223 6557

LONDON
Chats Palace, 42-44 Brooksby's Walk
Hackney, London E9 6DF
Website: www.chatspalace.com
e-mail: info@chatspalace.com
Centre Director: Sarah Wickens   BO/Admin: 020-8533 0227

LONDON
Cockpit Theatre, Gateforth Street, London NW8 8EH
Website: www.cockpittheatre.org.uk
e-mail: dave.wybrow@cwc.ac.uk
Fax: 020-7258 2921
BO: 020-7258 2925   Admin: 020-7258 2920

LONDON
The Drill Hall, 16 Chenies Street, London WC1E 7EX
Website: www.drillhall.co.uk
e-mail: boxoffice@drillhall.co.uk
Fax: 020-7307 5062
BO: 020-7307 5060   Admin: 020-7307 5061

LONDON
Hoxton Hall Arts Centre
130 Hoxton Street, London N1 6SH
Website: www.hoxtonhall.co.uk
e-mail: info@hoxtonhall.co.uk
Operations Manager: Jane Caley
Fax: 020-7729 3815   Admin: 020-7684 0060

LONDON
Institute of Contemporary Arts (No in-house productions
or castings)
The Mall, London SW1Y 5AH
Website: www.ica.org.uk
Live & Media Arts Director: Emma Quinn
Fax: 020-7306 0122
BO: 020-7930 3647   Admin: 020-7930 0493

LONDON
Islington Arts Factory
2 Parkhurst Road, London N7 0SF
e-mail: iaf@islingtonartsfactory.fsnet.co.uk
Fax: 020-7700 7229   Tel: 020-7607 0561

LONDON
Jacksons Lane
269A Archway Road, London N6 5AA
Website: www.jacksonslane.org.uk
e-mail: reception@jacksonslane.org.uk
Fax: 020-8348 2424
BO: 020-8341 4421   Admin: 020-8340 5226

LONDON
Menier Chocolate Factory
53 Southwark Street, London SE1 1RU
Website: www.menierchocolatefactory.com
e-mail: office@menierchocolatefactory.com
Artistic Director: David Babani
Fax: 020-7378 1713   Admin: 020-7378 1712

LONDON
The Nettlefold
West Norwood Library Centre
1 Norwood High Street, London SE27 9JX
Centre Development Officers: Joanne Johnson,
Mark Sheehan   Admin/BO: 020-7926 8070

LONDON
October Gallery
24 Old Gloucester Street, London WC1N 3AL
Website: www.octobergallery.co.uk
e-mail: rentals@octobergallery.co.uk
Contact: Stefani Crone
Fax: 020-7405 1851   Tel: 020-7831 1618

LONDON
Oval House Theatre
52-54 Kennington Oval, London SE11 5SW
Website: www.ovalhouse.com
e-mail: info@ovalhouse.com
Programmer: Ben Evans
Director: Deborah Bestwick   Tel: 020-7582 0080

LONDON
Polish Social & Cultural Association
238-246 King Street
London W6 0RF   Tel: 020-8741 1940

LONDON
Riverside Studios
Crisp Road
Hammersmith, London W6 9RL
Website: www.riversidestudios.co.uk
e-mail: admin@riversidestudios.co.uk
Fax: 020-8237 1001
BO: 020-8237 1111   Tel: 020-8237 1000

LONDON
The Stables Gallery & Arts Centre
Gladstone Park
Dollis Hill Lane, London NW2 6HT
e-mail: stablesgallery@msn.com   Tel: 020-8452 8655

MAIDENHEAD
Norden Farm Centre For The Arts
Altwood Road
Maidenhead SL6 4PF
Website: www.nordenfarm.org
e-mail: admin@nordenfarm.org
Director: Annabel Turpin
Fax: 01628 682525
BO: 01628 788997   Admin: 01628 682555

MAIDSTONE
Hazlitt Arts Centre
Earl Street
Maidstone, Kent ME14 1PL
Theatre & Events Manager: Mandy Hare
Fax: 01622 602194
BO: 01622 758611   Admin: 01622 753922

MANCHESTER
Greenroom
54-56 Whitworth Street West
Manchester M1 5WW
Website: www.greenroomarts.org
e-mail: info@greenroomarts.org
Artistic Director: Garfield Allen
Fax: 0161-615 0516
BO: 0161-615 0500   Admin: 0161-615 0515

MANCHESTER
The Lowry
Pier 8, Salford Quays M50 3AZ
Website: www.thelowry.com
e-mail: info@thelowry.com
Theatre Production Bookings: Steve Cowton
Fax: 0161-876 2021
BO: 0870 1112000   Admin: 0870 1112020

MILFORD HAVEN
Torch Theatre
St Peter's Road
Milford Haven
Pembrokeshire SA73 2BU
Website: www.torchtheatre.co.uk
e-mail: info@torchtheatre.co.uk
Artistic Director: Peter Doran
Fax: 01646 698919
BO: 01646 695267   Admin: 01646 694192

NEWCASTLE UPON TYNE
The Round
34 Lime Street
Ouseburn
Newcastle Upon Tyne NE1 2PQ
Website: www.the-round.com
e-mail: info@the-round.com
Theatre Manager: Ben Fletcher-Watson
                              Tel: 0191-260 5605

NEWPORT (Isle of Wight)
Quay Arts
Sea Street
Newport Harbour
Isle of Wight PO30 5BD
Website: www.quayarts.org
Fax: 01983 526606Tel: 01983 822490

NORWICH
Norwich Arts Centre
St Benedicts Street
Norwich, Norfolk NR2 4PG
Website: www.norwichartscentre.co.uk
e-mail: stuart@norwichartscentre.co.uk
BO: 01603 660352   Admin: 01603 660387

NUNEATON
Abbey Theatre & Arts Centre
Pool Bank Street
Nuneaton, Warks CV11 5DB
Website: www.abbeytheatre.co.uk
e-mail: admin@abbeytheatre.co.uk
Chairman: Tony Deeming
Tel: 024-7632 7359   BO: 024-7635 4090

PLYMOUTH
Plymouth Arts Centre
38 Looe Street
Plymouth, Devon PL4 0EB
Website: www.plymouthartscentre.org
e-mail: info@plymouthartscentre.org
Director: Ian Hutchinson
Fax: 01752 206118   Tel: 01752 206114

POOLE
Lighthouse Poole Centre for The Arts
Kingland Road
Poole
Dorset BH15 1UG
Website: www.lighthousepoole.co.uk
                        BO/Admin: 08700 668701

RADLETT
The Radlett Centre
1 Aldenham Avenue
Radlett, Herts WD7 8HL
Website: www.radlettcentre.co.uk
Fax: 01923 857592   Tel: 01923 857546

ROTHERHAM
Rotherham Civic Theatre
Catherine Street
Rotherham
South Yorkshire S65 1JH
Website: www.rotherham.gov.uk/theatres
Theatre Manager: Mark Scott
BO: 01709 823621   Admin: 01709 823641

SALISBURY
Salisbury Arts Centre
Bedwin Street, Salisbury, Wiltshire SP1 3UT
e-mail: info@salisburyarts.co.uk
Fax: 01722 343030   BO: 01722 321744

SHREWSBURY
Shrewsbury & District Arts Association
The Gateway, Chester Street
Shrewsbury, Shropshire SY1 1NB
e-mail: gateway.centre@shropshire-cc.gov.uk
                                     Tel: 01743 355159

SOUTHPORT
Southport Arts Centre
Lord Street
Southport
Merseyside PR8 1DB
Website: www.seftonarts.co.uk
e-mail: artsops@seftonarts.co.uk
BO: 01704 540011   Admin: 0151-934 2131

STAMFORD
Stamford Arts Centre
27 St Mary's Street
Stamford, Lincolnshire PE9 2DL
Website: www.stamfordartscentre.co.uk
General Manager: David Popple
Fax: 01780 766690
BO: 01780 763203   Admin: 01780 480846

STIRLING
MacRobert
University of Stirling, Stirling FK9 4LA
Website: www.macrobert.org
Director: Liz Moran
BO: 01786 466666   Admin: 01786 467155

SWANSEA
Taliesin Arts Centre
Swansea University, Singleton Park, Swansea SA2 8PZ
Website: www.taliesinartscentre.co.uk
e-mail: s.e.crouch@swansea.ac.uk
Head of Cultural Services: Sybil Crouch   Tel: 01792 295238

SWINDON
Wyvern Theatre, Theatre Square
Swindon, Wiltshire SN1 1QN
BO: 01793 524481   Admin: 01793 535534

TAUNTON
Brewhouse Theatre & Arts Centre
Coal Orchard, Taunton, Somerset TA1 1JL
Website: www.thebrewhouse.net
e-mail: info@thebrewhouse.net
Director: Robert Miles
BO: 01823 283244   Admin: 01823 274608

TOTNES
The Arts at Dartington
The Barn, Dartington Hall, Totnes, Devon TQ9 6DE
Website: www.dartington.org/arts
e-mail: arts@dartington.org
BO: 01803 847070   Admin: 01803 847074

TUNBRIDGE WELLS
Trinity Theatre, Church Road, Tunbridge Wells, Kent TN1 1JP
Director: Jonathan Salisbury
BO: 01892 678678   Admin: 01892 678670

ULEY
Prema
South Street, Uley, Nr Dursley, Glos GL11 5SS
Website: www.prema.demon.co.uk
e-mail: info@prema.demon.co.uk
Director: Gordon Scott   Tel: 01453 860703

VALE OF GLAMORGAN
St Donats Arts Centre
St Donats Castle, The Vale of Glamorgan CF61 1WF
e-mail: janetsmith@stdonats.com
General Manager: Janet Smith
Fax: 01446 799101
BO: 01446 799100   Tel: 01446 799099

WAKEFIELD
Wakefield Arts Centre
Wakefield College, Thornes Park Centre, Thornes Park,
Horbury Road, Wakefield WF2 8QZ
Website: www.theatreroyalwakefield.co.uk
BO: 01924 211311   Admin: 01924 215531

WALLSEND
Buddle Arts Centre
258B Station Road, Wallsend, Tyne & Wear NE28 8RG
Contact: Geoffrey A Perkins
Fax: 0191-200 7142   Tel: 0191-200 7132

WASHINGTON
The Arts Centre Washington
Biddick Lane, Fatfield, Washington, Tyne & Wear NE38 8AB
Fax: 0191-219 3458   Tel: 0191-219 3455

WELLINGBOROUGH
The Castle, Castle Way
Wellingborough, Northants NN8 1XA
Website: www.thecastle.org.uk
e-mail: info@thecastle.org.uk
Executive Director: Gail Arnott
Fax: 01933 229888   Tel: 01933 229022

WIMBORNE
Layard Theatre
Canford School, Canford Magna
Wimborne, Dorset BH21 3AD
e-mail: layardtheatre@canford.com
Director of Drama: Stephen Hattersley
Administrator: Christine Haynes
BO/Fax: 01202 847525   Admin: 01202 847529

WINCHESTER
The Tower @ Kings
Romsey Road
Winchester, Hampshire SO22 5PW
Website: www.towerarts.co.uk
Tower Co-ordinator: Ben Ward   Tel: 01962 867986

WINDSOR
The Firestation
The Old Court
St Leonards Road, Windsor, Berks SL4 3BL
Website: www.firestationartscentre.com
e-mail: info@firestationartscentre.com   Tel: 01753 866865

WREXHAM
Oriel Wrecsam/Wrexham Arts Centre
Rhosddu Road, Wrexham LL11 1AU
e-mail: arts.centre@wrexham.gov.uk
Fax: 01978 292611   Tel: 01978 292093

ARTS COUNCIL ENGLAND, EAST
(Norfolk, Suffolk, Bedfordshire, Cambridgeshire, Essex,
Hertfordshire and the unitary authorities of Luton,
Peterborough, Southend-on-Sea and Thurrock)

Eden House, 48-49 Bateman Street
Cambridge CB2 1LR
Website: www.artscouncil.org.uk
Fax: 0870 2421271   Tel: 0845 3006200

ARTS COUNCIL ENGLAND, EAST MIDLANDS
(Derbyshire, Leicestershire, Lincolnshire excluding North
and North East Lincolnshire, Northamptonshire,
Nottinghamshire and the unitary authorities of Derby,
Leicester, Nottingham and Rutland)

St Nicholas Court, 25-27 Castle Gate
Nottingham NG1 7AR
Website: www.artscouncil.org.uk
Fax: 0115-950 2467   Tel: 0845 3006200

ARTS COUNCIL ENGLAND, LONDON
(Greater London)

2 Pear Tree Court, London EC1R 0DS
Website: www.artscouncil.org.uk
Fax: 020-7608 4100   Tel: 0845 3006200

ARTS COUNCIL ENGLAND, NORTH EAST
(Durham, Northumberland, Metropolitan authorities of
Gateshead, Newcastle upon Tyne, North Tyneside, South
Tyneside, Sunderland and the unitary authorities of
Darlington, Hartlepool, Middlesborough, Red Car and
Cleveland, Stockton-on-Tees)

Central Square, Forth Street
Newcastle upon Tyne NE1 3PJ
Website: www.artscouncil.org.uk
Fax: 0191-230 1020   Tel: 0845 3006200

ARTS COUNCIL ENGLAND, NORTH WEST
(Lancashire, Cheshire, Cumbria and the metropolitan
authorities of Bolton, Bury, Knowsley, Liverpool,
Manchester, Oldham, Rochdale, St Helens, Salford, Sefton,
Stockport, Tameside, Trafford, Wigan, Wirral and the
unitary authorities of Blackburn with Darwen, Blackpool,
Halton & Warrington)

Manchester House
22 Bridge Street
Manchester M3 3AB
Website: www.artscouncil.org.uk
Fax: 0161-834 6969   Tel: 0845 3006200

ARTS COUNCIL ENGLAND, SOUTH EAST
(Buckinghamshire, East Sussex, Hampshire, Isle of Wight,
Kent, Oxfordshire, Surrey, West Sussex and the unitary
authorities of Bracknell Forest. Brighton & Hove, Medway
Towns, Milton Keynes, Portsmouth)

Sovereign House
Church Street
Brighton BN1 1RA
Website: www.artscouncil.org.uk
Fax: 0870 2421257   Tel: 0845 3006200

ARTS COUNCIL ENGLAND, SOUTH WEST
(Cornwall, Devon, Dorset, Gloucestershire, Somerset and
Wiltshire and the unitary authorities of Bristol, Bath,
Bournemouth, Plymouth, Poole, Torbay and Swindon)

Senate Court
Southernhay Gardens
Exeter, Devon EX1 1UG
Website: www.artscouncil.org.uk
Fax: 01392 498546   Tel: 0845 3006200

ARTS COUNCIL ENGLAND, WEST MIDLANDS
(Herefordshire, Worcestershire, Staffordshire,
Warwickshire and Shropshire, Stoke-on-Trent, Telford and
Wrekin and districts of Birmingham, Coventry, Dudley,
Sandwell, Solihull, Walsall & Wolverhampton)

82 Granville Street
Birmingham B1 2LH
Website: www.artscouncil.org.uk
Fax: 0121-643 7239   Tel: 0845 3006200

ARTS COUNCIL ENGLAND, YORKSHIRE
(North Yorkshire, metropolitan authorities of Barnsley,
Bradford, Calderdale, Doncaster, Kirklees, Leeds,
Rotherham, Sheffield, Wakefield and the unitary authorities
of East Riding of Yorkshire, Kingston upon Hull,
North Lincolnshire, North East Lincolnshire)

21 Bond Street
Dewsbury
West Yorkshire WF13 1AX
Website: www.artscouncil.org.uk
Fax: 01924 466522   Tel: 0845 3006200

ARTS COUNCIL OF WALES, NORTH WALES OFFICE
(Isle of Anglesey, Gwynedd, Conwy, Denbighshire,
Flintshire, Wrexham)

36 Prince's Drive
Colwyn Bay
Conwy LL29 8LA
Website: www.artswales.org
Fax: 01492 533677   Tel: 01492 533440

**ARTS COUNCIL OF WALES, SOUTH WALES & CENTRAL
OFFICE**
(Vale of Glamorgan, Cardiff, Newport, Monmouthshire,
Torfaen, Blaenau Gwent, Caerphilly, Merthyr Tydfil, Rhonda
Cynon Taff, Bridgend)

9 Museum Place
Cardiff CF10 3NX
Website: www.artswales.org
Fax: 029-2022 1447   Tel: 029-2037 6525

ARTS COUNCIL OF WALES, MID & WEST WALES OFFICE
(Ceredigion, Carmarthenshire, Pembrokeshire, Powys,
Swansea, Neath & Port Talbot)

6 Gardd Llydaw
Jacksons Lane
Carmarthen SA31 1QD
Website: www.artswales.org
Fax: 01267 233084   Tel: 01267 234248

C

Casting Directors

For information regarding membership of
the Casting Directors' Guild (CDG) please see
www.thecdg.co.uk

Consultants
Costumes, Wigs & Make-up
Critics

A C A CASTING
Contact: Catherine Arton
32A Edenvale Street, London SW6 2SF
e-mail: catherine@acacasting.com   Tel/Fax: 020-7384 2635

ADAMSON Jo
Northern Spirit Creative Casting
PO Box 140, Leeds LS13 9BS
Website: www.northernspiritcreative.co.uk
e-mail: jo@northernspiritcreative.co.uk
Mobile: 07787 311270   Tel: 0113-219 2896

AILION Pippa
(CDG Member)
3 Towton Road, London SE27 9EE
e-mail: enquiries@pippaailioncasting.co.uk
                                         Tel/Fax: 020-8670 4816

ALL DIRECTIONS OF LONDON
Contact: By Post Only
7 Rupert Court, Off Wardour Street
London W1D 6EB   Tel: 020-7437 5879

ANDERSON Jane
e-mail: casting@janeandersononline.com

ANDREW Dorothy CASTING
(CDG Member)
Campus Manor, Childwall Abbey Road
Childwall, Liverpool L16 0JP
Fax: 0151-737 4006   Tel: 0151-737 4044

AP CASTING
Contact: Annelie Powell
e-mail: apcasting@gmail.com   Mobile: 07821 440422

ASHTON HINKINSON CASTING
1 Charlotte Street, London W1T 1RD
Website: www.ashtonhinkinson.com
e-mail: casting@ahcasting.com
Fax: 020-7636 1657   Tel: 020-7580 6101

BAIG Shaheen CASTING
c/o Ground Floor
46 Mannock Road, London N22 6AA
e-mail: shaheen.baig@btconnect.com   Tel: 020-8889 9513

BARNES Derek
(CDG Member)
BBC DRAMA SERIES CASTING
BBC Elstree, Room N221
Neptune House, Clarendon Road
Borehamwood, Herts WD6 1JF
Fax: 020-8228 8311   Tel: 020-8228 7096

BATH Andrea
Contact: By Post/email/Telephone
Accepts Showreels. Theatre. Television
85 Brightwell Road, Watford WD18 0HR
e-mail: andreabath@btinternet.com   Tel: 01923 333067

BEACH CASTING Ltd
Contact: Brendan McNamara
BCM Box 4040, London WC1N 3XX
Website: www.beach-casting.com
e-mail: brendan@beach-casting.com   Tel: 08445 679595

BEASTALL AND NORTH Ltd
Contact: Lesley Beastall, Sophie North
41E Elgin Crescent, London W11 2JD
e-mail: lesley@beastallnorth.co.uk
Mobile: 07956 516606 (Sophie)   Mobile: 07956 516603 (Lesley)

Valerie Colgan

- For professional actors who need a voice production "MOT"
- Private individual classes
- Valerie Colgan and a consortium of tutors as appropriate

Ex Head of Drama at the City Lit · 5 Drama Schools · The Actors Centre

Tel: 020 7267 2153 The Green, 17 Herbert Street, London NW5 4HA

BEATTIE Victoria
Contact: By email
Accepts Showreels
Commercials. Feature Films. Television Drama
219B Westbourne Park Road, London W11 1EA
e-mail: victoria@victoriabeattie.com Mobile: 07976 395996

BEAUCHAMP Lauren CASTING
34A Brightside, Billericay CM12 0LJ
e-mail: laurenbeauchamp@tiscali.co.uk
Fax: 01277 656147   Mobile: 07961 982198

BECKLEY Rowland
BBC DRAMA SERIES CASTING, BBC Elstree
Room N222, Neptune House, Clarendon Road
Borehamwood, Herts WD6 1JF   Fax: 020-8228 7130

BERTRAND Leila CASTING
53 Hormead Road, London W9 3NQ
e-mail: leilabcasting@aol.com   Tel/Fax: 020-8964 0683

BEVAN Lucy
c/o Twickenham Studios
St Margaret's
Twickenham TW1 2AW   Tel: 020-8607 8888

BEWICK Maureen CASTING
104A Dartmouth Road, London NW2 4HB

BEXFIELD DEITCH ASSOCIATES
80-81 St. Martin's Lane, London WC2N 4AA
e-mail: casting@bexfielddeitch.co.uk   Tel: 020-7395 7525

BILL The
TalkbackThames Studios
1 Deer Park Road
London SW19 3TL   Tel: 020-8540 0600

BIRD Sarah
(CDG Member)
PO Box 32658, London W14 0XA
Fax: 020-7602 8601   Tel: 020-7371 3248

BIRKETT Hannah CASTING
26 Noko, 3/6 Banister Road, London W10 4AR
e-mail: hannah@hbcasting.com
Mobile: 07957 114175   Tel: 020-8960 2848

BRACKE Siobhan
(CDG Member)
Contact: By Post
Basement Flat, 22A The Barons
St Margaret's TW1 2AP   Tel: 020-8891 5686

BROWNING Grace
See CASTING COMPANY (UK) The

BUCKINGHAM Jo
Comedy. Entertainment
BBC Television Centre
Wood Lane, London W12 7RJ
e-mail: jo.buckingham@bbc.co.uk
Fax: 020-8576 4414   Tel: 020-8225 7585

CANDID CASTING
1st Floor, 32 Great Sutton Street
London EC1V 0NB
Website: www.candidcasting.co.uk
e-mail: mail@candidcasting.co.uk
Fax: 020-7490 8966   Tel: 020-7490 8882

Who are casting directors?

Casting directors are employed by directors / production companies to source the best available actors for roles across TV, film, radio, theatre and commercials. They do the groundwork and present a shortlist of artists to the director, who often makes the final selection. Many casting directors work on a freelance basis, others are employed permanently by larger organisations such as the BBC or the National Theatre. Discovering new and emerging talent also plays an important part in their job.

Why should I approach them?

If you are an actor looking for work, you can promote yourself directly to casting directors by sending them your photo and CV. They keep actors' details on file and may consider you for future productions. Bear in mind that you will not be guaranteed a response as casting directors are physically unable to reply to every one of the vast numbers of letters they receive from actors, but it is worth your while to explore this opportunity to find work.

How should I approach them?

Many of the following casting directors have indicated the method in which they prefer actors to contact them for the first time. This tends to be by post but some accept or prefer emails. Some are happy to receive telephone calls, but be aware that casting directors are very busy and you should not continually call them with questions or updates once you have sent your CV. If they have not specified whether they prefer postal or email contact, you should send them your CV, a headshot and a covering letter by post only, as this is the traditional method of contacting casting professionals. You should always include a stamped-addressed envelope (SAE) big enough to contain your 10 x 8 photo and with sufficient postage. This will increase your chances of getting a reply. Write your name and telephone number on the back of your headshot in case it gets separated from your CV.

Should I send a casting director my showreel and/or voicereel?

Some casting directors have also indicated that they are happy for actors to send showreels and/or voicereels along with their CVs and headshots, but if this is not indicated, we would recommend that you leave these out of your correspondence but indicate in your covering letter that they are available. If a casting director is interested in you, they can contact you later for these items, but they usually prefer not to sift through hundreds of unsolicited showreels until they have first established an interest in an actor.

How do I target my search?

It is not advisable to send a generic CV to every casting director listed in the following pages. Research the following names and companies and then target your letters accordingly. Find out what areas of the industry each one usually casts for (some specify this in their listing) and what productions they have previously cast. Keep an eye on TV, film and theatre credits so you become familiar with the casting directors used for different productions. Some of these casting directors have their own websites. If a casting director has 'CDG' after their name, it means they are a member of the Casting Directors' Guild, the professional organisation of casting directors working in the UK (see www.thecdg.co.uk for more information and their article over the page).

How do I write an effective CV and covering letter?

Once you have made a short-list of suitable casting directors you should send them your CV, your headshot, and an individually tailored covering letter. The covering letter should demonstrate that you have researched the casting director, and ideally you will have a particular reason for contacting them at this time: perhaps you can tell them about your next showcase, or where they can see you currently appearing on stage. Your CV should be no longer than one page, up-to-date and spell-checked. Please see the 'Promotional Services' section of Contacts for further advice on writing CVs and covering letters.

How do I prepare for a casting/audition?

Make sure you are fully prepared with accurate information about the audition time, venue, format and the people you will be meeting. Unless it's a last minute casting, you should always read the script in advance and try to have some opinions on it. If you are asked in advance to prepare a piece, always stick to the brief with something suitable and relevant. On the day, allow plenty of time to get there so you are not flustered when you arrive. Try to be positive and enjoy yourself. Remember, the casting director doesn't want to spend several days auditioning - they want you to get the job! Never criticise previous productions you have worked on. And at the end of the casting, remember to take your script away unless you are asked to leave it, otherwise it can look as if you're not interested. Please see 'Rehearsal Rooms and Casting Suites' for more detailed advice on preparing for and attending auditions.

Should I attend a casting in a house or flat?

Professional auditions are rarely held anywhere other than an official casting studio or venue. Be very wary if you are asked to go elsewhere. Trust your instincts. If something doesn't seem right to you, it probably isn't. Always take someone with you if you are in any doubt.

How do I become a casting director?

The best way to gain experience in this field is to work as a casting assistant. Vacancies are sometimes advertised in The Stage www.thestage.co.uk or PCR www.pcrnewsletter.com. Alternatively you could try sending your CV to casting directors asking for an internship. Just as we advise actors, remember to research any casting director you are considering approaching to make sure they actually work in the area you are interested in. The internship is likely to be unpaid, but the experience and contacts you gain will be invaluable.

When you read CDG after a Casting Director's name, you know he/she is a member of The Casting Directors' Guild and will therefore have a minimum of five years' experience. The current CDG Committee has prepared the following advice for actors.

Casting directors are there to help actors and not to hinder them. We want you to do your best as that reflects back on us, and you should realise that we are only as good as the actors we submit for each role.

Much of our work consists of creating a shortlist of potential actors and reducing it to a suitably sized group to present for audition. We also spend a great deal of time watching you work. Members of the CDG endeavour to cover as many performances as possible on film, television and in the theatre. There is no substitute to seeing you act.

When asked to attend an interview or audition, an actor should feel confident in asking his/her agent any relevant questions about the role and the project. If this is not forthcoming, arrive early and seek information from the casting director or, better still, contact him/her the day before. If it is only possible to speak to the casting director on the day, preferably do so before entering the audition room, rather than in front of the director or producer. The casting director will be happy to help.

Sometimes you will only receive pages for a role, but a casting director will always endeavour to give you as much information about a character as is available. When possible, read the entire play/screenplay rather than just the scenes your 'character' appears in, and ideally be able to talk about the script as a whole during the interview. Take your time when reading; preparation is worth a lot but don't be fazed if you get lost over their script. If you feel that a scene is going terribly it's ok to start again.

For most non-theatre jobs these days you will find that your meeting will be recorded on video tape. These tapes are then shown to the various producers involved, and this is when the process can slow down. It takes time to build a company and for final casting choices to be made.

Casting is a matter of interpretation. As well as character information derived from the script, the vision of the producer, director, casting director and indeed the actor all come into play. There are many reasons why one actor will be chosen over another, and even the best audition might not necessarily secure a part. Every aspect of the actor comes into play. Is he/she too young or too mature? Do they work as a family? Could they be mother and son? Does the chemistry work? There is also the frustrating problem of scripts, and parts, being re-written. A character may have an entirely different physical description in a later draft. Sadly we do not have control over this.

When it comes to contacting casting directors, most are happy to receive letters, updated photos and CVs. The best correspondence for casting directors to receive is performance information. Letters should be brief and to the point, with the production name, director, venue and/or TV channel clearly stated. If you are enquiring about work be as specific as possible, e.g. "I would like to be seen for the part of ... in ... because ..." or something similar. Dear Sir or Madam letters just don't work.

CVs should be well laid out. List most recent work first and use your spell checker. 6x4 photos are fine to send but include an SAE if you want them returned. Casting directors rarely like unsolicited DVDs and showreels: you must be aware that we do get inundated. Also bear in mind that not receiving a response to your letter does not mean it hasn't been read and filed: it is virtually impossible to reply to the volume of mail received from actors.

In our greener world it's great that Spotlight and other web media now have the facility for us to view CVs, photos and showreels online. Use the technology: it's very easy to keep your CV up-to-date online and you can change your photo at any time of year without having to do a huge mail out to let people know.

Actors are a fundamental tool of this industry: CDG members are aware of this and aim to put actors at their ease. Audition nerves are a given but you should feel secure that the reason you are in the room is because someone wants you to get that role and not because they want to see you fail.

Please visit www.thecdg.co.uk for further information about the CDG.

Sean Gleeson

STUARTALLEN
PHOTOGRAPHER

07776 258829

www.stuartallenphotos.com

Production, Publicity, Portraits

STUDENT DISCOUNTS

Natalie Barrett

CANNON DUDLEY & ASSOCIATES
Contact: Carol Dudley
By Post
Film. Stage. Television
43A Belsize Square, London NW3 4HN
e-mail: cdacasting@blueyonder.co.uk
Fax: 020-7813 2048   Tel: 020-7433 3393

CANNON John
(CDG Member)
BBC DRAMA SERIES CASTING
BBC Elstree, Room N223
Neptune House, Clarendon Road
Borehamwood, Herts WD6 1JF
Fax: 020-8228 8311   Tel: 020-8228 7322

CARLING Di CASTING
(CDG Member)
1st Floor, 49 Frith Street
London W1D 4SG
Fax: 020-7287 6844   Tel: 020-7287 6446

CARROLL Anji
(CDG Member)
Contact: By Post/email
4 Nesfield Drive, Winterley, Cheshire CW11 4NT
e-mail: anji@anjicarroll.tv   Tel: 01270 250240

CASTING COMPANY (UK) The
Contact: Michelle Guish, Grace Browning
3rd Floor, 112-114 Wardour Street
London W1F 0TS
Fax: 020-7434 2346   Tel: 020-7734 4954

CASTING CONNECTION The
Contact: Michael Syers
Dalrossie House, 16 Victoria Grove
Stockport, Cheshire SK4 5BU
Fax: 0161-442 7280   Tel: 0161-432 4122

CASTING COUCH The
Contact: Moira Townsend
213 Trowbridge Road
Bradford on Avon
Wiltshire BA15 1EU
e-mail: moiratownsend@yahoo.co.uk   Mobile: 07932 785807

CASTING UK
26-34 Emerald Street, London WC1N 3QA
Website: www.castinguk.com
e-mail: info@castinguk.com   Tel: 020-7400 1251

CATLIFF Suzy
(CDG Member)
PO Box 39492, London N10 3YX
e-mail: soose@soose.co.uk   Tel: 020-8442 0749

CHAND Urvashi
(CDG Member)
Cinecraft, 115A Kilburn Lane, London W10 4AN
e-mail: urvashi@cinecraft.biz
Fax: 020-8960 3167   Tel: 020-8968 7016

CHARD Alison
(CDG Member)
23 Groveside Court, 4 Lombard Road
Battersea, London SW11 3RQ
e-mail: chardcasting@btinternet.com   Tel: 020-7223 9125

jay

amy

alexa

john

sean ellis photographer   07702 381 258   sean@seanellis.co.uk   www.seanellis.co.uk   nr esher, surrey

CHARKHAM CASTING
Contact: Beth Charkham
Suite 361, 14 Tottenham Court Road
London W1T 1JY
e-mail: charkhamcasting@btconnect.com
Mobile: 07956 456630

CLARK Andrea
Contact: By Post.
Accepts Showreels
Commercials. Film. Stage. Television
PO Box 28895, London SW13 0WG
e-mail: andrea@aclarkcasting.com   Tel: 020-8876 6869

CLAYTON Rosalie
(CDG Member)
e-mail: rosalie@rosalieclayton.com   Tel/Fax: 020-7242 8109

COGAN Ben
BBC DRAMA SERIES CASTING
BBC Elstree, Room N221
Neptune House, Clarendon Road
Borehamwood, Herts WD6 1JF
Fax: 020-8228 8311   Tel: 020-8228 7516

COHEN Abi CASTING
London
e-mail: cohencasting@tinyonline.co.uk   Tel: 020-7687 9002

COLLINS Jayne CASTING
(CDG Member)
4th Floor, 20 Bedford Street, London WC2E 9HP
Website: www.jaynecollinscasting.com
e-mail: info@jaynecollinscasting.com
Fax: 020-7240 5323   Tel: 020-7836 9792

COMMERCIALS CASTING UK Ltd
Contact: Michelle Smith (CDG Member)
By Post
Accepts Showreels/Voicereels.
Commercials. Photographic. Street Casting. Voice Overs
Streaming/Uploading Service Available
220 Church Lane
Stockport SK7 1PQ
Fax: 0161-439 0622   Tel: 0161-439 6825

CORDORAY Lin
66 Cardross Street, London W6 0DR

COTTON Irene
(CDG Member)
25 Druce Road, Dulwich Village, London SE21 7DW
e-mail: irenecotton@btinternet.com
Tel/Fax: 020-8299 2787   Tel: 020-8299 1595

CRAMPSIE Julia
(Casting Executive)
BBC DRAMA SERIES CASTING
BBC Elstree, Room N224, Neptune House
Clarendon Road, Borehamwood
Herts WD6 1JF
Fax: 020-8228 8311   Tel: 020-8228 7170

CRANE Carole CASTING
e-mail: crane.shot@virgin.net   Mobile: 07976 869442

CRAWFORD Kahleen CASTING
Film City Glasgow, 4 Summertown Road, Glasgow G51 2LY
Website: www.kahleencrawford.com
e-mail: kahleen@kahleencrawford.com
Mobile: 07950 414164   Tel: 0141-425 1725

CROCODILE CASTING COMPANY The
Contact: Claire Toeman, Tracie Saban
9 Ashley Close, Hendon, London NW4 1PH
Website: www.crocodilecasting.com
e-mail: croccast@aol.com   Tel: 020-8203 7009

CROSS Louise
128A North View Road
London N8 7LP   Tel: 020-8341 2200

CROWE Sarah CASTING
75 Amberley Road, London W9 2JL
e-mail: sarah@sarahcrowecasting.co.uk
Fax: 020-7286 5030   Tel: 020-7286 5080

CROWLEY POOLE CASTING
11 Goodwins Court, London WC2N 4LL
Fax: 020-7379 5971   Tel: 020-7379 5965

CROWLEY Suzanne
(CDG Member) (See CROWLEY POOLE CASTING)

DAVIES Jane CASTING Ltd
Contact: Jane Davies (CDG), John Connor (CDG Member)
PO Box 680, Sutton, Surrey SM1 3ZG
e-mail: info@janedaviescasting.co.uk
Fax: 020-8644 9746   Tel: 020-8715 1036

DAVIS Leo (Miss)
(JUST CASTING)
20th Century Theatre
291 Westbourne Grove, London W11 2QA
Fax: 020-7792 2143   Tel: 020-7229 3471

DAVY Gary
(CDG Member)
Contact: By Post
Film. Television
1st Floor, 55-59 Shaftesbury Avenue, London W1D 6LD
Fax: 020-7437 0881   Tel: 020-7437 0880

DAWES Gabrielle
(CDG Member)
PO Box 52493, London NW3 9DZ
e-mail: gdawescasting@tiscali.co.uk   Tel: 020-7435 3645

DAY Kate
(CDG Member)
Pound Cottage, 27 The Green South
Warborough, Oxon OX10 7DR   Tel/Fax: 01865 858709

DE FREITAS Paul
(CDG Member)
e-mail: info@pauldefreitas.com

DENMAN Jack CASTING
Contact: By Post/Telephone
Commercials. Film. Role Play. Television
Burgess House, Main Street, Farnsfield
Notts NG22 8EF   Tel/Fax: 01623 882272

DENNISON Lee ASSOCIATES
(London & New York)
Contact: By Post/email
*Professional Featured Box Office Named Artists Only for
Major UK/USA Film and Television Features*
Fushion Pukka Bush
27 Old Gloucester Street, London WC1N 3XX
Website: www.ukscreen.com/crew/ldennison
e-mail: leedennison@fushion-uk.com
Fax: 08700 111020   Tel: 08700 111100

Jean Rogers

Steve McFadden

Shobna Gulati

SUE JONES ("Nil By Mouth", "Human Traffic", "Ronin") ONE TO ONE TUITION AND CASTING WORKSHOPS
An opportunity to get valuable insight into the casting process from the perspective of an experienced casting director. Examining the difference between a good performance and the successful performance. Demonstrating common pitfalls. The purpose of the workshops is to improve and refine actors' audition, interview and reading/performance technique, identifying and eliminating bad habits. Actors work in pairs on a script which is then directed and shot on camera and reviewed with observation and constructive criticism. To finish, there is a review of the session, general advice and a Q and A on any subject which the actors wish to pursue. One to one tuition, either for a specific important audition or to improve general technique. Available subject to availability. NB. THE WORKSHOPS ARE FOR PROFESSIONALS ONLY. SELECTION BY CV. **COMMERCIALS AND EPISODIC TV - 12 ACTORS PER 4 HR SESSION, FEATURES AND TV DRAMA - 10 ACTORS PER 4 HR SESSION** EMAIL info@suejones.net **FOR FULL DETAILS**

DICKENS Laura
(CDG Member)
197 Malpas Road
London SE4 1BH
e-mail: dickenscasting@aol.com   Mobile: 07958 665468

DOWD Kate
74 Wells Street, London W1T 3QG
Fax: 020-7580 6688   Tel: 020-7580 8866

DRURY Malcolm
(CDG Member)
34 Tabor Road
London W6 0BW   Tel: 020-8748 9232

DUDLEY Carol
(CDG Member) (See CANNON DUDLEY & ASSOCIATES)

DUFF Julia
(CDG Member)
73 Wells Street, London W1T 3QG
Fax: 020-7436 8859   Tel: 020-7436 8860

DUFF Maureen
(CDG Member)
PO Box 47340
London NW3 4TY
e-mail: belgrove@dircon.co.uk
Fax: 020-7681 7172   Tel: 020-7586 0532

DUFFY Jennifer
(CDG Member)
11 Portsea Mews
London W2 2BN   Tel: 020-7262 3326

EARNSHAW Rob
85B Jesmond Road
Newcastle upon Tyne NE2 1NH
Website: www.robertearnshawcasting.co.uk
e-mail: robertearnshaw@btinternet.com
Mobile: 07707 083674   Tel/Fax: 0191-209 1823

EAST Irene CASTING
(CDG Member)
Contact: By Post
Film. Theatre
40 Brookwood Avenue
Barnes, London SW13 0LR
e-mail: irneast@aol.com   Tel: 020-8876 5686

EJ CASTING
150 Tooley Street
London SE1 2TU
e-mail: info@ejcasting.com
Mobile: 07891 632946   Tel: 020-7564 2688

EMMERSON Chloe
96 Portobello Road
London W11 2QG
e-mail: c@ChloeEmmerson.com   Tel: 020-7792 8823

ET-NIK-A PRIME MANAGEMENT & CASTINGS Ltd
Contact: Aldo Arcilla
By Post
Accepts Showreels/Voicereels.
Commercials. Film. Television
30 Great Portland Street
London W1W 8QU
Website: www.etnikapmc.com
e-mail: info@etnikapmc.com
Fax: 020-7299 3558   Tel: 020-7299 3555

EVANS Richard
(CDG Member)
10 Shirley Road, London W4 1DD
Website: www.evanscasting.co.uk
e-mail: contact@evanscasting.co.uk   Tel: 020-8994 6304

EYE CASTING The
Tower Room, The Bath House
8 Chapel Place, Rivington Street
London EC2A 3DQ
Website: www.theeyecasting.com
e-mail: jody@theeyecasting.com
Fax: 020-7737 7895   Tel: 020-7729 9705

FEARNLEY Ali CASTING
3rd Floor
58-60 Rivington Street, London EC2A 3AU
e-mail: cast@alifearnley.com   Tel: 020-7613 7320

FIGGIS Susie
19 Spencer Rise
London NW5 1AR   Tel: 020-7482 2200

FILDES Bunny CASTING
(CDG Member)
56 Wigmore Street, London W1   Tel: 020-7935 1254

FINCHER Sally
(CDG Member)
e-mail: sally.fincher@btinternet.com

FOX CASTING
Pinewood Studios, Pinewood Road
Iver Heath, Bucks SL0 0NH
e-mail: julie.fox@virgin.net   Tel: 01753 656848

FOX Celestia
23 Leppoc Road, London SW4 9LS
e-mail: celestia.fox@virgin.net   Tel: 020-7720 6143

FRAZER Janie
(CDG Member)
ITV Productions, London TV Centre
South Bank, London SE1 9LT
e-mail: janie.frazer@granadamedia.com Tel: 020-7261 3848

FRECK Rachel
(CDG Member)
e-mail: casting@rachelfreck.com   Tel/Fax: 020-8673 2455

FREND Amanda
87 Swindon Road, Horsham, West Sussex RH12 2HF
e-mail: amandafrendcasting@hotmail.co.uk

FRISBY Jane CASTING
(CDG Member)
*Contact: By Post. Accepts Showreels/Voicereels
only on request. Commercials. Film. Theatre*
51 Ridge Road, London N8 9LJ
e-mail: jane.frisby@tiscali.co.uk   Tel: 020-8341 4747

FUNNELL Caroline
(CDG Member)
25 Rattray Road, London SW2 1AZ   Tel: 020-7326 4417

GALLIE Joyce
37 Westcroft Square, London W6 0TA   Tel: 020-8741 4009

GANE CASTING
Contact: Natasha Gane
52 Woodhouse Road, London N12 0RJ
e-mail: natasha@ganecasting.com
Fax: 020-8446 2508   Tel: 020-8446 2551

GB CASTING UK Ltd
Contact: Karin Grainger
65F Rowley Way, Abbey Road, London, NW8 0SJ
e-mail: kggbuk@lineone.net
Mobile: 07901 553075   Tel: 020-7328 8815

GILLHAM Tracey
(CDG Member)
Comedy. Entertainment
BBC Television Centre, Wood Lane, London W12 7RJ
Fax: 020-8576 4414   Tel: 020-8225 8648

GILLON Tamara CASTING
26 Carson Road, London SE21 8HU
e-mail: tamaragillon@yahoo.co.uk
Fax: 020-8265 6330   Tel: 020-8766 0099

GOLD Nina
(CDG Member)
117 Chevening Road, London NW6 6DU
e-mail: info@ninagold.co.uk
Fax: 020-8968 6777   Tel: 020-8960 6099

GOOCH Miranda CASTING
*Contact: By Post/email
Accepts Showreels/Voicereels. Film*
102 Leighton Gardens, London NW10 3PR
e-mail: mirandagooch@gmail.com
Fax: 020-8962 9579   Tel: 020-8962 9578

GREEN Jill CASTING
(CDG Member)
PO Box 56927
London N10 3UR   Tel: 0845 4786343

GREENE Francesca CASTING
79 Ashworth Mansions, London W9 1LN
e-mail: francesca@francescagreene.co.uk
          Tel: 020-7286 5957

GRESHAM Marcia
(CDG Member)
3 Langthorne Street
London SW6 6JT   Tel: 020-7381 2876

GROSVENOR Angela
(CDG Member) (Head of Casting)
Talkback Thames Studios
Talkback Thames
1 Deer Park Road
London SW19 3TL
Fax: 020-8543 2794   Tel: 020-8540 0600

GUISH Michelle
See CASTING COMPANY (UK) The

HALL David CASTING
2 The Shrubbery
2 Lavender Gardens
London SW11 1DL
Mobile: 07938 824830   Tel: 020-7223 4382

HALL Janet
69 Buckstones Road
Shaw, Oldham OL2 8DW
e-mail: stage@hall257.fsbusiness.co.uk
Mobile: 07956 822773   Tel: 01706 291306

HALL Pippa
Children. Teenagers
Rosebank, High Street
Blockley, Glos GL56 9EX
e-mail: pippa@pippahallcasting.com

HAMILTON Des CASTING
17F Clerkenwell Road
London EC1M 5RD
Website: www.deshamilton.com
e-mail: des@deshamilton.com   Tel: 020-7253 5558

HAMMOND Louis
6 Brewer Street, London W1F 0SD
e-mail: louis.hammond@virgin.net   Tel: 020-7734 1880

cwphotos
Clive Weeks LMPA
Photographer
Southampton
023 8073 2550
www.cwphotos.co.uk

HANCOCK Gemma
(CDG Member)
Contact: By email
North Lodge, Weald Chase
Staplefield Road, Cuckfield, West Sussex RH17 5HY
e-mail: gemma.hancock@virgin.net

HARKIN Julie
(CDG Member)
33 Fitzroy Street, London W1T 6DU
e-mail: julie@smithharkincasting.com   Tel: 020-7436 9255

HARRIS Lisa
290 Coulsdon Road, Old Coulsdon
Surrey CR5 1EB   Mobile: 07956 561247

HAWSER Gillian CASTING
24 Cloncurry Street, London SW6 6DS
e-mail: gillianhawser@btinternet.com
Fax: 020-7731 0738   Tel: 020-7731 5988

HAYFIELD Judi
(CDG Member)
6 Richmond Hill Road
Gatley, Cheadle, Stockport SK8 1QG
e-mail: judi.hayfield@hotmail.co.uk   Mobile: 07919 221873

HILL Serena
Sydney Theatre Company
Pier 4, Hickson Road
Walsh Bay, NSW 2000, Australia
e-mail: shill@sydneytheatre.com.au   Tel: 00 612 925 01727

HOOTKINS Polly
(CDG Member)
PO Box 52480, London NW3 9DH
e-mail: phootkins@clara.net   Tel: 020-7692 1184

HORAN Julia
(CDG Member)
26 Falkland Road
London NW5 2PX   Tel: 020-7267 5261

HOWE Gary CASTING
34 Orbit Street, Roath
Cardiff CF24 0JX   Tel/Fax: 029-2045 3883

HUBBARD CASTING
Contact: Ros Hubbard, John Hubbard
Dan Hubbard (CDG Member)
No Showreels
14 Rathbone Place, London W1T 1HT
e-mail: email@hubbardcasting.com
Fax: 020-7636 7117   Tel: 020-7631 4944

HUGHES Sarah
(CDG Member)
BBC Television Centre
Wood Lane, London W12 7RJ
e-mail: sarah.hughes@bbc.co.uk   Tel: 020-8225 8610

HUGHES Sylvia
Casting Suite, The Deanwater
Wilmslow Road, Woodford
Cheshire SK7 1RJ
e-mail: sylviahughes@hotmail.co.uk   Mobile: 07770 520007

JACKSON Sue
(CDG Member)
Contact: By Post
53 Moseley Wood Walk
Leeds LS16 7HQ   Tel: 0113-267 0819

JAFFA Janis CASTING
(CDG Member)
Contact: By Post
Accepts Showreels
67 Starfield Road, London W12 9SN
e-mail: janis@janisjaffacasting.co.uk
Fax: 020-8743 9561   Tel: 020-7565 2877

JAFFREY Jennifer
Contact: By Post
The Double Lodge, Pinewood Studios
Pinewood Road
Iver Heath, Bucks SL0 0NH
e-mail: jaffreymag@aol.com
Fax: 01753 785163   Tel: 01753 785162

JAY Jina CASTING
(CDG Member)
Office 2, Sound Centre
Twickenham Film Studios
The Barons, St Margarets
Twickenham, Middlesex TW1 2AW
Fax: 020-8607 8982   Tel: 020-8607 8888

JELOWICKI Ilenka
(Mad Dog Casting Ltd)
Contact: By Post/email
Accepts Showreels/Voicereels
Children. Real People. Street Casting
15 Leighton Place, London NW5 2QL
e-mail: ilenka@maddogcasting.com
Fax: 020-7284 2689   Tel: 020-7482 4703

JENKINS Lucy
(CDG Member)
Contact: By Post/Email
Accepts Showreels/Voicereels
Commercials. Film. Television. Theatre
74 High Street, Hampton Wick
Kingston on Thames KT1 4DQ
e-mail: lucy.jenkins@blueyonder.co.uk Tel: 020-8943 5328

JN PRODUCTION
16-24 Underwood Street, London N1 7JQ
e-mail: james@jnproduction.net
Fax: 020-7608 1876   Tel: 020-7278 8800

JOHN Priscilla
(CDG Member)
PO Box 22477, London W6 0GT
Fax: 020-8741 4005   Tel: 020-8741 4212

JOHNSON Alex CASTING
15 McGregor Road, London W11 1DE
e-mail: alex@alexjohnsoncasting.com
Fax: 020-7229 1665   Tel: 020-7229 8779

JOHNSON Marilyn
(CDG Member)
1st Floor, 11 Goodwins Court
London WC2N 4LL
e-mail: casting@marilynjohnsoncasting.com
Fax: 020-7497 5530   Tel: 020-7497 5552

JONES Doreen
(CDG Member)
PO Box 22478, London W6 0WJ
Fax: 020-8748 8533   Tel: 020-8746 3782

JONES Sue
(CDG Member)
e-mail: casting@suejones.net
Fax: 020-8838 1130   Tel: 020-8838 5153

KATE & LOU CASTING
The Basement, Museum House
25 Museum Street, London WC1A 1JT
Website: www.kateandloucasting.com
e-mail: cast@kateandloucasting.com
Mobile: 07976 252531   Mobile: 07885 763429

KENNEDY Anna CASTING
8 Rydal Road, London SW16 1QN
e-mail: anna@kennedycasting.com   Tel: 020-8677 6710

KEOGH Beverley CASTING Ltd
29 Ardwick Green North
Ardwick Green, Manchester M12 6DL
e-mail: beverley@beverleykeogh.tv
Fax: 0161-273 4401   Tel: 0161-273 4400

KESTER Gaby
e-mail: casting@gabykester.com

KIBBEY Leoni CASTING
Website: www.leonikibbey.com
e-mail: casting@leonikibbey.com
Mobile: 07855 313552   Tel: 01727 375166

KLIMEK Nana CASTING
2nd Floor Office
Unit 4, 18 Kingsland Road, Shoreditch, London E2 8DA
Website: www.headnodagency.com
e-mail: casting@headnodagency.com

KNIGHT-SMITH Jerry
(CDG Member)
Royal Exchange Theatre Company
St Ann's Square, Manchester M2 7DH
Fax: 0161-615 6691   Tel: 0161-615 6761

KOREL Suzy
(CDG Member)
20 Blenheim Road, London NW8 0LX
e-mail: suzy@korel.org
Fax: 020-7372 3964   Tel: 020-7624 6435

KRUGER Beatrice
(FBI Casting) 46 via della Pelliccia, 00153 Roma, Italy
Website: www.fbicasting.com
e-mail: beatrice.kruger@fbicasting.it
Fax: 00 39 06 23328203   Tel: 00 39 06 58332747

KYLE CASTING Ltd
71B North Worple Way
Mortlake, London SW14 8PR
e-mail: kylecasting@btinternet.com   Tel: 020-8876 6763

LARCA Ltd
(Welsh Language/English)
Commercials. Film. Stage. Television
Ynyslasuchaf Farm
Blackmill, Bridgend CF35 6DW
Fax: 01656 841815   Mobile: 07779 321954

LAYTON Claudie CASTING
Unit 308, Canalot Studios
222 Kensal Road, London W10 5BN
e-mail: casting@claudielayton.com
Fax: 020-8968 1330   Tel: 020-8964 2055

LEVENE Jon
e-mail: jonlevene@mac.com
Mobile: 07977 570899   Tel: 020-7792 8501

LEVINSON Sharon
30 Stratford Villas, London NW1 9SG
e-mail: sharonlev@blueyonder.co.uk   Tel: 020-7485 2057

LINDSAY-STEWART Karen
(CDG Member)
PO Box 2301, London W1A 1PT
Fax: 020-7439 0548   Tel: 020-7439 0544

LIP SERVICE CASTING Ltd
Contact: By Post
Accepts Voicereels
Voice overs only
60-66 Wardour Street, London W1F 0TA
Website: www.lipservice.co.uk
e-mail: bookings@lipservice.co.uk
Fax: 020-7734 3373   Tel: 020-7734 3393

LUNN Maggie
(CDG Member)
Unit HG14, Aberdeen Centre
22-24 Highbury Grove, London N5 2EA
e-mail: maggie@maggielunn.co.uk   Tel: 020-7226 7502

MAGSON Kay
(CDG Member)
Contact: By email. Theatre
PO Box 175, Pudsey, Leeds LS28 7WY
e-mail: kay.magson@btinternet.com   Tel: 0113-236 0251

MANN Andrew
26-34 Emerald Street
London WC1N 3QA
Website: www.castinguk.com
e-mail: drew@castinguk.com   Tel: 020-7400 1251

MANNING John
4 Holmbury Gardens, Hayes
Middlesex UB3 2LU   Tel: 020-8573 5463

MARCH Heather CASTING
Contact: By email
Commercials. Idents. Photographic. Pop Promos
The Aberdeen Centre
22-24 Highbury Grove, London N5 2EA
Website: www.heathermarchcasting.com
e-mail: hello@heathermarchcasting.com
Fax: 020-7704 6085   Tel: 020-7704 6464

McCANN Joan
(CDG Member)
26 Hereford Road, London W3 9JW
Fax: 020-8992 8715   Tel: 020-8993 1747

McLEOD Carolyn
Contact: By email
Commercials. Film. Television
PO Box 26495, London SE10 0WO
Website: www.cmcasting.co.uk
e-mail: info@cmcasting.co.uk   Tel/Fax: 07044 001720

McLEOD Thea
e-mail: mcleodcasting@hotmail.com
Mobile: 07941 541314   Tel: 020-8888 8993

McMURRICH Chrissie
Contact: By Post
Accepts Showreels
16 Spring Vale Avenue, Brentford
Middlesex TW8 9QH   Tel: 020-8568 0137

McSHANE Sooki
(CDG Member)
8A Piermont Road, East Dulwich
London SE22 0LN   Tel: 020-8693 7411

McWILLIAMS Debbie
e-mail: debbiemcwilliams@hotmail.com
   Mobile: 07785 575805

MEULENBERG Thea
Keizersgracht 116, 1015 CW
Amsterdam, The Netherlands
Website: www.theameulenberg.com
e-mail: info@theameulenberg.com
Fax: 00 31 20 622 9894   Tel: 00 31 20 626 5846

MILLER Hannah
(CDG Member)
(See ROYAL SHAKESPEARE COMPANY)

MOISELLE Frank
7 Corrig Avenue, Dun Laoghaire, Co. Dublin, Ireland
Fax: 00 353 1 2803277   Tel: 00 353 1 2802857

MOISELLE Nuala
7 Corrig Avenue, Dun Laoghaire, Co. Dublin, Ireland
Fax: 00 353 1 2803277   Tel: 00 353 1 2802857

MOORE Stephen
BBC DRAMA SERIES CASTING
BBC Elstree, Room N222
Neptune House, Clarendon Road
Borehamwood, Herts WD6 1JF
Fax: 020-8228 8311   Tel: 020-8228 7109

MORGAN Andy CASTING
Coach House, 114 Palace Road, London SW2 3JZ
e-mail: andymorgancasting@btinternet.com
   Tel: 020-8674 5375

MORRISON Melika
Contact: By Post.
Accepts Showreels.
Film. Radio. Television
12A Rosebank, Holyport Road
London SW6 6LG   Tel/Fax: 020-7381 1571

MUGSHOTS
Contact: Becky Kidd
153 Buckhurst Avenue
Carshalton, Surrey SM5 1PD
e-mail: becky@mugshots.co.uk
Fax: 020-8296 8056   Tel: 020-8296 0393

NATIONAL THEATRE CASTING DEPARTMENT
Contact: Wendy Spon, Head of Casting (CDG Member).
Deputy Head of Casting, Alastair Coomer. Casting Assistant,
Juliet Horsley)
Contact: By Post
Upper Ground, South Bank, London SE1 9PX
Website: www.nationaltheatre.org.uk
Fax: 020-7452 3340   Tel: 020-7452 3336

NEEDLEMAN Sue
19 Stanhope Gardens, London NW7 2JD
Fax: 020-8959 0225   Tel: 020-8959 1550

NORCLIFFE Belinda
Contact: Belinda Norcliffe, Matt Selby
23 Brougham Road, London W3 6JD
e-mail: belinda@bncasting.co.uk
Fax: 020-8992 5533   Tel: 020-8992 1333

O'BRIEN Debbie
72 High Street, Ashwell, Nr Baldock, Herts SG7 5NS
Fax: 01462 743110   Tel: 01462 742919

O'CONNOR Orla
The Out of The Blue Drill Hall
36 Dalmeny Street, Edinburgh EH6 8RG
e-mail: orlaoconnor@live.co.uk   Tel: 0131-553 0559

O'DONNELL Rory
178A Adelaide Avenue, London SE4 1JN
e-mail: rory@acting4camera.com
Fax: 020-8690 8005   Mobile: 07940 073165

ORANGE James CASTING
PO Box 51130, London SE13 7ZW
e-mail: casting@jamesorange.com
Fax: 020-8711 6942   Tel: 020-8297 0524

PALMER Helena CASTING
Contact: By email
Accepts Showreels
Film. Stage. Television
e-mail: helenamppalmer@hotmail.co.uk
   Mobile: 07779 220394

PARRISS Susie CASTING
(CDG Member)
PO Box 40, Morden SM4 4WJ
Fax: 020-8543 3327   Tel: 020-8543 3326

PERRYMENT Mandy CASTING
e-mail: mail@mandyperryment.com   Mobile: 07790 605191

PETTS Tree CASTING
125 Hendon Way, London NW2 2NA
e-mail: casting@treepetts.co.uk   Tel: 020-8458 8898

PLANTIN Kate
4 Riverside, Lower Hampton Road
Sunbury on Thames TW16 5PW
e-mail: kateplantin@hotmail.com
Fax: 01932 783235   Tel: 01932 782350

POLENTARUTTI Tania CASTING
(CDG Member)
Top Floor, 37 Berwick Street, London W1F 8RS
Fax: 020-7734 3549   Tel: 020-7734 1819

POOLE Gilly
(CDG Member) (See CROWLEY POOLE CASTING)

PROCTOR Carl
(CDG Member)
3rd Floor, 76 Neal Street
Covent Garden, London WC2H 9PL
Website: www.carlproctor.com
e-mail: carlproctor@btconnect.com
Mobile: 07956 283340   Tel: 020-7379 6200

PRYOR Andy
(CDG Member)
Suite 3, 15 Broad Court, London WC2B 5QN
Fax: 020-7836 8299   Tel: 020-7836 8298

RAFTERY Francesca CASTING
51 Purley Vale, Purley, Surrey CR8 2DU
Website: www.francescaraftery.com
e-mail: info@francescaraftery.com   Tel/Fax: 020-8763 0105

REICH Liora
25 Manor Park Road, London N2 0SN   Tel: 020-8444 1686

REYNOLDS Gillian CASTING
25 St Kevin's Parade, Dublin 8, Ireland
Website: www.gillianreynoldscasting.com
Tel: 00 353 1 4546309

REYNOLDS Simone
(CDG Member)
60 Hebdon Road, London SW17 7NN   Tel: 020-8672 5443

RHODES JAMES Kate
(CDG Member)
Suite 6, 135 High Street, Teddington TW11 8HH
e-mail: office@krjcasting.com
Fax: 020-8977 2624   Tel: 020-8977 1191

RIPLEY Jane
e-mail: jane@janeripleycasting.co.uk   Tel: 020-8342 8216

ROBERTSON Sasha CASTING Ltd
Contact: Sasha Robertson (CDG Member)
Associate, Maddy Hinton
19 Wendell Road, London W12 9RS
e-mail: casting@sasharobertson.com
Fax: 020-8740 1396   Tel: 020-8740 0817

ROFFE Danielle
(CDG Member)
71 Mornington Street, London NW1 7QE   Tel: 020-7388 1898

ROWAN Amy CASTING
PO Box 10247, Blackrock, Co. Dublin, Ireland
Fax: 00 353 1 2802005   Tel: 00 353 1 2140514

ROYAL SHAKESPEARE COMPANY
Contact: Hannah Miller, Head of Casting (CDG Member),
Helena Palmer, Janine Snape (CDG Member), Jim Arnold
Casting Department
1 Earlham Street, London WC2H 9LL
Website: www.rsc.org.uk
Fax: 020-7845 0505   Tel: 020-7845 0500

SALBERG Jane
86 Stade Street, Hythe, Kent CT21 6DY
e-mail: janesalberg@aol.com
Mobile: 07931 932103   Tel: 01303 239277

SCHILLER Ginny
(CDG Member)
180A Graham Road, London E8 1BS
e-mail: ginny.schiller@virgin.net
Fax: 020-8525 1049   Tel: 020-8525 1637

SCHOFIELD Gilly
(CDG Member) G S CASTING Ltd
e-mail: gillyschofield1@btinternet.com

SCOTT Laura
(CDG Member)
56 Rowena Crescent, London SW11 2PT
Website: www.thecdg.co.uk
e-mail: laurascottcasting@mac.com
Fax: 020-7924 1907   Tel: 020-7978 6336

SEARCHERS The
70 Sylvia Court, Cavendish Street, London N1 7PG
e-mail: waynesearcher@mac.com
Fax: 020-7684 5763   Mobile: 07958 922829

SEECOOMAR Nadira
PO Box 167, Twickenham TW1 2UP
Fax: 020-8744 1274   Tel: 020-8892 8478

SHAW David
(See KEOGH Beverley CASTING Ltd)

SHAW Phil
Suite 476, 2 Old Brompton Road
South Kensington, London SW7 3DQ
e-mail: shawcastlond@aol.com   Tel: 020-8715 8943

SHEPHERD Debbie CASTING
Suite 16, 63 St Martin's Lane, London WC2N 4JS
e-mail: debbie@debbieshepherd.com
Fax: 020-7240 4640   Tel: 020-7240 0400

SID PRODUCTIONS
110 Sandringham Flats
Charing Cross Road, London WC2H 0BP
Website: www.sidproductions.co.uk
e-mail: casting@sidproductions.co.uk   Tel: 01932 863194

SIMPSON Georgia
The Gate House, 20 Killaire Road
Bangor, Co Down, Northern Ireland BT19 1EY
e-mail: georgia@georgiasimpson.com   Tel: 028-9147 0800

Philip Quast

Rhys Rusbatch

Emma Williams

Nick james
PHOTOGRAPHER

STUDIO &
LOCATION

www.nickjamesphotography.co.uk

07961 122030

SINGER Sandra ASSOCIATES
Contact: By email
21 Cotswold Road, Westcliff-on-Sea
Essex SS0 8AA
Website: www.sandrasinger.com
e-mail: sandrasingeruk@aol.com
Fax: 01702 339393   Tel: 01702 331616

SMITH Michelle
(CDG Member)
Contact: By Post
Accepts Showreels/Voicereels. Animation. Commercials.
Corporate. Film. Television
220 Church Lane, Stockport SK7 1PQ
Fax: 0161-439 0622   Tel: 0161-439 6825

SMITH Suzanne
(CDG Member)
33 Fitzroy Street, London W1T 6DU
e-mail: zan@dircon.co.uk
Fax: 020-7436 9690   Tel: 020-7436 9255

SNAPE Janine
(CDG Member) (See ROYAL SHAKESPEARE COMPANY)

SOLOMON Alison
Birmingham Repertory Theatre, Centenary Square
Broad Street, Birmingham B1 2EP   Tel: 0121-245 2023

STAFFORD Emma CASTING
The Royal Exchange, St Ann's Square, Manchester M2 7BR
Website: www.emmastafford.tv
e-mail: info@emmastafford.tv
Fax: 0161-833 4264   Tel: 0161-833 4263

STARK CASTING
e-mail: stark.casting@virgin.net
Mobile: 07956 150689   Tel: 020-8800 0060

STEVENS Gail CASTING
(CDG Member)
Greenhill House, 90-93 Cowcross Street, London EC1M 6BF
Fax: 020-7253 6574   Tel: 020-7253 6532

STEVENS MILLEFIORINI Danny
Via Sillaro 14, Cerveteri, Rome, Italy 00052
e-mail: dannystevens62@gmail.com   Tel: 0039 348 26 82 015

STEVENSON Sam
(CDG Member)
e-mail: sam@hancockstevenson.com

STEWART Amanda CASTING
Apartment 1, 35 Fortess Road
London NW5 1AD
Tel: 020-7485 7973

STOLL Liz
BBC DRAMA SERIES CASTING
BBC Elstree, Room N223, Neptune House
Clarendon Road, Borehamwood, Herts WD6 1JF
Fax: 020-8228 8311
Tel: 020-8228 8285

STYLE Emma
(CDG Member)
1 Overton Cottages, Kings Lane
Cookham, Maidenhead SL6 9BA
Tel: 01628 483740

SUMMERS Mark CASTING
(Formerly CASTING UNLIMITED)
137 Freston Road, London W10 6TH
Website: www.marksummers.com
e-mail: mark@marksummers.com
Fax: 020-7243 1987
Tel: 020-7229 8413

SYERS Michael
(See CASTING CONNECTION The)

SYSON GRAINGER CASTING
Contact: Lucinda Syson (CDG Member)
Elaine Grainger (CDG Member)
1st Floor, 33 Old Compton Street, London W1D 5JT
e-mail: office@lucindasysoncasting.com
Fax: 020-7287 3629
Tel: 020-7287 5327

TABAK Amanda
(CDG Member) (See CANDID CASTING)

TEECE Shirley CASTING
Contact: By email
106 North View Road, London N8 7LP
e-mail: shirlteece@btinternet.com
Tel: 020-8347 9241

TOPOLSKI Tessa
25 Clifton Hill, London NW8 0QE
Tel: 020-7328 6393

TOPPING Nicci
The Media Centre
7 Northumberland Street HD1 1RL
Website: www.toppscasting.co.uk
e-mail: info@toppscasting.co.uk
Mobile: 07802 684256
Tel: 01484 511988

TRAMONTANO Luisa
Church Studios, 50 Church Road, London NW10 9PY
Website: www.luisatcasting.co.uk
e-mail: luisa@luisatcasting.co.uk
Mobile: 07767 438787

TREVELLICK Jill
(CDG Member)
92 Priory Road, London N8 7EY
e-mail: jill@trevellick.force9.co.uk
Fax: 020-8348 7400
Tel: 020-8340 2734

TREVIS Sarah
(CDG Member)
PO Box 47170, London W6 6BA
e-mail: info@sarahtrevis.com
Fax: 020-7602 8110
Tel: 020-7602 5552

TWIST & FLIC CASTING
Contact: Penny Burrows
1A Carlton Avenue, Dulwich Village, London SE21 7DE
Website: www.sportsmodels.com
e-mail: info@sportsmodels.com
Mobile: 07973 863263
Tel: 020-8299 8800

VAN OST & MILLINGTON CASTING
Contact: Valerie Van Ost, Andrew Millington
PO Box 115, Petersfield GU31 5BB
Tel: 01730 821530

VAUGHAN Sally
(CDG Member)
Contact: By Post
Accepts Showreels
Theatre
2 Kennington Park Place
London SE11 4AS
e-mail: srrvaughan@hotmail.com
Tel: 020-7735 6539

VITAL PRODUCTIONS
e-mail: mail@vital-productions.co.uk
Fax: 0870 3850168
Tel: 0870 0421276

VOSSER Anne CASTING
(CDG Member)
PO Box 408, Aldershot GU11 9DS
e-mail: anne@vosser-casting.co.uk
Mobile: 07968 868712
Tel: 01252 404716

WEIR Fiona
(CDG Member)
c/o Twickenham Studios
St Margaret's
Twickenham TW1 2AW
Tel: 020-8607 8888

WEST June
(CDG Member)
Granada Television, Quay Street
Manchester M60 9EA
Fax: 0161-827 2853
Tel: 0161-832 7211

WESTERN Matt CASTING
150 Blythe Road, London W14 0HD
e-mail: matt@mattwestern.co.uk
Tel: 020-7602 6646

WHALE Toby
(CDG Member)
80 Shakespeare Road, London W3 6SN
Website: www.whalecasting.com
e-mail: toby@whalecasting.com
Fax: 020-8993 8096
Tel: 020-8993 2821

WICKSTEED Rose CASTING
39 Sinclair Mansions
Richmond Way, London W12 8LN
Website: www.rosewicksteed.com
e-mail: casting@rosewicksteed.com
Tel: 020-8743 0193

WILDMANHALL CASTING
Contact: Vicky Wildman, Buffy Hall
1 Child's Place, London SW5 9RX
e-mail: wildmanhall@mac.com
Tel: 020-7373 2036

WILLIS Catherine
Contact: By email
e-mail: catherine@cwcasting.co.uk
Tel: 020-7697 4482

YOUNGSTAR CASTING
Children & Teenagers only
5 Union Castle House
Canute Road SO14 3FJ
Website: www.youngstar.tv
e-mail: info@youngstar.tv
Tel: 023-8047 7717

ZIMMERMANN Jeremy CASTING
36 Marshall Street, London W1F 7EY
Fax: 020-7437 4747
Tel: 020-7478 5161

VOCALEYES
Describing the arts for blind / partially sighted people in
• Theatres • Museums • Art Galleries • Heritage Sites

VOCALEYES T: 020 7375 1043 E: enquiries@vocaleyes.co.uk W: www.vocaleyes.co.uk

ACE FEATURE FILM
(Sourcing Investors, Product Placement, Cast & Crew)
70 Milson Road, London W14 0LA
Website: www.maggiessite.multiply.com
e-mail: acemaggiecooper@yahoo.com
Mobile: 07765 927008

ACTOR'S ONE-STOP SHOP The
(Showreels for Performing Artists)
First Floor, Above The Gate Pub
Station Road, London N22 7SS
Website: www.actorsonestopshop.com
e-mail: info@actorsonestopshop.com   Tel: 020-8888 7006

AGENTFILE
(Software for Agents)
Website: www.agentfile.com
e-mail: admin@agentfile.com   Mobile: 07050 683662

AKA PRODUCTIONS
(Advertising, Design, Sales, Promotions & Marketing)
1st Floor, 115 Shaftesbury Avenue
Cambridge Circus, London WC2H 8AF
Website: www.akauk.com
e-mail: aka@akauk.com
Fax: 020-7836 8787   Tel: 020-7836 4747

ARIAS Enrique
(Subtitles, Translations & Voice Overs)
602 Finchley Road, London NW11 7RX
Website: www.nwlondon.com/eag
e-mail: enriqueag@gmail.com   Mobile: 07956 261568

ARTS VA The
Contact: Bronwyn Robertson
(Experienced PA and Admin Support)
PO Box 2911 CV37 1WU
Website: www.theartsva.com
e-mail: bronwyn@theartsva.com
Fax: 01789 552818   Tel: 01789 552559

AUDIO DESCRIPTION (THEATRE DESCRIPTION)
(West End and On Tour)
e-mail: info@theatredescription.com   Mobile: 07747 655215

BARTERCARD
Lakeside House, 1 Furzeground Way
Stockley Park, Uxbridge UB11 1BD
Website: www.bartercard.co.uk
e-mail: info@ukbartercard.com   Tel: 0845 2197100

BIG PICTURE
(Casual Work in IT Field Marketing)
13 Netherwood Road, London W14 0BL
Website: www.ebigpicture.co.uk
e-mail: info@ebigpicture.co.uk   Tel: 020-7371 4455

BLUE SKY ENTERTAINMENT
(Corporate, Open Air & Specialist Entertainment)
8 Adelaide Grove, London W12 0JJ
Website: www.blueskyentertainment.co.uk
e-mail: info@blueskyentertainment.co.uk
Mobile: 07502 245540   Tel: 020-8723 2127

BRITISH ASSOCIATION OF DRAMATHERAPISTS
Waverley
Battledown Approach
Cheltenham, Glos GL52 6RE
Website: www.badth.org.uk
e-mail: enquiries@badth.org.uk   Tel/Fax: 01242 235515

BYFORD Simon PRODUCTION MANAGEMENT SERVICES
(Production & Event Management)
22 Freshfield Place
Brighton, East Sussex BN2 0BN
e-mail: simon@simonbyfordpms.com
Fax: 01273 606402   Tel: 01273 623972

BYRNE John
(The Stage's Agony Uncle)
71 Amina Way, London SE16 3UH
Website: www.showbusiness-success.com
e-mail: dearjohn@thestage.co.uk   Tel: 020-7231 4907

CAP PRODUCTION SOLUTIONS Ltd
(Technical Production Services)
20 Merton Industrial Park
Jubilee Way, Wimbledon, London SW19 3WL
e-mail: leigh@leighporter.com
Fax: 07970 763480   Tel: 020-8544 8668

CASTLE MAGICAL SERVICES
(Magical Consultants) Contact: Michael Shepherd
Broompark, 131 Tadcaster Road
Dringhouses, York YO24 1QJ
e-mail: info@castlemagicalservices.co.uk
Tel/Fax: 01904 709500

CAULKETT Robin Dip SM, MIIRSM
(Abseiling, Rope Work)
3 Churchill Way, Mitchell Dean
Glos GL17 0AZ   Mobile: 07970 442003

CELEBRITIES WORLDWIDE Ltd
(Celebrity on-line Media Database)
39-41 New Oxford Street
London WC1A 1BN
Website: www.celebritiesworldwide.com
e-mail: info@celebritiesworldwide.com
Fax: 020-7836 7701   Tel: 020-7836 7702

CHAPERONE AGENCY The
Website: www.chaperoneagency.com Mobile: 07960 075928

CIRCUS MANIACS
(Circus, Theatre, Dance, Choreography, Extreme Sports)
Office 8A
The Kingswood Foundation, Britannia Road
Kingswood, Bristol BS15 8DB
Website: www.circusmaniacsagency.com
e-mail: agency@circusmaniacs.com
Mobile: 07977 247287   Tel/Fax: 0117-947 7042

CLASS - CARLINE LUNDON ASSOCIATES
25 Falkner Square, Liverpool L8 7NZ
e-mail: carline.lundon@ukonline.co.uk
Mobile: 07853 248957

COBO MEDIA Ltd
(Performing Arts, Entertainment & Leisure Marketing)
43A Garthorne Road, London SE23 1EP
Website: www.cobomedia.com
e-mail: admin@cobomedia.com
Fax: 020-8291 4969   Tel: 020-8291 7079

COLCLOUGH John
(Practical Independent Guidance for Actors and Actresses)
Website: www.johncolclough.co.uk
e-mail: john@johncolclough.org.uk   Tel: 020-8873 1763

CREATIVE INDUSTRIES DEVELOPMENT AGENCY (CIDA)
(Professional Development & Business Support for Artists
& Creative Businesses)
Media Centre, Huddersfield, West Yorkshire HD1 1RL
Website: www.cida.org
e-mail: info@cida.org
Fax: 01484 483150   Tel: 01484 483140

CROFTS Andrew
(Book Writing Services)
Westlands Grange, West Grinstead
Horsham, West Sussex RH13 8LZ
Website: www.andrewcrofts.com   Tel/Fax: 01403 864518

DYNAMIC FX Ltd
(Entertainers and Magic Consultants)
Regent House, 291 Kirkdale, London SE26 4QD
e-mail: mail@dynamicfx.co.uk
Fax: 0845 0062443   Tel: 0845 0062442

EARLE Kenneth PERSONAL MANAGEMENT
214 Brixton Road, London SW9 6AP
e-mail: kennethearle@agents-uk.com
Fax: 020-7274 9529   Tel: 020-7274 1219

EQUIP
11 Balmoral Road, Gidea Park
Romford, Essex RM2 5XD
Website: www.equip-u.com
e-mail: sales@equip-u.com   Tel: 01708 479898

FACADE
(Creation & Production of Musicals)
43A Garthorne Road, London SE23 1EP
e-mail: facade@cobomedia.com   Tel: 020-8291 7079

FERRIS ENTERTAINMENT MUSIC
(Music for Film & Television)
Number 8, 132 Charing Cross Road, London WC2H 0LA
Website: www.ferrisentertainment.com
e-mail: info@ferrisentertainment.com   Mobile: 07801 493133

FLAMES MARTIAL ARTS ACADEMY
Contact: Adam Richards
Unit 2, 128 Milton Road Business Park
Gravesend, Kent DA12 2PG
Website: www.kuentao.com
e-mail: arstunts@yahoo.co.uk   Mobile: 07950 396389

FULL EFFECT The
(Live Event Producers including Choreographers)
Exchange Building
16 St Cuthbert's Street, Bedford MK40 3JG
Website: www.thefulleffect.co.uk
e-mail: mark.harrison@tfe.co.uk
Fax: 01234 214445   Tel: 01234 269099

GHOSTWRITER/AUTHOR
Contact: John Parker
21 Hindsleys Place, London SE23 2NF
e-mail: parkerwrite@aol.com   Tel: 020-8244 5816

GILMOUR Rev/Prof/Dr Glenn, MscD, SHsc.D, NFH, BCMA.Reg
(Fully Qualified/International Medium. Clairvoyant, Healer &
Holistic Therapist. Consultant Paranormal/Metaphysics/
Occult for Radio/TV)
Website: www.drglenngilmour.com
e-mail: drglenngilmour@yahoo.com   Tel: 0114-234 7726

GOLDIELLE PROMOTIONS
(Events)
68 Lynton Drive, Hillside
Southport, Merseyside PR8 4QQ
Website: www.goldiellepromotions.com
e-mail: goldielle@yahoo.co.uk   Tel: 01704 566604

HANDS UP PUPPETS
c/o Peter Charlesworth & Associates
68 Old Brompton Road, London SW7 3LD
Website: www.handsuppuppets.com
e-mail: enquiries@handsuppuppets.com   Tel: 020-7581 2478

HARLEY PRODUCTIONS
68 New Cavendish Street, London W1G 8TE
e-mail: harleyprods@aol.com
Fax: 020-8202 8863   Tel: 020-7580 3247

HATSTAND CIRCUS
(Specialist in Themed Performances for Events &
Promotions)
98 Milligan Street
Westferry, London E14 8AS
Website: www.hatstandcircus.co.uk
e-mail: helenahatstand@btconnect.com
Mobile: 07748 005839   Tel/Fax: 020-7538 3368

HAYES Susan
(Choreographer/Body Worker)
46 Warrington Crescent, London W9 1EP
e-mail: susan22@btinternet.com   Mobile: 07721 927714

HERITAGE RAILWAY ASSOCIATION
10 Hurdeswell, Long Hanborough
Witney, Oxfordshire OX29 8DH
Website: www.heritagerailways.com   Tel: 01993 883384

HGV THEATRICAL BRAND IDENTITY DESIGN CONSULTANTS
2-6 Northburgh Street, London EC1V 0AY
Website: www.hgv.co.uk
e-mail: pierre@hgv.co.uk
Fax: 020-7336 6345   Tel: 020-7336 6336

IMAGE DIGGERS
(Slide/Stills/Audio/Video Library & Theme Research)
618B Finchley Road, London NW11 7RR
Website: www.imagediggers.netfirms.com
e-mail: lambhorn@gmail.com   Tel: 020-8455 4564

IMPACT AGENCY The
(Public Relations)
3 Bloomsbury Place, London WC1A 2QL
e-mail: mail@impactagency.co.uk
Fax: 020-7580 7200   Tel: 020-7580 1770

I R A - INDEPENDENT REVIEWS ARTS SERVICES
(Stories from World of Film/Art/Showbiz)
12 Hemingford Close, London N12 9HF
e-mail: critic@independentradioarts.com
Mobile: 07956 212916   Tel/Fax: 020-8343 7437

JACKSON Kim
(Arts Education Consultancy)
1 Mellor Road, Leicester LE3 6HN
e-mail: jacksongillespie@hotmail.com   Tel: 0116-233 8432

JENKINS Andrew Ltd
(General Management & Accountancy)
63 Kidbrooke Park Road, London SE3 0EE
Website: www.andrewjenkinsltd.com
e-mail: info@andrewjenkinsltd.com
Fax: 020-8856 7106   Tel: 020-8319 3657

JFL SEARCH & SELECTION
(Recruitment Consultants)
27 Beak Street, London W1F 9RU
Website: www.jflrecruit.com
Fax: 020-7734 6501   Tel: 020-7009 3500

JORDAN Richard PRODUCTIONS Ltd
(General Management, UK and International Productions,
Festivals, Production Consultancy)
Mews Studios, 16 Vernon Yard, London W11 2DX
e-mail: richard.jordan@virgin.net
Fax: 020-7313 9667   Tel: 020-7243 9001

JOSHI CLINIC The
57 Wimpole Street, London W1G 8YW
Fax: 020-7486 9622   Tel: 020-7487 5456

KEAN LANYON Ltd
(Graphic Designers, PR & Marketing Consultants)
Rose Cottage, Aberdeen Centre
22 Highbury Grove, London N5 2EA
Website: www.keanlanyon.com
e-mail: iain@keanlanyon.com
Fax: 020-7359 0199   Tel: 020-7354 3362

KELLER Don
(Marketing Consultancy & Project Management)
65 Glenwood Road
Harringay, London N15 3JS
e-mail: info@dakam.org.uk
Fax: 020-8809 6825   Tel: 020-8800 4882

KIEVE Paul
(Magical Effects for Theatre & Film)
2 St. Philip's Road, London E8 3BP
Website: www.stageillusion.com
e-mail: mail@stageillusion.com   Tel/Fax: 020-7502 2213

LAMBOLLE Robert
(Script Evaluation/Editing)
618B Finchley Road, London NW11 7RR
Website: www.readingandrighting.netfirms.com
e-mail: lambhorn@gmail.com   Tel: 020-8455 4564

LEEP MARKETING & PR
(Marketing, Press and Publicity)
5 Nassau House
122 Shaftesbury Avenue, London W1D 5ER
e-mail: philip@leep.biz
Fax: 020-7439 8833   Tel: 020-7439 9777

LEO MEDIA & ENTERTAINMENT GROUP The
150 Minories, London EC3N 1LS
Website: www.leomediagroup.com
e-mail: info@leomediagroup.com
Fax: 0870 1330258   Tel: 020-8905 5191

LOCATION TUTORS NATIONWIDE
(Fully Qualified/Experienced Teachers working with
Children on Film Sets and Covering all Key Stages of
National Curriculum)
16 Poplar Walk, Herne Hill, London SE24 0BU
Website: www.locationtutors.co.uk
e-mail: locationtutorsnationwide@hotmail.com
Fax: 020-7207 8794   Tel: 020-7978 8898

LOVE Billie HISTORICAL PHOTOGRAPHS
(Picture Research. Formerly 'Amanda' Theatrical
Portraiture)
3 Winton Street, Ryde
Isle of Wight PO33 2BX
Fax: 01983 616565   Tel: 01983 812572

LUXFACTOR GROUP (UK) The
Fleet Place, 12 Nelson Drive
Petersfield, Hampshire GU31 4SJ
Website: www.luxfactor.co.uk
e-mail: info@luxfactor.co.uk
Fax: 0845 3700588   Tel: 0845 3700589

McCABE Michael
(Marketing Consultant)
2nd Floor, 23 Tavistock Street, London WC2E 7NX
Website: www.michaelmccabe.net
e-mail: mailbox@michaelmccabe.net
Fax: 020-7420 7748   Tel: 020-7420 7744

McKENNA Deborah Ltd
(Celebrity Chefs & Lifestyle Presenters)
64-66 Glentham Road, Barnes, London SW13 9PP
Website: www.deborahmckenna.com
e-mail: info@deborahmckenna.com
Fax: 020-8392 2462   Tel: 020-8876 7566

MEDIA LEGAL
(Education Services)
West End House, 83 Clarendon Road
Sevenoaks, Kent TN13 1ET   Tel: 01732 460592

MILDENBERG Vanessa
(Choreographer/Movement Director)
Flat 6, Cameford Court
New Park Road
London SW2 4LH   Mobile: 07796 264828

MILITARY ADVISORY & INSTRUCTION SPECIALISTS
(John Sessions) (Advice on Weapons, Drill, Period to
Present. Ex-Army Instructors)
38 Kempton Close, Strensall, York YO32 5ZF
e-mail: johnmusic1@hotmail.com   Tel: 01904 491198

MINISTRY OF FUN
(Provision of Performers/PR Marketing Campaigns)
Unit 1, Suffolk Studios
127-129 Great Suffolk Street, London SE1 1PP
Website: www.ministryoffun.net
e-mail: james@ministryoffun.net
Fax: 020-7407 5763   Tel: 020-7407 6077

MORGAN Jane ASSOCIATES (JMA)
(Marketing & Media)
8 Heathville Road, London N19 3AJ
e-mail: jma@janemorganassociates.com
Fax: 020-7263 9877   Tel: 020-7263 9867

MULLEN Julie
(Improvisors/Comedy Consultancy)
The Impro Lab, 34 Watts Lane
Teddington Lock TW11 8HQ   Mobile: 07956 877839

MUSIC SOLUTIONS Ltd
Garden Studios
11-15 Betterton Street, London WC2H 9BP
e-mail: mail@musicsolutions.ltd.uk   Tel: 020-7866 8160

NEATE Rodger PRODUCTION MANAGEMENT
15 Southcote Road, London N19 5BJ
e-mail: rneate@dircon.co.uk
Fax: 020-7697 8237   Tel: 020-7609 9538

NEXTSTOPLAX
(Relocation of Entertainment Industry Professionals)
Website: www.nextstoplax.com
e-mail: info@nextstoplax.com
Tel: (323) 363-9933   Tel: 020-7096 1301

NWA-UK HAMMERLOCK
(Wrestling Events, Training & Promotion)
PO Box 282
Ashford, Kent TN23 7ZZ
e-mail: nwauk@hammerlockwrestling.com
       Tel/Fax: 01233 663828

ORANGE TREE STUDIO Ltd & MUSIC SERVICES
(Original Music/Composition & Production, Saxophonist &
Brass Section For Hire)
PO Box 99, Kings Langley WD4 8FB
Website: www.orangetreestudio.com
e-mail: richard@orangetreestudio.com
Mobile: 07768 146200   Tel: 01923 440550

PB PRODUCTIVE
(Photographers' Agent. Shoot, Production & Event
Management)
2 Netherfield Road, London SW17 8AZ
Website: www.pbproductive.com
e-mail: info@pbproductive.com
Mobile: 07957 424776   Tel/Fax: 020-8767 7237

PENROSE Scott
(Magic for TV, Film & Theatre)
17 Berkeley Drive, Billericay, Essex CM12 0YP
Website: www.stagemagician.com
e-mail: mail@stagemagician.com   Mobile: 07767 336882

PINEWOOD NET
(Networking Group)
86 Hurst Farm Road, East Grinstead, West Sussex RH19 4DH
Website: www.pinewood.net
e-mail: kathy@pinewood.net   Mobile: 07882 794583

POLICE ACTION
(Police Personnel & Tactical Arms Group Inc./Riot Police
with Shields)
39 Gregson Close, Borehamwood WD6 5RW
e-mail: police-action@hotmail.co.uk
Mobile: 07899 651280   Tel: 020-8953 0166

PRODUCTIONS & PROMOTIONS Ltd
Apsley Mills Cottage
London Road, Hemel Hempstead, Herts HP3 9QU
Website: www.prodmotions.com
e-mail: reception@prodmotions.com   Tel: 01442 233372

PSYCHOLOGY GROUP The
(Expert Opinion, Assessments, Psychotherapy &
Counselling, Presentation. Nationwide Service)
Website: www.psychologygroup.co.uk
e-mail: info@psychologygroup.co.uk
Fax: 0845 2805243   Tel: 0870 6092445

PUPPET CENTRE TRUST
(Development & Advocacy Agency for Puppetry & Related
Theatre)
BAC Lavender Hill, London SW11 5TN
Website: www.puppetcentre.org.uk
e-mail: pct@puppetcentre.org.uk   Tel: 020-7228 5335

RICHARDS Adam
(Fight Director)
Unit 2, 128 Milton Road Business Park
Gravesend, Kent DA12 2PG
Website: www.kuentao.com   Mobile: 07950 396389

RIPLEY-DUGGAN PARTNERSHIP The
(Tour Booking)
26 Goodge Street, London W1T 2QG
e-mail: info@ripleyduggan.com   Tel: 020-7436 1392

SHAW Bernard
(Specialist in Recording & Directing Voice Tapes)
Horton Manor, Canterbury CT4 7LG
Website: www.bernardshaw.co.uk
e-mail: bernard@bernardshaw.co.uk   Tel/Fax: 01227 730843

SHAW Jennifer EVENTS
(Event Management & Promotions)
15 Ladyhouse Lane, Milnrow OL16 4EH
Website: www.jennifershawevents.co.uk
e-mail: jennifer@jennifershawevents.co.uk
       Tel: 0845 1309517

SHOWBIZ FRIENDS
(Community website for all showbiz people)
Website: www.showbizfriends.com

SINCLAIR Andy
(Mime)
7B Hart Grove, Ealing, London W5 3NA
Website: www.andyjsinclair.co.uk
e-mail: andynebular@hotmail.com   Mobile: 07831 196675

SPENCER Ivor
(Professional Toastmaster, Events Organiser & Principal of
Ivor Spencer International School for Butlers)
12 Little Bornes, Dulwich, London SE21 8SE
Website: www.ivorspencer.com
Fax: 020-8670 0055   Tel: 020-8670 5585

SPORTS PROMOTIONS Ltd
(Production Advisors, Sport, Stunts, Safety)
PO Box 878
Crystal Palace National Sports Centre
London SE19 2BH
e-mail: agent@sportspromotions.co.uk
Fax: 020-8776 7772   Tel: 020-8659 4561

STAGE CRICKET CLUB
(Cricketers & Cricket Grounds)
39-41 Hanover Steps
St George's Fields
Albion Street, London W2 2YG
Website: www.stagecc.co.uk
e-mail: brianjfilm@aol.com
Fax: 020-7262 5736
Tel: 020-7402 7543

STUDIO BOARDMAN Ltd
(Events Organisers)
143 Talgarth Road
Barons Court, London W14 9DA
Website: www.studioboardman.com
e-mail: hq@studioboardman.com
Fax: 020-8741 3171
Tel: 0845 2581111

STUNT ACTION SPECIALISTS (S.A.S.)
(Corporate & TV Stunt Work)
110 Trafalgar Road
Portslade
East Sussex BN41 1GS
Website: www.stuntactionspecialists.com
e-mail: wayne@stuntactionspecialists.co.uk
Fax: 01273 708699
Tel: 01273 230214

THEATRE PROJECTS CONSULTANTS
4 Apollo Studios
Charlton Kings Road
London NW5 2SW
Website: www.tpcworld.com
e-mail: post@tpcworld.net
Fax: 020-7284 0636
Tel: 020-7482 4224

TIGERLILIES
(Promotions & Events)
66 Cambie Crescent
Colchester, Essex CO4 5DW
Website: www.tigerliliesevents.piczo.com
e-mail: tigerlilies.info@yahoo.co.uk   Mobile: 07985 763518

TODD Carole
(Director/Choreographer)
c/o Chris Davis Management Ltd, Tenbury House
36 Teme Street
Tenbury Wells, Worcs WR15 8AA
e-mail: cdavis@cdm-ltd.com
Fax: 01584 819076
Tel: 01584 819005

UK THEATRE AVAILABILITY
(Bookings Service for Theatre Producers)
1 Hogarth Hill
London NW11 6AY
Website: www.uktheatreavailability.co.uk
e-mail: info@uktheatreavailability.co.uk
Tel: 020-8455 3278

UNITED KINGDOM COPYRIGHT BUREAU
(Script Services)
110 Trafalgar Road
Portslade
East Sussex BN41 1GS
Website: www.copyrightbureau.co.uk
e-mail: info@copyrightbureau.co.uk
Fax: 01273 705451
Tel: 01273 277333

UPFRONT TELEVISION Ltd
(Celebrity Booking for Events)
39-41 New Oxford Street, London WC1A 1BN
Website: www.celebritiesworldwide.com
e-mail: info@upfronttv.com
Fax: 020-7836 7701
Tel: 020-7836 7702

VERNON Doremy
(Author 'Tiller Girls'/Archivist/Dance Routines
Tiller Girl Style)
16 Ouseley Road
London SW12 8EF
Tel/Fax: 020-8767 6944

VOCALEYES
(Audio Description "Describing The Arts")
1st Floor, 54 Commercial Street, London E1 0LT
Website: www.vocaleyes.co.uk
e-mail: enquiries@vocaleyes.co.uk
Tel: 020-7375 1043

WELBOURNE Jacqueline
(Circus Trainer, Choreographer, Consultant)
c/o Circus Maniacs Agency
Office 8A, The Kingswood Foundation
Britannia Road
Kingswood, Bristol BS15 8DB
e-mail: jackie@circusmaniacs.com
Mobile: 07977 247287
Tel/Fax: 0117-947 7042

WEST END WORKSHOPS
(Audition Coaching/Arts Workshops)
Website: www.westendworkshops.co.uk
e-mail: info@westendworkshops.co.uk
Mobile: 07989 422808

WHITE Leonard
(Production & Script Consultant)
Highlands
40 Hill Crest Road, Newhaven, Brighton
East Sussex BN9 9EG
e-mail: leoguy.white@virgin.net
Tel: 01273 514473

WILD DREAM CONSULTANCY
(Audition Skills, Public Speaking, Confidence & Personal
Development)
Tel: 020-8374 3924

WILKINSON Gavin
(Choreographer/Director/Arts Consultant)
Website: www.westendworkshops.co.uk
e-mail: info@westendworkshops.co.uk
Mobile: 07989 422808

WISE MONKEY FINANCIAL COACHING
(Simonne Gnessen)
14 Eastern Terrace Mews
Brighton BN2 1EP
Website: www.financial-coaching.co.uk
e-mail: simonne@financial-coaching.co.uk
Tel: 01273 691223

WWW.EYENNCEE.COM
(Networking Site)
Website: www.eyenncee.com
e-mail: chris@internationalcollective.com

YOUNGBLOOD Ltd
(Fight Direction)
Website: www.youngblood.co.uk
e-mail: info@youngblood.co.uk
Tel: 020-7193 3207

Buxton Xmas '07

Rosemarie Swinfield
m a k e - u p   d e s i g n e r

Rosie's Make-up Box
6 Brewer Street Soho London W1R 3FS
m: 07976-965520
e: rosemarie@rosiesmake-up.co.uk
www.rosiesmake-up.co.uk

Author of:
* Stage Make-Up Step By Step
* Period Make-Up For The Stage
* Hair And Wigs For The Stage

Also
Courses, Workshops & Seminars

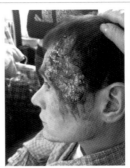

Royal Court '08

ACADEMY COSTUMES
50 Rushworth Street, London SE1 0RB
Website: www.academycostumes.com
e-mail: info@academycostumes.com
Fax: 020-7928 6287   Tel: 020-7620 0771

AJ COSTUMES Ltd
(Theatrical Costume Hire, Design & Making)
Sullom Lodge, Sullom Side Lane
Barnacre, Garstang PR3 1GH
Website: www.trendsgroup.co.uk
e-mail: info@trendsgroup.co.uk
Fax: 01253 407715   Tel: 0871 2003343

ALL-SEWN-UP
Mechanics Institute, 7 Church Street, Heptonstall
West Yorks HX7 7NS
Website: www.allsewnup.org.uk
e-mail: nwheeler_allsewnup@hotmail.com
Fax: 01422 845070   Tel: 01422 843407

ANELLO & DAVIDE
(Handmade Shoes)
15 St Albans Grove, London W8 5BP   Tel: 020-7938 2255

ANGELS
(Fancy Dress & Revue)
119 Shaftesbury Avenue, London WC2H 8AE
Website: www.fancydress.com
e-mail: party@fancydress.com
Fax: 020-7240 9527   Tel: 020-7836 5678

ANGELS THE COSTUMIERS
1 Garrick Road, London NW9 6AA
Website: www.angels.uk.com
e-mail: angels@angels.uk.com
Fax: 020-8202 1820   Tel: 020-8202 2244

ANGELS WIGS
(Wig Hire/Makers, Facial Hair Suppliers)
1 Garrick Road, London NW9 6AA
Website: www.angels.uk.com
e-mail: wigs@angels.uk.com
Fax: 020-8202 1820   Tel: 020-8202 2244

ANTOINETTE COSTUME HIRE
(Stage, Screen and Fancy Dress)
High Street Buildings, 134 Kirkdale, London SE26 4BB
Website: www.costumehirelondon.com
e-mail: antoinettehire@aol.com
Fax: 020-8699 1107   Tel: 020-8699 1913

ARMS & ARCHERY
(Armour, Weaponry, Chainmail, Warrior Costumes, Medieval
Tents, Banners)
Thrift Lane, off London Road, Ware, Herts SG12 9QS
e-mail: armsandarchery@btconnect.com
                                           Tel: 01920 460335

ATTLE Jamie COSTUME MAKER
4 Toynbee Road, Wimbledon, London SW20 8SS
e-mail: aalexiscolby@aol.com   Tel/Fax: 020-8540 3044

BAHADLY R
(Hair & Make-up Specialist, incl. Bald Caps,
Ageing & Casualty)
47 Ploughmans Way, Macclesfield, Cheshire SK10 2UN
Mobile: 07973 553073   Tel: 01625 615878

BEJEWELLED COSTUME JEWELLERY
23 Glenrise Close, St Mellons, Cardiff CF3 0AS
Website: www.bejewelledonline.com
e-mail: enquiries@bejewelledonline.com   Tel: 0845 3131081

BERTRAND Henry
(London Stockhouse for Silk)
52 Holmes Road, London NW5 3AB
Website: www.henrybertrand.co.uk
e-mail: sales@henrybertrand.co.uk
Fax: 020-7424 7001   Tel: 020-7424 7000

BIRMINGHAM COSTUME HIRE
Suites 209-210, Jubilee Centre
130 Pershore Street, Birmingham B5 6ND
e-mail: info@birminghamcostumehire.co.uk
Fax: 0121-622 2758   Tel: 0121-622 3158

BISHOP Kerry
(Hair & Make-up Artist)
Flat 4, 49 Upper Rock Gardens, Brighton, E Sussex BN2 1QF
e-mail: kerrybishop@email.com   Mobile: 07759 704394

BRIGGS Ron DESIGN
(Costume Making, Costume Design)
1 Bedford Mews, London N2 9DF
e-mail: costumes@ronbriggs.com   Tel: 020-8444 8801

BURLINGTONS
(Hairdressers)
14 John Princes Street, London W1G 0JS
Website: www.burlingtonsuk.com
Tel: 0870 8701299

CALICO FABRICS
(Suppliers of Unbleached Calico & other Fabrics for Stage,
Costumes, Backdrops etc)
3 Ram Passage, High Street
Kingston-upon-Thames, Surrey KT1 1HH
Website: www.calicofabrics.co.uk
e-mail: sales@calicofabrics.co.uk
Fax: 020-8546 7755
Tel: 020-8541 5274

CAPEZIO
(Dance Products)
95 Whiffler Road, Norwich, Norfolk NR3 2AW
Website: www.capezio.com
e-mail: eusales@balletmakers.com
Fax: 0870 3500074
Tel: 0870 3500073

CHRISANNE Ltd
(Specialist Fabrics & Accessories)
Chrisanne House, 14 Locks Lane, Mitcham, Surrey CR4 2JX
Website: www.chrisanne.com
e-mail: sales@chrisanne.co.uk
Fax: 020-8640 2106
Tel: 020-8640 5921

COLTMAN Mike
(See COSTUME CONSTRUCTION)

COOK Sheila TEXTILES
(Vintage Textiles, Costumes & Accessories for Sale)
(By Appointment)
105-107 Portobello Road, London W11 2QB
Website: www.sheilacook.co.uk
e-mail: sheilacook@sheilacook.co.uk
Tel: 020-7792 8001

COSPROP Ltd
(Costumes & Accessories)
469-475 Holloway Road, London N7 6LE
Website: www.cosprop.com
e-mail: enquiries@cosprop.com
Fax: 020-7561 7310
Tel: 020-7561 7300

COSTUME CONSTRUCTION
(Costumes, Masks, Props, Puppets)
Studio 1, Croft Street, Cheltenham GL53 0EE
Website: www.costumeconstruction.co.uk
Tel/Fax: 01242 581847

COSTUME CREATIONS
10 Olinthus Avenue, Wolverhampton WV11 3DE
e-mail: yourcostume@googlemail.com
Tel: 01902 738282

COSTUME GUIDE The
(Products & Suppliers Directory)
PO Box 54229, London W14 0SE
e-mail: tp@tessap.plus.com
Tel: 020-7602 2857

COSTUME SOLUTIONS
43 Rowan Road, London W6 7DT
Website: www.costumesolutions.co.uk
e-mail: karen@costumesolutions.co.uk
Tel: 020-7603 9035

COSTUME STORE Ltd The
(Costume Accessories)
16 Station Street, Lewes, East Sussex BN7 2DB
Website: www.thecostumestore.co.uk
e-mail: enquiries@thecostumestore.co.uk
Fax: 01273 477191
Tel: 01273 479727

COSTUME STUDIO Ltd
(Costumes & Wigs)
Montgomery House, 159-161 Balls Pond Road, London N1 4BG
Website: www.costumestudio.co.uk
e-mail: costume.studio@btconnect.com
Tel/Fax: 020-7923 9065
Tel: 020-7275 9614

COSTUMIA
Unit 9, Hockley Goods Yard
Pitsford Street, Hockley, Birmingham B18 6PT
Website: www.costumia.co.uk
e-mail: info@costumia.co.uk   Tel: 0121-551 2710

COUNTY DRAMA WARDROBE
(Costumes & Wigs - Hire only & Make-up for Sale)
25 Gwydir Street, Cambridge CB1 2LG   Tel: 01223 313423

COUTURE BEADING & EMBELLISHMENT
6 Milton Road, London E17 4SR
e-mail: dianavernon@mac.com   Tel: 020-8677 0810

CRAZY CLOTHES CONNECTION
(1920's-1970's for Sale or Hire)
134 Lancaster Road
Ladbroke Grove, London W11 1QU
Website: www.crazy-clothes.co.uk
e-mail: info@crazy-clothes.co.uk   Tel: 020-7221 3989

DANCIA INTERNATIONAL
168 Drury Lane, London WC2B 5QA
Website: www.dancia.co.uk
e-mail: dancialondon@btconnect.com
     Tel/Fax: 020-7831 9483

DAVIES Bryan Philip COSTUMES
(Lavish Pantomime, Musical Shows, Opera)
68 Court Road, Lewes, East Sussex BN7 2SA
Website: www.bpdcostumes.co.uk
e-mail: bryan@bpdcostumes.force9.co.uk
Mobile: 07931 249097   Tel: 01273 481004

DELAMAR ACADEMY
(Make-up Training)
Ealing Studios, Building D
2nd Floor, Ealing Green, London W5 5EP
Website: www.delamaracademy.co.uk
e-mail: info@delamaracademy.co.uk   Tel/Fax: 020-8579 9511

DESIGNER ALTERATIONS
(Restyling & Remodelling of Clothes & Costumes)
220A Queenstown Road, Battersea, London SW8 4LP
Website: www.designeralterations.com
e-mail: info@designalterations.com
Fax: 020-7622 4148   Tel: 020-7498 4360

EASTON Derek
(Wigs For Theatre, Film & TV)
1 Dorothy Avenue, Peacehaven, East Sussex BN10 8LP
Website: www.derekeastonwigs.co.uk
e-mail: wigs@derekeastonwigs.co.uk
Mobile: 07768 166733   Tel/Fax: 01273 588262

EVOLUTION SETS & COSTUMES Ltd
(Costume Hire)
Langdon Abbey, West Langdon, Dover, Kent CT15 5HJ
e-mail: sylviasims@btconnect.com
Fax: 01304 853506   Tel: 01304 853539

FOX Charles H. Ltd
(Professional Make-up & Wigs)
22 Tavistock Street, London WC2E 7PY
Website: www.charlesfox.co.uk
e-mail: makeup@charlesfox.co.uk
Fax: 0870 2001369   Tel: 0870 2000369

FREED OF LONDON
(Dancewear & Dance Shoes)
94 St Martin's Lane, London WC2N 4AT
Website: www.freedoflondon.com
e-mail: shop@freed.co.uk
Fax: 020-7240 3061   Tel: 020-7240 0432

FUNN Ltd
(Silk, Cotton Wool Stockings, Opaque Opera Tights & 40's
Rayon Stockings)
PO Box 102, Steyning, West Sussex BN44 3EB
e-mail: funn.biz@lycos.com
Fax: 0870 1361780   Tel: 0870 8794430

GAMBA THEATRICAL
(See THEATRICAL FOOTWEAR COMPANY Ltd The)

GAV NICOLA THEATRICAL FOOTWEAR
West Wick, Marshes, Burnham-on-Crouch, Essex CM0 8NE
e-mail: sale@gavnicola.freeserve.co.uk
Mobile: 07961 974278   Tel/Fax: 01621 785623

GILLHAM Felicite
(Wig Makers for Theatre, Opera & Film)
Trendle Cottage, Trendle Street
Sherborne, Dorset DT9 3NT
e-mail: f.gillham.wigs@gmx.net
Mobile: 07802 955908   Tel: 01935 814328

GREASEPAINT
143 Northfield Avenue, Ealing, London W13 9QT
Website: www.greasepaint.co.uk
e-mail: info@greasepaint.co.uk
Fax: 020-8840 3983   Tel: 020-8840 6000

GROVE Sue DESIGNS
(Costume Makers)
12 Ampthill Road, Shirley
Southampton, Hants SO15 8LP
e-mail: sue.grove1@tiscali.co.uk   Tel: 023-8078 6849

HAIRAISERS
(Wigs)
9-11 Sunbeam Road, Park Royal, London NW10 6JP
Website: www.hairaisers.com
e-mail: info@hairaisers.com
Fax: 020-8963 1600   Tel: 020-8965 2500

HAND & LOCK
86 Margaret Street, London W1W 8TE
Website: www.hand-embroidery.co.uk
e-mail: enquiries@hand-embroidery.co.uk
Fax: 020-7580 7499   Tel: 020-7580 7488

HARVEYS OF HOVE
(Theatrical Costumes & Military Specialists)
110 Trafalgar Road, Portslade, Sussex BN41 1GS
Website: www.harveysofhove.co.uk
e-mail: harveys.costume@ntlworld.com
Fax: 01273 708699   Tel: 01273 430323

HENRY Lewis Ltd
(Dress Makers)
111-113 Great Portland Street
London W1W 6QQ   Tel: 020-7636 6683

HERALD & HEART Ltd
(Men's & Women's Hats & Headdresses - Period & Modern)
102 High Street, Rye, East Sussex TN31 7JN
Website: www.heraldandheart.com
e-mail: heraldandheart2@mac.com   Tel: 01797 225261

HIREARCHY
(Classic & Contemporary Costume)
45-47 Palmerston Road, Boscombe
Bournemouth, Dorset BH1 4HW
Website: www.hirearchy.co.uk
e-mail: hirearchy1@aol.com   Tel: 01202 394465

HODIN Annabel
(Costume Designer/Stylist)
12 Eton Avenue, London NW3 3EH
e-mail: annabelhodin@aol.com
Mobile: 07836 754079   Tel: 020-7431 8761

INCE Katie
(Wig Maker & Make-up Artist)
15 Birchwood Gardens
Idle Park, Bradford BD10 9EW
e-mail: katieince@gmail.com   Tel: 07900 250853

INTERNATIONAL COLLECTIVE (CREATIVE)
Golden Cross House
8 Duncannon Street, The Strand, London WC2N 4JF
Website: www.inccreative.co.uk
e-mail: enquiries@internationalcollective.co.uk
Fax: 020-7484 5100   Tel: 020-7484 5080

INTERNATIONAL DANCE SUPPLIES/GRISHKO UK Ltd
(Importer & Distributor of Dance Shoes and Dancewear)
64 Butt Lane, Milton, Cambridge CB24 6DG
Website: www.grishko.co.uk
e-mail: info@grishko.co.uk
Fax: 01223 280388   Tel: 01223 861425

JULIE MAY'S BOUTIQUE
90 Anson Chase
Shoeburyness, Essex SS3 9RG
Website: www.julie-may.com/boutique.com
e-mail: juliemay@julie-may.com   Tel: 01702 290828

JULIETTE DESIGNS
(Diamante Jewellery Manufacturers)
90 Yerbury Road
London N19 4RS
Website: www.stagejewellery.com
Fax: 020-7281 7326   Tel: 020-7263 7878

KIDD Ella J.
(Bespoke Millinery, Wigs & Head-dresses for
Theatre, Film & TV)
Website: www.ellajkidd.co.uk   Tel: 020-8539 2786

LANDSFIELD Warren
(Period Legal Wigs)
47 Glenmore Road, London NW3 4DA   Tel: 020-7722 4581

LARGER THAN LIFE STAGEWEAR
(Theatrical Costumes for Hire)
2 Sundridge Parade, Bromley, Kent BR1 4DY
Website: www.largerthanlifestagewear.co.uk
e-mail: info@largerthanlifestagewear.co.uk
Tel/Fax: 020-8466 9010

MADDERMARKET THEATRE COSTUME HIRE
(Period Clothing, Costume Hire & Wig Hire)
St John's Alley, Norwich NR2 1DR
Website: www.maddermarket.co.uk
e-mail: mmtheatre@btconnect.com
Fax: 01603 661357   Tel: 01603 626292

MASK Kim
(Costume & Make-up Protection Masks)
PO Box 532, Isleworth, Middlesex TW7 6XP
Website: www.kimmask.com
e-mail: info@kimmask.com   Tel: 0845 0568482

MASTER CLEANERS The
(Dry Cleaning of Theatrical Costumes & Antique Garments)
189 Haverstock Hill, London NW3 4QG
e-mail: info@themastercleaners.com   Tel: 020-7431 3725

MEANANDGREEN.COM
17 Lichfield Street, Wolverhampton WV1 1EA
Website: www.meanandgreen.com
e-mail: custserv@meanandgreen.com
Fax: 01902 425564   Tel: 0845 899113

MIDNIGHT
Costume Design & Wardrobe Services (Music, Theatre,
Film, Tours)
e-mail: midnight_wardrobe@hotmail.com
Mobile: 07722 882847

MINHA CASA Ltd
51 Chalk Farm Road, London NW1 8AN
Website: www.minha-casa.co.uk
Fax: 020-7428 6901   Tel: 020-7428 6900

MORRIS Heather
(Wigs)
c/o The Hair Clinic at JBC
50-54 Wigmore Street, London W1U 2AU
Website: www.fortysevenhair.co.uk
e-mail: heather.morris@btconnect.com Tel: 020-7935 9200

NATIONAL THEATRE
(Costume, Furniture & Props Hire)
Chichester House, Kennington Park Estate
1-3 Brixton Road, London SW9 6DE
e-mail: costume_hire@nationaltheatre.org.uk
Tel: 020-7735 4774 (Costume)   Tel: 020-7820 1358 (Props)

NEW ID
(Makeover & Photographic Studios)
Third Floor, 17-18 Margaret Street, London W1W 8RP
Website: www.newidstudios.com
e-mail: bookings@newidstudios.co.uk   Tel: 0870 8701299

NORMAN Sam
(Hair & Make-up)
Website: www.samnorman.co.uk
e-mail: sam@samnorman.co.uk   Mobile: 07932 397465

ORIGINAL KNITWEAR
(Inc. Fake Fur) (Gina Pinnick)
Avalon, Tregoney Hill
Mevagissey, Cornwall PL26 6RG
e-mail: okgina@btinternet.com
Mobile: 07957 376855   Tel: 01726 844807

PATEY (LONDON) Ltd
Unit 1, 9 Gowlett Road, London SE15 4HX
Website: www.pateyhats.com
e-mail: pateyhats@aol.com
Fax: 020-7732 9538   Tel: 020-7635 0030

PEARCE Kate
(Costume Maker)
Thistledown, Wellfield Road
Marshfield, Near Newport CF3 2UB
e-mail: kpearce55@hotmail.com   Mobile: 07749 283802

PINK POINTES DANCEWEAR
1A Suttons Lane, Hornchurch, Essex RM12 6RD
e-mail: pink.pointes@btconnect.com
Tel/Fax: 01708 438584

PLAYHOUSE ENTERTAINMENT GROUP The
Playhouse Studios
2 Brampton Business Park, Eastbourne BN22 9AF
Website: www.playhousecostumes.co.uk
e-mail: enquiries@playhousecostumes.co.uk
Tel: 01323 501511

POLAND DENTAL STUDIO
(Film/Stage Dentistry)
1 Devonshire Place, London W1G 6HH
e-mail: robpoland@btconnect.com
Fax: 020-7486 3952   Tel: 020-7935 6919

PORSELLI
4 Frensham Road
Sweet Briar Industrial Estate
Norwich NR3 2BT
Website: www.porselli.com
e-mail: porselliuk@aol.com
Fax: 01603 406676   Tel: 0845 0170817

PROBLOOD
11 Mount Pleasant, Framlingham
Suffolk IP13 9HQ   Tel/Fax: 01728 723865

RAINBOW PRODUCTIONS Ltd
(Manufacture & Handling of Costume Characters)
Unit 3, Green Lea Park
Prince George's Road, London SW19 2JD
Website: www.rainbowproductions.co.uk
e-mail: info@rainbowproductions.co.uk
Fax: 020-8254 5306   Tel: 020-8254 5300

REPLICA WAREHOUSE
(Costumiers & Props)
200 Main Road, Goostrey, Cheshire CW4 8PD
Website: www.replicawarehouse.co.uk
e-mail: lesleyedwards@replicawarehouse.co.uk
                         Tel/Fax: 01477 534075

ROBBINS Sheila
(Wig Hire)
Broombarn, 7 Ivy Cottages
Hinksey Hill, Oxford OX1 5BQ   Tel/Fax: 01865 735524

ROBES D'EPOQUE
(Historical Costume Production)
12 Ampthill Road, Shirley
Southampton SO15 8LP   Tel: 023-8078 6849

ROLANDI Gianluca
(Hair & Make-up)
83 Deroy Lodge, Wicklow Street, London WC1X 3LF
Website: www.gluca.co.uk
e-mail: gluca@gluca.co.uk   Mobile: 07990 637299

ROSE Eda MILLINERY
(Ladies' Model Hat Design & Manufacture)
Lalique, Mongewell, Wallingford, Oxon OX10 8BP
Website: www.hatsbyedarose.co.uk
Fax: 01491 835909   Tel: 01491 837174

ROYAL EXCHANGE THEATRE COSTUME HIRE
(Period Costumes & Accessories)
47-53 Swan Street, Manchester M4 5JY
Website: www.royalexchange.co.uk
e-mail: costume.hire@royalexchange.co.uk
                         Tel/Fax: 0161-819 6660

ROYAL LYCEUM THEATRE COMPANY
(Theatrical Costume Hire)
29 Roseburn Street, Edinburgh EH12 5PE
Website: www.lyceum.org.uk
Fax: 0131-346 8072   Tel: 0131-337 1997

ROYER Hugo INTERNATIONAL Ltd
(Hair & Wig Materials)
10 Lakeside Business Park
Swan Lane, Sandhurst, Berkshire GU47 9DN
Website: www.hugoroyer.com
e-mail: enquiries@royer.co.uk
Fax: 01252 878852   Tel: 01252 878811

RSC COSTUME HIRE
28 Timothy's Bridge Road, Stratford Enterprise Park
Stratford-upon-Avon, Warwickshire CV37 9UY
e-mail: hire.wardrobe@rsc.org.uk   Tel/Fax: 01789 205920

RUMBLE Jane
(Masks, Millinery, Helmets Made to Order)
121 Elmstead Avenue, Wembley
Middlesex HA9 8NT   Tel: 020-8904 6462

SEXTON Sally Ann
(Hair & Make-up Designer)
31 Sylvester Road, East Finchley, London N2 4AW
e-mail: theharrisagency@btconnect.com
Mobile: 07973 802842   Tel: 01923 822744

SIDE EFFECTS
(Custom-made Character/FX Costumes)
92 Fentiman Road, London SW8 1LA
e-mail: sfx@lineone.net
Fax: 020-7207 0062   Tel: 020-7857 1116

SINGER Sandra ASSOCIATES
(Fashion Stylists for TV & Theatre, Costume/Designer)
21 Cotswold Road
Westcliff-on-Sea
Essex SS0 8AA
Website: www.sandrasinger.com
e-mail: sandrasingeruk@aol.com
Fax: 01702 339393   Tel: 01702 331616

SLEIMAN Hilary
(Specialist & Period Knitwear)
72 Godwin Road, London E7 0LG
e-mail: hilary.sleiman@ntlworld.com
Mobile: 07940 555663   Tel: 020-8555 6176

SOFT PROPS
(Costume & Model Makers)
92 Fentiman Road, London SW8 1LA
e-mail: jackie@softprops.co.uk
Fax: 020-7207 0062   Tel: 020-7587 1116

STAGEWORKS WORLDWIDE PRODUCTIONS
(Largest Costume Wardrobe in North)
525 Ocean Boulevard
Blackpool FY4 1EZ
Website: www.stageworkswwp.com
e-mail: simon.george@stageworkswwp.com
Fax: 01253 342702   Tel: 01253 342426

STRIBLING Joan
(Film & Television Make-up, Hair & Prosthetic Designer
/Artist, BAFTA, D & AD Awards)
Website: www.ilfracom.org.uk/stribling
e-mail: joanstribling@hotmail.com   Mobile: 07791 758480

SWINFIELD Rosemarie
(Make-up Design & Training)
Rosie's Make-Up Box
6 Brewer Street
Soho, London W1R 3FS
Website: www.rosiesmake-up.co.uk
e-mail: rosemarie@rosiesmake-up.co.uk
                                     Mobile: 07976 965520

TALK TO THE HAND PUPPETS
(Custom Puppets for Television & Theatre)
Studio 277, Wimbledon Art Studios
Riverside Yard, Riverside Road
Earlsfield, London SW17 0BB
Website: www.talktothehandproductions.com
e-mail: info@talktothehandproductions.com
Mobile: 07813 682293   Mobile: 07855 421454

THEATREKNITS
102C Belgravia Workshops
157-163 Marlborough Road, London N19 4NF
e-mail: trevorcollins@blueyonder.co.uk
                                 Tel/Fax: 020-7561 0044

THEATRICAL FOOTWEAR COMPANY Ltd The
(Trading as GAMBA Theatrical)
Unit 14, Chingford Industrial Centre
Hall Lane, Chingford
London E4 8DJ
e-mail: gambatheatrical1@btconnect.com
Fax: 020-8529 7995   Tel: 020-8529 9195

THEATRICAL SHOEMAKERS Ltd
(Footwear)
Unit 7A, Thames Road Industrial Estate
Thames Road, Silvertown, London E16 2EZ
Website: www.shoemaking.co.uk
e-mail: ts@shoemaking.co.uk
Fax: 020-7476 5220   Tel: 020-7474 0500

TRYFONOS Mary MASKS
(Designer & Maker of Masks & Costume Properties)
59 Shaftesbury Road
London N19 4QW
e-mail: marytryfonos@aol.com
Mobile: 07764 587433   Tel: 020-7561 9880

VINTAGE SHIRT COMPANY The
2 Mount Place, Lewes, East Sussex BN7 1YH
Website: www.vintageshirt.co.uk
e-mail: info@vintageshirt.co.uk   Tel/Fax: 01273 477699

WEST YORKSHIRE FABRICS Ltd
(Venetian, Crepe, Suiting, Barathea, Stretch Fabrics, Linen,
Cut Lengths)
West Yorkshire House
High Ash Drive, Leeds LS17 8RA
e-mail: neil@wyfabrics.com   Tel/Fax: 0113-225 6550

WIG EXPECTATIONS
3 Northernhay Walk
Morden, Surrey SM4 4BS
Website: www.wigexpectations.com
e-mail: wigexpectations@aol.com   Tel: 020-8540 5667

WIG ROOM The
22 Coronation Road
Basingstoke, Hants RG21 4HA
e-mail: darren@wigroom.co.uk   Tel/Fax: 01256 415737

WIG SPECIALITIES Ltd
(Hand Made Wigs & Facial Hair, Hair Extensions etc)
First Floor, 173 Seymour Place
London W1H 4PW
Website: www.wigspecialities.co.uk
e-mail: wigspecialities@btconnect.com
Fax: 020-7723 1566   Tel: 020-7262 6565

WIGGERY The
5 Kern Green, Stonehaugh
Hexham NE48 3DZ
Website: www.thewiggery.co.uk
e-mail: barb_alderson@yahoo.co.uk   Tel: 01434 344580

WILLIAMS Emma
(Costume Designer & Stylist - Film, TV & Theatre)
e-mail: emmacoz@dsl.pipex.com   Mobile: 07710 130345

WILSON Marian WIGS
(Theatrical & Film Wig Maker)
59 Gloucester Street
Faringdon, Oxon SN7 7JA
e-mail: gdwilly60@tiscali.co.uk
Fax: 01367 242438   Tel: 01367 241696

WRIGHT Fay
(Freelance Make-up Artist)
37 Veryan, Woking, Surrey GU21 3LL
e-mail: faylin_wright@hotmail.com   Mobile: 07816 128575

DAILY EXPRESS — Tel: 0871 4341010
Northern Shell Building
10 Lower Thames Street, London EC3R 6EN
Films: Alan Hunter
Television: Matt Baylis

DAILY MAIL — Tel: 020-7938 6000
Northcliffe House
2 Derry Street, Kensington, London W8 5TT
Theatre: Quentin Letts
Films: Chris Tookey

DAILY STAR — Tel: 0871 4341010
Northern Shell Building
10 Lower Thames Street, London EC3R 6EN
Show Business & Television: Nigel Pauley, Amy Watts,
Charli Morgan
Films & Video: Alan Frank

DAILY TELEGRAPH — Tel: 020-7931 2000
111 Buckingham Palace Road
London SW1W 0DT
Theatre: Charles Spencer, Dominic Cavendish
Films: Sukhdev Sandhu, Tim Robey
Radio: Gillian Reynolds Art: Richard Dorment
Dance: Sarah Crompton, Mark Monahan
Music: Geoffrey Norris, Ivan Hewitt

FINANCIAL TIMES — Tel: 020-7873 3000
1 Southwark Bridge
London SE1 9HL
Theatre: Sarah Hemmings, Ian Shuttleworth
Films: Nigel Andrews, Karl French
Television: Martin Hoyle, John Lloyd

GUARDIAN — Tel: 020-7278 2332
119 Farringdon Road
London EC1R 3ER
Theatre: Michael Billington
Films: Peter Bradshaw
Television: Nancy Banks-Smith
Radio: Elisabeth Mahoney

INDEPENDENT — Tel: 020-7005 2000
191 Marsh Wall
London E14 9RS
Television: Gerard Gilbert

LONDON EVENING STANDARD — Tel: 020-7938 6000
Northcliffe House
2 Derry Street, Kensington, London W8 5EE
Theatre: Nicholas de Jongh, Fiona Mountford,
Kieron Quirke
Films: Derek Malcolm Opera: Fiona Maddocks
Television: Ceri Thomas
Classical Music: Barry Millington

MAIL ON SUNDAY — Tel: 020-7938 6000
(Review Section)
Northcliffe House
2 Derry Street, London W8 5TS
Theatre: Georgina Brown
Films: Jason Solomons, Matthew Bond
Radio: Simon Garfield

MIRROR — Tel: 020-7510 3000
Mirror Group Newspapers Ltd
1 Canada Square, Canary Wharf, London E14 5AP
Films: Dave Edwards
Television: Mark Jefferies

MORNING STAR — Tel: 020-8510 0815
William Rust House
52 Beachy Road, London E3 2NS
Theatre & Films: Katie Lambert

NEWS OF THE WORLD — Tel: 020-7782 4000
News International Plc
1 Virginia Street, London E98 1NW
Show Business: Rav Singh
Films: Robbie Collin

OBSERVER — Tel: 020-7278 2332
3-7 Herbal Hill
London EC1R 5EJ
Theatre: Susanna Clapp
Films: Philip French, Akin Ojumu
Radio: Miranda Sawyer

PEOPLE — Tel: 020-7293 3000
1 Canada Square
Canary Wharf
London E14 5AP
Television & Radio: Sarah Moolla
Films: Richard Bacon
Show Business: Alice Walker
Features: Lloyd Embley

SPORT — Tel: 0161-238 8151
Sport Newspapers Ltd
19 Great Ancoats Street
Manchester M60 4BT
Showbusiness/Features: Neil Goodwin

SUN — Tel: 020-7782 4000
News International Plc
1 Virginia Street
Wapping, London E98 1SN
Television: Ally Ross
Films: Grant Rollings

SUNDAY EXPRESS — Tel: 0871 4341010
Northern Shell Building
10 Lower Thames Street
London EC3R 6EN
Theatre: Mark Shenton
Films: Henry Fitzherbert
Television: David Stephenson
Radio & Arts: Rachel Jane, Clare Heal

SUNDAY MIRROR — Tel: 020-7510 3000
Mirror Group
1 Canada Square
Canary Wharf, London E14 5AP
Theatre & Television: Kevin O'Sullivan
Films: Mark Adams
Showbiz: Zoe Griffin

SUNDAY TELEGRAPH — Tel: 020-7931 2000
111 Buckingham Palace Road
London SW1W 0DT
Theatre: Tim Walker
Films: Jenny McCartney
Television: John Preston

SUNDAY TIMES — Tel: 020-7782 5000
News International Plc
1 Pennington Street, London E98 1ST
Theatre: Christopher Hart
Films: Cosmo Landesman
Television: A. A. Gill
Radio: Paul Donovan

TIMES — Tel: 020-7782 5000
News International Plc
1 Pennington Street, London E98 1TT
Theatre: Benedict Nightingale
Films: James Christopher
Television: James Jackson
Video: Ed Potton Radio: Chris Campling

D

**Dance Companies & Organisations
Dance Training & Professional Classes
Drama Schools (Conference of)
Drama Training, Schools & Coaches**

AKADEMI SOUTH ASIAN DANCE UK
213 Haverstock Hill, Hampstead Town Hall
Haverstock Hill, London NW3 4QP
Website: www.akademi.co.uk
e-mail: info@akademi.co.uk
Fax: 020-7691 3211   Tel: 020-7691 3210

ANJALI DANCE COMPANY
The Mill Arts Centre, Spiceball Park
Banbury, Oxford OX16 5QE
Website: www.anjali.co.uk
e-mail: info@anjali.co.uk   Tel: 01295 251909

ARTSWORLD PRESENTATIONS Ltd
Vicarage House
58-60 Kensington Church Street, London W8 4DB
Website: www.arts-world.co.uk
e-mail: p@triciamurraybett.com
Fax: 020-7368 3338   Tel: 020-7368 3337

BALLROOM - LONDON THEATRE OF
(Artistic Director - Paul Harris)
24 Montana Gardens, Sutton, Surrey SM1 4FP
Website: www.londontheatreofballroom.com
e-mail: office@londontheatreofballroom.com
Mobile: 07958 784462   Tel/Fax: 020-8722 8798

BEDLAM DANCE COMPANY
Contact: By Post/email
18 St Augustine's Road, London NW1 9RN
Website: www.bedlamdance.com
e-mail: info@bedlamdance.com

BIRMINGHAM ROYAL BALLET
Thorp Street, Birmingham B5 4AU
Website: www.brb.org.uk
e-mail: administrator@brb.org.uk
Fax: 0121-245 3570   Tel: 0121-245 3500

BODY OF PEOPLE
(Jazz Theatre Company)
10 Stayton Road, Sutton, Surrey SM1 1RB
Website: www.bop.org.uk
e-mail: info@bop.org.uk   Tel: 020-8641 6959

BOLLYWOOD GROOVES DANCE COMPANY
7 Primrose Court
253 Cricklewood Lane, London NW2 2JG
Website: www.bollywoodgrooves.com
e-mail: info@bollywoodgrooves.com   Mobile: 07875 023744

BROWN Carole DANCES
Contact: Gwen Van Spijk
PO Box 563, Banbury OX16 6AQ
Website: www.cueperformance.com
e-mail: gwen@cueperformance.com   Tel: 01869 338458

CANDOCO DANCE COMPANY
2T Leroy House, 436 Essex Road, London N1 3QP
Website: www.candoco.co.uk
e-mail: info@candoco.co.uk
Fax: 020-7704 1645   Tel: 020-7704 6845

CHOLMONDELEYS & FEATHERSTONEHAUGHS The
LF1.1
Lafone House, The Leathermarket
11-13 Leathermarket Street, London SE1 3HN
Website: www.thecholmondeleys.org
e-mail: admin@thecholmondeleys.org
Fax: 020-7378 8810   Tel: 020-7378 8800

How do I become a professional dancer?

Full-time vocational training can start from as young as ten years old. A good starting point for researching the different schools and courses available is CDET (Council for Dance Education & Training) www.cdet.org.uk. There are over sixteen dance colleges offering professional training accredited by CDET, and nearly three hundred university courses which include some form of dance training. It is estimated that over one thousand dancers graduate from vocational training schools or university courses every year, so it is a highly competitive career. Therefore anyone wanting to be a professional dancer must obtain as many years of training and experience as possible, plus go to see plenty of performances spanning different types and genres of dance. If you require further information on vocational dance schools, applying to accredited dance courses, auditions and funding, contact CDET's information line 'Answers for Dancers' on 020-7240 5703 or see their article overleaf.

What are dance companies?

There are more than two hundred dance companies in the UK, spanning a variety of dance styles including ballet, contemporary, hip hop and African. A dance company will either be resident in a venue, be a touring company, or a combination of both. Many have websites which you can visit for full information. Most dance companies employ ensemble dancers on short to medium contracts, who may then work on a number of different productions for the same company over a number of months. In addition, the company will also employ principal / leading dancers on a role-by-role basis.

What are dance organisations?

There are numerous organisations which exist to support professional dancers, covering important areas including health and safety, career development, networking and legal and financial aspects. Other organisations (e.g. Regional / National Dance Agencies) exist to promote dance within the wider community.

I have already trained to be a dancer.
Why do I need further training?

Dance training should not cease as soon as you get your first job or complete a course. Throughout your career you should continuously strive to maintain your fitness levels, enhance and develop your existing skills and keep learning new ones in order to retain a competitive edge. You must also be prepared to continuously learn new dance styles and routines for specific roles. Ongoing training and classes can help you stay fit and active, and if you go through a period of unemployment you can keep your mind and body occupied, ready to take on your next job.

How should I use these listings?

The following pages will supply you with up-to-date contact details for a wide range of dance companies and organisations, followed by listings for dance training and professional classes. Always research schools and classes thoroughly, obtaining copies of prospectuses where available. Most vocational schools offer two and three year full-time training programmes, many also offer excellent degree programmes. Foundation Courses offer a sound introduction to the profession, but they can never replace a full-time vocational course. Many schools, organisations and studios also offer part-time / evening classes which offer a general understanding of dance and complementary technique or the opportunity to refresh specific dance skills; they will not, however, enable a student to become a professional dancer.

How else can I find work as a dancer?

Dance also plays a role in commercial theatre, musicals, opera, film, television, live music and video, corporate events and many other industries. Dancers may also want to be represented by an agent. Agents have many more contacts within the industry than an individual dancer can have, and can offer advice and negotiate contracts on your behalf as well as submit you for jobs. A number of specialist dance agencies are listed in the 'Agents – Dance' section towards the front of this book.

What is Spotlight Dancers?

Dancers wishing to promote themselves to these types of job opportunities should consider joining Spotlight's latest specialist directory for dancers. This is a central directory of dancers published annually which is used by dance employers throughout the UK to locate dancers and send out casting or audition information. Members receive a page in the directory containing a headshot and body shot, agency contact details and selected credits as well as an online CV. Please see www.spotlight.com/join for more information.

What other careers are available in dance?

Opportunities also exist to work as a teacher, choreographer, technician or manager. Dance UK www.danceuk.org is a valuable source of information for anyone considering this type of work.

What should I do to avoid injury?

An injury is more likely to occur if you are inflexible and unprepared for sudden physical exertion. The last thing you want to do is to pick up an injury, however minor, and be prevented from working, so continuous training during both employment and unemployment will help you to minimise the risk of an injury during a performance or rehearsal. If you do sustain an injury you will want to make sure it does not get any worse by getting treatment with a specialist. The British Association for Performing Arts Medicine (BAPAM) provides specialist health support for performers, free health assessment clinics and a directory of performing arts health practitioners and specialists. Visit their website www.bapam.org.uk for more information. You may also find the advice preceding the 'Health & Wellbeing' section of Contacts useful.

I'm not a professional dancer but I enjoy dancing. Why should I use these listings?

People don't just dance to perform, teach or advise within the industry. Dance can be pursued for fun, recreation, social reasons and for health. Training and professional advice should still be pursued to ensure that you do not injure yourself while dancing and prevent yourself from working. You can also use the 'Dance Training & Professional Classes' listings to find suitable dance lessons in your area, which you could attend to make friends, keep fit and stay occupied while unemployed.

Where can I find more information?

For further advice about the dance industry, you could try contacting CDET (www.cdet.org.uk) for training information, Dance UK (www.danceuk.org) regarding the importance and needs of dance and dancers, or BAPAM (www.bapam.org.uk) for health issues. You may want to get involved with Move It – the UK's biggest dance exhibition which takes place every year in March. Visit www.dance-london.co.uk for more information. If you are looking for a dance agent to promote you to job opportunities, please see the 'Agents – Dance' section of Contacts.

The Council for Dance Education and Training (CDET) is the accrediting body of the dance and musical theatre industry. It is the first point of contact for students wishing to work professionally in dance and musical theatre, students wanting to take dance or dance teaching qualifications and those who want to dance simply because it's there.

CDET runs a free information service – *Answers for Dancers (AfD)* – on all aspects of dance and musical theatre education and publishes the annual UK Handbook of Accredited Courses in Dance and Musical Theatre. The Handbook, sponsored by Spotlight, is the country's most comprehensive dance and musical theatre guide and is available free of charge from **www.samuelfrench-london.co.uk**. *Answers for Dancers* information sheets can be found on the CDET website and personal advice is also available by telephone. AfD addresses thousands of enquiries a year from students, parents, dancers and musical theatre artists. Here are some *Answers for Dancers*...

How do I become a professional dancer, dance teacher or musical theatre artist?
Whether you want to dance for leisure or professionally it is vitally important you get teaching of the highest quality in studios properly equipped to ensure you are safe and secure. Injury is an occupational hazard of the dancer and it is essential you are taught by professionals who understand the effect of hard, physical work on the body, that you dance on floors designed to minimise the risk of stress and strain and that you work in a space big enough to let you move freely and safely. Whether you dance professionally or as a serious hobby, injury means you have to stop until you have recovered. For professionals it might mean losing the next job.

Where can I find professional teachers who work to standards approved by the industry?
At a CDET accredited vocational dance or musical theatre school or college and at a CDET accredited Dance Awarding Body.

What makes CDET accredited education and training so special?
Every CDET accredited institution has been inspected by trained panels of dance and musical theatre professionals to ensure it meets the needs of both the industry and the student. Council inspection reports are used by the government, Ofsted, charitable foundations and trusts when making funding decisions. If a school or college fails to maintain its standards, it can lose its accreditation.

What is a CDET accredited vocational dance or musical theatre school?
A CDET accredited vocational school is a school or college offering performance or teaching courses for students over the age of 16 (Further Education) or 18 (Higher Education).

What is a CDET accredited Dance Awarding Body?
A CDET accredited Dance Awarding Body (and Dance Teaching Society) is an organisation offering qualifications by means of examinations and other forms of assessment.

What is a CDET Recognised pre-vocational School?
A CDET Recognised pre-vocational School (RS) is a dance or musical theatre school working with students under the age of 16. Schools awarded RS have confirmed in writing to the Council that they meet all nine requirements of the award, full details of which can be found in the pre-vocational dance section of the Council's website. The award is run in association with *Dancing Times and The Stage.*

Students applying to a vocational dance or musical theatre school, taking the qualifications of a Dance Awarding Body or attending a pre- or non-vocational dance or musical theatre school are **strongly advised** to ensure it holds CDET approval.

Competition for places at CDET accredited dance and musical theatre schools and colleges is fierce and you may be considering an offer from a vocational school not accredited by the Council. If so, make sure you are confident you will receive the quality of training you expect, that studio facilities and medical resources are suitable for the teaching of dance or musical theatre and that you request a written explanation as to why the school does not hold CDET accreditation.

Whatever your query regarding dance or musical theatre education and training visit the Council website at www.cdet.org.uk or telephone the Council on 020 7240 5703.

COMPANY OF CRANKS
1st Floor
62 Northfield House
Frensham Street, London SE15 6TN
Website: www.mimeworks.com
e-mail: mimetic16@yahoo.com   Mobile: 07963 617981

DANCE SOUTH WEST
PO Box 5457
Bournemouth, Dorset BH1 1WU
Website: www.dancesouthwest.org.uk
e-mail: info@dancesouthwest.org.uk   Tel/Fax: 01202 554131

DAVIES Siobhan DANCE
85 St George's Road
London SE1 6ER
Website: www.siobhandavies.com
e-mail: info@siobhandavies.com
Fax: 020-7091 9669   Tel: 020-7091 9650

DV8 PHYSICAL THEATRE
Arts Admin, Toynbee Studios
28 Commercial Street
London E1 6AB
Website: www.dv8.co.uk
e-mail: dv8@artsadmin.co.uk
Fax: 020-7247 5103   Tel: 020-7655 0977

ENGLISH NATIONAL BALLET Ltd
Markova House, 39 Jay Mews
London SW7 2ES
Website: www.ballet.org.uk
e-mail: comments@ballet.org.uk
Fax: 020-7225 0827   Tel: 020-7581 1245

ENGLISH YOUTH BALLET
Appledowne, The Hillside
Orpington, Kent BR6 7SD
Website: www.englishyouthballet.co.uk
e-mail: misslewis@englishyouthballet.co.uk
Mobile: 07732 383600   Tel/Fax: 020-8691 2806

GREEN CANDLE DANCE COMPANY
Oxford House
Derbyshire Street
Bethnal Green, London E2 6HG
Website: www.greencandledance.com
e-mail: info@greencandledance.com
Fax: 020-7729 8272   Tel: 020-7739 7722

IJAD
22 Allison Road
London N8 0AT
Website: www.ijad.freeserve.co.uk
e-mail: jouman@ijad.freeserve.co.uk   Mobile: 07930 378639

INDEPENDENT BALLET WALES
30 Glasllwch Crescent
Newport, South Wales NP20 3SE
Website: www.welshballet.co.uk
e-mail: dariusjames@welshballet.co.uk
Fax: 01633 221690   Tel: 01633 253985

JEYASINGH Shobana DANCE COMPANY
Moving Arts Base
134 Liverpool Road
Islington, London N1 1LA
Website: www.shobanajeyasingh.co.uk
e-mail: admin@shobanajeyasingh.co.uk Tel: 020-7697 4444

KHAN Akram COMPANY
Unit 232A
35A Britannia Row, London N1 8QH
Website: www.akramkhancompany.net
e-mail: office@akramkhancompany.net
Fax: 020-7354 5554   Tel: 020-7354 4333

KOSH The
(Physical Theatre)
59 Stapleton Hall Road
London N4 3QF
e-mail: info@thekosh.com   Tel/Fax: 020-8374 0407

LUDUS DANCE
Assembly Rooms
King Street
Lancaster LA1 1RE
Website: www.ludusdance.org
e-mail: info@ludusdance.org
Fax: 01524 847744   Tel: 01524 35936

MOVING EAST
St Matthias Church Hall
Wordsworth Road, London N16 8DD
Website: www.movingeast.co.uk
e-mail: admin@movingeast.co.uk   Tel: 020-7503 3101

MUDRALAYA DANCE THEATRE
(Formerly Pushkala Gopal Unnikrishnan & Co)
(Classical Indian Dance-Theatre)
20 Brisbane Road
Ilford, Essex IG1 4SR
e-mail: pushkala.gopal@gmail.com
Mobile: 07950 550550   Tel: 020-8554 4054

NEW ADVENTURES
Sadler's Wells
Rosebery Avenue, London EC1R 4TN
Website: www.new-adventures.net
e-mail: info@new-adventures.net   Tel/Fax: 020-7713 6766

NORTHERN BALLET THEATRE
West Park Centre
Spen Lane, Leeds LS16 5BE
e-mail: administration@northernballettheatre.co.uk
Fax: 0113-220 8007   Tel: 0113-274 5355

OGUIKE Henri DANCE COMPANY
Laban, The Cottages
Office No 2, Creekside, London SE8 3DZ
Website: www.henrioguikedance.co.uk
e-mail: info@henrioguikedance.co.uk
Fax: 020-8694 3669   Tel: 020-8694 7444

PHOENIX DANCE THEATRE
3 St Peter's Buildings
St Peter's Square, Leeds LS9 8AH
Website: www.phoenixdancetheatre.co.uk
e-mail: info@phoenixdancetheatre.co.uk
Fax: 0113-244 4736   Tel: 0113-242 3486

PIPER George DANCES
Sadler's Wells, Rosebery Avenue
Islington, London EC1R 4TN
Website: www.gpdances.com
e-mail: contact@gpdances.com
Fax: 020-7278 5684   Tel: 020-7278 5508

PLACE The
Robin Howard Dance Theatre
17 Duke's Road, London WC1H 9PY
Website: www.theplace.org.uk
e-mail: info@theplace.org.uk
Fax: 020-7121 1142   Tel: 020-7121 1000

RAMBERT DANCE COMPANY
94 Chiswick High Road
London W4 1SH
Website: www.rambert.org.uk
e-mail: rdc@rambert.org.uk
Fax: 020-8747 8323   Tel: 020-8630 0600

ROTIE Marie-Gabrielle PRODUCTIONS
7 Trinity Rise, London SW2 2QP
Website: www.rotieproductions.com
e-mail: rotiemanager@aol.com   Tel: 020-8674 1518

ROYAL BALLET The
Royal Opera House
Covent Garden, London WC2E 9DD
Fax: 020-7212 9121   Tel: 020-7240 1200 ext 712

RUSS Claire ENSEMBLE
(Choreography, Contemporary/Commercial/Corporate)
4 Heatham Park
Twickenham TW2 7SF
Website: www.clairerussensemble.com
e-mail: info@clairerussensemble.com
                                      Mobile: 07932 680224

SCOTTISH BALLET
261 West Princes Street
Glasgow G4 9EE
Website: www.scottishballet.co.uk
e-mail: sb@scottishballet.co.uk
Fax: 0141-331 2629   Tel: 0141-331 2931

SCOTTISH DANCE THEATRE
Dundee Repertory Theatre
Tay Square, Dundee DD1 1PB
Website: www.scottishdancetheatre.com
e-mail: achinn@dundeereptheatre.co.uk
Fax: 01382 228609   Tel: 01382 342600

SKY BLUE PINK
Website: www.skybluepinkproductions.com
e-mail: info@skybluepinkproductions.com
Mobile: 07779 866439   Tel: 020-8715 5007

SPRINGS DANCE COMPANY
99 Tressillian Road
London SE4 1XZ
Website: www.springsdancecompany.org.uk
e-mail: info@springsdancecompany.org.uk
Mobile: 07775 628442   Tel: 01634 817523

TRANSITIONS DANCE COMPANY
Creekside
London SE8 3DZ
e-mail: info@laban.org   Tel: 020-8691 8600

TWITCH EVENT CHOREOGRAPHY
5 Breakspears Mews
Brockley
London SE4 1PY
Website: www.twitch.uk.com
e-mail: info@twitch.uk.com
Mobile: 07932 656358   Mobile: 07747 770816

UNION DANCE
Top Floor
6 Charing Cross Road
London WC2H 0HG
Website: www.uniondance.co.uk
e-mail: info@uniondance.co.uk
Fax: 020-7836 7847   Tel: 020-7836 7837

ACCELERATE PRODUCTIONS Ltd
73 St Johns Street
Farringdon, London EC1M 4NJ
Website: www.accelerate-productions.co.uk
e-mail: info@accelerate-productions.co.uk
Tel: 020-7490 2772

AKADEMI SOUTH ASIAN DANCE UK
213 Haverstock Hill
Hampstead Town Hall
London NW3 4QP
Website: www.akademi.co.uk
e-mail: info@akademi.co.uk
Fax: 020-7691 3211
Tel: 020-7691 3210

ALLIED DANCING ASSOCIATION
137 Greenhill Road
Mossley Hill
Liverpool L18 7HQ
Tel: 0151-724 1829

ASSOCIATION OF DANCE OF THE AFRICAN DIASPORA
Urdang
The Old Finsbury Town Hall
Rosebery Avenue, London EC1R 4QT
Website: www.adad.org.uk
e-mail: info@adad.org.uk
Fax: 020-7833 2363
Tel: 020-7841 7357

BENESH INSTITUTE The
36 Battersea Square
London SW11 3RA
Website: www.benesh.org
e-mail: beneshinstitute@rad.org.uk
Tel: 020-7326 8000

BLUE EYED SOUL DANCE COMPANY
The Lantern
Meadow Farm Drive
Shrewsbury SY1 4NG
Website: www.blueeyedsouldance.com
e-mail: admin@blueeyedsouldance.com
Tel: 01743 210830

BRITISH ARTS The
12 Deveron Way, Rise Park
Romford RM1 4UL
Website: www.britisharts.org
Tel: 01708 756263

BRITISH ASSOCIATION OF TEACHERS OF DANCING
23 Marywood Square
Glasgow G41 2BP
Website: www.batd.co.uk
e-mail: katrina.allan@batd.co.uk
Tel: 0141-423 4029

BRITISH BALLET ORGANISATION
(Dance Examining Society & Teacher Training)
Woolborough House
39 Lonsdale Road
Barnes, London SW13 9JP
Website: www.bbo.org.uk
e-mail: info@bbo.org.uk
Tel: 020-8748 1241

BRITISH THEATRE DANCE ASSOCIATION
Garden Street
Leicester LE1 3UA
Website: www.btda.org.uk
e-mail: info@btda.org.uk
Fax: 0845 1662189
Tel: 0845 1662179

CHISENHALE DANCE SPACE
64-84 Chisenhale Road
Bow, London E3 5QZ
Website: www.chisenhaledancespace.co.uk
e-mail: rowena@chisenhaledancespace.co.uk
Fax: 020-8980 9323
Tel: 020-8981 6617

COUNCIL FOR DANCE EDUCATION & TRAINING
Old Brewer's Yard
17-19 Neal Street, Covent Garden
London WC2H 9UY
Website: www.cdet.org.uk
e-mail: info@cdet.org.uk
Fax: 020-7240 2547
Tel: 020-7240 5703

DANCE 4
(National Dance Agency)
3-9 Hockley, Nottingham NG1 1FH
Website: www.dance4.co.uk
e-mail: info@dance4.co.uk
Fax: 0115-941 0776
Tel: 0115- 941 0773

DANCE BASE NATIONAL CENTRE FOR DANCE
14-16 Grassmarket
Edinburgh EH1 2JU
Website: www.dancebase.co.uk
e-mail: dance@dancebase.co.uk
Fax: 0131-225 5234
Tel: 0131-225 5525

DANCE CITY
(National Dance Agency)
Temple Street
Newcastle-upon-Tyne NE1 4BR
Website: www.dancecity.co.uk
e-mail: info@dancecity.co.uk
Tel: 0191-261 0505

DANCE EAST
(National Dance Agency)
Northgate Arts Centre
Sidegate Lane West
Ipswich IP4 3DF
Website: www.danceeast.co.uk
e-mail: info@danceeast.co.uk
Fax: 01473 639236
Tel: 01473 639230

DANCE HOUSE
20 St Andrew's Street
Glasgow G1 5PD
Website: www.dancehouse.org
e-mail: info@dancehouse.org
Tel: 0141-552 2442

DANCE IN DEVON
(County Dance Development Agency)
Exeter Phoenix, Bradninch Place
Gandy Street, Exeter EX4 3LS
Website: www.danceindevon.org.uk
e-mail: info@danceindevon.org.uk
Tel: 01392 667050

DANCE INITIATIVE GREATER MANCHESTER
Zion Arts Centre
Stretford Road
Hulme, Manchester M15 5ZA
Website: www.digm.org
e-mail: info@digm.org.uk
Fax: 0161-232 7483
Tel: 0161-232 7179

DANCERS' CAREER DEVELOPMENT
220-221 Africa House
64 Kingsway
London WC2B 6BG
Website: www.thedcd.org.uk
e-mail: admin@thedcd.org.uk
Fax: 020-7424 3331   Tel: 020-7404 6141

DANCE SOUTH WEST
PO Box 5457
Bournemouth
Dorset BH1 1WU
Website: www.dancesouthwest.org.uk
e-mail: info@dancesouthwest.org.uk   Tel/Fax: 01202 554131

DANCE UK
(Including the Healthier Dancer Programme)
The Urdang
The Old Finsbury Town Hall
Rosebery Avenue
London EC1R 4QT
Website: www.danceuk.org
e-mail: info@danceuk.org
Fax: 020-7833 2363   Tel: 020-7713 0730

DANCE UMBRELLA
20 Chancellors Street
London W6 9RN
Website: www.danceumbrella.co.uk
e-mail: mail@danceumbrella.co.uk
Fax: 020-8741 7902   Tel: 020-8741 4040

DANCEXCHANGE
(National Dance Agency)
Birmingham Hippodrome
Thorp Street, Birmingham B5 4TB
Website: www.dancexchange.org.uk
e-mail: info@dancexchange.org.uk   Tel: 0121-689 3170

DAVIES Siobhan DANCE
(Professional Development for Dance Artists & Education)
85 St George's Road, London SE1 6ER
Website: www.siobhandavies.com
e-mail: info@siobhandavies.com
Fax: 020-7091 9669   Tel: 020-7091 9650

EAST LONDON DANCE
Stratford Circus
Theatre Square, London E15 1BX
Website: www.eastlondondance.org
e-mail: office@eastlondondance.org
Fax: 020-8279 1054   Tel: 020-8279 1050

ESSEXDANCE
2 Bond Street, Chelmsford, Essex CM1 1GH
Website: www.essexdance.co.uk
e-mail: info@essexdance.co.uk   Tel: 01245 346036

FOUNDATION FOR COMMUNITY DANCE
LCB Depot, 31 Rutland Street
Leicester LE1 1RE
Website: www.communitydance.org.uk
e-mail: info@communitydance.org.uk
Fax: 0116-261 6801   Tel: 0116-253 3453

The Council for Dance Education and Training is the national standards body of the professional dance industry. It accredits programmes of training in vocational dance schools and holds the Register of Dance Awarding Bodies - the directory of teaching societies whose syllabuses have been inspected and approved by the Council. It is the body of advocacy of the dance education and training communities and offers a free and comprehensive information service - *Answers for Dancers* - on all aspects of vocational dance provision to students, parents, teachers, dance artists and employers.

The Conference of Professional Dance Schools (CPDS) is a committee of the Council and provides a forum in which representatives from vocational dance training institutions may discuss policy and recommend action in relation to vocational dance training.

- Arts Educational School, Tring
- ArtsEd London
- Bird College
- Cambridge Performing Arts
- Elmhurst School for Dance
- Hammond School
- Italia Conti Academy of Theatre Arts Ltd
- LABAN
- Laine Theatre Arts
- Liverpool Theatre School and College
- London Studio Centre
- Northern Ballet School
- Performers College
- Stella Mann College
- Urdang Academy

For more info on the CPDS and CDET:
Contact:
Council for Dance Education & Training
Old Brewer's Yard
17-19 Neal Street
Covent Garden, London WC2H 9UY
Tel: 020 7240 5703
Email: info@cdet.org.uk
Website: www.cdet.org.uk

GREENWICH DANCE AGENCY
The Borough Hall
Royal Hill
London SE10 8RE
Website: www.greenwichdance.org.uk
e-mail: info@greenwichdance.org.uk   Tel: 020-8293 9741

IDTA
(INTERNATIONAL DANCE TEACHERS' ASSOCIATION)
International House
76 Bennett Road
Brighton
East Sussex BN2 5JL
Website: www.idta.co.uk
e-mail: info@idta.co.uk
Fax: 01273 674388   Tel: 01273 685652

ISLE OF WIGHT DANCE PROJECT
The Guildhall
High Street, Newport
Isle of Wight PO30 1TY
Website: www.isleofwight-arts.co.uk
e-mail: jane.bridle@iow.gov.uk   Tel: 01983 823813

LANGUAGE OF DANCE CENTRE
4th Floor, Charles House
375 Kensington High Street
London W14 8QH
Website: www.lodc.org
e-mail: info@lodc.org   Tel: 020-7603 8500

LONDON CONTEMPORARY DANCE SCHOOL
16 Flaxman Terrace
London WC1H 9AT
Website: www.theplace.org.uk
e-mail: lcds@theplace.org.uk
Fax: 020-7121 1142   Tel: 020-7121 1111

LUDUS DANCE
The Assembly Rooms
Kings Street, Lancaster LA1 1RE
Website: www.ludusdance.org
e-mail: info@ludusdance.org
Fax: 01524 847744   Tel: 01524 35936

MERSEYSIDE DANCE INITIATIVE
(National Dance Agency)
24 Hope Street
Liverpool L1 9BQ
Website: www.merseysidedance.co.uk
e-mail: info@mdi.org.uk   Tel: 0151-708 8810

MIDLAND INTERNATIONAL DANCE ARTS ASSOCIATION
29A Sycamore Road
Birmingham B23 5QP
Website: www.midaa.co.uk
e-mail: midaa.hq@hotmail.com
Fax: 0121-694 0013   Tel: 0121-694 0012

NATIONAL RESOURCE CENTRE FOR DANCE
University of Surrey
Guildford GU2 7XH
Website: www.surrey.ac.uk/nrcd
e-mail: nrcd@surrey.ac.uk
Fax: 01483 689500   Tel: 01483 689316

PLACE The
(National Dance Agency)
Robin Howard Dance Theatre
17 Duke's Road, London WC1H 9BY
Website: www.theplace.org.uk
e-mail: info@theplace.org.uk
Fax: 020-7121 1142   Tel: 020-7121 1000

PROFESSIONAL TEACHERS OF DANCING
Quay West Business Centre, Quay Lane
Gosport, Hants PO12 4LJ
Website: www.ptdance.com
e-mail: professionalteachersofdancing@msn.com
                                         Tel: 023-9260 4285

SOUTH-EAST DANCE
(National Dance Agency)
28 Kensington Street
Brighton BN1 4AJ
Website: www.southeastdance.org.uk
e-mail: info@southeastdance.org.uk
Fax: 01273 697212   Tel: 01273 696844

SURREY ARTS DANCE
Westfield School, Bonsey Lane
Woking, Surrey GU22 9PR
Website: www.surreycc.gov.uk/arts
e-mail: sa.dance@surreycc.gov.uk   Tel: 01483 776128

SWINDON DANCE
(National Dance Agency)
Town Hall Studios
Regent Circus, Swindon SN1 1QF
Website: www.swindondance.org.uk
e-mail: info@swindondance.org.uk   Tel: 01793 601700

TURTLE KEY ARTS
Ladbroke Hall
79 Barlby Road, London W10 6AZ
Website: www.turtlekeyarts.org.uk
e-mail: shaun@turtlekeyarts.org.uk
Fax: 020-8964 4080   Tel: 020-8964 5060

TWITCH EVENT CHOREOGRAPHY
5 Breakspears Mews
Brockley, London SE4 1PY
Website: www.twitch.uk.com
e-mail: info@twitch.uk.com
Mobile: 07932 656358   Mobile: 07747 770816

WELSH INDEPENDENT DANCE
Chapter, Market Road
Canton
Cardiff CF5 1QE
Website: www.welshindance.co.uk
e-mail: info@welshindance.co.uk   Tel: 029-2038 7314

YORKSHIRE DANCE
(National Dance Agency)
3 St Peters Buildings
St Peters Square
Leeds LS9 8AH
Website: www.yorkshiredance.com
e-mail: admin@yorkshiredance.com
Fax: 0113-259 5700   Tel: 0113-243 9867

PAUL HARRIS   07958-784462   www.paulharris.uk.com

Choreographer: "The Other Boleyn Girl" "Harry Potter 5" (Wand Combat)

Choreography and Coaching in Vintage and Contemporary Social Dance

* Swing * Waltz * Salsa * Tango * Charleston * Quadrille *etc.*

ACADEMY FOR THEATRE ARTS The
1 Vale View, Porthill
Newcastle under Lyme
Staffs ST5 0AF   Tel: 01782 751900

ARTS EDUCATIONAL SCHOOLS, LONDON
Cone Ripman House, 14 Bath Road
Chiswick, London W4 1LY
Website: www.artsed.co.uk
e-mail: reception@artsed.co.uk   Tel: 020-8987 6666

AVIV DANCE STUDIOS
Wren House, 1st Floor
19-23 Exchange Road
Watford WD18 0JD
Website: www.avivdance.com
e-mail: nikkiavron@btconnect.com   Tel/Fax: 01923 250000

BALLROOM - LONDON THEATRE OF
(Artistic Director - Paul Harris, Mentor "Faking It")
24 Montana Gardens
Sutton, Surrey SM1 4FP
Website: www.londontheatreofballroom.com
e-mail: office@londontheatreofballroom.com
Mobile: 07958 784462   Tel/Fax: 020-8722 8798

BHAVAN CENTRE
4A Castletown Road
London W14 9HE
Website: www.bhavan.net
e-mail: info@bhavan.net   Tel: 020-7381 3086

**BIRD COLLEGE DANCE MUSIC & THEATRE
PERFORMANCE**
(Dance & Theatre Performance HE & FE Programmes)
Birkbeck Centre, Birkbeck Road
Sidcup, Kent DA14 4DE
Website: www.birdcollege.co.uk
e-mail: admin@birdcollege.co.uk
Fax: 020-8308 1370   Tel: 020-8300 6004

BODENS STUDIOS
(Performing Arts Classes)
Bodens Studios & Agency
99 East Barnet Road
New Barnet, Herts EN4 8RF
Website: www.bodenstudios.com
e-mail: info@bodensagency.com
Fax: 020-8449 5212   Tel: 020-8449 0982

BRIGHTON DANCE DIVERSION
93 Sea Lane, Rustington
West Sussex BN16 2RS
Website: www.brightondancediversion.com
e-mail: info@brightondancediversion.com
    Tel: 01903 770304

CAMBRIDGE PERFORMING ARTS AT BODYWORK
Bodywork Company Dance Studios
25-29 Glisson Road
Cambridge CB1 2HA   Tel: 01223 314461

CANDOCO DANCE COMPANY
2T Leroy House
436 Essex Road, London N1 3QP
Website: www.candoco.co.uk
e-mail: foundationcourse@candoco.co.uk
    Tel: 020-7704 6845

CENTRAL SCHOOL OF BALLET
(Full Time Vocational Training, Open Classes
Beginner/Professional Level)
10 Herbal Hill
Clerkenwell Road
London EC1R 5EG
Website: www.centralschoolofballet.co.uk
e-mail: info@csbschool.co.uk
Fax: 020-7833 5571   Tel: 020-7837 6332

CENTRE - PERFORMING ARTS COLLEGE The
Building 62, Level 4, 37 Bowater Road
Charlton, London SE18 5TF
Website: www.thecentrepac.com
e-mail: dance@thecentrepac.com
Fax: 020-8855 6662   Tel: 020-8855 6661

COLLECTIVE DANCE & DRAMA
The Studio, Rectory Lane
Rickmansworth, Herts WD3 1FD
Website: www.collectivedance.co.uk
e-mail: info@collectivedance.co.uk   Tel/Fax: 020-8428 0037

CONTI Italia ACADEMY OF THEATRE ARTS
(Full-time 3 year Musical Theatre Course)
Italia Conti House
23 Goswell Road, London EC1M 7AJ
Website: www.italiaconti.com
e-mail: admin@italiaconti.co.uk
Fax: 020-7253 1430   Tel: 020-7608 0044

COUNCIL FOR DANCE EDUCATION & TRAINING (CDET) The
Old Brewer's Yard
17-19 Neal Street
Covent Garden, London WC2H 9UY
Website: www.cdet.org.uk
e-mail: info@cdet.org.uk
Fax: 020-7240 2547   Tel: 020-7240 5703

CPA COLLEGE
The Studios, 219B North Street
Romford RM1 4QA
Website: www.colinsperformingarts.co.uk
e-mail: admin@colinsperformingarts.co.uk
Fax: 01708 766077   Tel: 01708 766007

CUSTARD FACTORY
(Professional Dance Classes & Dance Studio Hire)
Gibb Street, Digbeth, Birmingham B9 4AA
e-mail: post@custardfactory.com
Fax: 0121-604 8888   Tel: 0121-224 7777

D & B SCHOOL OF PERFORMING ARTS
Central Studios, 470 Bromley Road
Bromley, Kent BR1 4PN
Website: www.dandbperformingarts.co.uk
e-mail: bonnie@dandbmanagement.com
Fax: 020-8697 8100   Tel: 020-8698 8880

DANCE BASE NATIONAL CENTRE FOR DANCE
14-16 Grassmarket
Edinburgh EH1 2JU
Website: www.dancebase.co.uk
e-mail: dance@dancebase.co.uk
Fax: 0131-225 5234   Tel: 0131-225 5525

DANCE HOUSE
20 St Andrew's Street, Glasgow G1 5PD
Website: www.dancehouse.org
e-mail: info@dancehouse.org   Tel: 0141-552 2442

DANCE RESEARCH COMMITTEE - IMPERIAL SOCIETY OF TEACHERS OF DANCING
(Training in Historical Dance)
c/o Ludwell House
Charing, Kent TN27 0LS
Website: www.istd.org
e-mail: n.gainesarmitage@tiscali.co.uk
Fax: 01233 712768   Tel: 01233 712469

DANCEWORKS
(Also Fitness, Yoga & Martial Arts Classes)
16 Balderton Street, London W1K 6TN
e-mail: info@danceworks.net   Tel: 020-7629 6183

DAVIES Siobhan STUDIOS
(Daily Professional Classes, open classes for wider community)
85 St George's Road
London SE1 6ER
Website: www.siobhandavies.com
e-mail: info@siobhandavies.com
Fax: 020-7091 9669   Tel: 020-7091 9650

DIRECTIONS THEATRE ARTS CHESTERFIELD Ltd
1A-2A Sheffield Road
Chesterfield, Derbyshire S41 7LL
Website: www.directionstheatrearts.org
e-mail: julie.cox5@btconnect.com   Tel/Fax: 01246 854455

D M AGENCY The
The Studios, Briggate, Shipley
Bradford, West Yorks BD17 7BT
Website: www.dmacademy.co.uk
e-mail: info@dmacademy.co.uk
Fax: 01274 592502   Tel: 01274 585317

DUFFILL Drusilla THEATRE SCHOOL
Grove Lodge, Oakwood Road
Burgess Hill, West Sussex RH15 0HZ
Website: www.drusilladuffilltheatreschool.co.uk
e-mail: drusilladschool@btclick.com
Fax: 01444 232680   Tel: 01444 232672

EAST LONDON DANCE
Stratford Circus
Theatre Square, London E15 1BX
Website: www.eastlondondance.org
e-mail: office@eastlondondance.org
Fax: 020-8279 1054   Tel: 020-8279 1050

EDINBURGH'S TELFORD COLLEGE
350 West Granton Road
Edinburgh EH5 1QE
Website: www.ed-coll.ac.uk
e-mail: mail@ed-coll.ac.uk
Fax: 0131-559 4111   Tel: 0131-559 4000

ELIE Mark DANCE FOUNDATION
The Tabernacle
Powis Square, London W11 2AY
Website: www.markelie-dancefoundation.co.uk
e-mail: markeliedancefoundation@uk2.net
                              Mobile: 07947 484021

ELMHURST SCHOOL FOR DANCE
249 Bristol Road
Edgbaston, Birmingham B5 7UH
Website: www.elmhurstdance.co.uk
e-mail: enquiries@elmhurstdance.co.uk
Fax: 0121-472 6654   Tel: 0121-472 6655

ENGLISH NATIONAL BALLET SCHOOL
Carlyle Building, Hortensia Road
London SW10 0QS
Website: www.enbschool.org.uk
e-mail: info@enbschool.org.uk
Fax: 020-7376 3404   Tel: 020-7376 7076

Stella Mann College has been invited to offer places under the Government's Dance and Drama Awards scheme.

This College offers the opportunity to study for the National Diploma in either Professional Dance or Professional Musical Theatre, both validated by Trinity College, London.

Course accredited by the Council for Dance Education and Training.

Stella Mann College promotes individuality and difference and welcomes applications from people from under-represented groups.

10 Linden Road, Bedford, Bedfordshire, MK40 2DA.   Tel: 01234 213331   Fax: 01234 217284
e-mail: info@stellamanncollege.co.uk   www.stellamanncollege.co.uk

...stretch yourself to the max!

The CENTRE	Performing Arts College	**Building 62, Level 4, 37 Bowater Road, Charlton, London SE18 5TF**
Principal: Karen King F.I.S.T.D., A.R.A.D.	Professional Development Programme	**T: +44 (0)20 8855 6661**
	Agency	**F: +44(0)20 8855 6662**
	Junior Department	**E: dance@thecentrepac.com**
		W: www.thecentrepac.com

EXCEL SCHOOL OF PERFORMING ARTS
KT Summit House, 100 Hanger Lane
Ealing, London W5 1EZ
Website: www.ktioe-excel.org
e-mail: excel@kt.org   Tel: 020-8799 6168

EXPRESSIONS ACADEMY OF PERFORMING ARTS
3 Newgate Lane, Mansfield
Nottingham NG18 2LB
Website: www.expressionsperformingarts.co.uk
e-mail: expressions-uk@btconnect.com
Fax: 01623 647337   Tel: 01623 424334

GEORGIE SCHOOL OF THEATRE DANCE
101 Lane Head Road
Shepley, Huddersfield, West Yorkshire HD8 8DB
e-mail: donna.george@virgin.net   Tel/Fax: 01484 606994

GREASEPAINT ANONYMOUS
4 Gallus Close, Winchmore Hill, London N21 1JR
e-mail: info@greasepaintanonymous.co.uk
Fax: 020-8882 9189   Tel: 020-8886 2263

HAMMOND SCHOOL The
Hoole Bank, Mannings Lane, Chester CH2 4ES
Website: www.thehammondschool.co.uk
e-mail: info@thehammondschool.co.uk
Fax: 01244 305351   Tel: 01244 305350

HARRIS Paul
(Movement for Actors, Choreography, Tuition in Traditional
& Contemporary Social Dance)
24 Montana Gardens
Sutton, Surrey SM1 4FP
Website: www.paulharris.uk.com
e-mail: office@paulharris.uk.com
Mobile: 07958 784462   Tel: 020-8771 4274

ISLINGTON ARTS FACTORY
2 Parkhurst Road, London N7 0SF
e-mail: iaf@islingtonartsfactory.fsnet.co.uk
Fax: 020-7700 7229   Tel: 020-7607 0561

LABAN
Creekside, London SE8 3DZ
Website: www.laban.org
e-mail: info@laban.org
Fax: 020-8691 8400   Tel: 020-8691 8600

LAINE THEATRE ARTS
The Studios, East Street
Epsom, Surrey KT17 1HH
Website: www.laine-theatre-arts.co.uk
e-mail: webmaster@laine-theatre-arts.co.uk
Fax: 01372 723775   Tel: 01372 724648

LEE Lynn THEATRE SCHOOL The
(Office)
126 Church Road, Benfleet, Essex SS7 4EP
e-mail: lynn@leetheatre.fsnet.co.uk   Tel: 01268 795863

LIVERPOOL THEATRE SCHOOL
(Musical Theatre & Professional Classes)
19 Aigburth Road, Liverpool, Merseyside L17 4JR
Website: www.liverpooltheatreschool.co.uk
e-mail: info@liverpooltheatreschool.co.uk
Fax: 0151-728 9582   Tel: 0151-728 7800

LONDON CONTEMPORARY DANCE SCHOOL
(Full-time Vocational Training at Degree, Certificate &
Postgraduate Level)
16 Flaxman Terrace, London WC1H 9AT
Website: www.theplace.org.uk
e-mail: lcds@theplace.org.uk
Fax: 020-7121 1145   Tel: 020-7121 1111

LONDON STUDIO CENTRE
42-50 York Way, London N1 9AB
Website: www.london-studio-centre.co.uk
e-mail: info@london-studio-centre.co.uk
Fax: 020-7837 3248   Tel: 020-7837 7741

MANN Stella COLLEGE OF PERFORMING ARTS Ltd
(Professional Training Course for Performers & Teachers)
10 Linden Road, Bedford, Beds MK40 2DA
Website: www.stellamanncollege.co.uk
e-mail: info@stellamanncollege.co.uk
Fax: 01234 217284   Tel: 01234 213331

MIDLANDS ACADEMY OF DANCE & DRAMA
Century House, Building B
428 Carlton Hill, Nottingham NG4 1QA
Website: www.maddcollege.co.uk
e-mail: admin@maddcollege.supanet.com
    Tel/Fax: 0115-911 0401

MILLENNIUM DANCE 2000 Ltd
Hampstead Town Hall Centre
213 Haverstock Hill, London NW3 4QP
Website: www.md2000.co.uk
e-mail: md2000hampstead@aol.com   Tel/Fax: 020-7916 9335

MOVING EAST
St Matthias Church Hall
Wordsworth Road, London N16 8DD
Website: www.movingeast.co.uk
e-mail: admin@movingeast.co.uk   Tel: 020-7503 3101

NEW LONDON PERFORMING ARTS CENTRE
(Performing Arts Classes 3-19 years/All Dance Styles, GCSE
Course, RAD & ISTD Exams)
76 St James Lane, Muswell Hill, London N10 3DF
Website: www.nlpac.co.uk
e-mail: nlpac@aol.com
Fax: 020-8444 4040   Tel: 020-8444 4544

NORTH LONDON DANCE STUDIO
843-845 Green Lanes, Winchmore Hill, London, N21 2RX
e-mail: thedancestudio@btopenworld.com
Fax: 020-8364 2009   Tel: 020-8360 5700

NORTHERN ACADEMY OF PERFORMING ARTS
Anlaby Road, Hull HU1 2PD
Website: www.northernacademy.org.uk
e-mail: napa@northernacademy.org.uk
Fax: 01482 212280   Tel: 01482 310690

NORTHERN BALLET SCHOOL
The Dancehouse, 10 Oxford Road
Manchester M1 5QA
Website: www.northernballetschool.co.uk
e-mail: enquiries@northernballetschool.co.uk
Fax: 0161-237 1408   Tel: 0161-237 1406

NORTHERN SCHOOL OF CONTEMPORARY DANCE The
98 Chapeltown Road, Leeds LS7 4BH
Website: www.nscd.ac.uk
e-mail: info@nscd.ac.uk   Tel: 0113-219 3000

NORTH LONDON DANCE STUDIO
843-845 Green Lanes
Winchmore Hill, London, N21 2RX
e-mail: thedancestudio@btopenworld.com
Fax: 020-8364 2009   Tel: 020-8360 5700

PAUL'S THEATRE SCHOOL
Ardleigh House, 42 Ardleigh Green Road
Hornchurch, Essex RM11 2LG
Website: www.paulstheatreschool.co.uk
e-mail: info@paulstheatreschool.co.uk   Tel: 01708 447123

PERFORMERS COLLEGE
Southend Road, Corringham, Essex SS17 8JT
Website: www.performerscollege.co.uk
e-mail: pdc@dircon.co.uk
Fax: 01375 672353   Tel: 01375 672053

PINEAPPLE DANCE STUDIOS
7 Langley Street, London WC2H 9JA
Website: www.pineapple.uk.com
e-mail: studios@pineapple.uk.com
Fax: 020-7836 0803   Tel: 020-7836 4004

PLACE The
Robin Howard Dance Theatre
17 Duke's Road, London WC1H 9BY
Website: www.theplace.org.uk
e-mail: info@theplace.org.uk
Fax: 020-7121 1142   Tel: 020-7121 1000

PROFESSIONAL TEACHERS OF DANCING
Quay West Business Centre
Quay Lane, Gosport, Hants PO12 4LJ
Website: www.ptdance.com
e-mail: professionalteachersofdancing@msn.com
          Tel: 023-9260 4285

RAMBERT SCHOOL OF BALLET & CONTEMPORARY DANCE
Clifton Lodge, St. Margaret's Drive
Twickenham, Middlesex TW1 1QN
Website: www.rambertschool.org.uk
e-mail: info@rambertschool.org.uk
Fax: 020-8892 8090   Tel: 020-8892 9960

REFLECTIONS PERFORMING ARTS AGENCY
34 Knowle Avenue
Bexleyheath, Kent DA7 5LX
Website: www.reflectionsperfarts.tripod.com
e-mail: c.johnson717@ntlworld.com
Mobile: 07958 617976   Tel/Fax: 01322 410003

RIDGEWAY STUDIOS PERFORMING ARTS COLLEGE
Fairley House, Andrews Lane
Cheshunt, Herts EN7 6LB
Website: www.ridgewaystudios.co.uk
e-mail: info@ridgewaystudios.co.uk
Fax: 01992 633844   Tel: 01992 633775

ROEBUCK Gavin
(Classical Ballet)
51 Earls Court Square
London SW5 9DG   Tel: 020-7370 7324

ROJO Y NEGRO
(Argentine Tango School of Dance)
52 Lloyd Baker Street
Clerkenwell, London WC1X 9AA
Website: www.rojoynegroclub.com
e-mail: info@rojoynegroclub.com   Tel: 020-8520 2726

ROTIE BUTOH Marie-Gabrielle UK
7 Trinity Rise, London SW2 2QP
Website: www.rotieproductions.com
e-mail: rotiemanager@aol.com   Tel: 020-8674 1518

ROYAL ACADEMY OF DANCE
36 Battersea Square, London SW11 3RA
Website: www.rad.org.uk
e-mail: info@rad.org.uk
Fax: 020-7924 2311   Tel: 020-7326 8000

SAFREY ACADEMY OF PERFORMING ARTS
10 St Julians Close, London SW16 2RY
Website: www.safreyarts.co.uk
e-mail: info@safreyarts.co.uk
Fax: 020-8488 9121   Tel: 020-8664 6676

TIFFANY THEATRE COLLEGE
969-973 London Road
Leigh on Sea, Essex SS9 3LB
Website: www.tiffanytheatrecollege.com
e-mail: info@tiffanytheatrecollege.com
Fax: 01702 715645   Tel: 01702 710069

URDANG ACADEMY The
Finsbury Town Hall
Rosebery Avenue
London EC1R 4RP
Website: www.theurdangacademy.com
e-mail: info@theurdangacademy.com
Fax: 020-7278 6727   Tel: 020-7713 7710

VALLÉ ACADEMY OF PERFORMING ARTS
The Vallé Academy Studios
Wilton House
Delamare Road, Cheshunt, Herts EN8 9SG
Website: www.valleacademy.co.uk
e-mail: enquiries@valleacademy.co.uk
Fax: 01992 622868   Tel: 01992 622862

WHITEHALL PERFORMING ARTS CENTRE
Rayleigh Road, Leigh-on-Sea
Essex SS9 5UU   Tel/Fax: 01702 529290

YOUNG Sylvia THEATRE SCHOOL
Rossmore Road
Marylebone, London NW1 6NJ
Website: www.sylviayoungtheatreschool.co.uk
e-mail: sylvia@sylviayoungtheatreschool.co.uk
Fax: 020-7723 1040   Tel: 020-7402 0673

SPOTLIGHT DANCERS

SPOTLIGHT'S latest directory, created especially for dancers
Promote yourself to dance jobs across the UK and worldwide

To join call 020 7437 7631 or visit www.spotlight.com/dancers

ALRA (ACADEMY OF LIVE AND RECORDED ARTS)
Studio One
The Royal Victoria Patriotic Building
John Archer Way, London SW18 3SX
Website: www.alra.co.uk
e-mail: info@alra.co.uk
Fax: 020-8875 0789   Tel: 020-8870 6475

ARTS EDUCATIONAL SCHOOLS LONDON
14 Bath Road, London W4 1LY
Website: www.artsed.co.uk
e-mail: drama@artsed.co.uk
Fax: 020-8987 6699   Tel: 020-8987 6666

BIRMINGHAM SCHOOL OF ACTING
Millennium Point
Curzon Street
Birmingham B4 7XG
Website: www.bsa.bcu.ac.uk
e-mail: info@bsa.bcu.ac.uk
Fax: 0121-331 7221   Tel: 0121-331 7200

BRISTOL OLD VIC THEATRE SCHOOL
2 Downside Road
Clifton, Bristol BS8 2XF
Website: www.oldvic.ac.uk
e-mail: enquiries@oldvic.ac.uk
Fax: 0117-923 9371   Tel: 0117-973 3535

CENTRAL SCHOOL OF SPEECH & DRAMA
Embassy Theatre, 64 Eton Avenue
Swiss Cottage, London NW3 3HY
Website: www.cssd.ac.uk
e-mail: enquiries@cssd.ac.uk   Tel: 020-7722 8183

CONTI Italia ACADEMY OF THEATRE ARTS
Avondale, 72 Landor Road
London SW9 9PH
Website: www.italiaconti-acting.co.uk
e-mail: acting@lsbu.ac.uk
Fax: 020-7737 2728   Tel: 020-7733 3210

CYGNET TRAINING THEATRE
New Theatre, Friars Gate
Exeter, Devon EX2 4AZ
e-mail: cygnetarts@btconnect.com   Tel/Fax: 01392 277189

DRAMA CENTRE LONDON
Central Saint Martins College of Art & Design
10 Back Hill
London EC1R 5EN
Website: www.csm.arts.ac.uk/drama
e-mail: drama@arts.ac.uk
Fax: 020-7514 8777   Tel: 020-7514 8778

DRAMA STUDIO LONDON
Grange Court
1 Grange Road, London W5 5QN
Website: www.dramastudiolondon.co.uk
e-mail: registrar@dramastudiolondon.co.uk
Fax: 020-8566 2035   Tel: 020-8579 3897

EAST 15 ACTING SCHOOL
Hatfields, Rectory Lane, Loughton IG10 3RY
Website: www.east15.ac.uk
e-mail: east15@essex.ac.uk
Fax: 020-8508 7521   Tel: 020-8508 5983

GSA, GUILDFORD SCHOOL OF ACTING
Millmead Terrace
Guildford, Surrey GU2 4YT
Website: www.gsauk.org
e-mail: enquiries@gsauk.org   Tel: 01483 560701

GUILDHALL SCHOOL OF MUSIC & DRAMA
Silk Street, Barbican, London EC2Y 8DT
Website: www.gsmd.ac.uk
e-mail: info@gsmd.ac.uk
Fax: 020-7256 9438   Tel: 020-7628 2571

LAMDA
155 Talgarth Road, London W14 9DA
Website: www.lamda.org.uk
e-mail: enquiries@lamda.org.uk
Fax: 020-8834 0501   Tel: 020-8834 0500

LIVERPOOL INSTITUTE FOR PERFORMING ARTS The
Mount Street
Liverpool L1 9HF
Website: www.lipa.ac.uk
e-mail: reception@lipa.ac.uk
Fax: 0151-330 3131   Tel: 0151-330 3000

MANCHESTER METROPOLITAN UNIVERSITY SCHOOL OF THEATRE
The Mabel Tylecote Building
Cavendish Street
Manchester M15 6BG
Website: www.capitoltheatre.co.uk   Tel: 0161-247 1305

MOUNTVIEW
Academy of Theatre Arts
Ralph Richardson Memorial Studios
Clarendon Road, London N22 6XF
Website: www.mountview.org.uk
e-mail: enquiries@mountview.org.uk
Fax: 020-8829 0034   Tel: 020-8881 2201

OXFORD SCHOOL OF DRAMA The
Sansomes Farm Studios
Woodstock, Oxford OX20 1ER
Website: www.oxforddrama.ac.uk
e-mail: info@oxforddrama.ac.uk
Fax: 01993 811220   Tel: 01993 812883

QUEEN MARGARET UNIVERSITY, EDINBURGH
Queen Margaret University Drive
Musselburgh
East Lothian EH21 6UU
Website: www.qmu.ac.uk
e-mail: admissions@qmu.ac.uk
Fax: 0131-474 0001   Tel: 0131-474 0000

ROSE BRUFORD COLLEGE
Lamorbey Park, Burnt Oak Lane
Sidcup, Kent DA15 9DF
Website: www.bruford.ac.uk
Fax: 020-8308 0542   Tel: 020-8308 2600

ROYAL ACADEMY OF DRAMATIC ART
62-64 Gower Street, London WC1E 6ED
Website: www.rada.org
e-mail: enquiries@rada.ac.uk
Fax: 020-7323 3865   Tel: 020-7636 7076

ROYAL SCOTTISH ACADEMY OF MUSIC & DRAMA
100 Renfrew Street, Glasgow G2 3DB
Website: www.rsamd.ac.uk
e-mail: registry@rsamd.ac.uk   Tel: 0141-332 4101

ROYAL WELSH COLLEGE OF MUSIC & DRAMA
Drama Department
Castle Grounds, Cathays Park
Cardiff CF10 3ER
Website: www.rwcmd.ac.uk
e-mail: drama.admissions@rwcmd.ac.uk
Fax: 029-2039 1302   Tel: 029-2039 1327

THE CONFERENCE OF DRAMA SCHOOLS

The Conference of Drama Schools comprises Britain's 22 leading Drama Schools. CDS exists to set and maintain the highest standards of training within the vocational drama sector and to make it easier for prospective students to understand the range of courses on offer and the application process. CDS member schools offer courses in Acting, Musical Theatre, Directing and Technical Theatre training.

CDS members offer courses which are:
Professional – you will be trained to work in the theatre by staff with professional experience and by visiting professionals.
Intensive – courses are full-time.
Work Orientated – you are being trained to do a job – these courses are practical training for work.

CDS publishes *The Conference of Drama Schools – Guide to Professional Training in Drama and*

Technical Theatre 2009 and *The CDS Guide to Careers Backstage*.

For links to CDS schools please visit the website at **www.drama.ac.uk**

The full texts of both guides are available on the website – if you would like a hard copy please contact French's Theatre Bookshop, by phone on 020 7255 4300 or by emailing **theatre@samuelfrench-london.co.uk** or by visiting the shop at 52 Fitzroy Street, London, W1T 5JR. Single copies will be sent free of charge to UK addresses.
To contact CDS please visit the website or write to the Executive Secretary, CDS Ltd, P.O. Box 34252, London NW5 1XJ.

in association with

Why do I need drama training?

The entertainment industry is an extremely competitive one, with thousands of performers competing for a small number of jobs. In such a crowded market, professional training will increase an actor's chances of success, and professionally trained artists are also more likely to be represented by agencies. Drama training can begin at any age and should continue throughout an actor's career.

I have already trained to be an actor.
Why do I need further training?

Drama training should not cease as soon as you graduate or get your first job. Throughout your career you should strive to enhance your existing skills and keep up-to-date with the techniques new actors are being taught, even straight after drama school, in order to retain a competitive edge. You must also be prepared to learn new skills for specific roles if required. Ongoing drama training and classes can help you stay fit and active, and if you go through a period of unemployment you can keep your mind and body occupied, ready to take on your next job.

What kind of training is available?

For the under 18's, stage schools provide specialist training in acting, singing and dancing. They offer a variety of full and part-time courses. After 18, students can attend drama school. The standard route is to take a three-year, full-time course, in the same way you would take a university degree. Some schools also offer one or two-year courses.

What is the Conference of Drama Schools (CDS)?

The Conference of Drama Schools was founded in 1969 and comprises Britain's twenty two leading Drama Schools. It exists in order to strengthen the voice of the member schools, to set and maintain the highest standards of training within the vocational drama sector, and to make it easier for prospective students to understand the range of courses on offer and the application process. The twenty two member schools listed in the section 'Drama Schools (Conference Of)' offer courses in Acting, Musical Theatre, Directing and Technical Theatre training. For more information you can visit their website www.drama.ac.uk

What is NCDT?

The National Council for Drama Training was established in 1976 and is a unique collaborative partnership of employers in the theatre, broadcast and media industry, employee representatives and training providers. Its aim is to champion and support professional drama training and education working to safeguard the highest standards and quality assurance through accreditation for vocational drama courses in the UK. This provides students with the confidence that the courses they choose are recognised by the drama profession as being relevant to the purposes of their employment. For more information please see www.ncdt.co.uk

How should I use these listings?

The following listings provide up-to-date contact details for a wide range of performance courses, classes and coaches. Every company listed is done so by written request to us. Some companies have provided contact names, areas of specialisation and a selection of courses on offer.

I want to apply to join a full-time drama course.
Where do I start?

Your first step should be to research as many different courses as possible. Have a look on each school's website and request a prospectus. Ask around to find out where other people have trained or are training now and who they recommend. You would be advised to begin your search by considering CDS courses. Please refer to the CDS Guide to Professional Training in Drama & Technical Theatre for a description of each school, its policy and the courses it offers together with information about funding, available from www.drama.ac.uk

What types of courses are available?

Drama training courses generally involve three-year degree or diploma courses or one-year postgraduate courses if you have already attended university or can demonstrate a certain amount of previous experience. Alternatively, short-term or part-time foundation courses are available, which can serve as an introduction to acting but are not a substitute for a full-time drama course.

When should I apply?

Deadlines for applications to drama courses vary between schools so make sure you check each school's individual deadlines. Most courses start in September. UCAS must receive your application between mid-September 2008 and 15th January 2009 to guarantee that your application will be considered for a course beginning in 2009. You can apply after that until 30th June, but the school is then under no obligation to consider your application.
See www.ucas.ac.uk/students/startapplication/whentoapply for more details.

What funding is available to me?

Drama courses are unavoidably expensive. Most students have to fund their own course fees and other expenses, whether from savings, part-time work or a student loan. However, if you are from a low-income household you may qualify for a maintenance grant from the government to cover some of the costs. Some NCDT accredited courses offer a limited number of students Dance and Drama Awards (DaDA) scholarships, introduced to increase access to dance, drama and stage management training for talented students. These scholarships include help with both course fees and living expenses. Find out what each school offers in terms of potential financial support before applying. See www.ncdt.co.uk/acourse.asp for details of accredited courses and funding options.

Another possibility is to raise funds from a charity, trust or foundation. As with applying to agents and casting professionals for representation and work, do your research first and target your letters to explain how your needs meet each organisation's objectives, rather than sending a generalised letter to everyone. You are much more likely to be considered if you demonstrate that you know the background of the organisation and what they can offer performers. You will find further advice and a list of charities and foundations you could approach at www.ncdt.co.uk/facts.asp

How can my child become an actor?

If your child is interested in becoming an actor, they should try to get as much practical experience as possible. They could also join a stage school or sign with an agent. Please see the 'Agents – Children's & Teenagers'' section for more information, or 'Drama Training, Schools & Coaches' for stage school listings.

What about other forms of training?

Building on your initial acting course is essential for both new and more experienced actors. There are so many new skills you can learn – you could take stage fighting classes, hire a vocal coach, attend singing and dance lessons, and many more. These will enhance your CV and will give you a competitive edge. It is also extremely useful to take occasional 'refresher' courses on audition skills, different acting techniques and so on in various forms such as one-to-one lessons, one-off workshops or evening classes, to make sure you are not rusty when your next audition comes along.

Where can I find more information?

The Actors Centre runs approximately 1700 classes and workshops a year to encourage performers to develop their talent throughout their career in a supportive environment. They also run introductory classes for people who are interested in becoming actors but currently have no training or experience. Visit their website www.actorscentre.co.uk for more information. You may also want to refer to the 'Dance Training & Professional Classes' to add additional skills to your CV as well as keep fit. If you are interested in a career behind rather than in front of the camera or stage, please see the *CDS Guide to Careers Backstage*, available from www.drama.ac.uk

Barbara Berkery is an international film dialect and dialogue coach. Her work includes *Shakespeare in Love* (Gwyneth Paltrow), *Bridget Jones* (Renée Zellweger) and *Pirates of the Caribbean* (Geoffrey Rush).

Ask anyone in Europe and beyond who is interested in theatre, and they'll extol the virtues of the British drama school. Our schools – in particular those which are members of the Conference of Drama Schools and have courses accredited by the National Council for Drama Training – are famous all over the world for their rigour, focus and the strength of their traditions. Most aspiring actors or technicians in this country seek this kind of solid training, which also attracts aspiring theatre and film artists and designers from all over the world. Studying at a British drama school is a wise investment, as graduates feel – quite rightly – ready to answer any question posed to them by this notoriously demanding profession.

But has it occurred to you that British drama schools may in some ways be too good? Yes, they give you solid skills and approaches to the work; they replicate industry conditions; they put you in contact with experienced professionals. They might even give you an artistic education which will underpin your work with something akin to a 'philosophy of art'. They then 'rev you up' to the point where you enter the profession full of confidence, ready to take on all comers and make your mark. Brilliant!

And then... that's it! Or at least this is how most of us in this country feel after our training. "I have served my time; earned my spurs and now I needn't think about swotting ever again. All I have to do now is 'do it!' "

I recall meeting a few years ago on a Hollywood film set a young actor recently graduated from an English drama school and with a couple of film parts already under his belt. This was his first Hollywood role, however, and the (American) director asked him at one point to work to change aspects of his voice. His reaction? "It's like being at drama school again!"

Yet this is not the attitude in other cultures: in North America, for example, or in Japan, actors and technicians take it for granted that their professional skills require constant updating and development. In France, the national insurance system contributes significantly to the professional development of artists in periods between jobs, on the solid ground that the more strings people acquire to their bows, the more likely they are to get back to work. Here we are not fortunate enough to have this kind of support and it requires a significant effort of will as well as an investment of money and time to 'go back to school' from time to time.

Yet I think this is an essential part of being an artist: not only do we need to acquire more and more skills, but – as our careers progress – we find ourselves revisiting familiar territory with the increased sophistication brought about by experience. You may want to improve your singing; keep up your fitness and suppleness; learn in middle age how to market yourself through a website; or may want to move into voice overs. Above all, you may feel the need to recharge your artistic batteries and find fresh material with which to stimulate your imagination! For all these things – as well as for information on fundamental training – you will find the pages that follow invaluable.

Members of the Conference of Drama Schools offer their students the highest quality training in the industry. Graduates from these schools are in a strong position to advise anyone thinking of following in their path. We have asked two recent graduates from CDS schools to share their thoughts on the benefits of drama training.

 Chloe Thorpe has just graduated from Queen Margaret University where she achieved a BA in Acting and Performance. She is a Spotlight Prize Winner and was awarded Best Female Actor for 2008.

I want to be the best actor that I can possibly be, and have always known that the first step is training. I was rejected for two years running, but I kept acting by getting a HND in Performing Arts from New College Nottingham. This course helped me and my acting mature. To feel rejection at the first hurdle is hard, but I knew that acting was something I just had to do. It is not an easy choice on so many levels, but I couldn't walk away.

Drama school stretched me and gave me personal and professional strength. Training from nine 'til five every day is physically, mentally and emotionally shattering, yet finding the energy to work weekends at a coffee shop helped me maintain a healthy balance between drama school and the rest of the world.

I was lucky enough to acquire an agent from my showcase before graduating. This gave me a little security about embarking into the business. If drama school taught me one thing, however, it is to be proactive: you have to make your own opportunities.

Drama school and the professional world both require positivity. After weeks of no good news and feeling disheartened, keeping busy, keeping a faith in my ability and remembering the passion and laughter that acting brings are what get me through this fun but extremely hard business!

 Francis Ortega recently graduated from Rose Bruford College where he completed a BA course in Acting. He is a Spotlight Prize Winner and was awarded Best Male Actor for 2008.

It was whilst doing my A levels, with the encouragement of an inspirational teacher, that I decided to seriously pursue acting. Actor training is incredibly beneficial. For three years you are submerged in your art form, learning techniques in voice, movement and approaches to text: all from tutors and external directors with a great wealth of passion, experience and knowledge. This training aims to help you find a process which works for you, along with the stamina to support it.

Whilst at drama school I was lucky enough to have incredibly supportive parents, which meant I could focus on my training and didn't need to work on the side to support myself. There are some grants and bursaries available from schools and other governing bodies for those in financial need, but these are limited.

My advice is this: at auditions, speak to existing students about their experience. Also try watching drama school productions. Information on a school's upcoming season can be found on their website. Seeing the work produced by drama schools is a great insight into the training itself.

I hope this has been of some help, and I wish you all the best for the future.

DRAMA TRAINING

ALISON MEAD. BA Hons; MA Drama; IPA Cert; RSA Dip;
Audition Coaching; Performance Techniques; Sight Reading
Tel: 020 8402 7858. www.dramatraininguk.co.uk

A & J THEATRE WORKSHOP
The Trinity Church
Beaumont Road, London SW19 6SP
Website: www.ajmanagement.co.uk
e-mail: info@ajmanagement.co.uk
Fax: 020-8342 0842 Tel: 020-8342 0542

A B ACADEMY THEATRE SCHOOL
Act Out Ltd, 22 Greek Street
Stockport, Cheshire SK3 8AB
e-mail: ab22actout@aol.com Tel/Fax: 0161-429 7413

ABOMELI TUTORING
Contact: Charles Abomeli BA LLAM
Stage & Screen Acting Technique. Characterisation Coach
Website: www.charlesabomeli.com
e-mail: charlesabm@aol.com Mobile: 07960 954904

ACADEMY OF CREATIVE TRAINING
8-10 Rock Place
Brighton, East Sussex BN2 1PF
Website: www.actedu.org.uk
e-mail: info@actedu.org.uk Tel: 01273 818266

ACADEMY OF THE SCIENCE OF ACTING AND DIRECTING The
67-83 Seven Sisters Road
London N7 6BU
Website: www.asad.org.uk
e-mail: info@asad.org.uk
Fax: 020-7272 0026 Tel: 020-7272 0027

ACADEMY SCHOOL OF PERFORMING ARTS The
Dance. Drama. Singing
PO Box 432, Oldham, Lancashire OL9 8ZS
Website: www.academy-sopa.co.uk
e-mail: theacademy@ntlworld.com Tel: 0161-287 9700

ACKERLEY STUDIOS OF SPEECH, DRAMA & PUBLIC SPEAKING
Contact: Margaret Christina Parsons (Principal)
Speech. Drama
5th Floor, Hanover House, Hanover Street
Liverpool L1 3DZ Tel: 0151-709 5995

ACT ONE DRAMA STUDIO
31 Dobbin Hill, Sheffield S11 7JA
Website: www.actonedrama.co.uk
e-mail: actonedramastudio@mypostoffice.co.uk
Tel: 0114-266 7209

ACT UP
Acting Classes for Everyone. Acting Workshops. Audition Technique. Pre-Drama School (18 yrs). Public Speaking. Vocal Coaching
Unit 88, Battersea Business Centre
99-109 Lavender Hill, London SW11 5QL
Website: www.act-up.co.uk
e-mail: info@act-up.co.uk
Fax: 020-7924 6606 Tel: 020-7924 7701

ACTING & AUDITION SUCCESS
Contact: Philip Rosch, Association of Guildhall Teachers FVCM, LGSM, LALAM, ATCL, ANEA, BA (Hons)
Audition Speeches/Effective Auditioning. Sight Reading & Expert Career Advice, RADA Acting Exams
53 West Heath Court, North End Road
London NW11 7RG Tel: 020-8731 6686

ACTION LAB
Contact: Miranda French, Peter Irving
Part-time Acting Courses. Private Coaching
18 Lansdowne Road
London W11 3LL
Mobile: 07979 623987 Tel: 020-7727 3474

ACTORS CENTRE The
1A Tower Street, London WC2H 9NP
Website: www.actorscentre.co.uk
e-mail: members@actorscentre.co.uk Tel: 020-7240 3940

ACTORS STUDIO
Accompanist. Acting Workshops. Audition Technique. Dialect/Accent Coaching. Elocution. Improvisation. Language Tutoring. Private Acting Classes. Public Speaking. Singing. Stage School for Children. Vocal Coaching
Pinewood Film Studios
Pinewood Road
Iver Heath, Bucks SL0 0NH
Website: www.actorsstudio.co.uk
e-mail: info@actorsstudio.co.uk
Fax: 01753 655622 Tel: 01753 650951

Unit 10, 21 Wren Street, London WC1X 0HF

ACTOR'S TEMPLE The
13 Warren Street, London W1T 5LG
Website: www.actorstemple.com
e-mail: info@actorstemple.com
Mobile: 07771 734670 Tel: 020-3004 4537

ACTORS' THEATRE SCHOOL
Foundation Course
32 Exeter Road
London NW2 4SB
Website: www.theactorstheatreschool.co.uk
e-mail: info@theactorstheatreschool.co.uk
Fax: 020-8450 1057   Tel: 020-8450 0371

ACTORSPACE.CO.UK
Acting in Business. Auditions. Improvisation. Roleplay.
Voice & Text
6 Chandos Court
The Green
Southgate, London N14 7AA
Website: www.actorspace.co.uk
e-mail: drama@london.com
Fax: 0870 1342719   Tel: 020-8886 8870

ACTOR WORKS The
1 Knighten Street
Wapping, London E1W 1PH
Website: www.theactorworks.co.uk
e-mail: info@theactorworks.co.uk   Tel: 020-7702 0909

ACTS
Ayres-Clark Theatre School
12 Gatward Close, Winchmore Hill
London N21 1AS   Tel: 020-8360 0352

ADVANCED PERFORMERS STUDIO The
Royal Academy of Music
Website: www.apstudios.co.uk
e-mail: info@apstudios.co.uk   Mobile: 07847 058666

ALEXANDER Helen
Audition Technique, Drama School Entry
14 Chestnut Road
Raynes Park
London SW20 8EB   Tel: 020-8543 4085

ALLSORTS - DRAMA
Part-time Courses & Drama Training
Kensington, Notting Hill, Hampstead
Fulham, Putney (3-18 yrs)
34 Pember Road, London NW10 5LS
Website: www.allsortsdrama.com
e-mail: info@allsortsdrama.com   Tel/Fax: 020-8969 3249

ALRA (ACADEMY OF LIVE & RECORDED ARTS)
See DRAMA SCHOOLS (Conference of)

AMERICAN VOICES
Contact: Lynn Bains
American Accent/Dialect Coach. Acting Teacher & Director
20 Craighall Crescent
Edinburgh EH6 4RZ
e-mail: mail@lynnbains.com   Mobile: 07875 148755

AMERSHAM & WYCOMBE COLLEGE
Dual Campuses: Amersham & Chesham
Website: www.amersham.ac.uk
e-mail: info@amersham.ac.uk   Tel: 0800 614016

AND ALL THAT JAZZ
Contact: Eileen Hughes
Accompanist. Vocal Coaching
165 Gunnersbury Lane, Acton Town
London W3 8LJ   Tel: 020-8993 2111

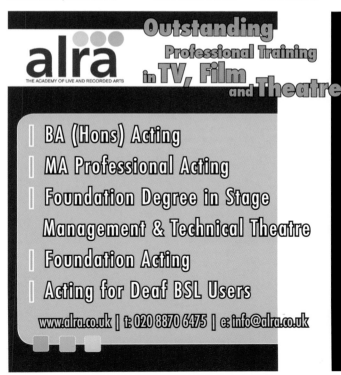

DIALECT COACH

LINDA JAMES R.A.M. Dip. Ed., I.P.D. (Lon Univ), L.R.A.M.

FILMS, T.V., STAGE & PRIVATE COACHING, ERADICATION OF ACCENT

020 8568 2390

ARDEN SCHOOL OF THEATRE The
Contact: Victoria Muir (Administrator)
Professional Stage Practice in Acting Studies & Musical
Theatre. HNC in Drama. PGDip in Writing for Performance
The Arden, 3 Universal Square
Devonshire Street North
Manchester M12 6JH
e-mail: ast@ccm.ac.uk
Fax: 0161-272 7645   Tel: 0161-279 7257

ARTEMIS SCHOOL OF SPEECH & DRAMA
Peredur Centre of The Arts
West Hoathly Road
East Grinstead
West Sussex RH19 4NF
Website: www.artemisspeechanddrama.org.uk
e-mail: office@artemisspeechanddrama.org.uk
          Tel/Fax: 01342 321330

ARTEMIS STUDIOS
30 Charles Square
Bracknell
Berkshire RG12 1AY
Website: www.artemis-studios.co.uk
e-mail: info@artemis-studios.co.uk   Tel: 01344 429403

ARTS EDUCATIONAL SCHOOL
Dance, Drama & Musical Theatre Training School (8-18 yrs)
Tring Park
Tring, Herts HP23 5LX
Website: www.aes-tring.com
e-mail: info@aes-tring.com   Tel: 01442 824255

ARTS EDUCATIONAL SCHOOLS LONDON
See DRAMA SCHOOLS (Conference of)

ASHCROFT ACADEMY OF DRAMATIC ART The
Drama LAMDA, Dance ISTD, Singing, (4-18 yrs)
Malcolm Primary School
Malcolm Road, Penge
London SE20 8RH
Website: www.ashcroftacademy.com
e-mail: geraldi.gillma@btconnect.com
Mobile: 07799 791586   Tel/Fax: 0844 8005328

ASHFORD Clare BSc, PGCE, LLAM, ALAM (Recital), ALAM (Acting)
20 The Chase
Coulsdon, Surrey CR5 2EG
e-mail: clareashford@handbag.com   Tel: 020-8660 9609

ASPIRE PRODUCTIONS
TV Presenter Training
34A Pollard Road, Morden, Surrey SM4 6EG
Website: www.aspirepresenting.com
e-mail: info@aspirepresenting.com   Tel: 020-8665 2275

AUDITION COACH
Contact: Martin Harris.
Acting Workshops. Audition Techniques. Private Acting
Classes. Group Evening Classes
245 Broadfield Road, Manchester M14 7JT
Website: www.auditioncoach.co.uk
e-mail: info@auditioncoach.co.uk
Mobile: 07788 723570   Tel: 0161-226 8788

BAC
Young People's Theatre Workshops & Performance Projects
(12-25 yrs)
Lavender Hill, London SW11 5TN
Website: www.bac.org.uk
e-mail: bacypt@bac.org.uk
Fax: 020-7978 5207   Tel: 020-7223 6557

BATE Richard MA (Theatre) LGSM (TD), PGCE (FE), Equity
Audition Technique. Vocal & Acting Training.
Drama School Entry
Apt 1, Broom Hall, High Street
Broom, Biggleswade
Bedfordshire SG18 9ND   Mobile: 07940 597738

BATES Esme CSSD STSD
Speech & Drama Coach. LAMDA Exam Specialist
2 Barons Court
Western Elmes Avenue
Reading, Berks RG30 2BP
e-mail: esmebates@btinternet.com
Mobile: 07941 700941   Tel: 0118-958 9330

BECK Eirene
Specialising in Voice & Audition Pieces
23 Rayne House, 170 Delaware Road
London W9 2LW   Tel: 020-7286 0588

BELCANTO LONDON ACADEMY
Stage School & Agency
Performance House, 20 Passey Place
Eltham, London SE9 5DQ
e-mail: agent@belcantolondonacademy.com
Fax: 020-8850 9944   Tel: 020-8850 9888

TRAIN AT ONE OF THE LEADING SCHOOLS FOR MUSICAL THEATRE AND PERFORMING ARTS

Former students include:
Julie Andrews, Sarah Brightman, Darcey Bussell,
Adam Cooper, Nigel Harman, Bonnie Langford,
Summer Strallen, Will Young and many more...

ARTS
ARTS EDUCATIONAL
SCHOOLS LONDON

President:
Lord Lloyd Webber

MUSICAL THEATRE

3yr BA Hons/Dip in Professional Musical Theatre

2yr Foundation in Musical Theatre (Sixth Form)

PERFORMING ARTS

3yr BA Hons/Dip in Professional Acting

1yr MA/Dip in Professional Acting

Post Diploma BA Hons in Performance Studies

1yr Part-Time Foundation Course

Indepdendent Vocational Day School - Aged 11-18

Saturday School

Short and Part-Time Courses

Summer Schools

Arts Educational Schools London
14 Bath Road, Chiswick, London W4 1LY
Telephone: 020 8987 6666   Email: receptionist@artsed.co.uk
WWW.ARTSED.CO.UK

BENCH Paul MEd, LGSM, ALAM, FRSA, LJBA (Hons), PGCE, ACP (Lings) (Hons), MASC (Ph), MIFA (Reg)
Corporate Vocal Presentation. Audition Technique. LAMDA Exams, Grades to Diploma Level. Private Acting Classes. Public Speaking. Vocal Coaching
1 Whitehall Terrace
Shrewsbury, Shropshire SY2 5AA
e-mail: pfbench@aol.com   Tel/Fax: 01743 233164

BENSKIN Eileen
Dialect Coach   Tel: 020-8455 9750

BERKERY Barbara
Dialogue/Dialect Coach for Film & Television
                Tel: 020-7281 3139

BEST THEATRE ARTS
PO Box 749, St Albans AL1 4YW
Website: www.besttheatrearts.com
e-mail: bestarts@aol.com   Tel: 01727 759634

BIG LITTLE THEATRE SCHOOL
Specialists in Musical Theatre & Acting Training (5-19 Years). Professional Development Programme & Youth Theatre.
Unit 305, Green Zone
Maycrete Road, Aviation Park West
Bournemouth Airport
Bournemouth BH23 6NW
Website: www.biglittletheatreschool.co.uk
e-mail: info@biglittletheatreschool.co.uk   Tel: 01202 574422

BIRD COLLEGE
Drama/Musical Theatre College
Birkbeck Centre, Birkbeck Road
Sidcup, Kent DA14 4DE
Website: www.birdcollege.co.uk
e-mail: admin@birdcollege.co.uk
Fax: 020-8308 1370   Tel: 020-8300 6004

BIRMINGHAM SCHOOL OF ACTING
See DRAMA SCHOOLS (Conference of)

BIRMINGHAM THEATRE SCHOOL The
The Old Rep Theatre
Station Street
Birmingham B5 4DY
Website: www.birminghamtheatreschool.co.uk
e-mail: info@birminghamtheatreschool.co.uk
                Tel: 0121-643 3300

BODENS STUDIOS
Contact: Adam Boden
Acting Workshops. Audition Technique. Dancing. Improvisation. Part-time Performing Arts Classes. Singing
Bodens Studio & Agency
99 East Barnet Road
New Barnet, Herts EN4 8RF
Website: www.bodenstudios.com
e-mail: info@bodenstudios.com
Fax: 020-8449 5212   Tel: 020-8449 0982

BOWES Sara
Child Acting Coach for Film & Commercials
23 John Aird Court
London W2 1UY
e-mail: sara@sarabowes.com
Mobile: 07830 375389   Tel: 020-7262 3543

BOYD Beth
Private Acting Classes
10 Prospect Road, Long Ditton, Surbiton
Surrey KT6 5PY   Tel: 020-8398 6768

BRADSHAW Irene
Private Coach. Voice & Audition Preparation
Flat F, Welbeck Mansions
Inglewood Road
West Hampstead, London NW6 1QX
Website: www.voicepowerworks.com   Tel: 020-7794 5721

BRAITHWAITE'S ACROBATIC SCHOOL
8 Brookshill Avenue
Harrow Weald
Middlesex   Tel: 020-8954 5638

BRANSTON Dale
Audition Techniques. Singing
Ground Floor Flat
16 Fernwood Avenue
Streatham, London SW16 1RD
e-mail: branpickle@yahoo.co.uk   Tel: 020-8696 9958

BRIDGE THEATRE TRAINING COMPANY The
Cecil Sharp House
2 Regent's Park Road
London NW1 7AY
Website: www.thebridge-ttc.org
e-mail: admin@thebridge-ttc.org
Fax: 020-7424 9118   Tel: 020-7424 0860

act up⸢ acting classes for everyone

Include:

⸺▷ act **for**   **a part-time foundation course in acting**

(for anyone auditioning for drama school).

Participants have gained places at: ALRA, The American Academy of Dramatic Arts (New York), ArtsEd, Birmingham School of Acting, Central School of Speech & Drama, Drama Studio London, E15, Lamda, Manchester Metropolitan University School of Theatre, Mountview, The Oxford School of Drama, The Poor School, RADA, Rose Bruford, Royal Welsh College of Music & Drama and Stella Adler Studio of Acting (New York).

⸺▷ act **too**

a series of workshops for professional actors

Also:
One to one tuition & industry advice.
Voice, presentation & communication skills training for the work place.

Tel 020 7924 7701 • Fax 020 7924 6606 • e-mail info@act-up.co.uk • website www.act-up.co.uk

---

BRIGHTON PERFORMERZONE
Contact: William Pool (ARCM)
Singing. Tuition. Workshops
33A Osmond Road, Hove, East Sussex BN3 1TD
Website: www.performerzone.co.uk
e-mail: info@performerzone.co.uk   Mobile: 07973 518643

BRIGHTON SCHOOL OF MUSIC & DRAMA
96 Claremont Road, Seaford
East Sussex BN25 2QA   Tel: 01323 492918

BRISTOL ACADEMY OF PERFORMING ARTS
The Academy Theatre, Market Place
Shepton Mallet, Somerset BA4 5AZ
Website: www.academytheatre.co.uk
e-mail: info@academytheatre.co.uk   Tel: 01749 347984

BRISTOL OLD VIC THEATRE SCHOOL
See DRAMA SCHOOLS (Conference of)

BRITISH AMERICAN DRAMA ACADEMY
14 Gloucester Gate
Regent's Park, London NW1 4HG
Website: www.badaonline.com
Fax: 020-7487 0731   Tel: 020-7487 0730

B.R.I.T. SCHOOL FOR PERFORMING ARTS & TECHNOLOGY The
60 The Crescent
Croydon CR0 2HN
Website: www.brit.croydon.sch.uk
e-mail: admin@brit.croydon.sch.uk
Fax: 020-8665 8676   Tel: 020-8665 5242

DAVID ROSS ACTING ACADEMY
"For Stage and Screen"
Run your own Acting School!
No marking or planning, fantastic curriculum, highly profitable Exiting lessons, work only 36 weeks, fantastic support network.

Call Clive Leach (National Marketing Director)
0800 288 9866
cliveleach@davidrossacting.com
w w w . d a v i d r o s s a c t i n g . c o m

BSA ACTOR TRAINING Ltd
Acting Workshops. Private Acting Classes. One Year Stage
& Screen Part Time Course. 10 Week Courses Including
Screen-Acting, Meisner Technique & Foundation
Admin Only:
First Floor
75 Brownlow Road, London N11 2BN
Website: www.bsa-actortraining.co.uk
e-mail: info@bsa-actortraining.co.uk   Tel: 020-3240 1064

CALE Bart TRAINING
Bristol
e-mail: bart.cale@virgin.net   Tel: 0117-969 2224

CAMERON BROWN Jo PGDVS
Dialect. Dialogue. Voice Coaching for films, TV,
Theatre & Auditions
6 The Bow Brook
Gathorne Street, London E2 0PW
e-mail: jocameronbrown@hotmail.com
Mobile: 07970 026621   Tel: 020-8981 1005

CAMPBELL Kenneth
Parkhills, 6 Clevelands Park
Northam, Bideford
North Devon EX39 3QH
e-mail: campbell870@btinternet.com   Tel: 01237 425217

CAMPBELL Ross ARCM, Dip RCM (Perf)
Head of Singing & Music, G.S.A. Singing Coach, Accompanist
& Music Director
17 Oldwood Chase
Farnborough
Hants GU14 0QS
e-mail: rosscampbell@ntlworld.com   Tel: 01252 510228

CAPITAL ARTS THEATRE SCHOOL
Contact: Kathleen Shanks
Wyllyotts Centre, Darkes Lane
Potters Bar, Herts EN6 2HN
e-mail: capitalarts@btconnect.com
Mobile: 07885 232414   Tel/Fax: 020-8449 2342

CARSHALTON COLLEGE
Nightingale Road
Carshalton, Surrey SM5 2EJ
Website: www.carshalton.ac.uk
e-mail: cs@carshalton.ac.uk
Fax: 020-8544 4440   Tel: 020-8544 4444

CELEBRATION THEATRE COMPANY FOR THE YOUNG
Contact: Neville Wortman
Summer Week Intensive Course. Acting Workshops.
Audition Technique. Dialect/Accent Coaching. Drama
School (over 18s). Elocution. Improvisation. Language
Tutoring. Private Acting Classes. Public Speaking. Stage
School for Children
48 Chiswick Staithe
London W4 3TP
Website: www.speakwell.co.uk
e-mail: wortman.speakwell@btinternet.com
Mobile: 07976 805976   Tel: 020-8994 8886

CENTRAL SCHOOL OF SPEECH & DRAMA
See DRAMA SCHOOLS (Conference of)

CENTRE STAGE SCHOOL OF PERFORMING ARTS
Students (4-18 yrs). North London
The Croft
7 Cannon Road
Southgate, London N14 7HJ
Website: www.centrestageuk.com
Fax: 020-8886 7555   Tel: 020-8886 4264

CENTRESTAGE SCHOOL OF PERFORMING ARTS
All Day Saturday Classes, Summer Courses, Private
Coaching for Professionals & Drama School Auditions
Centrestage House
117 Canfield Gardens
London NW6 3DY
Website: www.centrestageschool.co.uk
e-mail: vickiwoolf@centrestageschool.co.uk
Tel: 020-7328 0788

CHARD Verona LRAM, Dip RAM (Musical Theatre)
Teacher at Central School of Speech & Drama
Singing Tutor
Ealing House
33 Hanger Lane, London W5 3HJ
e-mail: veronachardmusic@aol.com   Tel: 020-8997 3355

CHARRINGTON Tim
Dialect/Accent Coaching
54 Topmast Point
Strafford Street
London E14 8SN
e-mail: tim.charrington@lycos.co.uk
Mobile: 07967 418236   Tel: 020-7987 3028

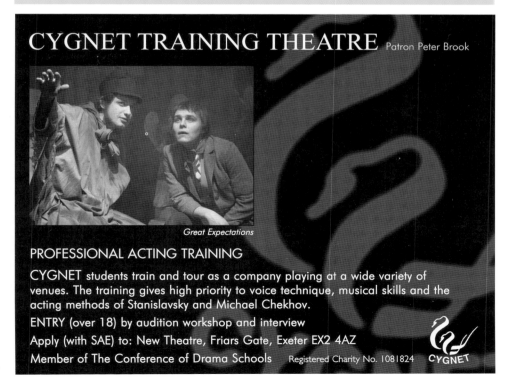

CHASE Stephan PRODUCTIONS Ltd
Private Coach for Acting Auditions & Public Speaking.
Dialect/Accent Coaching. Language Tutoring. Managing
Authentic Presence
The Studio
22 York Avenue
London SW14 7LG
Website: www.stephanchase.com
e-mail: stephan@stephanchase.com   Tel: 020-8878 9112

CHEKHOV Michael CENTRE
Acting Workshops. Audition Technique. Film Acting. Private
Acting Classes. Vocal Coaching, The Awakening,
The Deepening
Website: www.michaelchekhov.org.uk
e-mail: admin@michaelchekhov.org.uk   Tel: 01273 738238

CHRISKA STAGE SCHOOL
37-39 Whitby Road
Ellesmere Port
Cheshire L64 8AA   Tel: 01928 739166

CHRYSTEL ARTS THEATRE SCHOOL
Part-time classes for Children, Teenagers & Young Adults in
Dance, Drama & Musical Theatre. ISTD & LAMDA
Examinations
Edgware Parish Hall, Rectory Lane
Edgware, Middlesex HA8 7LG
e-mail: chrystelarts@waitrose.com   Tel/Fax: 01494 773336

CHURCHER Mel MA
Acting & Vocal Coach
Website: www.melchurcher.com
e-mail: melchurcher@hotmail.com   Mobile: 07778 773019

CHURCHER Teresa MASC
Acting, Audition & Career, Life Coach
London & Northampton
Website: www.teresachurcher.co.uk
e-mail: info@teresachurcher.co.uk   Mobile: 07966 228395

CIRCOMEDIA
Centre for Contemporary Circus & Physical Performance
Britannia Road
Kingswood, Bristol BS15 8DB
Website: www.circomedia.com
e-mail: info@circomedia.com   Tel/Fax: 0117-947 7288

CIRCUS MANIACS SCHOOL OF CIRCUS ARTS
Full & Part-time Courses, One-to-One Act Development &
Production Support
Office 8A
The Kingswood Foundation
Britannia Road
Kingswood, Bristol BS15 8DB
Website: www.circusmaniacs.com
e-mail: info@circusmaniacs.com
Mobile: 07977 247287   Tel/Fax: 0117-947 7042

CITY LIT The
Accredited & Non-Accredited Part-time & Full-time Day &
Evening Courses. Acting Workshops. Audition Technique.
Bi-Media Camera Training. Dancing. Dialect/Accent
Coaching. Directing. Drama School (over 18s). Elocution
Coaching. Improvisation. Language Tutoring. Presenting.
Professional Preparation. Public Speaking. Role-play
Training. Singing. Story Telling. Vocal Coaching
Keeley Street
Covent Garden
London WC2B 4BA
Website: www.citylit.ac.uk
e-mail: drama@citylit.ac.uk   Tel: 020-7492 2542

CLEMENTS Anne MA, LGSM, FRSA
Audition Technique. Back to Basics for Professional Actors.
Coaching. Dialect/Accent Coaching. Drama Preparation for
Drama School Entry. Private Acting Classes. Vocal Coaching
17 Gardnor Road
London NW3 1HA
e-mail: woodlandcreature10@hotmail.co.uk
                                    Mobile: 07963 818845

COLDIRON M J
Audition Preparation & Presentation Skills
Private Coaching
54 Millfields Road
London E5 0SB
e-mail: jiggs@blueyonder.co.uk   Tel: 020-8533 1506

COLGAN Valerie
Audition Technique & Voice Production
The Green
17 Herbert Street
London NW5 4HA   Tel: 020-7267 2153

PAUL GREGORY ACTOR / DRAMA COACH

EX RSC & RNT ACTOR. RECENTLY - DEMOCRACY & EMBERS.
Recent Film Sir Jack Crawford in SISTERHOOD (Comedy Feature).
Also HENRY V & FRANKENSTEIN with Kenneth Branagh.
Acted with & Directed by Sir Laurence Olivier, Robert De Niro, Anthony Hopkins,
Leonard Rossiter, Sir John Mills, Sir Anthony Sher, Jeremy Irons etc.

My students include: Louie Batley - HOLLYOAKS 2 Years
Stephanie Blacker - I WANT CANDY, Feature Film with Carmen Electra
Avtar Kaul - SHOOT ON SIGHT, Feature with Brian Cox
Kieran Leonard - HUSTLE, BBC TV with Robert Vaughn
Lauren Owen - LEND ME A TENOR, CBS New York
Peter Peralta - SUMMER, Short Feature, Berlin Film Festival & UK
Adrian Sharp - THE CLUB, Feature
Morgan Thrift - Bristol Old Vic Rep. Co., 1 Year
Scott Ryan Vickers - EMMERDALE
Sargon Yelda - MIDNIGHT MAN, ITV with James Nesbitt & SADDAM'S TRIBE, Channel 4

Private Coaching for Professionals and Students.

Successful applicants including Scholarships to ALL MAJOR DRAMA SCHOOLS
Many of my students also now represented by Top Agents.

Call me on: 020 8789 5726 or Mob: 07878 757814 *Putney Bridge Underground*

COMBER Sharrone BA (Hons) MAVS (CSSD) PGCE
Audition Technique. Dialect/Accent Coaching. Elocution.
Presentation Skills. Private Acting Classes. Public Speaking.
Vocal Coaching
8 Pinelands Close
St John's Park
Blackheath, London SE3 7TF
e-mail: sharronecomber@hotmail.com
Mobile: 07752 029422

COMEDY COACH
Contact: Jack Milner
43 Church Street
Chesham, Buckinghamshire HP5 1HU
Website: www.jackmilner.com
e-mail: jack@jackmilner.com
Tel: 01494 772908

COMPLETE WORKS CREATIVE COMPANY Ltd The
The Old Truman Brewery
91 Brick Lane, London E1 6QL
Website: www.tcw.org.uk
e-mail: info@tcw.org.uk
Fax: 0870 1431979
Tel: 0870 1431969

CONTI Italia ACADEMY OF THEATRE ARTS
See DRAMA SCHOOLS (Conference of)

CONTI Italia ACADEMY OF THEATRE ARTS
Italia Conti House
23 Goswell Road, London EC1M 7AJ
Website: www.italiaconti.com
e-mail: info@italiaconti.co.uk
Fax: 020-7253 1430
Tel: 020-7608 0044

CORNER Clive AGSM LRAM
Qualified Teacher, Private Coaching & Audition Training
3 Bainbridge Close
Ham
Middlesex TW10 5JJ
e-mail: cornerassociates@aol.com   Tel/Fax: 020-8332 1910

COURT THEATRE TRAINING COMPANY
55 East Road
London N1 6AH
Website: www.thecourtyard.org.uk
e-mail: info@thecourtyard.org.uk   Tel/Fax: 020-7251 6018

COX Jerry MA PGCE BA (Hons)
Flat 16 Aldermen Court
London N11 3GW
e-mail: jerrymarwood@hotmail.com   Mobile: 07957 654027

CPA COLLEGE
Full-time 3 yr Performing Arts College
The Studios, 219B North Street
Romford, Essex RM1 4QA
Website: www.colinsperformingarts.co.uk
e-mail: college@colinsperformingarts.co.uk
Fax: 01708 766077
Tel: 01708 766007

CREATIVE PERFORMANCE
Mobile Workshop in Circus Skills & Drama TIE. Events
Management for Communities
20 Pembroke Road
North Wembley, Middlesex HA9 7PD
e-mail: creative.performance@yahoo.co.uk
Tel/Fax: 020-8908 0502

CROWE Ben
Acting/Audition Tuition, Accent Coach
23 John Aird Court
London W2 1UY
e-mail: bencrowe@hotmail.co.uk
Mobile: 07952 784911   Tel: 020-7262 3543

CYGNET TRAINING THEATRE
See DRAMA SCHOOLS (Conference of)

D & B SCHOOL OF PERFORMING ARTS
Central Studios
470 Bromley Road
Bromley BR1 4PN
Website: www.dandbperformingarts.co.uk
e-mail: bonnie@dandbmanagement.com
Fax: 020-8697 8100   Tel: 020-8698 8880

DALLA VECCHIA Sara
Italian Teacher
13 Fauconberg Road
London W4 3JZ   Mobile: 07877 404743

DAVIDSON Clare
30 Highgate West Hill
London N6 6NP
Website: www.claredavidson.co.uk
e-mail: clare@claredavidson.co.uk   Tel: 020-8348 0132

DEBUT THEATRE SCHOOL OF PERFORMING ARTS
14 Titania Close
Cottingley
Bingley
West Yorkshire BD16 1WE
Website: www.debuttheatreschool.co.uk
Fax: 01274 564448   Tel: 01274 532347

DE COURCY Bridget
Singing Teacher
19 Muswell Road
London N10   Tel: 020-8883 8397

De FLOREZ Jane LGSM PG Dip
Singing Teacher, Auditions, Musical Theatre, Jazz, Classical
70 Ipsden Buildings
Windmill Walk
Waterloo, London SE1 8LT
Website: www.session-singer.archangel-promotions.co.uk
Tel: 020-7803 0835

DIGNAN Tess PDVS
Audition, Text & Voice Coach
004 Oregon Building
Deals Gateway
Lewisham SE13 7RR
e-mail: tessdignan60@tiscali.co.uk   Tel: 020-8691 4275

DI LACCIO Gabriela
Singing Teacher & Coach
165 Gunnersbury Lane
London W3 8LJ   Tel: 020-8993 2111

DIRECTIONS THEATRE ARTS (CHESTERFIELD) Ltd
Musical Theatre School & College
Studios: 1A/2A Sheffield Road
Chesterfield
Derby S41 7LL
Website: www.directionstheatrearts.org
e-mail: geoffrey.cox@btconnect.com
Mobile: 07973 768201   Tel/Fax: 01246 854455

DOGGETT Antonia MA
(Director of Cocksure Theatre Co)
Flat 2/2
131 Queen Margaret Drive
Glasgow G20 8PD
e-mail: antonia.doggett@googlemail.com
Mobile: 07814 155090

DONNELLY Elaine
Children's Acting Coach
Sangwin Associates
8-30 Galena Road, Hammersmith
London W6 0LT   Tel: 020-8748 8698

DRAGON DRAMA
Drama for Children
347 Hanworth Road
Hampton TW12 3EJ
Website: www.dragondrama.co.uk
e-mail: info@dragondrama.co.uk   Tel/Fax: 020-8255 8356

DRAMA ASSOCIATION OF WALES
Summer Courses for Amateur Actors & Directors
The Old Library
Singleton Road
Splott, Cardiff CF24 2ET
e-mail: aled.daw@virgin.net
Fax: 029-2045 2277   Tel: 029-2045 2200

DRAMA CENTRE LONDON
See DRAMA SCHOOLS (Conference of)

DRAMA STUDIO EDINBURGH The
Children's Weekly Drama Workshops
19 Belmont Road
Edinburgh EH14 5DZ
Website: www.thedramastudio.com
e-mail: info@thedramastudio.com
Fax: 0131-453 3108   Tel: 0131-453 3284

DRAMA STUDIO LONDON
See DRAMA SCHOOL (Conference of)

DREAM FACTORY The
*Accredited Professional Creative Arts Training Facility
Located within a UK Prison - Open to Offenders,
Ex-offenders & the Wider Community*
PO Box 31855
London SE17 3XP
Website: www.londonshakespeare.org.uk
e-mail: londonswo@hotmail.com   Tel: 020-7793 9755

DULIEU John
Acting Coach. Audition & Role Preparation
16 Fernwood Avenue
Streatham
London SW16 1RD
e-mail: john_dulieu@yahoo.com
Mobile: 07803 289599   Tel: 020-8696 9958

DUNMORE Simon
Acting & Audition Tuition
Website: www.simon.dunmore.btinternet.co.uk
e-mail: simon.dunmore@btinternet.com

DURRENT Peter
Audition & Rehearsal Pianist, Vocal Coach
Blacksmiths Cottage
Bures Road
Little Cornard
Sudbury
Suffolk CO10 0NR   Tel: 01787 373483

DYSON Kate LRAM
Audition Technique Coaching, Drama
39 Arundel Street
Kemptown BN2 5TH
Tel: 01273 607490   Mobile: 07812 949875

EARNSHAW Susi THEATRE SCHOOL
The Bull Theatre
68 High Street
Barnet
Herts EN5 5SJ
Website: www.susiearnshaw.co.uk
e-mail: info@sets.org.uk
Fax: 020-8364 9618   Tel: 020-8441 5010

EAST 15 ACTING SCHOOL
See DRAMA SCHOOLS (Conference of)

EASTON Helena BPSA MA ATC (CSSD)
Acting Coach
103 Red Square
Carysfort Road, London N16 9AG
e-mail: helena.easton@gmail.com   Mobile: 07985 931473

ECOLE INTERNATIONALE DE THEATRE JACQUES LECOQ
Contact: Rita Leys
Acting Workshops. Drama School (over 21yrs). Mime.
Movement & Creative Theatre. Play Writing
57 rue du Faubourg Saint-Denis
75010 Paris
Website: www.ecole-jacqueslecoq.com
e-mail: contact@ecole-jacqueslecoq.com
Fax: 00 331 45 23 40 14   Tel: 00 331 47 70 44 78

ELLIOTT CLARKE THEATRE SCHOOL & COLLEGE
Full-time Vocational Training. Saturday & Evening classes
132 Bold Street
Liverpool L1 4EZ   Tel: 0151-709 3323

EXCEL SCHOOL OF PERFORMING ARTS
KT Summit House
100 Hanger Lane, Ealing W5 1EZ
Website: www.ktioe-excel.org
e-mail: excel@kt.org   Tel: 020-8799 6168

EXPRESSIONS ACADEMY OF PERFORMING ARTS
3 Newgate Lane
Mansfield, Notts NG18 2LB
Website: www.expressionsperformingarts.co.uk
e-mail: expressions-uk@btconnect.com
Fax: 01623 647337   Tel: 01623 424334

FAIRBROTHER Victoria MA, CSSD, LAMDA Dip
Audition Technique. Improvisation. Private Acting Classes.
Public Speaking. Vocal Coaching. Vocal Connection to Self
& Text
15A Devenport Road
Shepherd's Bush
London W12 8NZ
e-mail: victoriafairbrother1@hotmail.com
Mobile: 07877 228990   Tel: 020-8749 1253

FAITH Gordon BA, IPA Dip, REM Sp, MCHC (UK), LRAM
Speech
1 Wavel Mews
Priory Road
London NW6 3AB   Tel: 020-7328 0446

FBI AGENCY Ltd
Acting Classes for Everyone
PO Box 250
Leeds LS1 2AZ
Website: www.fbi-agency.ltd.uk
e-mail: j.spencer@fbi-agency.ltd.uk   Tel/Fax: 07050 222747

FERRIS Anna MA (Voice Studies, CSSD)
Audition Technique. Private Acting Classes. Vocal Coaching
Gil'cup Leaze
Hilton
Blandford Forum
Dorset DT11 0DB   Tel: 01258 881098

FERRIS ENTERTAINMENT PERFORMING ARTS
London & Cardiff
Number 8
132 Charing Cross Road
London WC2H 0LA
Website: www.ferrisentertainment.com
e-mail: info@ferrisentertainment.com Mobile: 07801 493133

FINBURGH Nina
Sight Reading Specialist (Masterclasses & Individuals)
1 Buckingham Mansions
West End Lane
London NW6 1LR
e-mail: ninafinburgh@aol.com   Tel: 020-7435 9484

FOOTSTEPS THEATRE SCHOOL
Dance, Drama & Singing Training
145 Bolton Lane
Bradford BD2 4AT
e-mail: helen@footsteps.fslife.co.uk   Tel/Fax: 01274 626353

FORD Carole Ann ADVS
Acting Training & Communication Skills for Business
N10 2AL
e-mail: emko2000@aol.com   Tel: 020-8815 1832

FORREST Dee
Deputy Head of Voice. Mountview. Audition Technique.
Dialect/Accent Coaching for Film & Television. Elocution
NLP. Public Speaking. Vocal Coaching
20 Landseer Road
Hove BN3 7AF
Website: www.deeforrest4voice.com
e-mail: dee_forrest@yahoo.com
Mobile: 07957 211065   Tel: 01273 204779

FOX Betty STAGE SCHOOL
Slade Road, Erdington
Birmingham B23 7PX
e-mail: bettyfox.school@virgin.net
Mobile: 07703 436045   Tel/Fax: 0121-327 1020

FRANKLIN Michael
Meisner Technique
Correspondence:
c/o Spotlight
7 Leicester Place
London WC2H 7RJ   Tel/Fax: 020-8979 9185

FRANKLYN Susan
Audition Speeches. Confidence. Interview Technique.
Presentation. Sight Readings
Mobile: 07780 742891   Tel: 01306 884913

FRIEZE Sandra
English & Foreign Actors
London Area NW3/NW6   Mobile: 07802 865305

GAUNT Julia, ALCM, TD-Musical Theatre
Singing Teacher
116 Nottingham Road
Selston
Nottinghamshire
e-mail: joolsmusicbiz@aol.com   Mobile: 07712 624083

GLASGOW ACTING ACADEMY
34 Argyle Arcade Chambers
Buchanan Street
Glasgow G2 8BD
e-mail: info@glasgowactingacademy.com
                                        Tel: 0141-222 2942

GLYNNE Frances THEATRE STUDENTS
Flat 9
Elmwood, 6 The Avenue
Hatch End, Middlesex HA5 4EP
e-mail: franandmo@googlemail.com   Mobile: 07950 918355

GMA TELEVISION PRESENTER TRAINING
Audition Technique. Improvisation. Public Speaking. Radio
Presenting. Vocal Coaching
86 Beverley Gardens
Maidenhead
Berks SL6 6SW
e-mail: geoff@gma-training.co.uk
Mobile: 07769 598625   Tel: 01628 673078

GO FOR IT THEATRE SCHOOL
Contact: Teri Scoble
Acting Workshops. Audition Technique. Dancing.
Improvisation. Private Dance. Singing. Stage School for
Children
47 North Lane
Teddington
Middlesex TW11 0HU
Website: www.goforitts.com
e-mail: agency@goforitts.com   Tel: 020-8943 1120

GRAYSON John
Coaching for Drama Auditions
2 Jubilee Road
St Johns
Worcester WR2 4LY
e-mail: jgbizzybee@btinternet.com   Mobile: 07702 188031

GREASEPAINT ANONYMOUS
Youth Theatre & Training Company. Part-time Theatre
Workshops Run Weekly Through School Term Time. Holiday
Courses at Easter & Summer. Acting Workshops. Dancing.
Drama School (over 18s). Improvisation. Singing.
Stage School for Children
4 Gallus Close
Winchmore Hill
London N21 1JR
e-mail: info@greasepaintanonymous.co.uk
Fax: 020-8882 9189   Tel: 020-8886 2263

Gloria Lytton

Former Actress
Qualified Speech Therapist
Teacher at R.A.D.A. 1972-1986

Remedial Voice and Speech Work
Speaking with Confidence
Public Speaking
Audition Coaching

For people from all backgrounds
and walks of life

Tel: 020-8441 3118

GREGORY Lynda SCHOOL OF SPEECH & DRAMA
Speech and Drama Classes, All Ages
23 High Ash Avenue
Leeds LS17 8RS Tel: 0113-268 4519

GREGORY Paul
RSC & RNT Actor/Drama Coach
133 Kenilworth Court
Lower Richmond Road
Putney
London SW15 1HB
e-mail: paulgregory@paulgregorydramacoach.co.uk
Mobile: 07878 757814 Tel: 020-8789 5726

GREVILLE Jeannine THEATRE SCHOOL
Melody House, Gillott's Corner
Henley-on-Thames
Oxon RG9 1QU
e-mail: jeannines.dance@ukonline.co.uk Tel: 01491 572000

GROUT Philip
Theatre Director. Drama Coaching
81 Clarence Road
London N22 8PG
e-mail: philipgrout@hotmail.com Tel: 020-8881 1800

GSA, GUILDFORD SCHOOL OF ACTING
See DRAMA SCHOOLS (Conference of)

GUILDHALL SCHOOL OF MUSIC & DRAMA
See DRAMA SCHOOLS (Conference of)

HALL Michael THEATRE SCHOOL & CASTING AGENCY
Performing Arts Centre
19 Preston Old Road
Blackpool
Lancs FY3 9PR
e-mail: halljohn55@yahoo.com Tel: 01253 696990

HANCOCK Allison LLAM
Acting. Audition Coach. Dramatic Art. Elocution.
Speech Correction. Voice
38 Eve Road
Isleworth
Middlesex TW7 7HS Tel/Fax: 020-8891 1073

HARLEQUIN STUDIOS PERFORMING ARTS SCHOOL
Drama & Dance Training
122A Phyllis Avenue
Peacehaven
East Sussex BN10 7RQ Tel: 01273 581742

**HARRIS Sharon NCSD, LRAM, LAM, STSD, IPA Dip DA
(London Univ)**
Courses in Speech & Drama (RADA, LAMDA ESB).
Acting Workshops. Drama School (over 18s). Drama School
Entry. Improvisation. Private Acting Classes.
Stage School for Children
The Harris Drama School
Rajvilas
Kewferry Drive
Northwood
Middlesex HA6 2NT
e-mail: theharrisagency@btconnect.com
Fax: 01923 822253 Tel: 01923 822744

HARRISON Lucie MA Voice Studies, BA (Hons) Drama
Voice Teacher & Acting Coach
25 Shortlands Road
Kingston, Surrey KT2
Website: www.lucieharrison.co.uk
e-mail: info@lucieharrison.co.uk Mobile: 07773 798440

HASS Leontine
Vocal Coach
12 Silverton Road
London W6 9NY
Website: www.apstudios.co.uk
e-mail: info@apstudios.co.uk Mobile: 07801 270745

HEALING VOICES
Contact: Felicitas Ste. Croix. Singing Coach
London, Paris, Los Angeles, Athens
e-mail: healing.voices@yahoo.com Mobile: 07939 143721

HERTFORDSHIRE THEATRE SCHOOL
40 Queen Street
Hitchin
Herts SG4 9TS
Website: www.htstheatreschool.co.uk
e-mail: info@htstheatreschool.co.uk Tel: 01462 421416

HESTER John LLCM (TD)
(Member of The Society of Teachers of Speech & Drama)
Acting Courses for All Ages. Acting Workshops. Audition
Technique. Dialect/Accent Coaching. Drama School
Auditions (over 18s). Elocution Coaching. Private Acting
Classes. Public Speaking. Stage School for Children.
Vocal Coaching
105 Stoneleigh Park Road
Epsom
Surrey KT19 0RF
e-mail: hjohnhester@aol.com Tel: 020-8393 5705

HIGGS Jessica
Voice
41A Barnsbury Street
London N1 1PW
Mobile: 07940 193631 Tel/Fax: 020-7359 7848

H. J. A. (HERBERT JUSTICE ACADEMY)
PO Box 253
Beckenham
Kent BR3 3WH
Website: www.hjaworld.com
e-mail: mail@hjaworld.com
Fax: 020-8249 2616 Tel: 020-8249 3299

HOFFMANN-GILL Daniel
Acting & Audition Tuition
Flat 1, 28 Sidney Avenue
London N13 4UY
e-mail: danielhg@gmail.com
Mobile: 07946 433903   Tel: 020-8888 6045

HONEYBORNE Jack
Accompanist & Coach
The Studio, 165 Gunnersbury Lane
London W3 8LJ   Tel: 020-8993 2111

HOPE STREET Ltd
Physical & Multi-Media Perfomance, Training for Actors,
Designers, Directors & Participatory Arts Workers
13A Hope Street, Liverpool L1 9BQ
Website: www.hope-street.org
e-mail: arts@hope-street.org
Fax: 0151-709 3242   Tel: 0151-708 8007

HOPNER Ernest LLAM
Elocution. Public Speaking. Vocal Coaching
70 Banks Road
West Kirby CH48 0RD   Tel: 0151-625 5641

HOUSEMAN Barbara
Ex-RSC Voice Dept, Associate Director Young Vic
Acting. Confidence. Text. Voice
e-mail: barbarahouseman@hotmail.com
     Mobile: 07767 843737

HOWARD Ashley BA MA
Vocal Coach
87 Waddington Street, Norwich, Norfolk NR2 4JX
Website: www.vocalcoach.uk.com
e-mail: info@vocalcoach.uk.com   Mobile: 07821 213752

HUDDERSFIELD TECHNICAL COLLEGE
Courses in Acting, Dance & Musical Theatre
(BTec, GCSE & HNC)
Highfields Annexe
New North Road, Huddersfield HD1 5NN
e-mail: info@huddcoll.ac.uk   Tel: 01484 437047

HUGHES-D'AETH Charlie
Acting Workshops. Audition Techniques. Dialect/Accent
Coaching. Elocution. Private Acting Classes. Public
Speaking. Singing. Vocal Coaching
22 Osborne Road, Brighton BN1 6LQ
e-mail: chdaeth@aol.com   Mobile: 07811 010963

HUGHES Dewi
Accents. Auditions. Bodywork. Text. Voice
Flat 2, 4 Fielding Road, London W14 0LL
e-mail: dewi.hughes@gmail.com   Mobile: 07836 545717

IMPULSE COMPANY The
Meisner-Based Core Training
PO Box 158, Twickenham TW1 3WG
e-mail: info@impulsecompany.co.uk   Tel/Fax: 07525 264173

INDEPENDENT THEATRE WORKSHOP The
2 Mornington Road, Ranelagh, Dublin 6, Ireland
Website: www.independent-theatre-workshop.com
e-mail: info@independent-theatre-workshop.com
                                        Tel/Fax: 00 353 1 4968808

INTERACT
Contact: Lauren Bigby (LGSM)
Acting Workshops. Audition Technique. Elocution Coaching.
Private Acting Classes. Public Speaking
19 Raven Lane, Billericay, Essex CM12 0JB
Website: www.laurenbigby.me.uk
e-mail: renbigby@hotmail.com   Mobile: 07961 982198

INTERNATIONAL SCHOOL OF SCREEN ACTING
3 Mills Studios, Unit 3
24 Sugar House Lane, London E15 2QS
Website: www.screenacting.co.uk
e-mail: office@screenacting.co.uk   Tel: 020-8555 5775

JACK Andrew
Dialect Coach
Vrouwe Johanna
24 The Moorings, Willows Riverside, Windsor, Berks SL4 5TG
Website: www.andrewjack.com   Mobile: 07836 615839

JACK Paula
Dialect Coach & Language Specialist
Vrouwe Johanna
24 The Moorings, Willows Riverside
Windsor, Berks SL4 5TG
Website: www.paulajack.com   Mobile: 07836 615839

JACOBSEN Anja
German Language and Accent Tuition, Acting in German, Translation
54 Higham Hill Road
London E17 6ER   Tel: 020-8523 4950

JAM THEATRE COMPANY
21 Beechtree Avenue, Marlow, Bucks SL7 3NH
Website: www.jamtheatre.co.uk
e-mail: office@jamtheatre.co.uk   Tel: 01628 487773

JAMES Linda RAM Dip Ed, IPD, LRAM
Dialect Coach. Elocution Coaching
25 Clifden Road, Brentford
Middlesex TW8 0PB   Tel: 020-8568 2390

JAQUARELLO Roland BA
Audition, Drama School Entrance, Radio Coaching
41 Parfrey Street, London W6 9EW
Website: www.rolandjaquarello.com
e-mail: roland@jaquarellofulham.freeserve.co.uk
                                        Tel/Fax: 020-8741 2446

JIGSAW PERFORMING ARTS SCHOOL
64-66 High Street, Barnet, Herts EN5 5SJ
e-mail: admin@jigsaw-arts.co.uk   Tel: 020-8447 4530

JINGLES Jo
1 Boismore Road
Chesham, Bucks HP5 1SH
Website: www.jojingles.com
e-mail: headoffice@jojingles.co.uk   Tel: 01494 778989

JONES Desmond
Courses in Dynamic Acting, The Total Actor. Introduction to Mime & Physical Theatre. Physical Story Telling for the Theatre. Private Classes & Consultant - Freelance Choreography. Director. Teacher. Coach
20 Thornton Avenue, London W4 1QG
Website: www.desmondjones.com
e-mail: enquiries@desmondjones.com
                                        Tel/Fax: 020-8747 3537

JUDE'S DRAMA ACADEMY & MANAGEMENT
Manor House, Oldham Road
Springhead, Oldham OL4 4QJ
Website: www.judesdrama.com
e-mail: judesdrama@yahoo.co.uk   Tel: 0161-624 5378

KENT YOUTH THEATRE
Contact: Richard Andrews. Courses in Drama, Dance, Musical Theatre, Singing, Film Acting/Making. Improvisation. Private Acting Classes. Stage School for Children. Stage & Screen Academy
Mulberry Croft
Mulberry Hill
Chilham CT4 8AJ
Website: www.kentyouththeatre.co.uk
e-mail: richard@kyt.org.uk
Mobile: 07967 580213   Tel/Fax: 01227 730177

KERR Louise
Voice Coach
20A Rectory Road, London E17 3BQ
Website: www.resonancevoice.com
e-mail: louise@louisekerr.com
Mobile: 07780 708102
Tel: 020-8509 2767

KNYVETTE Sally
52 Burnfoot Avenue
London SW6 5EA
e-mail: salkny@aol.co.uk
Tel/Fax: 020-7731 0639

KRIMPAS Titania
One-to-one Tuition. Audition Technique. Drama School (over 18s)
The Garden Flat
23 Lambolle Road, London NW3 4HS
e-mail: titania@krimpas.freeserve.co.uk
Mobile: 07957 303958

LAINE THEATRE ARTS
Contact: Betty Laine
The Studios, East Street
Epsom, Surrey KT17 1HH
Website: www.laine-theatre-arts.co.uk
e-mail: info@laine-theatre-arts.co.uk
Fax: 01372 723775
Tel: 01372 724648

LAMDA
See DRAMA SCHOOLS (Conference of)

LAMONT DRAMA SCHOOL & CASTING AGENCY
Contact: Diane Lamont
Part-time Lessons. Audition Technique. Elocution Coaching. Improvisation
2 Harewood Avenue
Ainsdale, Merseyside PR8 2PH
Website: www.lamontcasting.co.uk
e-mail: diane@lamontcasting.co.uk
Mobile: 07736 387543

LAURIE Rona
Coach for Auditions & Voice and Speech Technique
Flat 1, 21 New Quebec Street
London W1H 7SA
Tel: 020-7262 4909

LEAN David Lawson BA Hons, PGCE
Acting Tuition for Children, LAMDA Exams, Licensed Chaperone
72 Shaw Drive
Walton-on-Thames, Surrey KT12 2LS
Website: www.davidlawsonlean.com
Tel: 01932 230231

LEE STAGE SCHOOL The
Office:
126 Church Road, Benfleet, Essex SS7 4EP
e-mail: lynn@leetheatre.fsnet.co.uk
Tel: 01268 795863

LESLIE Maeve
Classical & Musicals. Presentations. Singing. Voice Production
60 Warwick Square
London SW1V 2AL
Tel: 020-7834 4912

LEVENTON Patricia BA Hons
Audition & Dialect Coach
113 Broadhurst Gardens, West Hampstead, London NW6 3BJ
e-mail: patricia@lites2000.com
Mobile: 07703 341062
Tel: 020-7624 5661

BARBARA HOUSEMAN VOICE, TEXT, ACTING COACH
Author: Finding Your Voice & Tackling Text [and subtext]
RSC, WEST END, TV, FILM
barbarahouseman@hotmail.com

LINCOLN ACADEMY OF DRAMATIC ARTS
(6-18 yrs)
Sparkhouse Studios
Rope Walk, Lincoln, Lincs LN6 7DQ
Website: www.lada.org.uk/academy
e-mail: info@lada.org.uk
Fax: 01522 837201   Tel: 01522 837242

LIPTON Rick
Dialect/Accent Coaching
14 Lock Road
Richmond, Surrey TW10 7LH
e-mail: ricklipton@gmail.com   Mobile: 07961 445247

LIVERPOOL INSTITUTE FOR PERFORMING ARTS The
See DRAMA SCHOOLS (Conference of)

LIVINGSTON Dione LRAM, FETC
Audition Technique. Dialect/Accent Coaching. Elocution Coaching. Improvisation. Language Tutoring. Private Acting Classes. Public Speaking. Vocal Coaching
7 St Luke's Street
Cambridge CB4 3DA   Tel: 01223 365970

LOCATION TUTORS NATIONWIDE
Fully Qualified/Experienced Teachers Working with Children on Film Sets & Covering all Key Stages of National Curriculum
16 Poplar Walk
Herne Hill SE24 0BU
Website: www.locationtutors.co.uk
e-mail: locationtutorsnationwide@hotmail.com
Fax: 020-7207 8794   Tel: 020-7978 8898

LONDON ACTORS WORKSHOP
Pinewood Film Studios
Pinewood Road
Iver Heath, Bucks SL0 0NH
Website: www.londonactorsworkshop.co.uk
e-mail: info@londonactorsworkshop.co.uk
Mobile: 07748 846294

LONDON DRAMA SCHOOL
Acting. Singing. Speech Training
30 Brondesbury Park
London NW6 7DN
Website: www.startek-uk.com
e-mail: enquiries@startek-uk.com
Fax: 020-8830 4992   Tel: 020-8830 0074

LONDON INTERNATIONAL SCHOOL OF PERFORMING ARTS
Unit 8
Latimer Road
London W10 6RQ
Website: www.lispa.co.uk
e-mail: welcome@lispa.co.uk
Fax: 020-8964 9562   Tel: 020-8969 7004

LONDON REPERTORY COMPANY ACADEMY
27 Old Gloucester Street
London WC1N 3XX
Website: www.londonrepertorycompany.com
e-mail: academy@londonrepertorycompany.com
Tel/Fax: 020-7258 1944

LONDON SCHOOL OF DRAMATIC ART
Foundation & Advanced Diplomas in Acting (Full & Part-time). Drama School (over 18s)
4 Bute Street
South Kensington
London SW7 3EX
Website: www.lsda-acting.com
e-mail: enquiries@lsda-acting.com   Tel: 020-7581 6100

LONDON SCHOOL OF MUSICAL THEATRE
83 Borough Road
London SE1 1DN
e-mail: enquiries@lsmt.co.uk   Tel/Fax: 020-7407 4455

LONDON STUDIO CENTRE
Courses in Theatre Dance (3 yrs), Full-time, BA, FdA. 1 Year Professional Diploma. Summer Course. Evening & Saturday Classes
42-50 York Way
London N1 9AB
Website: www.london-studio-centre.co.uk
e-mail: info@london-studio-centre.co.uk
Fax: 020-7837 3248   Tel: 020-7837 7741

MACKINNON Alison
London SE6
e-mail: alison.mackinnon@tesco.net   Mobile: 07973 562132

MADDERMARKET THEATRE
Contact: Education Officer
Education Department
St John's Alley
Norwich NR2 1DR
Website: www.maddermarket.co.uk
e-mail: mmtedu@btconnect.com
Fax: 01603 661357   Tel: 01603 628600

MANCHESTER METROPOLITAN UNIVERSITY SCHOOL OF THEATRE
See DRAMA SCHOOLS (Conference of)

MANCHESTER SCHOOL OF ACTING
29 Ardwick Green North
Manchester M12 6DL
Website: www.manchesterschoolofacting.co.uk
e-mail: actorclass@aol.com   Tel/Fax: 0161-273 4738

MARLOW Jean LGSM
32 Exeter Road
London NW2 4SB   Tel: 020-8450 0371

MARTIN Liza GRSM, GRSM (Recital) ARMCM (Singing & Piano)
Singing Tuition   Tel: 020-8348 0346

MASTERS PERFORMING ARTS COLLEGE Ltd
Musical Theatre/Dance Course
Arterial Road
Rayleigh
Essex SS6 7UQ   Tel: 01268 777351

McCRACKEN Jenny
Acting Workshops. Audition Technique. Drama School (over 18s). Private Acting Classes
First Floor Flat
316A Chiswick High Road
London W4 5TA   Tel: 020-8747 6724

McDAID Marj
1 Chesholm Road
Stoke Newington
London N16 0DP
Website: www.voicings.co.uk
e-mail: marjmcdaid@hotmail.com
Fax: 020-7502 0412   Tel: 020-7923 4929

McKEAND Ian
Audition Technique. Drama School Entry
12 Linnet Close
Birchwood, Lincoln LN6 0JQ
Website: http://homepage.ntlworld.com/ian.mckeand1
e-mail: ian.mckeand@ntlworld.com   Tel: 01522 805966

McKELLAN Martin
Acting Workshops. Dialect/Accent Coaching. Private Acting Classes. Vocal Coaching
62A Neal Street
London WC2H 9PA
e-mail: mckellan@macunlimited.net   Tel: 020-7240 0145

MEAD Alison
Website: www.dramatraininguk.co.uk
e-mail: mail@dramatuition.co.uk   Tel: 020-8402 7858

MELLECK Lydia
Pianist & Coach for Auditions & Repertoire - RADA. Workshops on Sondheim. Accompanist. Singing for Beginners. Vocal Coaching
10 Burgess Park Mansions
London NW6 1DP   Tel: 020-7794 8845

METHOD STUDIO, LONDON The
*Dedicated to the Teaching of the 'Method' System of
Acting. Part-time & Full-time Classes Available. 1 Year
Acting Diploma Course ('Trinity Guildhall' ATCL Performing
Speech & Drama Exam). Acting for Film & TV. Acting
Workshops. Drama School (over 18s). Improvisation.
Shakespeare Text. Singing. Vocal Coaching*
Conway Hall
25 Red Lion Square, London WC1R 4RL
Website: www.themethodstudio.com
e-mail: info@themethodstudio.com
Fax: 020-7831 8319   Tel: 020-7831 7335

MICALLEF Marianne
Voice Coach, Accents, Text & Business Voice
Ealing, West London
e-mail: mariannemicallef@hotmail.com
Mobile: 07974 203001

MICHEL Hilary ARCM
*Accompanist. Auditions. Elocution for Songs. Language
Tutoring for Songs. Piano. Recorder. Singing Teacher.
Stage School for Children. Technique. Theory. Vocal Coach*
82 Greenway
Totteridge
London N20 8EJ
Mobile: 07775 780182   Tel: 020-8343 7243

MODEL CHILD AGENCY
York Chambers, Dukes Court
Macclesfield, Cheshire SK11 6NN
Website: www.modelchild.co.ok
e-mail: sam@modelchild.co.uk
Fax: 01625 442745   Tel: 01625 442742

MONTAGE THEATRE ARTS
*Contact: Judy Gordon (Artistic Director)
Dance. Drama. Singing. Children & Adults*
The Albany
Douglas Way, London SE8 4AG
Website: www.montagetheatre.com
e-mail: admin@montagetheatre.com   Tel: 020-8692 7007

MOORE Stefanie BA Hons LLAM
Audition Preparation, Public Speaking, Voice and Text
119 Francis Road, London E10 6PL
Website: www.tinbobbin.com
e-mail: stef@tinbobbin.com   Mobile: 07751 564223

www.zoenathenson.com

ZOE NATHENSON
SCHOOL OF FILM ACTING

- **FILM ACTING, AUDITION
  TECHNIQUE & SIGHT READING**
- **GROUP WORKSHOPS AND
  INTENSIVE COURSES AVAILABLE**

Zoe Nathenson School of Film Acting
55 St James' Lane, London N10 3DA
Mobile: 07956 833 850 Tel: 020 8883 7554
Email: zoe.act@btinternet.com

MORLEY ADULT EDUCATION COLLEGE
Day & Evening LOCN Accredited, Acting School Programme
61 Westminster Bridge Road
London SE1 7HT
Website: www.morleycollege.ac.uk
e-mail: dominic.grant@morleycollege.ac.uk
Tel: 020-7450 1925

MORRISON Elspeth
27 Oakworth Road
London W10 6DF
e-mail: elsp.morrison@talk21.com   Mobile: 07790 919870

MORRISON Stuart MA Voice Studies (CSSD)
Voice & Speech Coach
24 Deans Walk
Coulsdon, Surrey CR5 1HR
e-mail: stuartvoicecoach@yahoo.co.uk
Mobile: 07867 808648

MORTEMORE Sally BA, MA Voice Studies CSSD
Courses in Audition, Text, Voice & Accent Softening
7 Groton Road
Earlsfield, London SW18 4ER
Website: www.sallymortemore.com
e-mail: mortemores@aol.com   Tel: 020-8516 2192

MOUNTVIEW
See DRAMA SCHOOLS (Conference of)

MRS WORTHINGTON'S WORKSHOPS
Part-time Performing Arts for Children (6-16 yrs)
16 Ouseley Road
London SW12 8EF   Tel: 020-8767 6944

MTA
Musical Theatre Academy
The Drill Hall
16 Chenies Street
London WC1E 7EX
Website: www.thetma.co.uk
e-mail: annemarielthomas@aol.com   Tel: 020-8882 8181

MURRAY Barbara LGSM, LALAM
129 Northwood Way
Northwood
Middlesex HA6 1RF   Tel: 01923 823182

NATHENSON Zoe
*Audition Technique. Film Acting. Sight Reading
Group Classes*
55 St James's Lane
London N10 3DA
Website: www.zoenathenson.com
e-mail: zoe.act@btinternet.com   Mobile: 07956 833850

NATIONAL PERFORMING ARTS SCHOOL & AGENCY The
Liffey Trust Building
PO Box 8943
Dublin 4, Ireland
e-mail: info@npas.ie   Tel/Fax: 00 353 1 6684035

NEIL Andrew
Audition Technique. Private Acting Classes. Public Speaking
2 Howley Place
London W2 1XA
e-mail: andrewneil@talktalk.net
Mobile: 07979 843984   Tel/Fax: 020-7262 9521

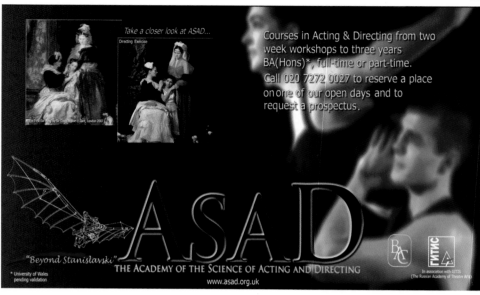

Take a closer look at ASAD...
Directing Exercise

Courses in Acting & Directing from two week workshops to three years BA(Hons)*, full-time or part-time. Call 020 7272 0027 to reserve a place on one of our open days and to request a prospectus.

"Beyond Stanislavski"

THE ACADEMY OF THE SCIENCE OF ACTING AND DIRECTING
www.asad.org.uk

* University of Wales pending validation

In association with GITIS
(The Russian Academy of Theatre Arts)

NEW LONDON PERFORMING ARTS CENTRE
Courses in Performing Arts (3-19 yrs). Dance. Drama
GCSE Courses, LAMDA, ISTD & RAD
76 St James Lane
Muswell Hill, London N10 3DF
Website: www.nlpac.co.uk
e-mail: nlpac@aol.com
Fax: 020-8444 4040   Tel: 020-8444 4544

NEWNHAM Caryll
Singing Teacher
35 Selwyn Crescent, Hatfield, Herts AL10 9NL
e-mail: caryll@ntlworld.com
Mobile: 07976 635745   Tel: 01707 267700

NORTHERN ACADEMY OF PERFORMING ARTS
Anlaby Road, Hull HU1 2PD
Website: www.northernacademy.org.uk
e-mail: napa@northernacademy.org.uk
Fax: 01482 212280   Tel: 01482 310690

NORTHERN FILM & DRAMA
Acting Workshops. Audition Technique. Dancing. Drama
School (over 18s). Film & Television Training. Improvisation.
Private Acting Classes. Stage School for Children.
PO Box 76, Leeds LS25 9AG
Website: www.northernfilmanddrama.com
e-mail: info@northernfilmanddrama.com
                                      Tel/Fax: 01977 681949

O'FARRELL STAGE & THEATRE SCHOOL
Dance, Drama, Singing
36 Shirley Street
Canning Town
London E16 1HU   Tel/Fax: 020-7511 9444

OLLERENSHAW Maggie BA (Hons), Dip Ed
Acting Workshops
Audition Technique. Career Guidance. Private Acting.
Television & Theatre Coaching
151D Shirland Road
London W9 2EP
e-mail: maggieoll@aol.com   Tel: 020-7286 1126

OLSON Lise
American Accents, Practical Voice, Vocal Coaching, Working
with Text
Midlands Based
c/o Birmingham School of Acting Millennium Point
Curzon Street, Birmingham B4 7XG
e-mail: lise.olson@bcv.ac.uk   Mobile: 07790 877145

OMOBONI Lino
Private Acting Classes
2nd Floor
12 Weltje Road
London W6 9TG
e-mail: bluewand@btinternet.com
Mobile: 07525 187468   Tel/Fax: 020-8741 2038

OPEN VOICE
Contact: Catherine Owen
Auditions. Consultancy. Personal Presentations
9 Bellsmains
Gorebridge
Near Edinburgh EH23 4QD   Tel: 01875 820175

OPPOSITE LEG Ltd
132 Bethwin Road
London SE5 0YY
Website: www.oppositeleg.co.uk
e-mail: david@oppositeleg.co.uk   Mobile: 07950 824123

ORAM Daron
Audition Preparation. Dialect/Accent Coaching
Voice Coaching
10 Winchelsea House
Swan Road
London SE16 4LH
e-mail: darono@yahoo.com   Mobile: 07905 332497

OSBORNE HUGHES John
Spiritual Psychology of Acting
Miracle Tree Productions Training Department
51 Church Road
London SE19 2TE
Website: www.spiritualpsychologyofacting.com
e-mail: johughes@miracletreeproductions.com
Mobile: 07801 950916   Tel: 020-8653 7735

OSCARS COLLEGE OF PERFORMANCE ARTS Ltd
103 Fitzwilliam Street
Huddersfield HD1 5PS
e-mail: oscars.college@virgin.net   Tel: 01484 545519

OVERSBY William
Singing & Vocal Projection
Petersfield, Hants
e-mail: billo363@msn.com
Mobile: 07811 946663   Tel: 01420 538549

OXFORD SCHOOL OF DRAMA The
See DRAMA SCHOOLS (Conference of)

PALMER Jackie STAGE SCHOOL
30 Daws Hill Lane
High Wycombe, Bucks HP11 1PW
Website: www.jackiepalmer.co.uk
e-mail: jackie.palmer@btinternet.com
Fax: 01494 510479   Tel: 01494 510597

PARKES Frances MA, AGSM
Voice & Acting Coach
451A Kingston Road
London SW20 8JP
Agent: Upson Edwards 020-8888 2525
Website: www.maxyourvoice.com
e-mail: frances25@blueyonder.co.uk
                    Tel/Fax: 020-8542 2777

PAUL'S THEATRE SCHOOL
Ardleigh House
42 Ardleigh Green Road
Hornchurch
Essex RM11 2LG
Website: www.paulstheatreschool.co.uk
e-mail: penny@paulstheatreschoolagency.co.uk
Tel: 01708 446167   Tel: 01708 447123

PERFORM
49 Charlton Street
London NW1 1HY
Website: www.perform.org.uk
e-mail: enquiries@perform.org.uk
Fax: 020-7691 4822   Tel: 0845 4004000

PERFORMANCE BUSINESS The
78 Oatlands Drive
Weybridge
Surrey KT13 9HT
Website: www.theperformance.biz
e-mail: michael@theperformance.biz   Tel: 01932 888885

PERFORMERS COLLEGE
Contact: Brian Rogers, Susan Stephens
Southend Road
Corringham
Essex SS17 8JT
Website: www.performerscollege.co.uk
e-mail: pdc@dircon.co.uk
Fax: 01375 672353   Tel: 01375 672053

PERFORMERS THEATRE SCHOOL
Hope Street, Liverpool L18 4QJ
& Royal Victoria Patriotic Buildings, London
Website: www.performerstheatre.co.uk
e-mail: info@performerstheatre.co.uk
Tel: 0151-708 4000   Tel: 020-8479 3000

PILATES INTERNATIONAL Ltd
Pilates Teacher Training (NVQ3 - Cert). Physical Coaching
Unit 1, Broadbent Close
20-22 Highgate High Street
London N6 5JG
Website: www.pilatesinternational.co.uk
Tel/Fax: 020-8348 1442

PLAIN SPEAKING
Also Available in London
64 Ferry Road
Sudbourne
Woodbridge
Suffolk IP12 2BJ
Website: www.plainspeaking.co.uk
e-mail: enquiries@plainspeaking.co.uk
Tel/Fax: 01394 450265

POLLYANNA CHILDREN'S TRAINING THEATRE
1 Knighten Street
Wapping
London E1W 1PH
Website: www.pollyannatheatre.co.uk
e-mail: pollyanna_mgmt@btinternet.com
Fax: 020-7480 6761   Tel: 020-7481 1911

POOR SCHOOL
242 Pentonville Road
London N1 9JY
Website: www.thepoorschool.com
e-mail: acting@thepoorschool.com   Tel: 020-7837 6030

PRECINCT THEATRE The
Units 2/3 The Precinct
Packington Square, London N1 7UP
Website: www.breakalegman.com
e-mail: theatre@breakalegman.com
Fax: 020-7359 3660   Tel: 020-7359 3594

QUEEN MARGARET UNIVERSITY, EDINBURGH
See DRAMA SCHOOLS (Conference of)

QUESTORS THEATRE EALING The
12 Mattock Lane
London W5 5BQ
Website: www.questors.org.uk
e-mail: jane@questors.org.uk
Fax: 020-8567 2275   Admin: 020-8567 0011

RADCLIFFE Tom
(Artistic Director at The Actor's Temple)
Sanford Meisner Technique/Actor Training
13-14 Warren Street
London W1T 5LG
e-mail: info@actorstemple.com   Tel: 020-7383 3535

RAVENSCOURT THEATRE SCHOOL Ltd
8-30 Galena Road
Hammersmith
London W6 0LT
Website: www.ravenscourt.net
e-mail: info@ravenscourt.net
Fax: 020-8741 1786   Tel: 020-8741 0707

RAW TALENT PRODUCTIONS & THE ACTORS CENTRE SCOTLAND
Contact: Helen Raw
Courses in Acting for Film, TV & Theatre (2 Days). Cold Reading & Audition Technique. Monologue & Character Development. Improvisation & Scene Study. After School Drama Classes
1 St Colme Street
Edinburgh EH3 6AA
Website: www.rawtalentproductions.co.uk
e-mail: info@rawtalentproductions.co.uk
Tel: 0131-220 8304

RC-ANNIE Ltd
For Dramatic Fight Services & Theatrical Blood Supplies
34 Pullman Place, London SE9 6EG
Website: www.rc-annie.com
e-mail: info@rc-annie.com
Tel: 020-8123 5936

REBEL SCHOOL OF THEATRE ARTS AND CASTING AGENCY Ltd
Based in Leeds
PO Box 169, Huddersfield HD8 1BE
e-mail: suerebeltheatre@aol.com
Mobile: 07808 803637
Tel: 0113-305 3796

RED ONION PERFORMING ARTS CENTRE
Dance. Drama. Vocal Training (8 yrs - Adult)
26-28 Hatherley Mews, London E17 4QP
Website: www.redonion.uk.com
e-mail: info@redonion.uk.com
Fax: 020-8521 6646
Tel: 020-8520 3975

REDROOFS THEATRE SCHOOL
Littlewick Green
Maidenhead, Berks SL6 3QY
Website: www.redroofs.co.uk
e-mail: sam@redroofs.co.uk
Fax: 01628 822461
Tel: 01628 822982

REFLECTIONS AGENCY
9 Weavers Terrace
Fulham
London SW6 1QE
Website: www.reflectionsperfarts.tripod.com
Mobile: 07951 191468
Tel/Fax: 01322 410003

REP COLLEGE The
17 St Mary's Avenue
Purley on Thames
Berks RG8 8BJ
Website: www.repcollege.com
e-mail: tudor@repcollege.co.uk
Tel: 0118-942 1144

RICHMOND DRAMA SCHOOL
1 Year Course
Richmond Adult College
Parkshot
Richmond
Surrey TW9 2RE
e-mail: mark.woolgar@racc.ac.uk
Tel: 020-8439 8944

RIDGEWAY STUDIOS PERFORMING ARTS COLLEGE
Fairley House
Andrews Lane
Cheshunt
Herts EN7 6LB
Website: www.ridgewaystudios.co.uk
e-mail: info@ridgewaystudios.co.uk
Fax: 01992 633844
Tel: 01992 633775

RISING STARS DRAMA SCHOOL
PO Box 6281
Dorchester
Dorset DT1 9BB
Website: www.risingstarsdramaschool.co.uk
e-mail: info@risingstarsdramaschool.co.uk
Tel: 0845 2570127

ROFFE Danielle
Acting Workshops. Audition Techniques Dialect/Accent Coaching. Drama School (over 18s). Elocution. Private Acting Classes. Public Speaking. Vocal Coaching
71 Mornington Street
London NW1 7QE
Tel: 020-7388 1898

ROSCH Philip
Association of Guildhall Teachers, FVCM, LALAM, ATCL, LGSM, ANEA, BA Hons
Auditions for Top UK Drama Schools. Audition Speeches. Effective Sight-reading. Commercial Castings. Expert Career Guidance. Private Acting Classes. RADA Acting Exams
53 West Heath Court
London NW11 7RG
Tel: 020-8731 6686

ROSE BRUFORD COLLEGE
See DRAMA SCHOOLS (Conference of)

ROSS David ACTING ACADEMY
8 Farrier Close
Sale
Cheshire M33 2ZL
Website: www.davidrossacting.com
e-mail: info@davidrossacting.com   Mobile: 07957 862317

ROSSENDALE DANCE & DRAMA CENTRE
Contact: Chris Marlow. LAMDA, LCM, TCL
Grade & Diploma Courses & Exams.
Acting Workshops. Audition Technique. Dancing.
Dialect/Accent Coaching. Drama School (over 18s).
Elocution. Improvisation. Private Acting Classes. Public
Speaking. Stage School for Children. Vocal Coaching
52 Bridleway
Waterfoot
Rossendale
Lancs BB4 9DS
e-mail: rddc@btinternet.com   Tel: 01706 211161

ROYAL ACADEMY OF DRAMATIC ART
See DRAMA SCHOOLS (Conference of)

ROYAL ACADEMY OF MUSIC
Musical Theatre Department
Marylebone Road, London NW1 5HT
Website: www.ram.ac.uk
e-mail: mth@ram.ac.uk   Tel: 020-7873 7483

ROYAL SCOTTISH ACADEMY OF MUSIC & DRAMA
See DRAMA SCHOOLS (Conference of)

ROYAL WELSH COLLEGE OF MUSIC & DRAMA
See DRAMA SCHOOLS (Conference of)

RUMBELOW Sam
Acting & Method Acting Coach
84 Union Road, London SW4 6JU
Website: www.methodacting.co.uk
e-mail: samson@methodacting.co.uk   Tel: 020-7622 9742

RYDER Richard
Voice & Speech Coach
15A Worlingham Road, East Dulwich, London SE22 9HD
e-mail: richard_j_ryder@hotmail.com   Mobile: 07967 352551

Sam Rumbelow
t: 020 7622 9742
m: 07764 680 232
www.methodacting.co.uk
Acting Classes & Coaching

method. Acting
To develop & strengthen your work

SALES Stephanie
61 Brookfield Road
Chiswick
London W4 1DF
Website: www.stephaniesales.co.uk/dramacoaching
e-mail: steph@stephaniesales.co.uk   Tel: 020-8995 9127

SCALA SCHOOL OF PERFORMING ARTS
Audition Technique. Dancing. Dialect/Accent Coaching.
Improvisation. Singing. Stage School for Children
Vocal Training
Office: 42 Rufford Avenue
Yeadon, Leeds LS19 7QR
Website: www.scalakids.com
e-mail: office@scalakids.com
Fax: 0113-250 8806   Tel: 0113-250 6823

SEMARK Rebecca LLAM
Audition Technique. Drama School Entry. Speech Faults.
Voice & Speech Coach
11 Charles Street
Epping, Essex CM16 7AU
Website: www.semark.biz
e-mail: rebecca@semark.biz   Mobile: 07956 850330

SHAW Phil
Actors' Consultancy Service. Audition Technique/Voice
Coaching
Suite 476, 2 Old Brompton Road
South Kensington, London SW7 3DQ
e-mail: shawcastlond@aol.com   Tel: 020-8715 8943

SHENEL Helena
Singing Teacher
80 Falkirk House
165 Maida Vale, London W9 1QX
Tel: 020-7328 2921   Tel: 020-7724 8793

SHOWSONG ACCOMPANIST
Showsong Accompanist
165 Gunnersbury Lane
London W3 8LJ   Tel: 020-8993 2111

SIMMONS Jacki BA (Hons) PGCE MA (CSSD)
Audition Technique. Private Acting Classes
16 Tower Terrace
London N22 6SX
e-mail: jacki_@hotmail.com   Mobile: 07989 389183

SIMMONS Ros MA
Auditions. Dialects/Accents. Presentations. Voice
The Real Speaking Company
120 Hillfield Avenue
Crouch End, London N8 7DN
Website: www.realspeaking.co.uk
e-mail: info@realspeaking.co.uk
Mobile: 07957 320572   Tel: 020-8347 8089

SIMPKIN Heather
Morriston, Fairmile
Henley-on-Thames
Oxon RG9 2JX
e-mail: heathersimpkin@btinternet.com   Tel: 01491 574349

SINGER Sandra ASSOCIATES
LAMDA & ISTD Exams. Acting Workshops. Audition
Technique. Dancing. Dialect/Accent Coaching. Part-time
Drama School (over 18s). Improvisation. Private Acting
Classes. Singing. Stage School for Children. Vocal Coaching
21 Cotswold Road
Westcliff-on-Sea, Essex SS0 8AA
Website: www.sandrasinger.com
e-mail: sandrasingeruk@aol.com
Fax: 01702 339393   Tel: 01702 331616

SINGER STAGE SCHOOL
Part-time Vocational Stage School & Summer School.
Adult Classes (16+ yrs) for Singing, Acting & Tap. Acting
Workshops. Audition Technique. Dancing. Dialect/Accent
Coaching. Drama School (over 18s). Improvisation. Private
Acting Classes. Singing. Stage School for Children. Vocal
Coaching
21 Cotswold Road
Westcliff-on-Sea
Essex SS0 8AA
Website: www.sandrasinger.com
e-mail: sandrasingeruk@aol.com
Fax: 01702 339393   Tel: 01702 331616

SOCIETY OF TEACHERS OF SPEECH & DRAMA The
The Registered Office:
73 Berry Hill Road
Mansfield, Notts NG18 4RU
Website: www.stsd.org.uk
e-mail: ann.k.jones@btinternet.com   Tel: 01623 627636

SPEAKE Barbara STAGE SCHOOL
East Acton Lane, London W3 7EG
e-mail: speakekids3@aol.com   Tel/Fax: 020-8743 1306

**SPEED Anne-Marie Hon ARAM, MA (Voice Studies),
CSSD, ADVS, BA**
Accents. Auditions. Coaching. Vocal Technique
PO Box 235
19-21 Crawford Street
London W1H 1PJ
Website: www.thevoiceexplained.com
e-mail: anne-marie.speed@virgin.net
Mobile: 07957 272554   Tel: 020-7644 5947

SPIRITUAL PSYCHOLOGY OF ACTING The
51 Church Road, London SE19 2TE
Website: www.spiritualpsychologyofacting.com
e-mail: info@miracletreeproductions.com
     Tel: 020-8653 7735

SPONTANEITY SHOP The
85-87 Bayham Street, London NW1 0AG
Website: www.the-spontaneity-shop.com
e-mail: info@the-spontaneity-shop.com   Tel: 020-7788 4080

STAGE 84 YORKSHIRE SCHOOL OF PERFORMING ARTS
Evening & Weekend Classes & Summer Schools
Old Bell Chapel, Town Lane
Idle, West Yorks BD10 8PR
e-mail: valeriejackson@stage84.com
Mobile: 07785 244984   Tel: 01274 569197

STAGE CENTRAL THEATRE ARTS
St John Fisher High School
Harrogate, North Yorkshire HG2 8PT
Website: www.stagecentral.co.uk
e-mail: darren@stagecentral.co.uk   Tel: 01423 540533

**STAGECOACH TRAINING CENTRES FOR THE
PERFORMING ARTS**
The Courthouse, Elm Grove
Walton-on-Thames, Surrey KT12 1LZ
Website: www.stagecoach.co.uk
e-mail: mail@stagecoach.co.uk
Fax: 01932 222894   Tel: 01932 254333

STAGEFIGHT
138 Wilden Lane
Stourport-on-Severn
Worcestershire DY13 9LP
Website: www.stagefight.co.uk
e-mail: raph@stagefight.co.uk   Mobile: 07813 308672

STAR-BRIGHT DRAMA WORKSHOPS
Royal Exchange, St Ann's Square
Manchester M2 7BR
Website: www.emmastafford.tv
e-mail: workshops@emmastafford.tv
Fax: 0161-833 4264   Tel: 0161-833 4263

STE. CROIX Felicitas
Former Assistant to Jack Waltzer
Audition Preparation. Meisner.
Meyerhold. Chekhov. Sense Memories
London & Los Angeles
e-mail: felicitasstecroix@yahoo.com   Mobile: 07939 143721

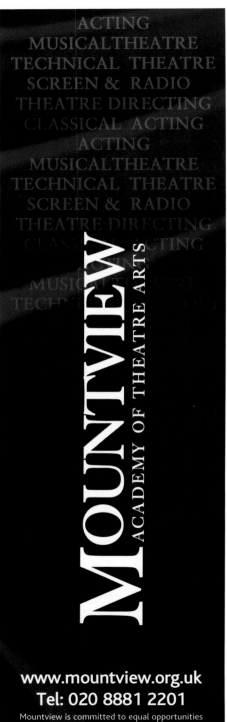

STEPHENSON Sarah
Musical Director. Pianist. Vocal Coach
8A Edgington Road
Streatham
London SW16 5BS
e-mail: s.stephenson@ntlworld.com
Mobile: 07957 477642   Tel: 020-8425 1225

STEWART Carola LRAM NCSD LUD
*Audition Technique. CV Advice. Dialect/Accent Coaching.
Elocution. Interview Technique. LAMDA Exams. Private
Acting Classes. Public Speaking.*
13 Church Lane, East Finchley, London N2 8DX
e-mail: carolastewart@msn.com   Tel: 020-8444 5994

STIRLING ACADEMY
Contact: Glen Mortimer
*Acting Workshops. Audition Techniques. Audition Training
for Camera. Drama School (over 18s). Improvisation.
Private Acting Classes*
c/o Melody Pop Tuition Building
174-176 St Georges Road
Bolton
Greater Manchester BL1 2NZ
Website: www.stirlingacademy.co.uk
e-mail: admin@stirlingacademy.co.uk
Fax: 0844 4128689   Tel: 0845 0176500

STOCKTON RIVERSIDE COLLEGE
Education & Training
Harvard Avenue, Thornaby, Stockton TS17 6FB
Website: www.stockton.ac.uk   Tel: 01642 865400

STOMP! THE SCHOOL OF PERFORMING ARTS
*Stage School for Children. Street Dance. Acting & Singing
Classes (6-19 yrs). Evenings & Weekends*
Mill Hill & Finchley Areas
c/o Suite 5, Lyndhurst House
120 Bunns Lane
Mill Hill, London NW7 2AR
Website: www.stompschool.com
e-mail: stompschoolnw7@aol.com   Tel/Fax: 020-8959 5353

STREETON Jane
Singing Teacher - RADA
24 Richmond Road
Leytonstone
London E11 4BA   Tel: 020-8556 9297

Voice and Elocution Coach

Bart Cale

www.english-elocution.com

Tel Bristol 0117 9692224

SUPPORT ACT SERVICES
Contact: Ian McCracken
Services for Actors including Stage Combat Instruction
243A Lynmouth Avenue
Morden, Surrey SM4 4RX
Website: www.supportact.co.uk
e-mail: info@supportact.co.uk   Tel: 0845 0940796

SWINFIELD Rosemarie
Make-Up Design & Training
Rosie's Make-Up Box
6 Brewer Street
Soho, London W1R 3FS
Website: www.rosiesmake-up.co.uk
e-mail: rosemarie@rosiesmake-up.co.uk
                              Mobile: 07976 965520

TALENTED KIDS PERFORMING ARTS SCHOOL & AGENCY
Contact: Maureen V. Ward
*Acting Workshops. Audition Technique. Dance. Drama
School (over 18s). Elocution. Improvisation. Musical
Theatre. Singing. Stage School for Children. Vocal Coaching*
23 Burrow Manor
Calverstown
Kilcullen, Co. Kildare, Ireland
Website: www.talentedkidsireland.com
e-mail: talentedkids@hotmail.com
Mobile: 00 353 872480348   Tel/Fax: 00 353 45 485464

TEAM ACTIVATE
Auditions & Presentation Skills
38 Highbury Hill
London N5 1AL
Website: www.teamactivate.com
e-mail: teamactivate@fastmail.fm   Mobile: 07837 712323

THAT'S A WRAP PERFORMING ARTS SCHOOL
*Accompanist. Acting Workshops. Audition Technique.
Dialect & Accent Coaching. Elocution. Improvisation. Private
Acting Classes. Singing. Stage School for Children*
The Actors Studio
Pinewood Studios
Pinewood Road
Iver Heath, Bucks SL0 0NH
Website: www.actorsstudio.co.uk
e-mail: info@actorsstudio.co.uk   Tel: 01753 650951

Unit 10, 21 Wren Street
London WC1X 0HF

THEATRETRAIN
Annual West End Productions Involving all Pupils (6-18 yrs)
121 Theydon Grove
Epping CM16 4QB
Website: www.theatretrain.co.uk
e-mail: info@theatretrain.co.uk   Tel: 01992 577977

TIP TOE STAGE SCHOOL
Dance, Drama, Singing & Performing Arts Part-time Training
For correspondence only:
45 Viola Close
South Ockendon
Essex RM15 6JF
Website: www.tiptoestageschool1.piczo.com
e-mail: julieecarter@aol.com   Mobile: 07914 899438

TLC COACHING

Contact: Teresa Churcher.
Acting & Audition Coaching. Audition Technique
Career & Life Coaching. Group Workshops
One to One Public Speaking
Herne Hill, London SE24
Website: www.teresachurcher.co.uk
e-mail: info@teresachurcher.co.uk   Mobile: 07966 228395

TO BE OR NOT TO BE

Contact: Anthony Barnett
LAMDA Exams. Showreels. Theatre/Audition Pieces.
TV/Film Acting Technique
40 Gayton Road
King's Lynn, Norfolk PE30 4EL
Website: www.showreels.org.uk
e-mail: tony@tobeornottobe.org.uk
Mobile: 07958 996227   Tel/Fax: 01553 776995

TODD Paul

Audition Technique. Improvisation. Vocal Coaching
3 Rosehart Mews
London W11 3JN
e-mail: paultodd@talk21.com   Tel: 020-7229 9776

TOMORROW'S TALENT THEATRE ARTS

Theatre Training for students (6-16 yrs)
Website: www.tomorrowstalent.co.uk
e-mail: info@tomorrowstalent.co.uk   Mobile: 07989 422808

TOP HAT STAGE SCHOOL

Part-time Theatre Arts Training in Hertforshire (4-17 yrs).
Schools in Potters Bar
Welwyn, Stevenage
St Albans & Hertford
PO Box 860, St Albans
Herts AL1 9BR
Website: www.tophatstageschool.co.uk
e-mail: admin@tophatstageschool.co.uk
                            Tel/Fax: 01727 812666

TOP TV ACADEMY

Presenter Training. Researcher Workshop
309 Kentish Town Road
London NW5 2TJ
Website: www.toptvacademy.co.uk
e-mail: liza@toptvacademy.co.uk
Fax: 020-7485 7536   Tel: 020-7267 3530

TROTTER William BA, MA, PGDVS

25 Thanet Lodge
Mapesbury Road
London NW2 4JA
Website: www.ukspeech.co.uk
e-mail: william.trotter@ukspeech.co.uk
                            Tel/Fax: 020-8459 7594

TUCKER John

Audition Technique. Dialect/Accent Coaching. Public
Speaking. Singing. Vocal Coaching
503 Mountjoy House
Barbican
London EC2Y 8BP
Website: www.john-tucker.com
e-mail: mail@john-tucker.com   Mobile: 07903 269409

TIM CHARRINGTON

Dip. C.S.S.D., A.D.V.S., ACTOR & TEACHER

ACCENT & DIALECTS T: 020 7987 3028 M: 07967 418 236

TV ACTING CLASSES
Contact: Elisabeth Charbonneau
14 Triangle Place
Clapham
London SW4 7HS
e-mail: ejcharbonneau@aol.com   Mobile: 07885 621061

TWICKENHAM THEATRE WORKSHOP FOR CHILDREN
29 Campbell Road
Twickenham
Middlesex TW2 5BY   Tel: 020-8898 5882

UK DRAMA EDUCATION
Contact: Esme Bates CSSD STSD
2 Barons Court
Western Elms Avenue
Reading, Berks RG30 2BP
e-mail: esmebates@btinternet.com
Mobile: 07941 700941   Tel: 0118-958 9330

URQUHART Moray
Private Coaching for Auditions, Schools, Showbiz, etc
61 Parkview Court
London SW6 3LL
e-mail: nmuphelps@yahoo.co.uk   Tel: 020-7731 3604

VALLÉ ACADEMY OF PERFORMING ARTS
The Vallé Academy Studios
Wilton House
Delamare Road
Cheshunt, Herts EN8 9SG
Website: www.valleacademy.co.uk
e-mail: enquiries@valleacademy.co.uk
Fax: 01992 622868   Tel: 01992 622862

VERRALL Charles
19 Matilda Street
London N1 0LA
Website: www.learntoact.co.uk
e-mail: charles.verrall@virgin.net   Tel: 020-7833 1971

VIVIAN Michael
Acting Workshops. Audition Technique. Improvisation.
Private Acting Classes. Public Speaking
15 Meredyth Road
Barnes
London SW13 0DS
e-mail: vivcalling@aol.com   Tel: 020-8876 2073

VOCAL CONFIDENCE FOR SPEECH & SINGING
Contact: Alix Longman
98C Balham Park Road
London SW12 8EA
Website: www.vocalconfidence.com
e-mail: alix@vocalconfidence.com   Tel: 020-8767 6463

VOICE MASTER
Specialized Training for Voice-Overs & TV Presenters
88 Erskine Hill
London NW11 6HR
Website: www.voicemaster.co.uk
e-mail: stevehudson@voicemaster.co.uk Tel: 020-8455 2211

VOICE-OVERS-UK
Presentation Skills
Middle Highfield Barn
Lancaster LA2 6PQ
Website: www.ace-presentations.co.uk
                    Tel/Fax: 07000 802280

VOICE TAPE SERVICES INTERNATIONAL
Professional Management/Voice-Over Direction & CDs
80 Netherlands Road
New Barnet, Herts EN5 1BS
Website: www.vtsint.co.uk
e-mail: info@vtsint.co.uk
Fax: 020-8441 4828   Tel: 020-8440 4848

VOICES LONDON
Vocal Coaching. Technique. Auditions
36 Wigmore Street
London W1U 2BP
Website: www.voicesvocal.co.uk
e-mail: info@voicesvocal.co.uk   Tel: 01279 655542

VOXTRAINING Ltd
Voice-Over Training & Demo CDs
20 Old Compton Street
London W1D 4TW
Website: www.voxtraining.com
e-mail: info@voxtraining.com   Tel: 020-7434 4404

WALLACE Elaine BA
Voice
249 Goldhurst Terrace
London NW6 3EP
e-mail: im@voicebiz.biz   Tel: 020-7625 4049

R. The Royal Shakespeare Company · Rose Bruford College **C.**
A.   **TESS DIGNAN** PDVS   **S.**
D.   (preparing to audition...need some help?!)   **S.**
          Auditions, Sight Reading, Text Work, Voice & Speech, R.P....**Tel: 020-8691 4275**
A. The Moscow Arts Theatre School · BBC · LAMDA **D.**

❧ Eileen Benskin ❧

Dialect/Dialogue Coach

R.A.D.A. dip., C.P.E.P. University College London

FILMS • TELEVISION • THEATRE

Specialist in Standard British English (R.P.)
and American, British & Foreign Accents & Dialects

Tel/Fax: 020-8455 9750 or Spotlight 020-7437 7631   Mobile 07785 791715

WALSH Anne
Accents. Dialect. Speech
45B Windsor Road
Willesden Green
London NW2 5DT
Mobile: 07932 440043   Tel: 020-8459 8071

WALSH Genevieve
Acting Tuition. Audition Coaching
37 Kelvedon House
Guildford Road
Stockwell
London SW8 2DN   Tel: 020-7627 0024

WALTZER Jack
Professional Acting Workshops
5 Minetta Street Apt 2B
New York NY 10012
Website: www.jackwaltzer.com
e-mail: jackwaltzer@hotmail.com
Tel: 001 (212) 840-1234   Mobile: 07847 126318 (London)

WEAKLIAM Brendan
Presentation. Singing. Voice Production
100 Gillespie Road
London N5 1LP
e-mail: brenweakliam@hotmail.com   Mobile: 07724 558955

WEBB Bruce
Audition Technique. Singing
Abbots Manor
Kirby Cane
Bungay, Suffolk NR35 2HP   Tel: 01508 518703

WELBOURNE Jacqueline
Circus Trainer, Choreographer, Consultant
c/o Circus Maniacs Agency
Office 8A
Britannia Road
The Kingswood Foundation
Kingswood
Bristol BS15 8DB
Website: www.circusmaniacs.com
e-mail: jackie@circusmaniacs.com
Mobile: 07977 247287   Tel/Fax: 0117-947 7042

WEST END WORKSHOPS
Arts Workshops. Audition Coaching
Website: www.westendworkshops.co.uk
e-mail: info@westworkshops.co.uk   Tel: 07989 422808

WESTMINSTER KINGSWAY COLLEGE
Performing Arts
Regent's Park Centre
Longford Street, London NW1 3HB
Website: www.westking.ac.uk
e-mail: courseinfo@westking.ac.uk
Fax: 020-7391 6400   Tel: 0870 0609800

WHITE Susan
BA TEFL LGSM MA Voice Studies Distinction
*Coach of Spoken Voice & Personal
Presence/Ego State Practitioner*
Central London
Website: www.per-sona.com
e-mail: susan@per-sona.com   Tel: 020-7244 0402

WHITEHALL PERFORMING ARTS CENTRE
Rayleigh Road
Leigh-on-Sea
Essex SS9 5UU
e-mail: info@whitehallcollege.co.uk   Tel: 01702 529290

WHITWORTH Geoffrey LRAM, MA
Piano Accompanist
789 Finchley Road
London NW11 8DP   Tel: 020-8458 4281

WILDER Andrea
23 Cambrian Drive
Colwyn Bay
Conwy LL28 4SL
Website: www.awagency.co.uk
e-mail: andrea@awagency.co.uk
Fax: 07092 249314   Mobile: 07919 202401

WILSON Holly
3 Worple Street
Mortlake
London SW14 8HE   Tel: 020-8878 0015

WIMBUSH Martin Dip GSMD
*Audition Technique. Drama School (over 18s). Elocution.
Public Speaking. Vocal Coaching*
Flat 4
289 Trinity Road
Wandsworth Common
London SW18 3SN
Website: www.martinwimbush.com
e-mail: martinwimbush@btinternet.com   Tel: 020-8877 0086

WINDSOR Judith Ph. D
American Accents/Dialects
Woodbine
Victoria Road
Deal
Kent CT14 7AS
e-mail: sarah.upson@voicecoach.tv
Fax: 01782 728004   Tel: 01782 827222

WITH PANACHE THEATRE ACADEMY
22 St. David's Close
Maidenhead
Berkshire SL6 3BB
Website: www.withpanache.co.uk
e-mail: info@withpanache.co.uk   Tel: 07881 656575

WOOD Tessa Teach Cert AGSM, CSSD, PGDVS
Voice Coach
43 Woodhurst Road
London W3 6SS
e-mail: tessaroswood@aol.com   Tel: 020-8896 2659

WOODHOUSE Alan AGSM ADVS
Acting Coach. Acting Workshops. Elocution Coaching. Private Acting Classes. Public Speaking. Vocal Coaching
33 Burton Road
Kingston upon Thames
Surrey KT2 5TG
Website: www.woodhouse-voice.co.uk
e-mail: alanwoodhouse50@hotmail.com
Tel/Fax: 020-8549 1374

WOODHOUSE Nan (Playwright & LAMDA Examiner)
LGSM (Hons Medal) LLAM, LLCM (TD), ALCM
Mobile: 07812 921625

WORTMAN Neville
Voice Training & Speech Coach
11 Mandeville Place, London W1U 3AJ
Website: www.speakwell.co.uk
e-mail: wortman.speakwell@btinternet.com
Mobile: 07976 805976
Tel: 020-8994 8886

WYNN Madeleine
Acting Workshops. Audition Technique. Directing & Acting Coach. LAMDA Exams. Private Acting Classes. Public Speaking. Drama School (over 18s)
40 Barrie House, Hawksley Court
Albion Road, London N16 0TX
e-mail: madeleine@onetel.com
Tel: 01394 450265

YOUNG ACTORS THEATRE
70-72 Barnsbury Road
London N1 0ES
Website: www.yati.org.uk
e-mail: info@yati.org.uk
Fax: 020-7833 9467
Tel: 020-7278 2101

YOUNG VICTORIA The
Drama Training. Singing
Correspondence: 35 Thorpes Crescent
Skelmanthorpe
Huddersfield HD8 9DH
Tel: 01484 866401

YOUNGSTAR TELEVISION & FILM ACTING SCHOOL
Part-time Schools across the UK (8-20 yrs)
Head Office
5 Union Castle House
Canute Road
Southampton SO14 3FJ
Website: www.youngstar.tv
e-mail: info@youngstar.tv
Fax: 023-8045 5816
Tel: 023-8047 7717

YOUNGSTARS
Contact: Coralyn Canfor-Dumas
Dancing. Drama. Part-time Children's Theatre School (5-16 yrs). Singing. Voice Overs
4 Haydon Dell
Bushey
Herts WD23 1DD
e-mail: youngstars@bigfoot.com
Fax: 020-8950 5701
Tel: 020-8950 5782

YOUNG Sylvia THEATRE SCHOOL
Acting Workshops. Audition Technique. Dancing. Improvisation. Singing. Stage School for Children Summer Schools. Vocal Coaching
Rossmore Road
Marylebone
London NW1 6NJ
Website: www.sylviayoungtheatreschool.co.uk
e-mail: info@sylviayoungtheatreschool.co.uk
Fax: 020-7723 1040
Tel: 020-7402 0673

ZANDER Peter
Acting in Drama & Opera. Breathing. German. Improvisation. Linguist. Movement. Posture Public Speaking. Relaxation. Speech. Voice
22 Romilly Street
London W1D 5AG
e-mail: peterzan.berlin@virgin.net
Mobile: 07920 125509
Tel: 020-7437 4767

**Festivals
Film & Video Facilities
Film, Radio, Television & Video
  Production Companies
Film & Television Schools
Film & Television Studios**

[CONTACTS 2009]

24:7 THEATRE FESTIVAL
(20 - 26 July 2009)
PO Box 247
Manchester M60 2ZT
Website: www.247theatrefestival.co.uk
e-mail: info@247theatrefestival.co.uk   Tel: 0845 4084101

ALDEBURGH FESTIVAL OF MUSIC AND THE ARTS
(12 - 28 June 2009)
Aldeburgh Music
Snape Maltings Concert Hall
Snape Bridge
Nr Saxmundham
Suffolk IP17 1SP
Website: www.aldeburgh.co.uk
e-mail: enquiries@aldeburgh.co.uk
Fax: 01728 687120
BO: 01728 687110   Admin: 01728 687100

ALMEIDA OPERA
(July - August 2009)
Almeida Street
Islington, London N1 1TA
Website: www.almeida.co.uk
e-mail: patrick@almeida.co.uk
Fax: 020-7288 4901
BO: 020-7359 4404   Admin 020-7288 4900

ARUNDEL FRINGE FESTIVAL
Arundel Town Hall
Arundel
West Sussex BN18 9AP
Director: Kevin Williams
Website: www.arundelfestival.net
e-mail: arundelfringe@aol.com   Tel/Fax: 01903 889821

BARBICAN INTERNATIONAL THEATRE EVENT (BITE)
(Year-Round Festival)
Barbican Theatre
Silk Street
London EC2Y 8DS
Website: www.barbican.org.uk
e-mail: theatre@barbican.org.uk
Fax: 020-7382 7377   Tel: 020-7382 7372

BATH INTERNATIONAL MUSIC FESTIVAL
(22 May - 5 June 2009)
Bath Festivals
Abbey Chambers
Kingston Buildings
Bath BA1 1NT
Website: www.bathmusicfest.org.uk
e-mail: info@bathfestivals.org.uk
Fax: 01225 445551
BO: 01225 463362   Tel: 01225 462231

BATH LITERATURE FESTIVAL
(28 February - 8 March 2009)
Bath Festivals, Abbey Chambers
Kingston Buildings
Bath BA1 1LY
Website: www.bathlitfest.org.uk
e-mail: info@bathfestivals.org.uk
Fax: 01225 445551
BO: 01225 463362   Tel: 01225 462231

What do I need to know about the listed festivals?

The festivals listed in this section are all dedicated to creative and performing arts. Festivals are an opportunity for like-minded people to gather together to appreciate and learn from both well-established and new and up-and-coming acts and performers.

Why should I get involved?

Being a spectator at a festival is a chance to see others in action and to see a variety of shows that are not necessarily mainstream. This is an opportunity to see talent in its rawest form, which is exactly why casting directors often attend drama festivals: they may spot someone who is just what they are looking for, who would otherwise have gone unnoticed in a pile of CVs.

Taking part in festivals will be something else to add to your CV and will help develop your skills. This not only means performance skills but social skills as well: you will meet hundreds of new faces with the same passion for their work as you, so this is a great opportunity to make friends and useful contacts in the industry.

What do I need to bear in mind?

Before committing to performing at a festival, there are a number of issues to take into consideration. You will usually be unpaid and you will have to set aside enough money to fund the time spent rehearsing for and performing at the festival, not to mention travel, accommodation and food expenses. Not only that, you must also consider that you will be putting yourself out of the running for any paid work offered to you during this time. Make sure you let your agent know the dates you will be unavailable for work.

You may be required to not just perform but help out with any odd jobs involved with your show, such as setting up the stage and handing out flyers. If you are considering taking your own show to a festival, you will have to think well in advance about entrance fees, choosing and hiring a suitable venue, publicising your show, casting if necessary, finding technicians, buying or hiring props, costumes, sets, and so on. You must weigh up the financial outlays and potential headaches with the learning and networking opportunities that come with being involved in festivals.

How can I get involved?

If you are a performer at a festival, casting professionals could be there looking for you! Let them know that you will be performing and where and when. Send them a covering letter giving details and enclose your CV and headshot if you have not already done so in previous correspondence. You could do the same with agents if you are currently searching for new representation.

Spotlight members performing at the Edinburgh Fringe Festival can now promote themselves for free in the new Spotlight Edinburgh directory. You can add your photo, contact details and production information for maximum promotion during the Festival. Visit www.spotlight.com/edinburgh for more details and check for updated information each year during July and August.

Most festivals have websites which you can browse for further information on what to expect and how to get involved. Even if you simply go as a spectator to a festival, you will learn a lot and will have the opportunity to network. If you are performing in or organising a show, make sure you know exactly what you are letting yourself in for and make the most of your time there!

PLEASANCE

Anthony Alderson is Artistic Director of the Pleasance at the Edinburgh Festival Fringe. Here he shares his experiences of past festivals and offers advice to anyone interested in getting involved with performing arts festivals.

Festival, fair, carnival, gala, fête, jubilee, party, fiesta, jamboree, holiday or feast. Whichever way you put it, we are a sociable bunch and we love to gather. With new festivals popping up almost every weekend, I imagine you could travel from one end of the county to the other, and always be celebrating.

There is a mass of great talent out there, and festivals are often the only places where some of that talent gets its chance to be seen. Festivals are vital to the rich stew of artistic endeavour we are surrounded by. They are places to showcase new work, discover new people, challenge or strengthen perceptions, learn and develop new skills and above all to discuss and share ideas. This is where much of the art in this country begins.

Festivals have become a vital platform for the arts industry; many are programmed by invitation, and others are free to all. The majority have one thing in common; each is a market place, and an intricate part of the foundations of our arts industry. Festivals provide a breeding ground for new talent. Whether writers, producers, actors, stage managers, directors or designers, they are for many the first rung on the ladder of an increasingly competitive industry. It's a place to seek advice, to create ties, find inspiration and, most importantly, work.

The Edinburgh Festival Fringe is the largest festival in the world; it has grown in success because it is free of censorship and is open to all. Some of the most inspirational work I have ever seen, I found in the most unlikely of places. This is a community that is often fearless, challenging and wonderfully enthralling. We all need a jolt from normality, and festivals provide us with an excursion from our routine. They provide a pressure valve for society, a place to let off steam and an environment to challenge our humanity. I am still haunted by Badac Theatre Company's production of *Cage*, a brutal play about domestic violence, and Iris Bahr's portrayal of life in Israel in her solo performance of *Dai (Enough)*. Every year I have discovered something new and exciting, and my belief in what we do is confirmed.

With the right planning and preparation festivals can be enormously beneficial and provide numerous possibilities. If you wish to get involved, then find out what each festival is about and how it works. Bringing work to festivals can be expensive, finding support is often difficult and it can also be gruelling when things go wrong. There is a huge amount of information to be found on the various festivals, and this is a perfect place to start. Make sure you are primed from the start and never be afraid to ask.

Whether theatre, music, literature, comedy or even beer, the festival experience is all-embracing. You don't always need wellies and you don't necessarily have to stay in a tent. It's not all jugglers, face painters, stilt walkers or loud music, and at most, it is even acceptable to wash. Every festival is different, every year unique... So go on, I dare you, get festive!

BRIGHTON DOME & FESTIVAL Ltd
(2 - 24 May 2009)
12A Pavilion Buildings
Castle Square, Brighton BN1 1EE
Chief Executive:Andrew Comben
Website: www.brightonfestival.org
e-mail: info@brightonfestival.org
BO: 01273 709709   Admin: 01273 700747

BUXTON FESTIVAL
(8 - 26 July 2009)
3 The Square
Buxton, Derbyshire SK17 6AZ
Website: www.buxtonfestival.co.uk
e-mail: info@buxtonfestival.co.uk
BO: 0845 1272190   Admin: 01298 70395

CHESTER MUSIC FESTIVAL
(11 - 19 July 2009)
4 Abbey Square, Chester CH1 2HU
Contact: Kate Sawallisch
Website: www.chesterfestivals.co.uk/music
BO: 01244 304618   Admin: 01244 320722

CHICHESTER FESTIVITIES
(Not Chichester Festival Theatre)
(26 June - 12 July 2009)
Canon Gate House
South Street
Chichester, West Sussex PO19 1PU
Website: www.chifest.org.uk
e-mail: info@chifest.org.uk
Fax: 01243 528356   Tel: 01243 785718

DANCE UMBRELLA
(October 2009)
Annual Contemporary Dance Festival
20 Chancellors Street
London W6 9RN
Website: www.danceumbrella.co.uk
e-mail: mail@danceumbrella.co.uk
Fax: 020-8741 7902   Tel: 020-8741 4040

DUBLIN THEATRE FESTIVAL
(1 - 18 October 2009)
44 East Essex Street, Temple Bar
Dublin 2, Ireland
Contact: Jessica Hilliard
Website: www.dublintheatrefestival.com
e-mail: info@dublintheatrefestival.com
Fax: 00 353 1 6797709   Tel: 00 353 1 6778439

EDINBURGH FESTIVAL FRINGE
(7 - 31 August 2009)
Festival Fringe Society Ltd
180 High Street
Edinburgh EH1 1QS
Website: www.edfringe.com
e-mail: admin@edfringe.com
Fax: 0131-226 0016
BO: 0131-226 0000   Tel: 0131-226 0013

EDINBURGH INTERNATIONAL FESTIVAL
(14 August - 6 September 2009)
The Hub, Castlehill, Edinburgh EH1 2NE
Website: www.eif.co.uk
e-mail: eif@eif.co.uk
BO: 0131-473 2000   Admin: 0131-473 2099

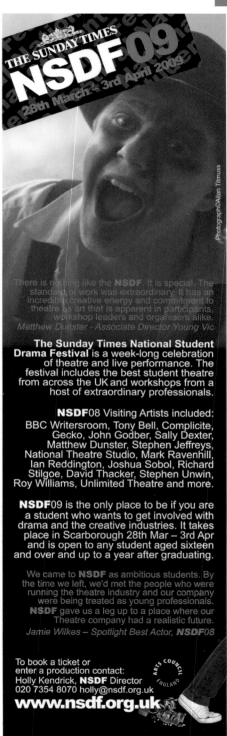

HARROGATE INTERNATIONAL FESTIVAL
(16 July - 1 August 2009)
Raglan House, Raglan Street
Harrogate, North Yorkshire HG1 1LE
Website: www.harrogate-festival.org.uk
e-mail: info@harrogate-festival.org.uk
Fax: 01423 521264   Tel: 01423 562303

KING'S LYNN FESTIVAL
(12 - 25 July 2009)
5 Thoresby College
Queen Street
King's Lynn, Norfolk PE30 1HX
Website: www.kingslynnfestival.org.uk
Fax: 01553 767688   Tel: 01553 767557

LIFT
(Annual Festival)
19-20 Great Sutton Street
London EC1V 0DR
Website: www.liftfestival.com
e-mail: info@liftfest.org.uk
Fax: 020-7490 3976   Tel: 020-7490 3964

LLANDOVERY THEATRE ARTS FESTIVAL
Llandovery Theatre
Stone Street
Llandovery
Carmarthenshire SA20 0DQ   Tel: 01550 720113

LUDLOW FESTIVAL SOCIETY Ltd
(20 June - 5 July 2009)
Festival Office, Castle Square
Ludlow, Shropshire SY8 1AY
Website: www.ludlowfestival.co.uk
e-mail: admin@ludlowfestival.co.uk
Fax: 01584 877673
BO: 01584 872150   Admin: 01584 875070

RE VAMP - READY MADE STREET FESTIVALS
Ealing House
33 Hanger Lane, London W5 3HJ
e-mail: verona.chard@vampevents.com Tel: 020-8997 3355

**THE SUNDAY TIMES NATIONAL STUDENT DRAMA
FESTIVAL**
(28 March - 3 April 2009)
AH107 Aberdeen Centre
22-24 Highbury Grove
London N5 2DQ
Director: Holly Kendrick
Website: www.nsdf.org.uk
e-mail: admin@nsdf.org.uk   Tel: 020-7354 8070

ULSTER BANK BELFAST FESTIVAL AT QUEEN'S
(October/November 2009)
8 Fitzwilliam Street
Belfast BT9 6AW
Website: www.belfastfestival.com
e-mail: evs.festivals@qub.ac.uk
Fax: 028-9097 1336   Tel: 028-9097 1034

WINCHESTER HAT FAIR, FESTIVAL OF STREET THEATRE
(2 - 5 July 2009)
5A Jewry Street
Winchester, Hampshire SO23 8RZ
Website: www.hatfair.co.uk
e-mail: info@hatfair.co.uk   Tel: 01962 849841

ACTOR'S ONE-STOP SHOP The
(Showreels for Performing Artists)
First Floor, Above The Gate Pub
Station Road, London N22 7SS
Website: www.actorsonestopshop.com
e-mail: info@actorsonestopshop.com   Tel: 020-8888 7006

ANVIL POST PRODUCTION
Contact: Mike Anscombe (Studio Manager)
Perivale Park, Horsenden Lane South, Perivale UB6 7RL
Website: www.anvilpost.com
e-mail: mike.anscombe@thomson.net   Tel: 020-8799 0555

ARRI MEDIA
3 Highbridge, Oxford Road
Uxbridge, Middlesex UB8 1LX
Website: www.arrimedia.com
e-mail: info@arrimedia.com
Fax: 01895 457101   Tel: 01895 457100

ASCENT MEDIA CAMDEN Ltd
(Post-Production Film Facilities)
13 Hawley Crescent, London NW1 8NP
Website: www.ascentmedia.co.uk
Fax: 020-7284 1018   Tel: 020-7284 7900

ASCENT MEDIA Ltd
(Post-Production Facilities), Film House
142 Wardour Street, London W1F 8DD
Website: www.ascentmedia.co.uk
Fax: 020-7878 7800   Tel: 020-7878 0000

AXIS FILMS
(Film Equipment Rental)
Shepperton Studios
Studios Road, Middlesex TW17 0QD
Website: www.axisfilms.co.uk
e-mail: info@axisfilms.co.uk
Fax: 01932 592246   Tel: 01932 592244

CENTRAL FILM FACILITIES
(Camera Tracking Specialists)
c/o Myddle Cottage
Plaish, Church Stretton
Shropshire SY6 7HX
Website: www.centralfilmfacilities.com   Tel: 07966 421878

CENTRELINE VIDEO Ltd
138 Westwood Road, Tilehurst, Reading RG31 6LL
Website: www.centrelinevideo.com   Tel: 0118-941 0033

CHANNEL 2020 Ltd
The Clerkenwell Workshops
27/31 Clerkenwell Close, London EC1R 0AT
Website: www.channel2020.co.uk
e-mail: info@channel2020.co.uk   Tel: 0844 8402020

2020 House, 26-28 Talbot Lane
Leicester LE1 4LR
Fax: 0116-222 1113   Tel: 0844 8402020

CINE TO VIDEO & FOREIGN TAPE CONVERSION & DUPLICATING
(Peter J Snell Enterprises)
Amp House, Grove Road
Rochester, Kent ME2 4BX
e-mail: pjstv@blueyonder.co.uk
Fax: 01634 726000   Tel: 01634 723838

CLICKS
Media Studios, Grove Road
Rochester, Kent ME2 4BX
e-mail: info@clicksstudios.co.uk
Fax: 01634 726000   Tel: 01634 723838

CLUB The
35 Bedfordbury, Covent Garden
London WC2N 4DU
Website: www.theclubpc.co.uk
e-mail: production@theclubpc.co.uk
Fax: 020-7379 5210   Tel: 020-7759 7100

CRYSTAL MEDIA
28 Castle Street, Edinburgh EH2 3HT
Website: www.crystal-media.co.uk
e-mail: hello@crystal-media.co.uk
Fax: 0131-240 0989   Tel: 0131-240 0988

DE LANE LEA
(Film & TV Sound Dubbing & Editing Suite)
75 Dean Street, London W1D 3PU
Website: www.delanelea.com
e-mail: solutions@delanelea.com
Fax: 020-7432 3838   Tel: 020-7432 3800

DENMAN PRODUCTIONS
(3D Computer Animation, Film/Video CD Business Card
Showreels)
60 Mallard Place, Strawberry Vale
Twickenham TW1 4SR
Website: www.denman.co.uk
e-mail: info@denman.co.uk   Tel: 020-8891 3461

DIVERSE PRODUCTION Ltd
(Pre & Post-Production)
6-12 Gorleston Street, London W14 8XS
Website: www.diverse.tv
e-mail: reception@diverse.tv
Fax: 020-7603 2148   Tel: 020-7603 4567

EXECUTIVE AUDIO VISUAL
(Showreels for Actors & TV Presenters)
80 York Street, London W1H 1QW   Tel: 020-7723 4488

FARM DIGITAL POST PRODUCTION The
27 Upper Mount Street
Dublin 2, Ireland
Website: www.thefarm.ie
e-mail: info@thefarm.ie
Fax: 00 353 1 676 8816   Tel: 00 353 1 676 8812

FROME SILK MILL STUDIOS
Westbrook House
33 Vicarage Street, Frome BA11 1PU
e-mail: damonmoore@macace.net
Mobile: 07811 440584   Tel: 01373 473246

GREENPARK PRODUCTIONS Ltd
(Film Archives)
Illand, Launceston
Cornwall PL15 7LS
Website: www.greenparkimages.co.uk
e-mail: info@greenparkimages.co.uk
Fax: 01566 782127   Tel: 01566 782107

HARLEQUIN PRODUCTIONS
Suite 5, Woodville Court
31 Sylvan Road
London SE19 2SG
Website: www.harlequinproductions.co.uk
e-mail: neill@harlequinproductions.co.uk
     Tel: 020-8653 2333

HUNKY DORY PRODUCTIONS Ltd
(Facilities & Crew, Also Editing: Non-Linear)
57 Alan Drive
Barnet, Herts EN5 2PW
Website: www.hunkydory.tv   Tel: 020-8440 0820

MOVING PICTURE COMPANY The
(Post-Production)
127-133 Wardour Street
London W1F 0NL
Website: www.moving-picture.com
e-mail: mailbox@moving-picture.com
Fax: 020-7287 5187   Tel: 020-7434 3100

OCEAN OPTICS
(Underwater Camera Sales & Operator Rental)
Archer Fields, Burnt Mills Industrial Estate
Basildon, Essex SS13 1DL
Website: www.oceanoptics.co.uk
e-mail: optics@oceanoptics.co.uk
Fax: 01268 523795   Tel: 01268 523786

PANAVISION UK
The Metropolitan Centre
Bristol Road
Greenford, Middlesex UB6 8GD
Website: www.panavision.co.uk
Fax: 020-8839 7300   Tel: 020-8839 7333

PEDIGREE PUNKS
(Shooting Crews, Editing, Compositing, Encoding, Mastering
to all formats)
49 Woolstone Road
Forest Hill, London SE23 2TR
Website: www.pedigree-punks.com
e-mail: video@pedigree-punks.com
Fax: 020-8291 5801   Tel: 020-8314 4580

PLACE The
Robin Howard Dance Theatre
17 Duke's Road
London WC1H 9PY
Website: www.theplace.org.uk
e-mail: info@theplace.org.uk
Fax: 020-7121 1142   Tel: 020-7121 1000

PRO-LINK RADIO SYSTEMS Ltd
(Radio Microphones & Communications)
5, B Block, Saxon Business Park
Hanbury Road, Bromsgrove, Worcestershire B60 4AD
Website: www.prolink-radio.com
e-mail: service@prolink-radio.com
Fax: 01527 577757   Tel: 01527 577788

RICH VIDEO Ltd
Houldsworth Mill, Houldsworth Street
Reddish, Stockport, Cheshire SK5 6DA
Website: www.richvideo.co.uk
e-mail: sales@richvideo.co.uk   Tel: 0161-975 6207

SALON Ltd
(Post-Production & Editing Equipment Hire)
12 Swainson Road, London W3 7XB
Website: www.salonrentals.com
e-mail: hire@salonrentals.com   Tel: 020-8746 7611

SOUNDHOUSE The
10th Floor, Ashley House
Quay Street, Manchester M3 4AE
Website: www.thesoundhouse.tv
e-mail: suekeane@thesoundhouse.tv
Fax: 0161-832 7266   Tel: 0161-832 7299

TVMS (SCOTLAND)
(Corporate & Broadcast Facilities)
3rd Floor, 420 Sauchiehall Street, Glasgow G2 3JD
e-mail: mail@tvms.co.uk
Fax: 0141-332 9040   Tel: 0141-331 1993

VECTOR PRODUCTIONS Ltd
(Visual Effects & Motion Graphics)
12 Mill Fields
Higham Ferrers, Northants NN10 8ND
Website: www.vectortv.co.uk
e-mail: production@vectortv.co.uk
Tel: 01933 355442   Tel: 020-7193 5655

VIDEO INN PRODUCTION
(AV Equipment Hire)
Glebe Farm, Wooton Road
Quinton, Northampton NN7 2EE
Website: www.videoinn.co.uk
e-mail: post@videoinn.co.uk   Tel: 01604 864868

VIDEOSONICS CINEMA SOUND
(Film & Television Dubbing Facilities)
68A Delancey Street
London NW1 7RY
Website: www.videosonics.com
e-mail: info@videosonics.com
Fax: 020-7419 4470   Tel: 020-7209 0209

VSI - VOICE & SCRIPT INTERNATIONAL
(Dubbing, Editing & DVD Encoding & Authoring Facilities)
132 Cleveland Street, London W1T 6AB
Website: www.vsi.tv
e-mail: info@vsi.tv
Fax: 020-7692 7711   Tel: 020-7692 7700

W6 STUDIO
(Video Production & Editing Facilities)
359 Lillie Road, Fulham, London SW6 7PA
Website: www.w6studio.co.uk
Fax: 020-7381 5252   Tel: 020-7385 2272

30 BIRD PRODUCTIONS
17 Emery Street, Cambridge CB1 2AX
Website: www.30birdproductions.org
e-mail: info@30birdproductions.org   Mobile: 07970 960995

303 PRODUCTIONS
11 D'Arblay Street, London W1T 8DT
e-mail: lucy@303productions.co.uk
Fax: 020-7494 0956   Tel: 020-7494 0955

ACADEMY
16 West Central Street, London WC1A 1JJ
Website: www.academyfilms.com
e-mail: post@academyfilms.com
Fax: 020-7240 0355   Tel: 020-7395 4155

ACTAEON FILMS Ltd
Contact: Daniel Cormack. By Post/email.
Comedy & Light Entertainment. Documentaries. Drama.
Feature Films. Films. Television.
50 Gracefield Gardens, London SW16 2ST
Website: www.actaeonfilms.com
e-mail: info@actaeonfilms.com
Fax: 0870 1347980   Tel: 020-8769 3339

AGILE FILMS
Unit 1, 68-72 Redchurch Street, London E2 7DD
Website: www.agilefilms.com
e-mail: info@agilefilms.com   Tel: 020-7000 2882

ALGERNON Ltd
24B Cleveleys Road, London E5 9JN
Website: www.algernonproductions.com
e-mail: info@algernonproductions.com
Fax: 0870 1388516   Mobile: 07092 805026

AN ACQUIRED TASTE TV CORP
51 Croham Road, South Croydon CR2 7HD
e-mail: cbennetttv@aol.com
Fax: 020-8686 5928   Tel: 020-8686 1188

APT FILMS
Ealing Studios, Ealing Green, London W5 5EP
Website: www.aptfilms.com
e-mail: admin@aptfilms.com
Fax: 020-8280 9111   Tel: 020-8280 9125

APTN
The Interchange, Oval Road, Camden Lock, London NW1 7DZ
Fax: 020-7413 8312   Tel: 020-7482 7400

ARIEL PRODUCTIONS Ltd
46 Melcombe Regis Court, 59 Weymouth Street
London W1G 8NT   Tel/Fax: 020-7935 6636

ARLINGTON PRODUCTIONS Ltd
Cippenham Court, Cippenham Lane, Cippenham
Nr Slough, Berkshire SL1 5AU
Fax: 01753 691785   Tel: 01753 516767

ASCENT MEDIA Ltd
Film House, 142 Wardour Street, London W1F 8DD
Website: www.ascentmedia.co.uk
Fax: 020-7878 7870   Tel: 020-7878 0000

ASF PRODUCTIONS Ltd
Contact: Alan Spencer, Malcolm Bubb
Commercials. Corporate Videos. Documentaries
Feature Films. Films
38 Clunbury Court, Manor St, Berkhamsted, Herts HP4 2FF
e-mail: info@asfproductions.co.uk
Fax: 01442 872536   Tel: 01442 872999

ASHFORD ENTERTAINMENT CORPORATION Ltd The
20 The Chase, Coulsdon, Surrey CR5 2EG
Website: www.ashford-entertainment.co.uk
e-mail: info@ashford-entertainment.co.uk
Tel: 020-8668 8188

ATTICUS TELEVISION Ltd
5 Clare Lawn, London SW14 8BH
e-mail: attwiz@aol.com
Fax: 020-8878 3821   Tel: 020-8487 1173

AVALON TELEVISION Ltd
4A Exmoor Street, London W10 6BD
Fax: 020-7598 7313   Tel: 020-7598 8000

BAILEY Catherine Ltd
110 Gloucester Avenue
Primrose Hill, London NW1 8JA
Website: www.cbltd.net   Tel: 020-7483 3330

BANANA PARK Ltd
Animation Production Company
Banana Park, 6 Cranleigh Mews, London SW11 2QL
Website: www.bananapark.co.uk
e-mail: studio@bananapark.co.uk
Fax: 020-7738 1887   Tel: 020-7228 7136

BARFORD PRODUCTIONS
35 Bedfordbury, London WC2N 4DU
Website: www.barford.co.uk
e-mail: info@barford.co.uk
Fax: 020-7379 5210   Tel: 020-7240 4188

BARRATT Michael
9 Andrews Reach, Bourne End, Bucks SL8 5EA
e-mail: michael@mbarratt.co.uk   Tel: 01628 530895

BBC WORLDWIDE Ltd
Woodlands, 80 Wood Lane, London W12 0TT
Website: www.bbcworldwide.com   Tel: 020-8433 2000

BIG RED BUTTON Ltd
Contact: By Post
91 Brick Lane, London E1 6QL
Website: www.bigredbutton.tv
e-mail: info@bigredbutton.tv

BLACKBIRD PRODUCTIONS
6 Molasses Row, Plantation Wharf
Battersea, London SW11 3UX
e-mail: enquiries@blackbirdproductions.co.uk
Tel: 020-7924 6440

BLUE FISH MEDIA
39 Ratby Close, Lower Earley, Reading RG6 4ER
Website: www.bfmedia.co.uk
e-mail: ideas@bfmedia.co.uk   Tel: 0118-975 0272

BLUE SKY ENTERTAINMENT
Contact: Robert J. Williamson. By email.
Corporate. Documentaries. Films. Live Events. Open Air &
Specialist Entertainment. Television
8 Adelaide Grove, London W12 0JJ
Website: www.blueskyentertainment.co.uk
e-mail: info@blueskyentertainment.co.uk
Mobile: 07502 245540   Tel: 020-8723 2127

BLUE WAND PRODUCTIONS Ltd
Contact: By email. Films
2nd Floor, 12 Weltje Road, London W6 9TG
e-mail: bluewand@btinternet.com
Mobile: 07525 187468   Tel/Fax: 020-8741 2038

BLUELINE PRODUCTIONS Ltd
Contact: David Tranter
Corporate Videos
16 Five Oaks Close, Woking, Surrey GU21 8TU
e-mail: david@blue-line.tv   Tel: 01483 797002

BRUNSWICK FILMS Ltd
Formula One Grand Prix Film Library
26 Macroom Road
Maida Vale, London W9 3HY
Website: www.brunswickfilms.com
e-mail: info@brunswickfilms.com
Fax: 020-8960 4997   Tel: 020-8960 0066

BRYANT WHITTLE Ltd
49 Federation Road, Abbey Wood, London SE2 0JT
Website: www.bryantwhittle.com
e-mail: bryant.whittle@virgin.net
Fax: 020-8311 5827   Tel: 020-8311 8752

BUCKMARK PRODUCTIONS
Commer House, Station Road
Tadcaster, North Yorkshire LS24 9JF
Website: www.buckmark.com
e-mail: info@buckmark.com
Fax: 01937 835901   Tel: 01937 835900

BUENA VISTA PRODUCTIONS
3 Queen Caroline Street, Hammersmith, London W6 9PE
Fax: 020-8222 2795   Tel: 020-8222 1000

BURDER FILMS
37 Braidley Road, Meyrick Park
Bournemouth BH2 6JY
Website: www.johnburder.co.uk
e-mail: burderfilms@aol.com   Tel: 01202 295395

CALDERDALE TELEVISION
Dean Clough, Halifax HX3 5AX
e-mail: ctv@calderdaletv.co.uk   Tel: 01422 253100

CAMBRIDGE FILM & TELEVISION PRODUCTIONS Ltd
Contact: By Post/email/Telephone
Commercials. Corporate Videos. Documentaries. Drama
The Old Chapel, Butchers Row, Ely, Cambs CB7 4NA
Website: www.cftp.co.uk
e-mail: contact@cftp.co.uk
Fax: 01323 653279   Tel: 01323 653260

CARDINAL BROADCAST
Cutting Room 13, Pinewood Studios
Iver Heath, Bucks SL0 0NH   Tel: 01753 639210

CARNIVAL FILM & TELEVISION Ltd
47 Marylebone Lane, London W1U 2NT
Website: www.carnivalfilms.co.uk
Fax: 020-7317 1380   Tel: 020-7317 1370

CELADOR PRODUCTIONS Ltd
39 Long Acre, London WC2E 9LG
Fax: 020-7845 6975   Tel: 020-7240 8101

CELTIC FILMS ENTERTAINMENT Ltd
Lodge House
69 Beaufort Street, London SW3 5AH
Website: www.celticfilms.co.uk
e-mail: info@celticfilms.co.uk
Fax: 020-7351 4139   Tel: 020-7351 0909

CENTRAL OFFICE OF INFORMATION
Television
Hercules House, Hercules Road, London SE1 7DU
Website: www.coi.gov.uk
e-mail: eileen.newton@coi.gsi.gov.uk
Fax: 020-7261 8776   Tel: 020-7261 8220

CENTRE SCREEN PRODUCTIONS
Eastgate, Castle Street
Castlefield, Manchester M3 4LZ
Website: www.centrescreen.co.uk
e-mail: info@centrescreen.co.uk
Fax: 0161-832 8934   Tel: 0161-832 7151

CHANNEL 2020 Ltd
2020 House, 26-28 Talbot Lane, Leicester LE1 4LR
Website: www.channel2020.co.uk
e-mail: info@channel2020.co.uk
Fax: 0116-222 1113   Tel: 0844 8402020

CHANNEL TELEVISION PRODUCTION
The Television Centre, La Pouquelaye
St Helier, Jersey JE1 3ZD
e-mail: production@channeltv.co.uk
Fax: 01534 816889   Tel: 01534 816816

CHANNEL X Ltd
3rd Floor, Cairo Studios, 4 Nile Street, London N1 7RF
e-mail: firstname.lastname@channelx.co.uk
Fax: 020-7566 8161   Tel: 020-7566 8160

CHILDREN'S FILM & TELEVISION FOUNDATION Ltd
e-mail: annanhome@cftf.org.uk   Mobile: 07887 573479

CINEMANX Ltd
13 Manette Street, London W1D 4AW
Fax: 020-7439 4901   Tel: 020-7439 4900

CLASSIC MEDIA GROUP
Shepperton Studios, Studios Road
Shepperton, Middlesex TW17 0QD
e-mail: lyn.beardsall@classic-media-group.com
Fax: 01932 592046   Tel: 01932 592016

COLLINGWOOD O'HARE ENTERTAINMENT Ltd
10-14 Crown Street, Acton, London W3 8SB
e-mail: info@crownstreet.co.uk
Fax: 020-8993 9595   Tel: 020-8993 3666

COMMERCIAL BREAKS
Anglia House, Norwich NR1 3JG
Website: www.commercialbreaks.co.uk
e-mail: commercialbreaks@itv.com
Fax: 01603 752610   Tel: 01603 752600

COMMUNICATOR Ltd
199 Upper Street, London N1 1RQ
e-mail: info@communicator.ltd.uk
Fax: 020-7704 8444   Tel: 020-7704 8333

COMPLETE WORKS The
The Old Truman Brewery, 91 Brick Lane, London E1 6QL
Website: www.tcw.org.uk
e-mail: info@tcw.org.uk
Fax: 0870 1431979   Tel: 0870 1431969

COMTEC Ltd
Unit 19, Tait Road, Croydon, Surrey CR0 2DP
Website: www.comtecav.co.uk
e-mail: info@comtecav.co.uk
Fax: 020-8684 6947   Tel: 020-8684 6615

COURTYARD PRODUCTIONS
TV Production Company
Little Postlings Farmhouse
Four Elms, Kent TN8 6NA
e-mail: courtyard@mac.com   Tel: 01732 700324

CREATIVE PARTNERSHIP The
13 Bateman Street, London W1D 3AF
Website: www.creativepartnership.co.uk
Fax: 020-7437 1467   Tel: 020-7439 7762

CROFT TELEVISION
Croft House, Progress Business Centre
Whittle Parkway, Slough, Berkshire SL1 6DQ
Fax: 01628 668791   Tel: 01628 668735

CROSSROADS FILMS
2nd Floor, 87 Notting Hill Gate, London W11 3JZ
Website: www.crossroadsfilms.co.uk
e-mail: info@crossroadsfilms.co.uk
Fax: 020-7792 0592   Tel: 020-7792 5400

CUTHBERT Tony PRODUCTIONS
Suite 14, 7 Dials Court, 3 Shorts Gardens, London WC2H 9AT
Website: www.tonycuthbert.com
e-mail: tonycuthbert@btconnect.com   Tel: 020-7836 3432

DALTON FILMS Ltd
127 Hamilton Terrace, London NW8 9QR
e-mail: dalton@robdal.demon.co.uk
Fax: 020-7624 4420   Tel: 020-7328 6169

DARLOW SMITHSON PRODUCTIONS Ltd
Highgate Studios, 53-79 Highgate Road, London NW5 1TL
Website: www.darlowsmithson.com
e-mail: mail@darlowsmithson.com
Fax: 020-7482 7039   Tel: 020-7482 7027

DAWSON FILMS
Suite 114, The Business Design Centre
52 Upper Street, London N1 0QH
Website: www.dawsonfilms.com
e-mail: contactus@dawsonfilms.com
Fax: 020-7288 1386   Tel: 020-7704 9386

DIALOGICS
249-251 Kensal Road, London W10 5DB
e-mail: peter@dialogics.com
Fax: 020-8968 1517   Tel: 020-8960 6069

DLT ENTERTAINMENT UK Ltd
10 Bedford Square, London WC1B 3RA
Fax: 020-7636 4571   Tel: 020-7631 1184

DON PRODUCTIONS Ltd
2 Soskett Mews, Shacklewell Lane, London E8 2BZ
Website: www.donproductions.com
e-mail: info@donproductions.com
Fax: 07092 273283   Tel: 020-7254 0044

DRAMATIS PERSONAE Ltd
Contact: Nathan Silver, Nicolas Kent
19 Regency Street, London SW1P 4BY
e-mail: ns@nathansilver.com
                                      Tel: 020-7834 9300

DREAMING WILL INITIATIVE The
PO Box 38155, London SE17 3XP
Website: www.lswproductions.co.uk
e-mail: londonswo@hotmail.com   Tel/Fax: 020-7793 9755

DVA
8 Campbell Court, Bramley, Hampshire RG26 5EG
Website: www.dvafacilities.co.uk
e-mail: barrieg@dva.co.uk
Fax: 01256 882024   Tel: 01256 882032

ECOSSE FILMS Ltd
Brigade House, 8 Parsons Green, London SW6 4TN
Website: www.ecossefilms.com
e-mail: info@ecossefilms.com
Fax: 020-7736 3436   Tel: 020-7371 0290

EDGE PICTURE COMPANY Ltd The
7 Langley Street, London WC2H 9JA
Website: www.edgepicture.com
e-mail: ask.us@edgepicture.com
Fax: 020-7836 6949   Tel: 020-7836 6262

EFFINGEE PRODUCTIONS Ltd
13 Colquhoun Avenue, Hillington Park, Glasgow G52 4BN
Website: www.effingee.com
e-mail: info@effingee.com
Fax: 0141-576 1138   Tel: 0141-579 2921

ENDEMOL UK Plc
(Including Endemol UK Productions, Initial, Brighter
Pictures & Victoria Real)
Shepherds Building Central
Charecroft Way, Shepherd's Bush, London W14 0EE
Fax: 0870 3331800   Tel: 0870 3331700

ENLIGHTENMENT INTERACTIVE
East End House, 24 Ennerdale, Skelmersdale WN8 6AJ
Website: www.trainingmultimedia.co.uk   Tel: 01695 727555

ENTERTAINMENT RIGHTS Plc
Colet Court, 100 Hammersmith Road, London W6 7JP
e-mail: enquiries@entertainmentrights.com
Fax: 020-8762 6299   Tel: 020-8762 6200

EON PRODUCTIONS Ltd
Eon House, 138 Piccadilly, London W1J 7NR
Fax: 020-7408 1236   Tel: 020-7493 7953

EXTRA DIGIT Ltd
PO Box 51736, London NW1 5ZJ
Website: www.extradigit.com
e-mail: info@extradigit.com   Mobile: 07956 859449

EYE FILM & TELEVISION
Chamberlain House, 2 Dove Street, Norwich NR2 1DE
Website: www.eyefilmandtv.co.uk
e-mail: production@eyefilmandtv.co.uk
Fax: 01603 762420   Tel: 01603 762551

FARNHAM FILM COMPANY The
34 Burnt Hill Road, Lower Bourne, Farnham GU10 3LZ
Website: www.farnfilm.com   e-mail: info@farnfilm.com
Fax: 01252 725855   Tel: 01252 710313

FEELGOOD FICTION Ltd
49 Goldhawk Road, London W12 8QP
Website: www.feelgoodfiction.co.uk
e-mail: feelgood@feelgoodfiction.co.uk
Fax: 020-8740 6177   Tel: 020-8746 2535

FERRIS ENTERTAINMENT FILMS
Number 8, 132 Charing Cross Road, London WC2H 0LA
Website: www.ferrisentertainment.com
e-mail: info@ferrisentertainment.com Mobile: 07801 493133

FESTIVAL FILM & TELEVISION Ltd
Festival House, Tranquil Passage
Blackheath Village, London SE3 0BJ
Website: www.festivalfilm.com
e-mail: info@festivalfilm.com
Fax: 020-8297 1155   Tel: 020-8297 9999

FILM & GENERAL PRODUCTIONS Ltd
4 Bradbrook House, Studio Place, London SW1X 8EL
Fax: 020-7245 9853   Tel: 020-7235 4495

FILMS OF RECORD Ltd
2 Elgin Avenue, London W9 3QP
Website: www.filmsofrecord.com
Fax: 020-7286 0444   Tel: 020-7286 0333

FIRST WRITES RADIO COMPANY
Radio Drama Company
Lime Kiln Cottage, High Starlings
Banham, Norfolk NR16 2BS
Website: www.first-writes.co.uk
e-mail: ellen@first-writes.co.uk
Fax: 01953 888974   Tel: 01953 888525

FLASHBACK TELEVISION Ltd
58 Farringdon Road, London EC1R 3PB
Website: www.flashbacktelevision.com
e-mail: mailbox@flashbacktv.co.uk
Fax: 020-7253 8765   Tel: 020-7253 8768

FLYING DUCKS GROUP
Oakridge, Weston Road, Stafford ST16 3RS
Website: www.flyingducks.biz
e-mail: enquiries@flyingducks.biz
Fax: 01785 252448   Tel: 0700 3401211

FOCUS PRODUCTIONS Ltd
58 Shelley Road, Stratford-upon-Avon
Warwickshire CV37 7JS
Website: www.focusproductions.co.uk
e-mail: maddern@focusproductions.co.uk
Fax: 01789 294845   Tel: 01789 298948

FORSTATER Mark PRODUCTIONS
11 Keslake Road
London NW6 6DJ   Tel/Fax: 020-8933 5475

FREMANTLEMEDIA TALKBACKTHAMES
1 Stephen Street, London W1T 1AL
Fax: 020-7691 6100   Tel: 020-7691 6000

FULMAR TELEVISION & FILM Ltd
Pascoe House, 54 Bute Street
Cardiff Bay, Cardiff CF10 5AF
Fax: 029-2045 5111   Tel: 029-2045 5000

FUNNY FACE FILMS Ltd
8A Warwick Road
Hampton Wick, Surrey KT1 4DW
e-mail: stevendrew40@hotmail.com   Mobile: 07951 344602

GALA PRODUCTIONS Ltd
25 Stamford Brook Road, London W6 0XJ
Website: www.galaproductions.co.uk
e-mail: info@galaproductions.co.uk
Fax: 020-8741 2323   Tel: 020-8741 4200

GALLEON FILMS Ltd
Greenwich Playhouse, Station Forecourt
189 Greenwich High Road, London SE10 8JA
Website: www.galleonfilms.co.uk
e-mail: alice@galleontheatre.co.uk   Tel/Fax: 020-8310 7276

GAY Noel TELEVISION Ltd
Shepperton Studios, Studios Road
Shepperton, Middlesex TW17 0QD
e-mail: charles.armitage@virgin.net
Fax: 01932 592172   Tel: 01932 592569

GHA GROUP
1 Great Chapel Street, London W1F 8FA
Website: www.ghagroup.co.uk
e-mail: sales@ghagroup.co.uk
Fax: 020-7437 5880   Tel: 020-7439 8705

GLASS PAGE Ltd The
15 De Montfort Street, Leicester LE1 7GE
Fax: 0116-249 2188   Tel: 0116-249 2199

GOLDHAWK ESSENTIAL
Radio Productions
20 Great Chapel Street, London W1F 8FW
e-mail: enquiries@goldhawk.eu
Fax: 020-7287 3597   Tel: 020-7439 7113

GRANT NAYLOR PRODUCTIONS Ltd
Room 964, David Lean Buildings, Shepperton Studios
Studios Road, Shepperton, Middlesex TW17 0QD
Fax: 01932 592484   Tel: 01932 592175

GREAT GUNS Ltd
43-45 Camden Road, London NW1 9LR
e-mail: greatguns@greatguns.com
Fax: 020-7692 4422   Tel: 020-7692 4444

GUERILLA FILMS Ltd
35 Thornbury Road
Isleworth, Middlesex TW7 4LQ
Website: www.guerilla-films.com
e-mail: david@guerilla-films.com
Fax: 020-8758 9364   Tel: 020-8758 1716

HAMMERWOOD FILM PRODUCERS
110 Trafalgar Road, Portslade, Sussex BN41 1GS
Website: www.filmangel.co.uk
e-mail: filmangels@freenetname.co.uk
Fax: 01273 705451   Tel: 01273 277333

HARBOUR PICTURES
6 Providence Villas Studio
Brackenbury Road, London W6 0BA
Website: www.harbourpictures.com
e-mail: info@harbourpictures.com
Fax: 020-8740 1937   Tel: 020-8749 4100

HARTSWOOD FILMS
Twickenham Studios, The Barons, St Margaret's
Twickenham, Middlesex TW1 2AW
Fax: 020-8607 8744   Tel: 020-8607 8736

HAT TRICK PRODUCTIONS Ltd
10 Livonia Street, London W1F 8AF
Fax: 020-7287 9791   Tel: 020-7434 2451

HAWK EYE FILMS
82 Kenley Road, St Margarets
Twickenham TW1 1JU   Tel: 020-8241 7089

HEAD Sally PRODUCTIONS
Twickenham Film Studios
The Barons, St Margaret's Twickenham
Middlesex TW1 2AW
e-mail: admin@shpl.demon.co.uk
Fax: 020-8607 8964   Tel: 020-8607 8730

HEAVY ENTERTAINMENT Ltd
111 Wardour Street, London W1F 0UH
Website: www.heavy-entertainment.com
e-mail: info@heavy-entertainment.com
Fax: 020-7494 1100   Tel: 020-7494 1000

HIT ENTERTAINMENT Ltd
5th Floor, Maple House
149 Tottenham Court Road, London W1T 7NF
Website: www.hitentertainment.com
e-mail: creative@hitentertainment.com
Fax: 020-7388 9321   Tel: 020-7554 2500

HOLMES ASSOCIATES & OPEN ROAD FILMS
The Studio, 37 Redington Road, London NW3 7QY
e-mail: holmesassociates@blueyonder.co.uk
Fax: 020-7813 4334   Tel: 020-7813 4333

HUDSON FILM Ltd
24 St Leonard's Terrace
London SW3 4QG   Tel: 020-7730 0002

HUNGRY MAN Ltd
1-2 Herbal Hill, London EC1R 5EF
Website: www.hungryman.com
e-mail: ukreception@hungryman.com
Fax: 020-7239 4589   Tel: 020-7239 4550

HUNKY DORY PRODUCTIONS Ltd
57 Alan Drive, Barnet, Herts EN5 2PW
Website: www.hunkydory.tv
e-mail: adrian@hunkydory.tv   Mobile: 07973 655510

HURRICANE FILMS Ltd
19 Hope Street, Liverpool L1 9BQ
Website: www.hurricanefilms.net
e-mail: sol@hurricanefilms.co.uk
Fax: 0151-707 9149   Tel: 0151-707 9700

Television & Film Production
Studio and Production Offices for Hire
13 Colquhoun Avenue, Hillington Park, Glasgow, G52 4BN
Tel: 0141 579 2921 Fax: 0141 576 1138
www.effingee.com

Effingee Productions Ltd

IAMBIC PRODUCTIONS Ltd
89 Whiteladies Road
Clifton, Bristol BS8 2NT
e-mail: admin@iambic.tv
Fax: 0117-923 8343   Tel: 0117-923 7222
ICON FILMS Ltd
1-2 Fitzroy Terrace, Bristol BS6 6TF
Fax: 0117-973 3890   Tel: 0117-317 1717
INFORMATION TRANSFER Ltd
Training Video Packages
Burleigh House
15 Newmarket Road, Cambridge CB5 8EG
Fax: 01223 310200   Tel: 01223 312227
ISIS PRODUCTIONS Ltd
387B King Street, London W6 9NJ
Website: www.isis-productions.com
e-mail: hello@isis-productions.com
Fax: 020-8748 7634   Tel: 020-8748 3042
IWC MEDIA
The Gloucester Building
Kensington Village
Avonmore Road, London W14 8RF
e-mail: info@iwcmedia.co.uk
Fax: 020-7013 4012   Tel: 020-7013 4040
JACKSON Brian FILMS Ltd
39-41 Hanover Steps
St George's Fields
Albion Street, London W2 2YG
Website: www.brianjacksonfilms.com
Fax: 020-7262 5736   Tel: 020-7402 7543
J. I. PRODUCTIONS
10 Linden Grove, Great Linford
Milton Keynes, Bucks MK14 5HF
Website: www.jasonimpey.co.uk
e-mail: jason.impey@freeuk.com
Mobile: 07732 476409   Tel: 01908 676081
JMS GROUP Ltd
Hethersett, Norwich
Norfolk, NR9 3DL
Website: www.jms-group.com
e-mail: info@jms-group.com
Fax: 01603 812255   Tel: 01603 811855
KNOWLES Dave FILMS
Also Multimedia Interactive CD-Roms
34 Ashleigh Close
Hythe SO45 3QP
Website: www.dkfilms.co.uk
e-mail: mail@dkfilms.co.uk
Fax: 023-8084 1600   Tel: 023-8084 2190
LANDSEER PRODUCTIONS Ltd
140 Royal College Street, London NW1 0TA
Website: www.landseerfilms.com
e-mail: ken@landseerproductions.com   Tel: 020-7485 7333
LIME PICTURES
Campus Manor, Childwall, Abbey Road, Liverpool L16 0JP
Fax: 0151-722 6839   Tel: 0151-722 9122
LITTLE BIRD TELEVISION
9 Grafton Mews, London W1T 5HZ
e-mail: info@littlebird.co.uk
Fax: 020-7380 3981   Tel: 020-7380 3980

LITTLE KING COMMUNICATIONS
The Studio, 2 Newport Road
Barnes, London SW13 9PE
Fax: 020-8653 2742   Tel: 020-8741 7658
LOOKING GLASS FILMS Ltd
103 Brittany Point, Ethelred Estate
Kennington, London SE11 6UH
e-mail: lookingglassfilm@aol.com   Tel/Fax: 020-7735 1363
LOOP COMMUNICATION AGENCY The
Hanover House
Queen Charlotte Street, Bristol BS1 4EX
e-mail: mail@theloopagency.com
Fax: 0117-311 2041   Tel: 0117-311 2040
MAGPIE FILM PRODUCTIONS Ltd
471 Birmingham Road
Boardsley, Worcs B97 6RL
Website: www.magpiefilms.co.uk
e-mail: jim@magpiefilms.co.uk
Fax: 01527 64134   Tel: 01527 60264
MALLINSON TELEVISION PRODUCTIONS
Commercials
29 Lynedoch Street, Glasgow G3 6EF
e-mail: shoot@mtp.co.uk
Fax: 0141-332 6190   Tel: 0141-332 0589
MALONE GILL PRODUCTIONS Ltd
27 Campden Hill Road, London W8 7DX
e-mail: malonegill@aol.com
Fax: 020-7460 3750   Tel: 020-7937 0557
MANS Johnny PRODUCTIONS Ltd
PO Box 196, Hoddesdon
Herts EN10 7WG
Website: www.johnnymansproductions.co.uk
e-mail: johnnymansagent@aol.com
Fax: 01992 470516   Tel: 01992 470907
MANSFIELD Mike TELEVISION Ltd/MANSFIELD
PRODUCTIONS Ltd
The Gatehouse
4 Ellerton Road, London SW20 0EP
e-mail: mikemantv@aol.com   Tel: 020-8947 6884
MARTIN William PRODUCTIONS
The Studio, Tubney Warren Barns
Tubney, Oxfordshire OX13 5QJ
Website: www.wmproductions.co.uk
e-mail: info@wmproductions.co.uk
Fax: 01865 390148   Tel: 01865 390258
MAVERICK TELEVISION
Progress Works, Heath Mill Lane
Birmingham B9 4AL
Website: www.mavericktv.co.uk
e-mail: mail@mavericktv.co.uk
Fax: 0121-771 1550   Tel: 0121-771 1812
MAX MEDIA
Contact: Martin Franks.
Comedy & Light Entertainment. Corporate Videos.
Documentaries. Drama
The Lilacs, West End, Woodhurst
Huntingdon, Cambridge PE28 3BH
Website: www.therealmaxmedia.com
e-mail: martin@therealmaxmedia.com
Fax: 01487 825299   Tel: 01487 823608

MBP TV
Saucelands Barn, Coolham
Horsham, West Sussex RH13 8QG
Website: www.mbptv.com
e-mail: info@mbptv.com
Fax: 01403 741647   Tel: 01403 741620

McINTYRE Phil ENTERTAINMENT
2nd Floor, 35 Soho Square, London W1D 3QX
e-mail: info@mcintyre-ents.com
Fax: 020-7439 2280   Tel: 020-7439 2270

MENTORN
77 Fulham Palace Road, London W6 8JA
Fax: 020-7258 6888   Tel: 020-7258 6800

MINAMON FILM
Contact: Min Clifford
By email/Telephone
Corporate Videos. Documentaries. Drama. Films
117 Downton Avenue, London SW2 3TX
Website: www.minamonfilm.co.uk
e-mail: studio@minamonfilm.co.uk
Fax: 020-8674 1779   Tel: 020-8674 3957

MINISTRY OF VIDEO
Contact: Chris, Andy
By email/Telephone
Casting Videos. Children's Entertainment. Commercials.
Corporate Videos. Live Events. Live Stage Productions.
Music Videos. Showreels
1533 High Road, Whetstone, London N20 9PP
Website: www.ministryofvideo.co.uk
e-mail: info@ministryofvideo.co.uk Tel: 020-8369 5956

MISTRAL FILMS Ltd
31 Oval Road, London NW1 7EA
e-mail: info@mistralfilm.co.uk
Fax: 020-7284 0547   Tel: 020-7284 2300

MODUS OPERANDI FILMS
10 Brackenbury Road, London W6 0BA
Website: www.mofilms.com   Tel: 020-7243 8199

MOVE A MOUNTAIN PRODUCTIONS
5 Ashchurch Park Villas, London W12 9SP
Website: www.moveamountain.com
e-mail: mail@moveamountain.com   Tel: 020-8743 3017

MURPHY Patricia FILMS Ltd
Lock Keepers Cottage,
Lyme Street, London NW1 0SF
e-mail: office@patriciamurphy.co.uk
Fax: 020-7485 0555   Tel: 020-7267 0007

NEAL STREET PRODUCTIONS Ltd
1st Floor, 26-28 Neal Street, London WC2H 9QQ
e-mail: post@nealstreetproductions.com
Fax: 020-7240 7099   Tel: 020-7240 8890

NEW MOON TELEVISION
8 Ganton Street, London W1F 7QP
Website: www.new-moon.co.uk
e-mail: production@new-moon.co.uk
Fax: 020-7479 7011   Tel: 020-7479 7010

NEXUS PRODUCTIONS Ltd
Animation for Commercials, Broadcast
Pop Promos & Title Sequences
113-114 Shoreditch High Street, London E1 6JN
Website: www.nexusproductions.com
e-mail: info@nexusproductions.com
Fax: 020-7749 7501   Tel: 020-7749 7500

NFD PRODUCTIONS Ltd
Contact: By Post/email/Telephone
Children's Entertainment. Commercials. Corporate Videos.
Drama. Films. Television. Short Films. Showreels
PO Box 76, Leeds LS25 9AG
Website: www.nfdproductions.com
e-mail: info@nfdproductions.com
Mobile: 07932 653466   Tel/Fax: 01977 681949

OLD VIC PRODUCTIONS (FILMS) Plc
The Old Vic Theatre
The Cut, Waterloo, London SE1 8NB
e-mail: becky.barber@oldvictheatre.com
Fax: 020-7981 0946   Tel: 020-7928 2651

OMNI PRODUCTIONS Ltd
Location House, Westside Entrance
5 Dove Lane, Bristol BS2 9HP
Website: www.omniproductions.co.uk
e-mail: info@omniproductions.co.uk   Tel: 0117-954 7170

ON COMMUNICATIONS/ONTV OXFORD & LONDON
Work across all Media in Business Communications
5 East St Helen Street, Abingdon, Oxford OX14 5EG
Website: www.oncommunication.com
e-mail: info@oncommunication.com
Fax: 01235 530581   Tel: 01235 537400
33 James's Square, London SW1Y 4JS Tel: 020-3170 7235

ON SCREEN PRODUCTIONS Ltd
Ashbourne House, 33 Bridge Street
Chepstow, Monmouthshire NP16 5GA
Website: www.onscreenproductions.co.uk
e-mail: action@onscreenproductions.co.uk
Fax: 01291 636301   Tel: 01291 636300

OPEN MIND PRODUCTIONS
3 Waxhouse Gate, St Albans, Herts AL3 4EW
e-mail: production.manager@openmind.co.uk
                                     Tel: 0845 8909192

OPEN SHUTTER PRODUCTIONS Ltd
Contact: John Bruce
Corporate Videos. Documentaries. Drama. Television
100 Kings Road, Windsor, Berkshire SL4 2AP
e-mail: jonthebruce@talktalk.net
Mobile: 07753 618875   Tel: 01753 841309

OPUS PRODUCTIONS Ltd
9A Coverdale Road
Shepherds Bush, London W12 8JJ
Website: www.opusproductions.co.uk
e-mail: claire.bidwell@opusproductions.com
Fax: 020-8749 4537   Tel: 020-8743 3910

ORIGINAL FILM & VIDEO PRODUCTIONS Ltd
84 St Dionis Road, London SW6 4TU
e-mail: original.films@btinternet.com Tel: 020-7731 0012

OVC MEDIA Ltd
Contact: Eliot M. Cohen. By email
Animation. Documentaries. Drama. Feature Films
Films. Television
88 Berkeley Court, Baker Street, London NW1 5ND
Website: www.ovcmedia.com
e-mail: eliot@ovcmedia.com
Fax: 020-7723 3064   Tel: 020-7402 9111

PALADIN INVISION
8 Barb Mews, London W6 7PA
Fax: 020-7371 2160   Tel: 020-7348 1950

PAPER MOON PRODUCTIONS
Wychwood House, Burchetts Green Lane
Littlewick Green, Maidenhead, Berkshire SL6 3QW
e-mail: david.haggas@paper-moon.co.uk
                                  Tel/Fax: 01628 829819

PARADINE David PRODUCTIONS Ltd
The Penthouse
346 Kensington High Street, London W14 8NS
e-mail: mail@paradine-productions.com
Fax: 020-7602 0411   Tel: 020-7371 3111

PARALLAX EAST Ltd
Victoria Chambers, St Runwald Street
Colchester CO1 1HF   Tel: 01206 574909

PARK VILLAGE Ltd
1 Park Village East, London NW1 7PX
e-mail: info@parkvillage.co.uk
Fax: 020-7388 3051   Tel: 020-7387 8077

PASSION PICTURES Ltd
Animation. Documentary. Television
3rd Floor, 33-34 Rathbone Place, London W1T 1JN
e-mail: info@passion-pictures.com
Fax: 020-7323 9030   Tel: 020-7323 9933

PATHE PICTURES Ltd
Kent House, 14-17 Market Place
Great Titchfield Street, London W1W 8AR
Website: www.pathe.co.uk
Fax: 020-7631 3568   Tel: 020-7323 5151

PICTURE PALACE FILMS Ltd
13 Egbert Street, London NW1 8LJ
Website: www.picturepalace.com
e-mail: info@picturepalace.com
Fax: 020-7586 9048   Tel: 020-7586 8763

PIER PRODUCTIONS Ltd
Lower Ground Floor, 1 Marlborough Place, Brighton BN1 1UB
e-mail: info@pierproductionsltd.co.uk
Fax: 01273 693658   Tel: 01273 691401

PIEREND PRODUCTIONS
34 Fortis Green, London N2 9EL
e-mail: russell@richardsonassoc.co.uk
    Tel/Fax: 020-8444 0138

POKER Ltd
143B Whitehall Court, London SW1A 2EL
e-mail: pokerfilms@yahoo.co.uk   Tel/Fax: 020-7839 6070

POSITIVE IMAGE Ltd
25 Victoria Street, Windsor, Berkshire SL4 1HE
Fax: 01753 830878   Tel: 01753 842248

POTBOILER PRODUCTIONS Ltd
9 Greek Street, London W1D 4DQ
e-mail: edie@potboiler.co.uk
Fax: 020-7287 5228   Tel: 020-7734 7372

POZZITIVE TELEVISION Ltd
Paramount House
162-170 Wardour Street, London W1F 8AB
e-mail: pozzitive@pozzitive.co.uk
Fax: 020-7437 3130   Tel: 020-7734 3258

PRETTY CLEVER PICTURES
Iping Mill, Iping, Midhurst, West Sussex GU29 0PE
e-mail: pcpics@globalnet.co.uk
Mobile: 07836 616981   Tel: 01730 817899

PRISM ENTERTAINMENT
Television Production & Website Design Company
The Clockhouse
220 Latimer Road, London W10 6QY
Website: www.prismentertainment.co.uk
e-mail: info@prism-e.com
Fax: 020-8969 1012   Tel: 020-8969 1212

PRODUCERS The
8 Berners Mews, London W1T 3AW
Website: www.theproducersfilms.co.uk
e-mail: info@theproducersfilms.co.uk
Fax: 020-7636 4099   Tel: 020-7636 4226

PRODUCTIONS & PROMOTIONS Ltd
Apsley Mills Cottage, London Road
Hemel Hempstead, Herts HP3 9QU
Website: www.prodmotions.com
e-mail: reception@prodmotions.com   Tel: 01442 233372

PROMENADE ENTERPRISES Ltd
6 Russell Grove, London SW9 6HS
Website: www.promenadeproductions.com
e-mail: info@promenadeproductions.com
    Tel: 020-7582 9354

PSA Ltd
52 The Downs, Altrincham WA14 2QJ
e-mail: andy@psafilms.co.uk
Fax: 0161-924 0022   Tel: 0161-924 0011

PVA MANAGEMENT Ltd
Hallow Park, Hallow, Worcs WR2 6PG
e-mail: films@pva.co.uk
Fax: 01905 641842   Tel: 01905 640663

QUADRILLION
The Old Barn, Kings Lane
Cookham Dean, Berkshire SL6 9AY
Website: www.quadrillion.tv
e-mail: enqs@quadrillion.tv
Fax: 01628 487523   Tel: 01628 487522

READ Rodney
45 Richmond Road, Twickenham, Middlesex TW1 3AW
Website: www.rodney-read.com
e-mail: rodney_read@blueyonder.co.uk
Fax: 020-8744 9603   Tel: 020-8891 2875

RECORDED PICTURE COMPANY Ltd
24 Hanway Street, London W1T 1UH
Fax: 020-7636 2261   Tel: 020-7636 2251

RED KITE ANIMATION
89 Giles Street, Edinburgh EH6 6BZ
Website: www.redkite-animation.com
e-mail: info@redkite-animation.com
Fax: 0131-553 6007   Tel: 0131-554 0060

RED ROSE CHAIN
1 Fore Hamlet, Ipswich IP3 8AA
Website: www.redrosechain.co.uk
e-mail: info@redrosechain.co.uk   Tel: 01473 288886

REDWEATHER PRODUCTIONS
Easton Business Centre
Felix Road, Bristol BS5 0HE
Website: www.redweather.co.uk
e-mail: info@redweather.co.uk
Fax: 0117-941 5851   Tel: 0117-941 5854

REEL THING Ltd The
20 The Chase, Coulsdon, Surrey CR5 2EG
Website: www.reelthing.tv
e-mail: info@reelthing.tv   Tel: 020-8668 8188

REPLAY Ltd
Contact: Danny Scollard
Animation. Corporate Videos. Documentaries. Drama E-Learning. Live Events. Script Writing. Web Design
Museum House, 25 Museum Street, London WC1A 1JT
Website: www.replayfilms.co.uk
e-mail: sales@replayfilms.co.uk   Tel: 020-7637 0473

RESOURCE BASE
Fairways House, Mount Pleasant Road
Southampton SO14 0QB
Website: www.resource-base.co.uk
e-mail: jane@resource-base.co.uk
Fax: 023-8023 6816   Tel: 023-8023 6806

REUTERS Ltd
The Reuters Building, South Collonade
Canary Wharf, London E14 5EP   Tel: 020-7250 1122

REVERE ENTERTAINMENT
22 Poland Street, London W1F 8QQ
Fax: 020-7292 7391   Tel: 020-7292 8370

RIVERSIDE TV STUDIOS
Riverside Studios
Crisp Road, London W6 9RL
Website: www.riversidetv.co.uk
e-mail: info@riversidetv.co.uk
Fax: 020-8237 1121   Tel: 020-8237 1123

ROGERS Peter PRODUCTIONS Ltd
Pinewood Studios, Iver Heath
Bucks SL0 0NH   Tel: 01753 651700

ROOKE Laurence PRODUCTIONS
14 Aspinall House, 155 New Park Road, London SW2 4EY
Mobile: 07765 652058   Tel: 020-8674 3128

RSA FILMS
42-44 Beak Street, London W1F 9RH
Fax: 020-7734 4978   Tel: 020-7437 7426

RUSSO Denis ASSOCIATES
Animation
161 Clapham Road, London SW9 0PU
Fax: 020-7582 2725   Tel: 020-7582 9664

SANDS FILMS
(Squirrel Films Distribution Ltd)
Grice's Wharf, 119 Rotherhithe Street, London SE16 4NF
Website: www.sandsfilms.co.uk
Fax: 020-7231 2119   Tel: 020-7231 2209

SCALA PRODUCTIONS Ltd
2nd Floor, 37 Foley Street, London W1W 7TN
e-mail: scalaprods@aol.com   Tel: 020-7637 5720

SCIMITAR FILMS Ltd
219 Kensington High Street, London W8 6BD
e-mail: winner@ftech.co.uk
Fax: 020-7602 9217   Tel: 020-7734 8385

SCREEN FIRST Ltd
The Studios, Funnells Farm, Down Street
Nutley, East Sussex TN22 3LG
e-mail: paul.madden@virgin.net   Tel: 01825 712034

SCREEN VENTURES
49 Goodge Street, London W1T 1TE
Website: www.screenventures.com
e-mail: info@screenventures.com
Fax: 020-7631 1265   Tel: 020-7937 5553

SEPTEMBER FILMS Ltd
Glen House, 22 Glenthorne Road
Hammersmith, London W6 0NG
Fax: 020-8741 7214   Tel: 020-8563 9393

SEVEN STONES MEDIA Ltd
The Old Butcher's Shop
St Briavels, Gloucestershire GL15 6TA
e-mail: info@sevenstonesmedia.com
Fax: 01594 530094   Tel: 01594 530708

SEVENTH ART PRODUCTIONS
63 Ship Street, Brighton BN1 1AE
Website: www.seventh-art.com
e-mail: info@seventh-art.com
Fax: 01273 323777   Tel: 01273 777678

SHED PRODUCTIONS
2 Holford Yard, London WC1X 9HD
Website: www.shedproductions.com
e-mail: shed@shedproductions.com
Fax: 020-7239 1011   Tel: 020-7239 1010

SHELL FILM & VIDEO UNIT
Shell Centre, York Road, London SE1 7NA
Fax: 020-7934 7490   Tel: 020-7934 3318

SHELL LIKE RADIO
Whitfield House, 81 Whitfield Street, London W1T 4HG
Website: www.shelllike.com
e-mail: enquiries@shelllike.com
Fax: 020-7255 5255   Tel: 020-7255 5204

SIGHTLINE
CD-Rom. Commercials. DVD. Video. Websites
Dylan House, Town End Street
Godalming, Surrey GU7 1BQ
Website: www.sightline.co.uk
e-mail: action@sightline.co.uk
Fax: 01483 861516   Tel: 01483 861555

SILK SOUND
Commercials. Corporate Videos. Documentaries
13 Berwick Street, London W1F 0PW
Website: www.silk.co.uk
e-mail: bookings@silk.co.uk
Fax: 020-7494 1748   Tel: 020-7434 3461

SILVER PRODUCTIONS Ltd
Bridge Farm, Lower Road, Britford
Salisbury, Wiltshire SP5 4DY
Website: www.silver.co.uk
Fax: 01722 336227   Tel: 01722 336221

SINDIBAD FILMS Ltd
79 Knightsbridge, 4th Floor, London SW1X 7RB
Website: www.sindibad.co.uk
e-mail: info@sindibad.co.uk   Tel: 020-7823 7488

SITCH LIVE
2D & 3D Design. Film & Video. Live Design
Exhibitions. Live Events
G4 Harbour Yard, Chelsea Harbour, London SW10 0XD
Fax: 020-7352 7906   Tel: 020-7544 7500

SMITH & WATSON PRODUCTIONS
The Gothic House
Fore Street, Totnes, Devon TQ9 5EH
Website: www.smithandwatson.com
e-mail: info@smithandwatson.com
Fax: 01803 864219   Tel: 01803 863033

SNEEZING TREE FILMS
1st Floor, 37 Great Portland Street, London W1W 8QH
Website: www.sneezingtree.com
e-mail: firstname@sneezingtree.com
Fax: 020-7580 1957   Tel: 020-7436 8036

SOLOMON THEATRE COMPANY
Penny Black, High Street
Fordingbridge, Hants SP6 3EU
Website: www.solomon-theatre.co.uk
e-mail: office@solomon-theatre.co.uk   Tel/Fax: 01725 518760

SONY PICTURES
25 Golden Square, London W1F 9LU
Fax: 020-7533 1015   Tel: 020-7533 1000

SPACE CITY PRODUCTIONS
77 Blythe Road, London W14 0HP
Website: www.spacecity.co.uk
e-mail: info@spacecity.co.uk
Fax: 020-7371 4001   Tel: 020-7371 4000

SPEAKEASY PRODUCTIONS Ltd
Wildwood House, Stanley, Perth PH1 4NH
Website: www.speak.co.uk
e-mail: info@speak.co.uk
Fax: 01738 828419   Tel: 01738 828524

SPECIFIC FILMS Ltd
25 Rathbone Street, London W1T 1NQ
e-mail: info@specificfilms.com
Fax: 020-7636 6886   Tel: 020-7580 7476

SPIRAL PRODUCTIONS Ltd
Aberdeen Studios
22 Highbury Grove, London N5 2EA
Fax: 020-7359 6123   Tel: 020-7354 5492

STAFFORD Jonathan PRODUCTIONS
Shepperton Studios, Studios Road
Shepperton, Middlesex TW17 0QD
e-mail: jon@staffordproductions.com
Fax: 01932 592617   Tel: 01932 562611

STANDFAST FILMS
The Studio, 14 College Road, Bromley, Kent BR1 3NS
Fax: 020-8313 0443   Tel: 020-8466 5580

STANTON MEDIA
6 Kendal Close, Aylesbury, Bucks HP21 7HR
Website: www.stantonmedia.com
e-mail: info@stantonmedia.com   Tel/Fax: 01296 489539

STEEL SPYDA Ltd
96-98 Undley, Lakenheath, Suffolk IP27 9BY
Website: www.steelspyda.com
e-mail: kay.hill@steelspyda.com
Fax: 01842 862875   Tel: 01842 862880

STONE PRODUCTIONS CREATIVE Ltd
Lakeside Studio, 62 Mill Street
St Osyth, Essex CO16 8EW
Website: www.stone-productions.co.uk
e-mail: kevin@stone-productions.co.uk
Fax: 01255 822160   Tel: 01255 822172

STUDIO AKA
Animation
30 Berwick Street, London W1F 8RH
Website: www.studioaka.co.uk
Fax: 020-7437 2309   Tel: 020-7434 3581

TABARD PRODUCTIONS Ltd
Contact: John Herbert
By email
Corporate Videos. Documentaries
Adam House, 7-10 Adam Street
London WC2N 6AA
Website: www.tabardproductions.com
e-mail: johnherbert@tabard.co.uk
Fax: 020-7497 0850   Tel: 020-7497 0830

TABLE TOP PRODUCTIONS
Contact: Ben Berry
By email
Drama. Feature Films
1 The Orchard, Bedford Park
Chiswick, London W4 1JZ
e-mail: berry@tabletopproductions.com
Tel/Fax: 020-8742 0507   Tel: 020-8994 1269

TAKE 3 PRODUCTIONS Ltd
72-73 Margaret Street, London W1W 8ST
Website: www.take3.co.uk
e-mail: mail@take3.co.uk
Fax: 020-7637 4678   Tel: 020-7637 2694

TAKE FIVE PRODUCTIONS
37 Beak Street, London W1F 9RZ
Website: www.takefivestudio.com
e-mail: info@takefivestudio.com
Fax: 020-7287 3035   Tel: 020-7287 2120

TALKBACKTHAMES
20-21 Newman Street, London W1T 1PG
Fax: 020-7861 8001   Tel: 020-7861 8000

TALKING PICTURES
Pinewood Studios, Pinewood Road
Iver Heath, Bucks SL0 0NH
Website: www.talkingpictures.co.uk
e-mail: info@talkingpictures.co.uk
Fax: 01753 650048   Tel: 01753 655744

TANDEM TV & FILM Ltd
Charleston House, 13 High Street
Hemel Hempstead, Herts HP1 3AA
Website: www.tandemtv.com
e-mail: info@tandemtv.com
Fax: 01442 219250   Tel: 01442 261576

THIN MAN FILMS
9 Greek Street, London W1D 4DQ
e-mail: info@thinman.co.uk
Fax: 020-7287 5228   Tel: 020-7734 7372

TIGER ASPECT PRODUCTIONS
7 Soho Street
London W1D 3DQ
Website: www.tigeraspect.co.uk
e-mail: general@tigeraspect.co.uk
Fax: 020-7434 1798   Tel: 020-7434 6700

TKO COMMUNICATIONS Ltd
(A Division of The Kruger Organisation Inc)
PO Box 130
Hove, Sussex BN3 6QU
e-mail: tkoinc@tkogroup.com
Fax: 01273 540969   Tel: 01273 550088

TOP BANANA
The Studio, Stourbridge
West Midlands DY9 0HA
Website: www.top-b.com
e-mail: info@top-b.com
Fax: 01562 700930   Tel: 01562 700404

TOPICAL TELEVISION Ltd
61 Devonshire Road, Southampton SO15 2GR
Fax: 023-8033 9835   Tel: 023-8071 2233

TRAFALGAR 1 Ltd
Contact: Hasan Shah
By Post/email
Documentaries. Feature Films. Film. Music Videos.
Television.
153 Burnham Towers
Adelaide Road, London NW3 3JN
Fax: 020-7483 0662   Tel: 020-7722 7789

TV PRODUCTION PARTNERSHIP Ltd
4 Fullerton Manor, Fullerton, Hants SP11 7LA
Website: www.tvpp.tv
e-mail: dbj@tvpp.tv   Tel: 01264 861440

TVE Ltd
Broadcast Facilities. Non-Linear Editing
TVE House
Wick Drive
New Milton, Hampshire BH25 6RH
e-mail: enquiries@tvehire.com
Fax: 01425 625021   Tel: 01425 625020

TVF
375 City Road, London EC1V 1NB
Fax: 020-7833 2185   Tel: 020-7837 3000

TVMS (SCOTLAND)
3rd Floor, 420 Sauchiehall Street
Glasgow G2 3JD
e-mail: mail@tvms.co.uk
Fax: 0141-332 9040   Tel: 0141-331 1993

TWOFOUR
Corporate Videos. Documentaries. Live Events. Television.
TwoFour Studios, Estover, Plymouth PL6 7RG
Website: www.twofour.co.uk
e-mail: enq@twofour.co.uk
Fax: 01752 727450   Tel: 01752 727400

TYBURN FILM PRODUCTIONS Ltd
Cippenham Court, Cippenham Lane
Cippenham, Nr Slough, Berkshire SL1 5AU
Fax: 01753 691785   Tel: 01753 516767

VERA
3rd Floor, 66-68 Margaret Street
London W1W 8SR
e-mail: phoebe@vera.co.uk
Fax: 020-7436 6117   Tel: 020-7436 6116

VERA MEDIA
Video Production & Training Company
30-38 Dock Street, Leeds LS10 1JF
e-mail: vera@vera-media.co.uk
Fax: 0113-242 8739   Tel: 0113-242 8646

VIDEO & FILM PRODUCTION
Robin Hill, The Ridge
Lower Basildon, Reading, Berks
Website: www.videoandfilm.co.uk
e-mail: david.fisher@videoandfilm.co.uk
Mobile: 07836 544955   Tel: 0118-984 2488

VIDEO ARTS
6-7 St Cross Street, London EC1N 8UA
e-mail: sales@videoarts.co.uk
Fax: 020-7400 4900   Tel: 020-7400 4800

VIDEO ENTERPRISES
12 Barbers Wood Road
High Wycombe, Bucks HP12 4EP
Website: www.videoenterprises.co.uk
e-mail: videoenterprises@ntlworld.com
Fax: 01494 534145   Tel: 01494 534144

VIDEOTEL PRODUCTIONS
Corporate Videos
84 Newman Street, London W1T 3EU
Fax: 020-7299 1818   Tel: 020-7299 1800

VILLAGE PRODUCTIONS
4 Midas Business Centre, Wantz Road
Dagenham, Essex RM10 8PS
e-mail: village000@btclick.com
Fax: 020-8593 0198   Tel: 020-8984 0322

W3KTS Ltd
10 Portland Street, York YO31 7EH
e-mail: chris@w3kts.com   Tel: 01904 647822

W6 STUDIO
359 Lillie Road, Fulham, London SW6 7PA
Website: www.w6studio.co.uk
Fax: 020-7381 5252   Tel: 020-7385 2272

WALKING FORWARD Ltd
Studio 1, 35 Britannia Row, London N1 8QH
Website: www.walkingforward.co.uk
e-mail: info@walkingforward.co.uk
Fax: 020-7359 5091   Tel: 020-7359 5249

WALKOVERS VIDEO
Willow Cottage, Church Lane, Kington Langley
Chippenham, Wiltshire SN15 5NR
e-mail: walkoversvideo@btinternet.com   Tel: 01249 750428

WALSH BROS Ltd
Contact: By email
Animation. Documentaries. Drama. Feature Films. Films.
Television
4 Trafalgar Grove, Greenwich, London SE10 9TB
Website: www.walshbros.co.uk
e-mail: info@walshbros.co.uk   Tel/Fax: 020-8858 6870

WALSH Steve PRODUCTIONS Ltd
Contact: Wendy Wolfcarius
Animation. Feature Films. Films. Television
352 Banbury Road, Oxford OX2 7PP
Website: www.steve-walsh.com
e-mail: info@steve-walsh.com
Fax: 020-7580 6567   Tel: 020-7580 6553

WARNER BROS PRODUCTIONS Ltd
Warner Suite, Leavesden Studios
South Way, Leavesden, Herts WD25 7LT
Fax: 01923 685221   Tel: 01923 685222

WARNER SISTERS PRODUCTIONS Ltd
Ealing Studios, Ealing Green, London W5 5EP
e-mail: ws@warnercini.com   Tel: 020-8567 6655

WEST DIGITAL
Broadcast Post-Production
65 Goldhawk Road, London W12 8EG
Fax: 020-8743 2345   Tel: 020-8743 5100

WHITE CROW PRODUCTIONS Ltd
24 Telegraph Lane, Claygate
Surrey KT10 0DU   Tel: 01372 460674

WHITEHALL FILMS
10 Lower Common South
London SW15 1BP
e-mail: mwhitehall@msn.com
Fax: 020-8788 2340   Tel: 020-8785 3737

WINNER Michael Ltd
219 Kensington High Street
London W8 6BD
e-mail: winner@ftech.co.uk
Fax: 020-7602 9217   Tel: 020-7734 8385

WORKING TITLE FILMS Ltd
Oxford House, 76 Oxford Street
London W1D 1BS
Fax: 020-7307 3001   Tel: 020-7307 3000

WORLD PRODUCTIONS & WORLD FILM SERVICES Ltd
16 Dufours Place, London W1F 7SP
Website: www.world-productions.com
Fax: 020-7758 7000   Tel: 020-7734 3536

WORLD WIDE PICTURES
21-25 St Anne's Court, London W1F 0BJ
Website: www.worldwidepictures.tv
e-mail: reception@worldwidepictures.tv
Fax: 020-7734 0619   Tel: 020-7494 8000

WORLD'S END TELEVISION
16-18 Empress Place, London SW6 1TT
Website: www.worldsendproductions.com
e-mail: info@worldsendproductions.com
Fax: 020-7386 4901   Tel: 020-7386 4900

WORTHWHILE MOVIE Ltd
Providing the services of Bruce Pittman as Film Director
191 Logan Avenue
Toronto, Ontario
Canada M4M 2NT   Tel: 00 1 (416) 4690459

XINGU FILMS
12 Cleveland Row, London SW1A 1DH
Fax: 020-7451 0601   Tel: 020-7451 0600

YOUNGSTAR PRODUCTIONS
Television Drama
Suite 10, 3rd Floor
Royal Mail House
Terminus Terrace, Southampton SO14 3FD
Website: www.youngstar.tv
e-mail: info@youngstar.tv   Tel: 023-8033 9322

ZEPHYR FILMS Ltd
33 Percy Street, London W1T 2DF
e-mail: info@zephyrfilms.co.uk
Fax: 020-7255 3777   Tel: 020-7255 3555

What are Film & Television Schools?

The schools listed in this section offer various courses to those who wish to become part of the behind-camera world of the entertainment industry. These courses include filmmaking, producing, screenwriting and animation, to name a few. Students taking these courses usually have to produce a number of short films in order to graduate and need actors willing to work for nothing or next to nothing to play parts in these productions. The following advice has been divided into two sections: for potential students and for actors.

Advice For Actors:

Why should I get involved?
All actors experience periods of unemployment during their career, particularly new performers striving to make a name for themselves. Unpaid work on student films can offer new actors the chance to develop skills and experience in front of a camera, learning scripts, working with other actors and working with crew members. Making new contacts and learning how to get on with those you are working with, whether in front of or behind camera, is a vital part of getting along in the acting community.

In addition, you are likely to receive a certain amount of exposure from the film. The student filmmaker may show it to teachers, other students, other actors, and most importantly directors when applying for jobs, and you would normally be given your own copy of the film which you can show to agents or casting directors if requested, or use a clip of it in your showreel (see below).

What if I am not new to acting?
For more experienced actors who are between jobs, unpaid work provides an opportunity to hone existing skills and keep involved within the industry. If an audition does come up after a long period without paid work, you will feel more prepared and less rusty if you have been 'practicing'. It is also useful to observe new actors and keep up-to-date with new training ideas and techniques.

What should I bear in mind about unpaid work?
The major downside, of course, is that you are extremely unlikely to benefit financially from a student film. Travel and food expenses are sometimes, but not always, offered.

You will not be working with professionals but with inexperienced directors, writers and sometimes unskilled actors. You will also be taking time out from paid work while rehearsing and filming so make sure your agent knows what you are doing. These things must be borne in mind and weighed against the benefits to your experience, skills and involvement in the industry in whatever form available. Keeping your finger on the pulse ensures you don't miss out on any news and gets you out of the house, keeping you positive and motivated mentally as well as your physical acting skills sharp and ready for your next audition.

Equity recommends that if taking on unpaid work in any capacity you make sure you always sign a contract to ensure that, should a film or other production become a commercial success, you are remunerated retrospectively.

How do I get involved?
It may be helpful to see if the schools' websites have any advice for actors interested in being considered for parts in student films and suggesting how they should make contact. If there is no advice of this kind, it would be worth either phoning or emailing to ask if the school or its students would consider actors previously unknown to them. If this is the case, ask who CVs and headshots should be sent to, and whether they would like to see a showreel or voicereel (for animation courses).

If you are asked to play a role in a student film, make sure you are not going to a student's home and that someone knows where you are going and when.

Should I use a clip of a student film on my showreel?
Casting directors would generally prefer to see some form of showreel than none at all. If you do not have anything else you can show that has been professionally broadcast, or do not have the money to get a showreel made from scratch, then a student film is an acceptable alternative. See the 'Promotional Services' section for more information on showreels.

Should I include unpaid acting work on my CV?
Again, casting professionals understand that actors have to start somewhere, and in such a competitive industry there are likely to be periods of unemployment. They will not judge you for having done unpaid work. Whether to include such work on your CV, however, is another question. We would normally recommend that you exclude these credits and only include paid professional work.

Where can I find more information?
Actors and students may want to visit Shooting People's website www.shootingpeople.org for further advice and daily email bulletins of student and unpaid film and TV castings. Filmmakers can upload their films to the site for others to view.

BRIGHTON FILM SCHOOL
Contact: Senior Lecturer Franz von Habsburg FBKS (BAFTA) (Member of the National Association for Higher Education in the Moving Image (NAHEMI) and the University Film and Video Association (UFVA). Part-time Day or Evening Film Directors' Courses includes Screen Writing, Cinematography etc)
Website: www.brightonfilmschool.org.uk
e-mail: info@brightonfilmschool.org.uk Tel: 01273 302166

LEEDS METROPOLITAN UNIVERSITY
(PG Dip/MA's in Film & Moving Image Production or Fiction Screenwriting, and BA (Hons) in Film & Moving Image Production and Cert HE/FdA in Film & Television Production)
and Cert HE/FdA in Film & Television Production,
Northern Film School
Electric Press
1 Millennium Square
Leeds LS2 3AD
Website: www.leedsmet.ac.uk
Fax: 0113-812 8080   Tel: 0113-812 0000

LONDON COLLEGE OF COMMUNICATION
(Film & Video Course)
Elephant & Castle
London SE1 6SB
Fax: 020-7514 6843   Tel: 020-7514 7935

LONDON FILM ACADEMY
The Old Church
52A Walham Grove, London SW6 1QR
Website: www.londonfilmacademy.com
e-mail: info@londonfilmacademy.com
Fax: 020-7381 6116   Tel: 020-7386 7711

LONDON FILM SCHOOL The
(2-year MA Course in Film Making, 1-year MA in Screenwriting)
24 Shelton Street, London WC2H 9UB
Website: www.lfs.org.uk
e-mail: info@lfs.org.uk
Fax: 020-7497 3718   Tel: 020-7836 9642

MIDDLESEX UNIVERSITY
(School of Arts)
Cat Hill, Barnet, Herts EN4 8HT
Website: www.mdx.ac.uk   Tel: 020-8411 5555

NATIONAL FILM AND TELEVISION SCHOOL
(MA and Diploma Courses in the Key Filmmaking Disciplines & Short Courses for Freelancers)
Beaconsfield Studios, Station Road
Beaconsfield, Bucks HP9 1LG
Website: www.nfts.co.uk
e-mail: info@nfts.co.uk
Fax: 01494 674042   Tel: 01494 731425

UCCA - FARNHAM
(3-year BA (Hons) Photography, BA (Hons) Journalism, Film Production, Digital Screen Arts, Arts & Media, Animation)
Falkner Road
Farnham
Surrey GU9 7DS
Website: www.ucreative.ac.uk   Tel: 01252 722441

UNIVERSITY OF WESTMINSTER SCHOOL OF MEDIA ARTS & DESIGN
(Undergraduate courses in Film and Television Production and Contemporary Media Practice. Postgraduate Courses in Screenwriting and Producing, Film and Television; Theory, Culture and Industry)
Admissions & Enquiries:
Watford Road
Northwick Park
Harrow
Middlesex HA1 3TP
Website: www.wmin.ac.uk/filmschool   Tel: 020-7911 5000

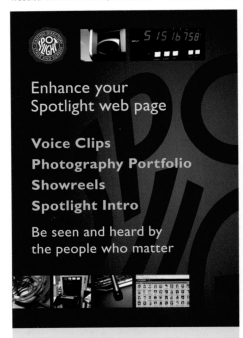

3 MILLS STUDIOS
Three Mill Lane, London E3 3DU
Website: www.3mills.com
e-mail: info@3mills.com
Fax: 08715 944028   Tel: 020-7363 3336

ARDMORE STUDIOS Ltd
Herbert Road
Bray, Co. Wicklow, Ireland
Website: www.ardmore.ie
e-mail: film@ardmore.ie
Fax: 00 353 1 2861894   Tel: 00 353 1 2862971

BBC TELEVISION
Television Centre
Wood Lane, Shepherds Bush
London W12 7RJ   Tel: 020-8743 8000

BRAY FILM STUDIOS
Down Place, Water Oakley
Windsor, Berkshire SL4 5UG
Fax: 01628 623000   Tel: 01628 622111

BRIGHTON FILM STUDIOS Ltd
The Brighton Forum
95 Ditchling Road, Brighton BN1 4ST
Website: www.brightonfilmstudios.com
e-mail: franz@brightonfilmstudios.com   Tel: 01273 302166

CAPITAL STUDIOS
Wandsworth Plain, London SW18 1ET
Website: www.capitalstudios.com
e-mail: info@capitalstudios.com
Fax: 020-8877 0234   Tel: 020-8877 1234

CHELTENHAM FILM STUDIOS Ltd
Arle Court
Hatherley Lane
Cheltenham, Gloucestershire GL51 6PN
Website: www.cheltenhamphotostudios.com
e-mail: hollycfs@yahoo.com   Tel: 01242 542708

EALING STUDIOS
Ealing Green, London W5 5EP
Website: www.ealingstudios.com
e-mail: info@ealingstudios.com
Fax: 020-8758 8658   Tel: 020-8567 6655

ELSTREE STUDIOS
Shenley Road
Borehamwood, Herts WD6 1JG
Website: www.elstreestudios.co.uk
e-mail: info@elstreestudios.co.uk
Fax: 020-8905 1135   Tel: 020-8953 1600

LONDON STUDIOS The
London Television Centre
Upper Ground, London SE1 9LT
Website: www.londonstudios.co.uk
Fax: 020-7928 8405   Tel: 020-7737 8888

PINEWOOD STUDIOS
Pinewood Road, Iver Heath
Buckinghamshire SL0 0NH
Website: www.pinewoodgroup.com   Tel: 01753 651700

REUTERS TELEVISION
The Reuters Building
South Colonnade
Canary Wharf
London E14 5EP   Tel: 020-7250 1122

RIVERSIDE STUDIOS
Crisp Road, London W6 9RL
Website: www.riversidestudios.co.uk
e-mail: info@riversidestudios.co.uk
Fax: 020-8237 1001   Tel: 020-8237 1000

SHEPPERTON STUDIOS
Studios Road
Shepperton, Middlesex TW17 0QD
Website: www.pinewoodgroup.com
Fax: 01932 568909   Tel: 01932 562611

SQUIRREL & SANDS FILMS/ROTHERHITHE STUDIOS
119 Rotherhithe Street
London SE16 4NF
Website: www.sandsfilms.co.uk
Fax: 020-7231 2119   Tel: 020-7231 2209

TEDDINGTON STUDIOS
Broom Road
Teddington
Middlesex TW11 9NT
Website: www.pinewoodgroup.com
Fax: 020-8943 4050   Tel: 020-8977 3252

TWICKENHAM FILM STUDIOS Ltd
The Barons
St Margaret's
Twickenham
Middlesex TW1 2AW
Website: www.twickenhamstudios.com
Fax: 020-8607 8889   Tel: 020-8607 8888

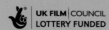

G

Good Digs Guide

Compiled By Janice Cramer and David Banks

This is a list of digs recommended by those who have used them.

To keep the list accurate please send recommendations for inclusion to

GOOD DIGS GUIDE
Spotlight
7 Leicester Place
London WC2H 7RJ

If you are a digs owner wishing to be listed, your application must contain a recommendation from a performer who has stayed in your accommodation.

Entries in **BOLD** have been paid for by the digs concerned.

ABERDEEN
Milne, Mrs A
5 Sunnyside Walk
Aberdeen AB24 3NZ   Tel: 01224 638951

Woods, Pat
62 Union Grove
Aberdeen AB10 6RX   Tel: 01224 586324

AYR
Dunn, Sheila
The Dunn-Thing Guest House
13 Park Circus
Ayr KA7 2DJ
Mobile: 07887 928685   Tel: 01292 284531

BATH
Hutton, Mrs Celia
Bath Holiday Homes
Terranova
Shepherds Walk
Bath BA2 5QT
Website: www.bathholidayhomes.co.uk
e-mail: bhh@virgin.net   **Tel: 01225 830830**

Tapley, Jane
Camden Lodgings
3 Upper Camden Place
Bath BA1 5HX   Tel: 01225 446561

BELFAST
McCully, Mrs S
28 Eglantine Avenue
Belfast BT9 6DX
e-mail: shealaghmccully@hotmail.com
Mobile: 07985 947673   Tel: 028-9068 2031

BILLINGHAM
Gibson, Mrs S
Northwood
61 Tunstall Avenue
Billingham TS23 3QB
Mobile: 07813 407674   Tel: 01642 561071

BIRMINGHAM
Baker, Mr N K
41 King Edward Road
Mosley
Birmingham B13 8HR   Tel: 0121-449 8220

Mountain, Marlene P
268 Monument Road
Edgbaston
Birmingham B16 8XF   **Tel: 0121-454 5900**

Wilson, Mrs
17 Yew Tree Road
Edgbaston
Birmingham B15 2LX   Tel: 0121-440 5182

BLACKPOOL
Lees, Jean
Ascot Flats
6 Hull Road
Central Blackpool FY1 4QB   Tel: 01253 621059

Somerset Apartments
22 Barton Avenue
Blackpool FY1 6AP
Website: www.blackpool-somerset-apartments.co.uk
    Tel/Fax: 01253 346743

[CONTACTS 2009]

BLACKPOOL Cont'd
Waller, Veronica & Bob
The Brooklyn Hotel
7 Wilton Parade
Blackpool FY1 2HE
Website: enquiries@brooklynhotel.co.uk   Tel: 01253 627003

BOLTON
Duckworth, Paul
19 Burnham Avenue
Bolton BL1 6DB
Mobile: 07762 545129   Tel: 01204 495732

White, Mrs M
20 Heywood Gardens
Great Lever
Bolton BL3 6RB   Tel: 01204 531589

BOURNEMOUTH
Sitton, Martin
Flat 2, 9 St Winifreds Road
Meyrick Park
Bournemouth BH2 6NX   Tel: 01202 293318

BRADFORD
Smith, Theresa
8 Moorhead Terrace
Shipley
Bradford BD18 4LA
e-mail: theresaannesmith@hotmail.com   Tel: 01274 778568

BRIGHTON
Benedict, Peter
19 Madeira Place, Brighton BN2 1TN
e-mail: peterdbenedict@hotmail.com
Mobile: 07752 810122   Tel: 020-7703 4104

Cleveland, Carol
13 Belgrave Street
Brighton BN2 9NS
Mobile: 07973 363939   Tel: 01273 602607

Dyson, Kate
39 Arundel Street
Kemptown BN2 5TH
Tel: 01273 607490   Mobile: 07812 949875

Stanfield-Miller, Ms
Flat 1, 154 Freshfield Road
Brighton BN2 9YD
Website: www.geocities.com/rowanstanfield/brightondigs
e-mail: rowanstanfield@yahoo.com
Mobile: 07747 725331   Tel: 01273 696080

BURY ST EDMUNDS
Bird, Mrs S
30 Crown Street
Bury St Edmunds
Suffolk IP33 1QU   Tel: 01284 754492

Harrington-Spie, Sue
39 Well Street
Bury St Edmunds
Suffolk IP33 1EQ   Tel: 01284 768986

BUXTON
Kitchen, Mrs M
Flat 1
17 Silverlands
Buxton
Derbyshire SK17 6QH   Tel: 01298 79381

CAMBRIDGE
O'Bernon, Mrs S
7 St Lukes Mews
Sealle Street
Cambridge   Tel: 01223 351440

CANTERBURY
Ellen, Nikki
Crockshard Farmhouse
Wingham
Canterbury CT3 1NY
Website: www.crockshard.com
e-mail: crockshard_bnb@yahoo.com   Tel: 01227 720464

CARDIFF
Blade, Mrs Anne
25 Romilly Road
Canton
Cardiff CF5 1FH   Tel: 029-2022 5860

Kennedy, Rosie
Duffryn Mawr Cottages
Pendoylan
Vale of Glamorgan
e-mail: rosie.kennedy@ukonline.co.uk   Mobile: 07746 946118

Lewis, Nigel
66 Donald Street
Roath, Cardiff CF24 4TR
e-mail: nigel.lewis66@btinternet.com
Mobile: 07813 069822   Tel: 029-2049 4008

Nelmes, Michael
12 Darran Street
Cathays
Cardiff
South Glamorgan CF24 4JF   Tel: 029-2034 2166

CHESTERFIELD
Cook, Linda & Chris
27 Tennyson Avenue
Chesterfield
Derbyshire
Mobile: 07929 850561   Tel: 01246 202631

Foston, Mr & Mrs
Anis Louise Guest House
34 Clarence Road
Chesterfield S40 1LN
Website: www.anislouiseguesthouse.co.uk
e-mail: anislouise@gmail.com   Tel: 01246 235412

Popplewell, Mr & Mrs
23 Tennyson Avenue
Chesterfield
Derbyshire S40 4SN   Tel: 01246 201738

CHICHESTER
Potter, Iain & Lyn
Hunston Mill Cottages, Selsey Road
Chichester PO20 1AU   Tel: 01243 783375

COVENTRY
Snelson, Paddy & Bob
Banner Hill Farmhouse
Rouncil Lane
Kenilworth CV8 1NN   Tel: 01926 852850

DARLINGTON
Bird, Mrs
Gilling Old Mill
Gilling West, Richmond
N Yorks DL10 5JD   Tel: 01748 822771

Graham, Anne
Holme House
Piercebridge, Darlington DL2 3SY
Website: www.holmehouse.com
e-mail: graham.holmehouse@gmail.com   Tel: 01325 374280

The Proprietor
George Hotel, Piercebridge
Darlington DL2 3SW   Tel: 01325 374576

DUNDEE
Hill, Mrs J
Ash Villa, 216 Arbroath Road
Dundee DD4 7RZ   Tel: 01382 450831

EASTBOURNE
Allen, Peter
Flat 1, 16 Enys Road
Eastbourne BN21 2DN
Mobile: 07712 439289   Tel: 01323 730235

Guess, Maggie
3 Hardy Drive, Langney Point
Eastbourne, East Sussex BN23 6ED
e-mail: guesswhom@btinternet.com
Mobile: 07710 273288   Tel: 01323 736689

EDINBURGH
Glen Miller, Edna
25 Bellevue Road
Edinburgh EH7 4DL   Tel: 0131-556 4131

Stobbart, Joyce
84 Bellevue Road, Edinburgh EH7 4DE
Mobile: 07740 503951   Day Tel: 0131-222 9889

Tyrrell, Helen
9 Lonsdale Terrace, Edinburgh EH3 9HN
e-mail: helen.tyrrell@vhscotland.org.uk
Tel: 0131-229 7219   Tel: 0131-652 5992 (Office)

GLASGOW
Baird, David W
6 Beaton Road
Maxwell Park, Glasgow G41 4LA
Mobile: 07842 195597   Tel: 0141-423 1340

Leslie-Carter, Simon
52 Charlotte Street
Glasgow G1 5DW
Website: www.52charlottestreet.com
e-mail: slc@52charlottestreet.co.uk
Fax: 01436 810520   Tel: 0845 2305252

Robinson, Lesley
28 Marywood Square
Glasgow G41 2BJ
Tel: 0141-423 6920   Mobile: 07957 188922

GRAVESEND
Greenwood, Mrs S
8 Sutherland Close
Chalk
Gravesend, Kent DA12 4XJ
Website: www.chalkbedandbreakfast.co.uk   Tel: 01474 350819

HULL
The Arches Guesthouse
38 Saner Street
Hull HU3 2TR   Tel: 01482 211558

INVERNESS
Blair, Mrs
McDonald House Hotel
1 Ardross Terrace
Inverness IV3 5NQ   Tel: 01463 232878

Kerr-Smith, Jennifer
Ardkeen Tower, 5 Culduthel Road
Inverness IV2 4AD   Tel: 01463 233131

IPSWICH
Ball, Bunty
56 Henley Road
Ipswich IP1 3SA   Tel: 01473 256653

Bennett, Liz
Gayfers
Playford, Ipswich IP6 9DR
e-mail: lizzieb@clara.co.uk   Tel: 01473 623343

Hyde-Johnson, Anne
64 Benton Street
Hadleigh, Ipswich
Suffolk IP7 5AT   Tel: 01473 823110

ISLE OF WIGHT
Ogston, Sue
Windward House
69 Mill Hill Road
Cowes
Isle of Wight PO31 7EQ   Tel: 01983 280940

KESWICK
Bell, Miss A
Flat 4, Skiddaw View
Penrith Road
Keswick CA12 5HF   Mobile: 07740 949250

KIRKCALDY
Nicol, Mrs
44 Glebe Park, Kirkcaldy
Fife KY1 1BL   Tel: 01592 264531

LEEDS
Baker, Mrs M
2 Ridge Mount
(off Cliff Road)
Leeds LS6 2HD   Tel: 0113-275 8735

LINCOLN
Carnell, Andrew
Tennyson Court Cottages
3 Tennyson Street, Lincoln LN1 1LZ
Website: www.tennyson-court.co.uk
Tel: 01522 569892   Tel: 0800 9805408

Sharpe, Mavis S
Bight House, 17 East Bight
Lincoln LN2 1QH   Tel: 01522 534477

Ye Olde Crowne Inn (Theatre Pub)
Clasketgate
Lincoln LN2 1JS   Tel: 01522 542896

LIVERPOOL
De Leng, Ms S
7 Beach Lawn, Waterloo
Liverpool L22 8QA   Tel: 0151-476 1563

Double, Ross
5 Percy Street
Liverpool L8 7LT   Tel: 0151-708 8821

Maloney, Anne
16 Sandown Lane, Wavertree
Liverpool L15 8HY   Tel: 0151-734 4839

LLNADUDNO
Blanchard, Mr D & Mrs A
Oasis Hotel, 4 Neville Crescent
Central Promenade, Llandudno LL30 1AT
e-mail: ann@oasis-hotel.co.uk   Tel: 01492 877822

LONDON
Allen, Mrs I
Flat 2
9 Dorset Square
London NW1 6QB   Tel: 020-7723 3979

Broughton, Mrs P A
31 Ringstead Road
Catford
London SE6 2BU   Tel: 020-8461 0146

Cardinal, Maggie
17A Gaisford Street
London NW5 2EB   Tel: 020-7681 7376

Maya, Ms Y
23 Lena Crescent
London N9 0FB   Mobile: 07958 461468

Mesure, Nicholas
16 St Alfege Passage
Greenwich
London SE10 9JS   Tel: 020-8853 4337

Montagu, Beverley
13 Hanley Road
London N4 3DU   Tel: 020-7263 3883

Rothner, Dora
23 The Ridgeway
Finchley
London N3 2PG   Tel: 020-8346 0246

Rothner, Stephanie
44 Grove Road
North Finchley
London N12 9DY
Mobile: 07956 406446   Tel: 020-8446 1604

Shaw, Lindy
11 Baronsmede
London W5 4LS   Tel: 020-8567 0877

Walsh, Genevieve
37 Kelvedon House
Guildford Road
Stockwell
London SW8 2DN   Tel: 020-7627 0024

Warren, Mrs Sally
28 Prebend Gardens
Chiswick
London W4 1TW   Tel: 020-8994 0560

Zahri, L
79 Hazlewood Road
London E17 7AJ
e-mail: lindiblue@hotmail.co.uk   Tel: 020-8281 5050

MALVERN
Emuss, Mrs
Priory Holme
18 Avenue Road
Malvern WR14 3AR   Tel: 01684 568455

Martin, Mr N
37 Quest Hills Road
Malvern WR14 1RL
e-mail: nick@questhills.co.uk
Mobile: 07979 851529   Tel: 01684 562442

McLeod, Mr & Mrs
Sidney House
40 Worcester Road
Malvern WR14 4AA
Website: www.sidneyhouse.co.uk
e-mail: info@sidneyhouse.co.uk   Tel: 01684 574994

MANCHESTER
Dyson, Mrs Edwina
33 Danesmoor Road
West Didsbury
Manchester M20 3JT   Tel: 0161-434 5410

Heaton, Miriam
58 Tamworth Avenue
Whitefield
Manchester M45 6UA   Tel: 0161-773 4490

Higgins, Mark, Tanzey & Mathew
103 The Arthouse
43 George Street
China Town
Manchester M1 4AB
Mobile: 07904 520898   Tel: 0161-234 0705

Jones, P M
375 Bury New Road
Whitefield
Manchester M45 7SU   Tel: 0161-766 9243

Prichard, Fiona & John
45 Bamford Road
Didsbury
Manchester M20 2QP   Tel: 0161-434 4877

Twist, Susan
45 Osborne Road, Levenshulme
Manchester M19 2DU   Tel: 0161-225 1591

MILFORD HAVEN
Henricksen, Bruce & Diana
Belhaven House Hotel Ltd
29 Hamilton Terrace
Milford Haven SA73 3JJ
Website: www.westwaleshotel.com
e-mail: hbhl@mac.com
Fax: 01646 690787   Tel: 01646 695983

NEWCASTLE UPON TYNE
The Manager
Rosebery Hotel
2 Rosebery Crescent
Jesmond, Newcastle upon Tyne NE2 1ET
Website: www.roseberyhotel.co.uk   Tel: 0191-281 3363

NEWPORT
Price, Mrs Dinah
Great House, Isca Road
Old Village, Caerleon
Gwent NP18 1QG
Website: www.greathousebb.co.uk
e-mail: dinah.price@amserve.net   Tel: 01633 420216

NORWICH
Busch, Julia
8 Chester Street, Norwich NR2 2AY
e-mail: juliacbusch@aol.com
Mobile: 07920 133250   Tel: 01603 612833

Youd, Cherry
Whitegates, 181 Norwich Road
Wroxham NR12 8RZ   Tel: 01603 781037

NOTTINGHAM
Davis, Barbara
3 Tattershall Drive
The Park, Nottingham NG7 1BX   Tel: 0115-947 4179

Offord, Mrs
5 Tattershall Drive
The Park, Nottingham NG7 1BX   Tel: 0115-947 6924

Santos, Mrs S
Eastwood Farm
Hagg Lane, Epperstone
Nottingham NG14 6AX   Tel: 0115-966 3018

Walker, Christine
18A Cavendish Crescent North
The Park, Nottingham NG7 1BA
e-mail: walker.ce@virgin.net   Tel: 0115-947 2485

OXFORD
Petty, Susan
74 Corn Street
Witney, Oxford OX28 6BS   Tel: 01993 703035

PETERBOROUGH
Smith, J
Fen-Acre, 19 Barber Drove
Crowland, Peterborough PE6 0BE
e-mail: julie@fen-acreholidaylet.com   Tel: 01733 211947

PLYMOUTH
Carson, Mr & Mrs
6 Beech Cottages, Parsonage Road
Newton Ferrers, Nr Plymouth PL8 1AX
e-mail: beechcottages@aol.com   Tel: 01752 872124

Humphreys, John & Sandra
Lyttleton Guest House (Self-Catering)
4 Crescent Avenue
Plymouth PL1 3AN   Tel: 01752 220176

Mead, Teresa
Ashgrove House
218 Citadel Road
The Hoe, Plymouth PL1 3BB   Tel: 01752 664046

Spencer, Hugh & Eloise
10 Grand Parade, Plymouth PL1 3DF
Mobile: 07966 412839   Tel: 01752 664066

POOLE
Saunders, Mrs
1 Harbour Shallows
15 Whitecliff Road
Poole BH14 8DU   Tel: 01202 741637

READING
Estate Office
Mapledurham House and Watermill
Mapledurham Estate
Reading RG4 7TR   Tel: 0118-972 3350

SALISBURY
Brumfitt, Ms S
26 Victoria Road, Salisbury
Wilts SP1 3NG   Tel: 01722 334877

SHEFFIELD
Craig, J & Rosen, B
59 Nether Edge Road, Sheffield S7 1RW   Tel: 0114-258 1337

Slack, Penny
Rivelin Glen Quarry, Rivelin Valley Road, Sheffield S6 5SE
Website: www.quarryhouse.org.uk
e-mail: pennyslack@aol.com   Tel: 0114-234 0382

SOUTHSEA & PORTSMOUTH
Tyrell, Wendy
Douglas Cottage, 27 Somerset Road
Southsea PO5 2NL   **Tel: 023-9282 1453**

STOKE-ON-TRENT
Griffiths, Dorothy
40 Princes Road
Hartshill, Stoke-on-Trent ST4 7JQ
Mobile: 07789 362960   Tel: 01782 416198

Hindmoor, Mrs
Verdon Guest House, 44 Charles Street, Hanley
Stoke-on-Trent ST1 3JY   Tel: 01782 264244

Meredith, Mr K
2 Bank End Farm Cottage
Hammond Avenue, Brown Edge
Stoke-on-Trent, Staffs ST6 8QU   **Tel: 01782 502160**

STRATFORD-UPON-AVON
Caterham House
58-59 Rother Street, Stratford-upon-Avon CV37 6LT
e-mail: caterhamhousehotel@btconnect.com
    Tel: 01789 267309

WESTCLIFF
Hussey, Joy
42A Ceylon Road
Westcliff-on-Sea SS0 7HP   Mobile: 07946 413496

WOLVERHAMPTON
Nixon, Sonia
39 Stubbs Road, Pennfields
Wolverhampton WV3 7DJ   Tel: 01902 339744

Prior, Julia
Treetops, The Hem, Shifnal
Shropshire TF11 9PS   Tel: 01952 460566

Riggs, Peter A
'Bethesda'
56 Chapel Lane, Codsall, Nr Wolverhampton WV8 2EJ
Mobile: 07930 967809   Tel: 01902 844068

WORTHING
Stewart, Mollie
School House, 11 Ambrose Place
Worthing BN11 1PZ   **Tel: 01903 206823**

Symonds, Mrs Val
23 Shakespeare Road, Worthing BN11 4AR
Mobile: 07951 183252   Tel: 01903 201557

YORK
Blacklock, Tom
155 Lowther Street, York YO3 7LZ   Tel: 01904 620487

Blower, Iris & Dennis
Dalescroft Guest House
10 Southlands Road, York YO23 1NP
Website: www.dalescroft-york.co.uk
e-mail: info@dalescroft-york.co.uk   Tel: 01904 626801

Harrand, Greg
Hedley House Hotel & Apts
3 Bootham Terrace
York YO30 7DH   Tel: 01904 637404

AHLOWALIA Dr B.S.
(Dentist & Botox)
3 Victoria Place, Biddleswade, Bedfordshire SG18 9RN
Website: www.thechrysalis.co.uk
e-mail: info@thechrysalis.co.uk   Tel: 01767 315278

ALEXANDER ALLIANCE
(Alexander Technique, Voice & Audition Coaching)
3 Hazelwood Drive, St Albans, Herts
Website: www.alextech.co.uk
e-mail: bev.keech@ntlworld.com   Tel: 01727 843633

ALEXANDER CENTRE The Bloomsbury
(Alexander Technique)
Bristol House, 80A Southampton Row, London WC1B 4BB
Website: www.alexcentre.com
e-mail: enquiries@alexcentre.com   Tel: 020-7404 5348

ALEXANDER TECHNIQUE
Contact: Robert Macdonald
13 Ascot Lodge, Greville Place, London NW6 5JD
Website: www.voice.org.uk   Mobile: 07956 852303

ALEXANDER TECHNIQUE
Contact: Jackie Coote MSTAT
27 Britannia Road, London SW6 2HJ
Website: www.alexandertec.co.uk
e-mail: jackiecoote@alexandertec.co.uk   Tel: 020-7731 1061

ALL ABOUT TEETH Ltd
The Club Room, Miserden, Gloucestershire GL6 7JA
e-mail: nicolas@ceramiccentre.com   Tel: 01285 821220

ALTERED IMAGE LIFE COACHING
Primrose Cottage
6 Lee Place, Ilfracombe EX34 9BQ
Website: www.alteredimage2.co.uk
e-mail: lifecoach@merseymail.com
Fax: 08709 133624   Mobile: 07050 644101

ARTS CLINIC The
(Psychological Counselling, Personal & Professional
Development)
14 Devonshire Place, London W1G 6HX
e-mail: mail@artsclinic.co.uk
Fax: 020-7224 6256   Tel: 020-7935 1242

ASPEY ASSOCIATES
(Management & Team Training, Executive Coaching, Human
Resources)
90 Long Acre,
Covent Garden, London WC2E 9RZ
Website: www.aspey.com
e-mail: hr@aspey.com   Tel: 0845 1701300

AUTOGENIC THERAPY
(Stress Management & Relaxation Training)
Hammersmith, London W6
e-mail: autogenictherapy@talktalk.net   Tel: 020-8741 2595

BENWOODFITNESS.COM
37 Nevil Road
Stoke Newington, London N16 8SW
Website: www.benwoodfitness.com
e-mail: benwood@benwoodfitness.com
          Mobile: 07776 222526

BODY CLINIC The
(Skincare Specialists)
Harley Street, South Woodford & Gidea Park
Website: www.thebodyclinic.co.uk   Tel: 0800 5424809

BODYWISE YOGA & NATURAL HEALTH CENTRE
119 Roman Road, London E2 0QN
Website: www.bodywisehealth.org
e-mail: info@bodywisehealth.org   Tel: 020-8981 6938

Health & Wellbeing

[CONTACTS 2009]

BOWES Sara
(Holistic Massage & Reflexology)
23 John Aird Court, London W2 1UY
e-mail: sara@sarabowes.com
Mobile: 07830 375389   Tel: 020-7262 3543

BREATHE FITNESS/ANTHONY MAYATT
22A Station Approach
Hayes, Bromley, Kent BR2 7EH
Website: www.breathefitness.uk.com
e-mail: anthony@breathefitness.uk.com
    Mobile: 07840 180094

BRITISH DOULAS
(Baby Care Services)
49 Harrington Gardens, London SW7 4JU
Website: www.britishdoulas.co.uk
e-mail: info@britishdoulas.co.uk
Fax: 020-7244 9035   Tel: 020-7244 6053

BURGESS Chris
(Counselling for Performing Artists)
81 Arne House, Tyers Street
London SE11 5EZ   Tel: 020-7582 8229

BURT Andrew
(Counselling)
74 Mill Hill Road, London W3 8JJ
Website: www.andrewburtcounselling.co.uk
e-mail: burt.counsel@tiscali.co.uk   Tel: 020-8992 5992

COCKBURN Daisy
Alexander Technique Teacher (MSTAT)
Bloomsbury Alexander Centre
Bristol House
80A Southampton Row, London WC1B 4BB
e-mail: daisycockburn@btinternet.com
    Mobile: 07734 725445

CONSTRUCTIVE TEACHING CENTRE Ltd
(Alexander Technique Teacher Training)
18 Lansdowne Road, London W11 3LL
Website: www.alexandertek.com
e-mail: constructiveteachingcentre@gmail.com
    Tel: 020-7727 7222

CORTEEN Paola MSTAT
(Alexander Technique)
10A Eversley Park Road, London N21 1JU
e-mail: pmcorteen@yahoo.co.uk   Tel: 020-8882 7898

COURTENAY Julian
(NLP Hypnotherapy)
42 Langdon Park Road, London N6 5QG
e-mail: julian@mentalfitness.uk.com   Mobile: 07973 139376

DAVIES Siobhan STUDIOS
(Treatment Room: Deep Tissue Massage, Homeopathy,
Suppleworx & Craniosacral Therapy)
85 St George's Road, London SE1 6ER
Website: www.siobhandavies.com
e-mail: info@siobhandavies.com
Fax: 020-7091 9669   Tel: 020-7091 9650

DREAM
(Massage, Reflexology & Yoga for Events, the Workplace
and Home)
117B Gaisford Street, London NW5 2EG
Website: www.dreamtherapies.co.uk
e-mail: heidi@dreamtherapies.co.uk   Mobile: 07973 731026

EDGE OF THE WORLD HYPNOTHERAPY AND NLP
Central London, Essex/Suffolk
Website: www.edgehypno.com
e-mail: info@edgehypno.com   Mobile: 07960 755626

EDWARDS Simon MCA Hyp
(Hypnotherapy for Professionals in Film, TV & Theatre)
15 Station Road, Quainton
Nr Aylesbury, Buckinghamshire HP22 4BW
e-mail: hypnotherapisttothestars@o2.co.uk
Mobile: 07889 333680   Tel: 01296 651259

FAITH Gordon BA DHC MCHC (UK)
(Hypnotherapy, Obstacles to Performing, Positive
Affirmation, Focusing)
1 Wavel Mews, Priory Road
West Hampstead, London NW6 3AB   Tel: 020-7328 0446

FIT 4 THE PART
Contact: Jon Trevor, (Personal Training)
One Malthus Path, London SE28 8AJ
Website: www.jontrevor.com
e-mail: info@jontrevor.com
Fax: 0845 4664477   Tel: 0845 0066348

FITNESS COACH The
Contact: Jamie Baird
Agua at The Sanderson
50 Berners Street, London W1T 3NG
e-mail: jamie@thefitnesscoach.com
Mobile: 07970 782476   Tel: 020-7300 1414

FOCUSING EXPERIENTIAL SESSIONS
(Existential Dialogue) (Central London & Brighton)
25 Sheffield Court, Brighton BN1 4HA
Website: www.gregmadison.net/focusbrighton
e-mail: info@gregmadison.net   Mobile: 07941 300871

HAMMOND John B. Ed (Hons) ICHFST
(Fitness Consultancy, Sports & Relaxation Massage)
4 Glencree, Billericay, Essex CM11 1EB
Mobile: 07703 185198   Tel/Fax: 01277 632830

HARLEY STREET VOICE CENTRE The
The Harley Street ENT Clinic
109 Harley Street, London W1G 6AN
Website: www.harleystreetent.com
e-mail: info@harleystreetent.com
Fax: 020-7935 7701   Tel: 020-7224 2350

HYPNOSIS WORKS
Tulip House, 70 Borough High Street, London SE1 1XE
Website: www.hypnosisdoeswork.net
e-mail: sssp@hypnosisdoeswork.net   Tel: 020-7237 5815

HYPNOTHERAPY & PSYCHOTHERAPY
(Including Performance Improvement, Karen Mann DCH
DHP)
9 Spencer House, Vale of Health
Hampstead, London NW3 1AS
Website: www.karenmann.co.uk   Tel: 020-7794 5843

INSPIRATIONAL WELLBEING
(Energy Healer)
Avda Alcoy, 123, 2°E, 03009, Alicante, Spain
Website: www.inspirationalwellbeing.com
e-mail: inspirationalwellbeing@f2s.com   Tel: 638577438

JLP FITNESS
(Personal Training. Group Sessions. Kick/Muay-Thai Boxing
& Boxing)
e-mail: jlpthecoach@jacquileepryce.com
    Mobile: 07930 304809

LIFE COACHING
Contact: Dr Elspeth Reid
(Including Career, Relationship, Self-Confidence Coaching)
102 Clarence Road, Wimbledon SW19 8QD
Website: www.elspethreid.com
e-mail: coach@elspethreid.com   Tel: 020-8879 7676

How should I use these listings?

You will find a variety of companies in this section which could help you enhance your health and wellbeing physically and mentally. They include personal fitness and lifestyle coaches, counsellors, exercise classes and beauty consultants amongst others. It is worth researching any company or service you are considering using. Many of these listings have websites which you can browse. Even if you feel you have your career and lifestyle under control, you may still find the following advice helpful:

Your body is part of your business

Your mental and physical health is vital to your career as a performer. Just from a business perspective, your body is part of your promotional package and it needs to be maintained. Try to keep fit and eat healthily to enhance both your outward appearance and your inner confidence. This is particularly important if you are unemployed. You need to ensure that if you are suddenly called for an audition you look suitable for and feel positive about the part you are auditioning for.

Injury

Keeping fit also helps you to minimise the risk of an injury during a performance. The last thing you want to do is to be prevented from working. An injury is more likely to occur if you are inflexible and unprepared for sudden physical exertion. If you do pick up an injury or an illness you will want to make sure it does not get any worse by getting treatment with a specialist.

Unemployment

If you are unemployed, it can be difficult to retain a positive mindset. The best thing you can do is to keep yourself occupied. You could join a dance or drama class, which would help to maintain your fitness levels as well as developing contacts and keeping involved within the industry. Improve your CV by learning to speak a new language or play a musical instrument. Think about taking on temporary or part-time work outside of acting to earn money until the next job comes along, or you could put yourself forward for unpaid acting work in a student film (see 'Film & Television Schools' for more information).

Where can I find more information?

For more information on health and wellbeing you may wish to contact the British Association for Performing Arts Medicine (BAPAM) www.bapam.org.uk. You may also find their article overleaf helpful. Please refer to the 'Drama Training, Schools & Coaches' and 'Dance Training & Professional Classes' sections if you are interested in taking drama or dance courses or lessons to improve your fitness, keep your auditioning skills sharp between jobs and/or stay occupied and motivated.

Please note that while Spotlight takes every care in screening the companies featured in this section, it cannot be held responsible for services or treatments received.

BRITISH ASSOCIATION FOR
PERFORMING ARTS MEDICINE
CARING FOR PERFORMERS' HEALTH

Actors who are never out of work are rare creatures. But you can use your resting periods to invest in your physical and mental health. Here are a few suggestions from BAPAM, the charity that provides free health-assessment clinics and reduced-price treatments to artists with performance-related health problems.

- **Look after your health on a budget**
  If you can't justify the cost of keeping up your gym membership, go for cheaper forms of exercise:
- **Walk or cycle** instead of driving or using public transport. If you haven't ridden a bike for years, build your confidence by taking a course.
- **Run** in the open air instead of on a treadmill at a gym. It's much better to be in the fresh air – and it's more sociable.
- **Swimming** is a cheap and effective form of exercise. Think about taking lessons to make your stroke more efficient and avoid putting unnecessary pressure on your joints – especially your neck.
- **Team sports** combine fresh air and being sociable; now could be the time to take up football or netball again. Be careful, though – you wouldn't want a sports injury to come between you and your next job!
- Learn a technique to help with posture, such as Alexander Technique, Feldenkrais or Pilates. Techniques that are taught one-to-one can be expensive, but you can often find taster sessions at adult education colleges.
- **Take a refresher** in all those stagecraft skills (breathing; warm-up exercises; stage fighting) you learned at drama school. Enrol on a short course or read some books. When the next job comes up you need to be in peak condition and able to perform safely.

Think about your diet while you're resting

Everyone knows that eating well has a positive effect on your mental and physical well-being – especially important when you need to keep your spirits up.

- Learn about **healthy eating**, and expand your repertoire of recipes. Farmers' markets save money and you'll learn what's in season. Then you can maintain good habits when you're running around or on tour.
- If you ration your **treats**, you make them more special. If a treat becomes a daily habit you won't enjoy real treats so much.
- Now is the time to **phase out junk food**. Why spend money on processed food when you could eat so much better for less? See the BAPAM factsheet Sensible eating for performers.
- Don't rely on **alcohol** to keep you going. You develop expectations around alcohol, and that will take its toll on your liver (and your wallet!). Try to make a drink last longer, or alternate alcohol and water over the course of an evening. See the BAPAM factsheet *The drinks are on me!* for more information about drinking responsibly.

Invest in your mental health too.

- Think strategically about your career. Do a **skills audit**, remembering all the skills you've accumulated (numeracy, fundraising, any IT skills). Be creative about how you can put them to use, and fill any skill gaps. Focusing on something developmental can take your mind off your current circumstances.
- Use quiet periods to **organise** your paperwork and electronic filing systems. You will feel empowered when you know everything is in order; it saves time and stress when you do get busy if you already have a workable system in place. Learn to use **spreadsheets** to keep track of your finances. You'll save yourself endless headaches when it's time to file your tax return, and you'll save yourself money on an accountant.
- **Volunteering** is great for stopping you feeling isolated. Try and find an activity that involves physical exercise – such as working in a community garden. It might even lead to a job!
- Remember, there's no need to suffer alone if being out of work is beginning to get you down. A few sessions with a **counsellor** can make a big difference. Check out the BAPAM Directory online at **www.bapam.org.uk to locate a performer-friendly counsellor in your area.**

To find out more about performance-related health issues and BAPAM services, please see the website www.bapam.org.uk.

smile@richardcasson.com

cosmetic fillings, orthodontics, bleaching, veneers
crowns and bridges, implants, hygienist

Dr. Richard Casson, Dental Care
For further information phone 020 7580 9696
Flat 6, Milford House, 7 Queen Anne Street, London W1G 9HN
Website: www.richardcasson.com

LIFE PRACTICE UK Ltd
(NLP and Clinical Hypnosis)
Woodlands, Preston Road
Gosmore, Hitchin, Herts SG4 7QS
Website: www.lifepractice.co.uk
e-mail: info@lifepractice.co.uk   Tel/Fax: 01462 451473

LUCAS Hazel
(Qualified Holistic Masseur)
119 Brightwell Avenue
Westcliff-on-Sea, Essex SS0 9EQ
e-mail: hazeystar@blueyonder.co.uk   Mobile: 07870 862939

MAGIC KEY PARTNERSHIP The
Contact: Lyn Burgess (Life Coach)
151A Moffat Road, Thornton Heath, Surrey CR7 8PZ
Website: www.magickey.co.uk
e-mail: lyn@magickey.co.uk   Tel: 0845 1297401

MATRIX ENERGY FIELD THERAPY
(Accredited Healer)
Deal Castle House, 31 Victoria Road
Deal, Kent CT14 7AS
e-mail: donnie@lovingorganization.org
Mobile: 07762 821828   Tel: 01304 379466

McCALLION Anna
(Alexander Technique)
Flat 2, 11 Sinclair Gardens
London W14 0AU
e-mail: hildegarde007@yahoo.com   Tel: 020-7602 5599

MINDSCI CLINIC
(Clinical Hypnotism)
34 Willow Bank, Ham, Richmond, Surrey TW10 7QX
Website: www.mindsci-clinic.com
e-mail: bt@mindsci-clinic.com   Tel/Fax: 020-8948 2439

NORTON Michael R
(Implant/Reconstructive Dentistry)
104 Harley Street, London W1G 7JD
Website: www.nortonimplants.com
e-mail: linda@nortonimplants.com
Fax: 020-7486 9119   Tel: 020-7486 9229

NUTRITIONAL THERAPY FOR PERFORMERS
Contact: Vanessa May BSc
18 Oaklands Road
Ealing, London W7 2DR
Website: www.wellbeingandnutrition.co.uk
e-mail: vanessamay9@yahoo.co.uk   Mobile: 07962 978763

OGUNLARU Rasheed
(Life & Business Coach)
The Coaching Studio
223A Mayall Road, London SE24 0PS
Website: www.rasaru.com
e-mail: rasheed@rasaru.com
Tel: 020-7207 1082

PEAK PERFORMANCE TRAINING
Contact: Tina Reibl, Hypnotherapy, NLP, Success Strategies
42 The Broadway
Maidenhead, Berkshire SL6 1LU
e-mail: tina.reibl@tesco.net
Tel: 01628 633509

POLAND DENTAL STUDIOS
(Film/Stage Dentistry)
1 Devonshire Place, London W1G 6HH
e-mail: robpoland@btconnect.com
Fax: 020-7486 3952
Tel: 020-7935 6919

RUOK4SPEX.COM
PO Box 1027 PE12 0SQ
Website: www.ruok4spex.com
e-mail: info@ruok4spex.com

SELFSIGHT
(Counselling & EMDR)
Psycholsynthesis & Education Trust
92-94 Tooley Street
London Bridge, London SE1 2TH
Website: www.selfsight.com
e-mail: rickylock@btinternet.com
Mobile: 07961 152740
Tel: 020-8740 8678

SEYRI Kayvan BSc (Hons), NSCA-CPT*D, PES
(Personal Training & Nutrition Advice)
Unit 3, 69 St Mark's Road, London W10 6JG
Website: www.ultimatefitpro.com
e-mail: info@ultimatefitpro.com
Mobile: 07881 554636

SHENAS Dr DENTAL STUDIO
51 Cadogan Gardens
Sloane Square, London SW3 2TH
Website: www.shenasdental.co.uk
e-mail: info@shenasdental.co.uk
Tel: 020-7589 2319

SHER SYSTEM The
(Helping Skin with Acne & Rosacea)
30 New Bond Street, London W1S 2RN
Website: www.sher.co.uk
e-mail: skincare@sher.co.uk
Fax: 020-7629 7021
Tel: 020-7499 4022

SHIATSU HEALTH CENTRE
Moving Arts Base
134 Liverpool Road, London N1 1LA
Website: www.shiatsuhealth.com
e-mail: japaneseyoga@btinternet.com
Mobile: 07905 504418

SMILE NW
(Dentist)
17 Hallswelle Parade, Finchley Road
Temple Fortune, London NW11 0DL
Website: www.smile-nw.co.uk
e-mail: enquiries@smile-nw.co.uk
Fax: 020-8458 5681
Tel: 020-8458 2333

SMILE SOLUTIONS
(Dental Practice)
24 Englands Lane
London NW3 4TG
Website: www.smile-solutions.info
e-mail: enquiries@smile-solutions.info
Fax: 020-7449 1769
Tel: 020-7449 1760

SMILESTUDIO
First Floor, Wingate House
93-107 Shaftesbury Avenue
London W1D 5DY
Website: www.smile-studio.co.uk
Tel: 020-7439 0888

STAT (The Society of Teachers of the Alexander Technique)
1st Floor Linton House
39-51 Highgate Road
London NW5 1RS
Website: www.stat.org.uk
e-mail: enquiries@stat.org.uk
Fax: 020-7482 5435
Tel: 0845 2307828

THEATRICAL DENTISTRY
Contact: Richard D Casson (Cosmetic Dentist)
6 Milford House
7 Queen Anne Street
London W1G 9HN
Website: www.richardcasson.com
e-mail: smile@richardcasson.com
Tel/Fax: 020-7580 9696

VITAL TOUCH Ltd The
(On-site Massage Company)
11 Evering Road, London N16 7PX
Website: www.thevitaltouch.com
e-mail: suzi@thevitaltouch.com
Mobile: 07976 263691

WALK-IN BACKRUB
(On-site Massage Company)
14 Neals Yard, London WC2H 9DP
Website: www.walkinbackrub.co.uk
Tel/Fax: 020-7436 9875

WELLBEING
Contact: Leigh Jones (Personal Training, Yoga, Tai Chi)
22 Galloway Close, Broxbourne, Herts EN10 6BU
e-mail: williamleighjones@hotmail.com
Mobile: 07957 333921

WOODFORD HOUSE DENTAL PRACTICE
162 High Road, Woodford Green
Essex IG8 9EF
Website: www.improveyoursmile.co.uk
e-mail: info@improveyoursmile.co.uk
Fax: 020-8252 0835
Tel: 020-8504 2704

OPERA COMPANIES

ARTSWORLD PRESENTATIONS Ltd
Vicarage House
58-60 Kensington Church Street
London W8 4DB
Website: www.arts-world.co.uk
e-mail: p@triciamurraybett.com
Fax: 020-7368 3338   Tel: 020-7368 3337

CARL ROSA OPERA
359 Hackney Road
London E2 8PR
Website: www.carlrosaopera.co.uk
e-mail: info@carlrosaopera.co.uk
Fax: 020-7613 0859   Tel: 020-7613 0777

ENGLISH NATIONAL OPERA
London Coliseum
St Martin's Lane
London WC2N 4ES
Website: www.eno.org
Fax: 020-7845 9277   Tel: 020-7836 0111

ENGLISH TOURING OPERA
(James Conway)
1st Floor
52-54 Rosebery Avenue,
London EC1R 4RP
Website: www.englishtouringopera.org.uk
e-mail: admin@englishtouringopera.org.uk
Fax: 020-7713 8686   Tel: 020-7833 2555

GLYNDEBOURNE FESTIVAL OPERA
Glyndebourne
Lewes
East Sussex BN8 5UU
Website: www.glyndebourne.com   Tel: 01273 812321

GRANGE PARK OPERA
24-26 Broad Street
Alresford
Hampshire SO24 9AQ
Website: www.grangeparkopera.co.uk
e-mail: info@grangeparkopera.co.uk   Tel: 01962 737360

GUBBAY Raymond Ltd
Dickens House
15 Tooks Court
London EC4A 1QH
Website: www.raymondgubbay.co.uk
e-mail: info@raymondgubbay.co.uk
Fax: 020-7025 3751   Tel: 020-7025 3750

KENT Ellen PRODUCTIONS
The Admiral's Offices
The Historic Dockyard
Chatham
Kent ME4 4TZ
Website: www.ellenkent.com
e-mail: info@ellenkentinternational.co.uk
Fax: 01634 819149   Tel: 01634 819141

O

**Opera Companies
Organisations**

[CONTACTS 2009]

KENTISH OPERA
Watermede
Wickhurst Road, Sevenoaks
Weald, Kent TN14 6LX
Website: www.kentishopera.fsnet.co.uk
e-mail: sl.sweald@fsmail.net
Tel: 01732 463284

MUSIC THEATRE LONDON
Chertsey Chambers
12 Mercer Street
London WC2H 9QD
Website: www.capriolfilms.co.uk
e-mail: musictheatre.london@virgin.net
Mobile: 07831 243942

OPERA DELLA LUNA
7 Cotmore House, Fringford
Bicester, Oxfordshire OX27 8RQ
Website: www.operadellaluna.org
e-mail: operadellaluna@aol.com
Fax: 01869 323533
Tel: 01869 325131

OPERA NORTH
Grand Theatre
46 New Briggate, Leeds LS1 6NU
Website: www.operanorth.co.uk
Fax: 0113-244 0418
Tel: 0113-243 9999

OPERAUK
177 Andrewes House
Barbican, London EC2Y 8BA
Website: www.operauk.co.uk
e-mail: rboss@aol.com
Tel: 020-7628 0025

PEGASUS OPERA COMPANY Ltd
The Brix
St Matthew's
Brixton Hill
London SW2 1JF
Website: www.pegopera.org
Tel/Fax: 020-7501 9501

PIMLICO OPERA
24 Broad Street
Alresford
Hampshire SO24 9AQ
Website: www.grangeparkopera.co.uk
e-mail: pimlico@grangeparkopera.co.uk
Tel: 01962 737360

ROYAL OPERA The
Royal Opera House
Covent Garden
London WC2E 9DD
Website: www.roh.org.uk
Tel: 020-7240 1200

SCOTTISH OPERA
39 Elmbank Crescent
Glasgow G2 4PT
Website: www.scottishopera.org.uk
Tel: 0141-248 4567

WELSH NATIONAL OPERA
Wales Millennium Centre
Bute Place
Cardiff CF10 5AL
Website: www.wno.org.uk
e-mail: marketing@wno.org.uk
Fax: 029-2063 5099
Tel: 029-2063 5000

ACTORS' ADVISORY SERVICE
Provides Advice to Actors, Agents, Photographers etc
29 Talbot Road, Twickenham
Middlesex TW2 6SJ Tel: 020-8287 2839

ACTORS' BENEVOLENT FUND
6 Adam Street, London WC2N 6AD
Website: www.actorsbenevolentfund.co.uk
e-mail: office@abf.org.uk
Fax: 020-7836 8978 Tel: 020-7836 6378

ACTORS CENTRE (LONDON) The
1A Tower Street, London WC2H 9NP
Website: www.actorscentre.co.uk
e-mail: admin@actorscentre.co.uk
Fax: 020-7240 3896 Tel: 020-7240 3940

ACTORS CENTRE NORTH
Contact: Maggie Lackey
Charity. Provides Advice, Support & Information
Workshops in continuing professional development for
professionally trained actors
21-23 Oldham Street, Manchester M1 1JG
Website: www.actorscentrenorth.com
e-mail: info@actorscentrenorth.com Tel/Fax: 0161-819 2513

ACTORS' CHARITABLE TRUST
Provides Advice & Support. Grants for Actors' Children
58 Bloomsbury Street, London WC1B 3QT
e-mail: robert@tactactors.org
Fax: 020-7637 3368 Tel: 020-7636 7868

ACTORS' CHURCH UNION
St Paul's Church, Bedford Street, London WC2E 9ED
e-mail: actors-church.union@tiscali.co.uk
Tel: 020-7240 0344

ADVERTISING ASSOCIATION
7th Floor North, Artillery House
11-19 Artillery Row, London SW1P 1RT
Website: www.adassoc.org.uk
e-mail: aa@adassoc.org.uk
Fax: 020-7222 1504 Tel: 020-7340 1100

AGENTS' ASSOCIATION (Great Britain)
54 Keyes House, Dolphin Square, London SW1V 3NA
Website: www.agents-uk.com
e-mail: association@agents-uk.com
Fax: 020-7821 0261 Tel: 020-7834 0515

ARTS & BUSINESS
Nutmeg House, 60 Gainsford Street
Butlers Wharf, London SE1 2NY
Website: www.aandb.org.uk
e-mail: head.office@aandb.org.uk
Fax: 020-7407 7527 Tel: 020-7378 8143

**ARTS & ENTERTAINMENT TECHNICAL TRAINING
INITIATIVE (AETTI)**
73 Potley Hill Road, Yately, Hants GU46 6AG
Website: www.aetti.org.uk
e-mail: aetti.office@btinternet.com Tel: 01252 8733339

ARTS CENTRE GROUP
Menier Chocolate Factory
51 Southwark Street, London SE1 1RU
Website: www.artscentregroup.org.uk
e-mail: info@artscentregroup.org.uk
Tel: 020-7407 1881 Tel: 0845 4581881

ARTS COUNCIL ENGLAND
2 Pear Tree Court, London EC1R 0DS
Website: www.artscouncil.org.uk
e-mail: enquiries@artscouncil.org.uk
Fax: 020-7608 4100 Tel: 0845 300 6200

ARTS COUNCIL OF NORTHERN IRELAND
MacNeice House, 77 Malone Road, Belfast BT9 6AQ
Website: www.artscouncil-ni.org
Fax: 028-9066 1715 Tel: 028-9038 5200

ARTS COUNCIL OF WALES The
9 Museum Place, Cardiff CF10 3NX
Website: www.artswales.org.uk
e-mail: info@artswales.org.uk
Fax: 029-2022 1447 Tel: 029-2037 6500

ARTSLINE
Disability Access Information Service
54 Chalton Street, London NW1 1HS
Website: www.artsline.org.uk
e-mail: admin@artsline.org.uk
Fax: 020-7383 2653 Tel: 020-7388 2227

ASSITEJ UK
(UK Centre of the International Association of Theatre for
Children and Young People)
c/o Kevin Lewis, Secretary, Theatre Iolo
The Old School Building, Cefn Road
Mynachdy, Cardiff CF14 3HS
Website: www.assitejuk.org
e-mail: admin@theatriolo.com Tel: 029-2061 3782

ASSOCIATION OF BRITISH THEATRE TECHNICIANS
4th Floor, 55 Farringdon Road, London EC1M 3JB
Website: www.abtt.org.uk
e-mail: office@abtt.org.uk
Fax: 020-7242 9303 Tel: 020-7242 9200

ASSOCIATION OF LIGHTING DESIGNERS
PO Box 680, Oxford OX1 9DG
Website: www.ald.org.uk
e-mail: office@ald.org.uk Mobile: 07817 060189

ASSOCIATION OF MODEL AGENTS
11-29 Fashion Street, London E1 6PX
e-mail: amainfo@btinternet.com
Info. Line: 09068 517644   Tel: 020-7422 0699

BFI SOUTH BANK
Belvedere Road, South Bank, London SE1 8XT
Website: www.bfi.org.uk   Tel: 020-7928 3535

**BRITISH ACADEMY OF COMPOSERS
& SONGWRITERS The**
2nd Floor, British Music House
26 Berners Street, London W1T 3LR
Website: www.britishacademy.com
e-mail: info@britishacademy.com
Fax: 020-7636 2212   Tel: 020-7636 2929

BRITISH ACADEMY OF FILM & TELEVISION ARTS The
195 Piccadilly, London W1J 9LN
Website: www.bafta.org
e-mail: membership@bafta.org
Fax: 020-7292 5868   Tel: 020-7734 0022

**BRITISH ACADEMY OF FILM & TELEVISION ARTS/LOS
ANGELES The**
8533 Melrose Avenue, West Hollywood, CA 90069
e-mail: info@baftala.org
Fax: (310) 854-6002   Tel: (310) 652-4121

BRITISH ACADEMY OF STAGE & SCREEN COMBAT
Suite 280, 10 Great Russell Street, London WC1B 3BQ
Website: www.bassc.org
e-mail: info@bassc.org   Mobile: 07981 806265

**BRITISH ASSOCIATION FOR PERFORMING ARTS
MEDICINE (BAPAM)**
Charity
4th Floor, Totara Park House
34-36 Gray's Inn Road, London WC1X 8HR
Website: www.bapam.org.uk
e-mail: clinic@bapam.org.uk   Tel: 020-7404 5888

BRITISH ASSOCIATION OF DRAMATHERAPISTS The
Waverley, Battledown Approach
Cheltenham, Glos GL52 6RE
Website: www.badth.org.uk
e-mail: enquiries@badth.org.uk   Tel: 01242 235515

BRITISH BOARD OF FILM CLASSIFICATION
3 Soho Square, London W1D 3HD
Website: www.bbfc.co.uk
Fax: 020-7287 0141   Tel: 020-7440 1570

BRITISH COUNCIL The
Performing Arts Department
10 Spring Gardens, London SW1A 2BN
Website: www.britishcouncil.org/arts
e-mail: arts@britishcouncil.org   Tel: 020-7389 3194

BRITISH EQUITY COLLECTING SOCIETY
Hudson House, 8 Tavistock Street, London WC2E 7PP
Website: www.equitycollecting.org.uk
e-mail: becs@equity.org.uk   Tel: 020-3178 6885

BRITISH FILM INSTITUTE
21 Stephen Street, London W1T 1LN
Website: www.bfi.org.uk
e-mail: library@bfi.org.uk
Fax: 020-7436 2338   Tel: 020-7255 1444

BRITISH LIBRARY SOUND ARCHIVE
96 Euston Road, London NW1 2DB
Website: www.bl.uk/soundarchive
e-mail: sound-archive@bl.uk
Fax: 020-7412 7441   Tel: 020-7412 7676

BRITISH MUSIC HALL SOCIETY
Contact: Daphne Masterton (Secretary)
Meander, 361 Watford Road, Chiswell Green
St Albans, Herts AL2 3DB   Tel: 01727 768878

CATHOLIC STAGE GUILD
Contact: Ms Molly Steele (Hon Secretary)
By Post (SAE)
1 Maiden Lane, London WC2E 7NB
e-mail: mary40steele@btinternet.com   Tel: 020-7240 1221

CELEBRITY BULLETIN The
8-10 Wiseton Road, London SW17 7EE
e-mail: enquiries@celebrity-bulletin.co.uk
Fax: 020-8672 2282   Tel: 020-8672 3191

CHILDREN'S FILM & TELEVISION FOUNDATION Ltd
e-mail: annahome@cftf.org.uk   Mobile: 07887 573479

CHRISTIANS IN ENTERTAINMENT
Charity
PO Box 223, Bexhill-on-Sea TN40 9DP
Website: www.cieweb.org.uk
e-mail: chris@cieweb.org.uk   Tel: 01737 550375

CIDA (CREATIVE INDUSTRIES DEVELOPMENT AGENCY)
*Professional Development & Business Support for Artists &
Creative Businesses*
Media Centre, Huddersfield
West Yorkshire HD1 1RL
Website: www.cida.org
e-mail: info@cida.org
Fax: 01484 483150   Tel: 01484 483140

CINEMA & TELEVISION BENEVOLENT FUND (CTBF)
22 Golden Square, London W1F 9AD
Website: www.ctbf.co.uk
e-mail: charity@ctbf.co.uk
Fax: 020-7437 7186   Tel: 020-7437 6567

CINEMA EXHIBITORS' ASSOCIATION
22 Golden Square, London W1F 9JW
Website: www.cinemauk.org.uk
e-mail: cea@cinemauk.ftech.co.uk
Fax: 020-7734 6147   Tel: 020-7734 9551

CLUB FOR ACTS & ACTORS
(Incorporating Concert Artistes Association)
20 Bedford Street, London WC2E 9HP
Website: www.thecaa.org
e-mail: office@thecaa.org
Office: 020-7836 3172   Members: 020-7836 2884

COMBINED THEATRICAL CHARITIES The
West Suite, 2nd Floor
11 Garrick Street, London WC2E 9AR
e-mail: ctc@trtf.com
Fax: 020-7379 8273   Tel: 020-7379 6978

COMPANY OF CRANKS
1st Floor, 62 Northfield House
Frensham Street, London SE15 6TN
Website: www.mimeworks.com
e-mail: mimetic16@yahoo.com   Mobile: 07963 617981

CONCERT ARTISTES ASSOCIATION
(See CLUB FOR ACTS & ACTORS)

CONFERENCE OF DRAMA SCHOOLS
Contact: Saul Hyman
*Comprises Britain's 22 Leading Drama Schools. Offers
advice, sets standards of training*
PO Box 34252, London NW5 1XJ
Website: www.drama.ac.uk
e-mail: info@cds.drama.ac.uk

COUNCIL FOR DANCE EDUCATION & TRAINING (CDET)
The
Old Brewer's Yard
17-19 Neal Street, London WC2H 9UY
Website: www.cdet.org.uk
e-mail: info@cdet.org.uk
Fax: 020-7240 2547   Tel: 020-7240 5703

CPMA
(Co-operative Personal Management Association)
The Secretary
c/o 1 Mellor Road
Leicester LE3 6HN
Website: www.cpma.co.uk
e-mail: cpmauk@yahoo.co.uk   Mobile: 07984 345310

CRITICS' CIRCLE The
c/o Catherine Cooper Events
69 Marylebone Lane, London W1U 2PH
Website: www.criticscircle.org.uk   Tel: 020-7224 1410

DANCE HOUSE
20 St Andrews Street, Glasgow G1 5PD
Website: www.dancehouse.org
e-mail: info@dancehouse.org   Tel: 0141-552 2442

DANCE UK
(Including the Healthier Dancer Programme & 'The UK Choreographers' Directory')
Professional Body & Charity, providing Advice, Funding, Information & Support
The Urdang, The Old Finsbury Town Hall
Rosebery Avenue, London EC1R 4QT
Website: www.danceuk.org
e-mail: info@danceuk.org
Fax: 020-7833 2363   Tel: 020-7713 0730

DENVILLE HALL
Provides residential & nursing care to actors 70+ and other theatrical professions
62 Ducks Hill Road, Northwood, Middlesex HA6 2SB
Website: www.denvillehall.org
e-mail: denvillehall@yahoo.com   Fax: 01923 841855
Residents: 01923 820805   Office: 01923 825843

DIRECTORS UK
20-22 Bedford Row, London WC1R 4EB
Website: www.directors.uk.com
e-mail: info@directors.uk.com
Fax: 020-7269 0676   Tel: 020-7269 0677

Rc-Annie provides the following Fight services:
Fight Choreography, Fight Performers, Fake Blood and Fight Training for Theatre and Film. BADC certified Stage Combat Classes. Specialist workshops from Slapstick to Handguns.
www.rc-annie.com. info@rc-annie.com. 0208 5936123.

D'OYLY CARTE OPERA COMPANY
First Floor, 295 Kennington Road, London SE11 4QE
Website: www.doylycarte.org.uk
e-mail: ian@doylycarte.org.uk
Fax: 020-7820 0240   Tel: 020-7793 7100

DRAMA ASSOCIATION OF WALES
Specialist Drama Lending Library
The Old Library, Singleton Road, Splott, Cardiff CF24 2ET
e-mail: aled.daw@virgin.net
Fax: 029-2045 2277   Tel: 029-2045 2200

DRAMATURGS' NETWORK
Network of Professional Dramaturgs
10 Glengarry Road, East Dulwich, London SE22 8PZ
Website: www.dramaturgy.co.uk
e-mail: info@dramaturgy.co.uk   Mobile: 07939 270566

ENGLISH FOLK DANCE & SONG SOCIETY
Cecil Sharp House, 2 Regent's Park Road, London NW1 7AY
Website: www.efdss.org
e-mail: info@efdss.org
Fax: 020-7284 0534   Tel: 020-7485 2206

ETF (Equity Trust Fund)
Suite 222, Africa House
64 Kingsway, London WC2B 6BD
Fax: 020-7831 4953   Tel: 020-7404 6041

FILM LONDON
Suite 6.10, The Tea Building
56 Shoreditch High Street, London E1 6JJ
Website: www.filmlondon.org.uk
e-mail: info@filmlondon.org.uk
Fax: 020-7613 7677   Tel: 020-7613 7676

GLASGOW FILM OFFICE
Advice and Liaison Support for Feature Films
City Chambers, Glasgow G2 1DU
Fax: 0141-287 0311   Tel: 0141-287 0424

GRAND ORDER OF WATER RATS
328 Gray's Inn Road, London WC1X 8BZ
Website: www.gowr.net
e-mail: info@gowr.net
Fax: 020-7278 1765   Tel: 020-7278 3248

GROUP LINE
Group Bookings for London Theatre
22-24 Torrington Place, London WC1E 7HJ
Website: www.groupline.com
e-mail: tix@groupline.com
Fax: 020-7436 6287   Tel: 020-7580 6793

GUY Gillian ASSOCIATES
84A Tachbrook Street, London SW1V 2NB
e-mail: gillian@gillianguyassoc.com   Tel: 020-7976 5888

HAMMER FILMS PRESERVATION SOCIETY
Fan Club
14 Kingsdale Road
Plumstead, London SE18 2DG
e-mail: devohammerfilms29@yahoo.co.uk
                             Tel: 020-8854 7383

INDEPENDENT THEATRE COUNCIL (ITC)
Professional Body offering Advice, Information, Support and Political Representation
12 The Leathermarket, Weston Street, London SE1 3ER
Website: www.itc-arts.org
e-mail: admin@itc-arts.org
Fax: 020-7403 1745   Tel: 020-7403 1727

IRVING SOCIETY The
Contact: Michael Kilgarriff (Hon. Secretary)
10 Kings Avenue, London W5 2SH
e-mail: secretary@theirvingsociety.org.uk
                             Tel: 020-8566 8301

ITC
(See INDEPENDENT THEATRE COUNCIL)

ITV Plc
200 Gray's Inn Road, London WC1X 8HF
Website: www.itv.com   Tel: 020-7156 6000

LONDON SCHOOL OF CAPOEIRA The
Units 1 & 2 Leeds Place, Tollington Park, London N4 3RF
Website: www.londonschoolofcapoeira.co.uk
e-mail: info@londonschoolofcapoeira.co.uk
                             Tel: 020-7281 2020

LONDON SHAKESPEARE WORKOUT
PO Box 31855, London SE17 3XP
Website: www.londonshakespeare.org.uk
e-mail: londonswo@hotmail.com   Tel/Fax: 020-7793 9755

MANDER & MITCHENSON THEATRE COLLECTION
Jerwood Library of the Performing Arts
King Charles Building, Old Royal Naval College
Greenwich, London SE10 9JF
e-mail: rmangan@tcm.ac.uk
Fax: 020-8305 9426   Tel: 020-8305 4426

NATIONAL ASSOCIATION OF YOUTH THEATRES (NAYT)
Contact: Jo Harker
Charity, providing Advice, Information & Support. Founded in 1982, the National Association of Youth Theatres (NAYT) is the flagship/registration organisation for youth theatre practice in England, supporting the development of Youth Theatre Activity through programmes of Training, Advocacy & Participation
Arts Centre, Vane Terrace,
Darlington, County Durham DL3 7AX
Website: www.nayt.org.uk
e-mail: nayt@btconnect.com
Fax: 01325 363313   Tel: 01325 363330

NATIONAL CAMPAIGN FOR THE ARTS
1 Kingly Street, London W1B 5PA
Website: www.artscampaign.org.uk
e-mail: nca@artscampaign.org.uk
Fax: 020-7287 4777   Tel: 020-7287 3777

NATIONAL COUNCIL FOR DRAMA TRAINING
1-7 Woburn Walk, Bloomsbury, London WC1H 0JJ
Website: www.ncdt.co.uk
e-mail: info@ncdt.co.uk
Fax: 020-7387 3860   Tel: 020-7387 3650

NATIONAL ENTERTAINMENT AGENTS COUNCIL
PO Box 112, Seaford, East Sussex BN25 2DQ
Website: www.neac.org.uk
e-mail: chrisbray@neac.org.uk
Fax: 0844 8155958   Tel: 0844 8155957

NATIONAL RESOURCE CENTRE FOR DANCE
University of Surrey, Guildford, Surrey GU2 7XH
Website: www.surrey.ac.uk/nrcd
e-mail: nrcd@surrey.ac.uk
Fax: 01483 689500   Tel: 01483 689316

NEW PRODUCERS ALLIANCE
Unit 7.03, The Tea Building
56 Shoreditch High Street, London E1 6JJ
Website: www.npa.org.uk
e-mail: queries@npa.org.uk
Fax: 020-7729 7852   Tel: 020-7613 0440

NODA (National Operatic & Dramatic Association)
Contact: K Doherty
*Charity, providing Advice, Information & Support. Largest
umbrella body for amateur theatre in the UK offering
advice and assistance on all aspects of amateur theatre
plus workshops, summer school and social events*
Noda House, 58-60 Lincoln Road, Peterborough PE1 2RZ
Website: www.noda.org.uk
e-mail: info@noda.org.uk
Fax: 0870 7702490   Tel: 0870 7702480

NORTH WEST PLAYWRIGHTS
18 Express Networks
1 George Leigh Street, Manchester M4 5DL
Website: www.newplaysnw.co.uk
e-mail: newplaysnw@hotmail.com   Tel/Fax: 0161-237 1978

OFCOM
Ofcom Media Office, Riverside House
2A Southwark Bridge Road, London SE1 9HA
Website: www.ofcom.org.uk
e-mail: mediaandcorporaterelations@ofcom.org.uk
                                     Tel: 020-7981 3033

PACT
*Trade Association for Independent Television, Feature Film
& New Media Production Companies*
2nd Floor, Procter House
1 Procter Street, London WC1V 6DW
Website: www.pact.co.uk
e-mail: enquiries@pact.co.uk
Fax: 020-7067 4377   Tel: 020-7067 4367

PERFORMING RIGHT SOCIETY Ltd
29-33 Berners Street, London W1T 3AB
Website: www.mcps-prs-alliance.co.uk
Fax: 020-7306 4455   Tel: 020-7580 5544

RICHARDSON Ralph & Meriel FOUNDATION
c/o Suite 23, 19 Cavendish Square, London W1A 2AW
Website: www.sirralphrichardson.org.uk
e-mail: manager@sirralphrichardson.org.uk
Fax: 020-7664 4489   Tel: 020-7636 1616

ROYAL TELEVISION SOCIETY
5th Floor, Kildare House, 3 Dorset Rise, London EC4Y 8EN
Website: www.rts.org.uk
e-mail: info@rts.org.uk
Fax: 020-7822 2811   Tel: 020-7822 2810

ROYAL THEATRICAL FUND
11 Garrick Street, London WC2E 9AR
e-mail: admin@trtf.com
Fax: 020-7379 8273   Tel: 020-7836 3322

SAMPAD SOUTH ASIAN ARTS
Promotes the appreciation & practice of South Asian Arts
c/o Mac
Cannon Hill Park
Birmingham B12 9QH
Website: www.sampad.org.uk
e-mail: info@sampad.org.uk   Tel: 0121-446 4312

SAVE LONDON'S THEATRES CAMPAIGN
Guild House
Upper St Martin's Lane, London WC2H 9EG
Website: www.savelondonstheatres.org.uk
e-mail: contactus@savelondonstheatres.org.uk
Fax: 020-7379 7001   Tel: 020-3077 1021

SCOTTISH SCREEN
249 West George Street, Glasgow G2 4QE
Website: www.scottishscreen.com
e-mail: info@scottishscreen.com
Fax: 0141-302 1711   Tel: 0141-302 1700

SCRIPT
*West Midlands Playwrights, Scriptwriters. Provides Training
& Support*
Unit 107 The Greenhouse
The Custard Factory
Gibb Street, Birmingham B9 4AA
Website: www.scriptonline.net   Tel: 0121-224 7415

SOCIETY OF AUTHORS
*Trade Union for Professional Writers. Providing Advice,
Funding, Information & Support*
84 Drayton Gardens, London SW10 9SB
Website: www.societyofauthors.org
e-mail: info@societyofauthors.org   Tel: 020-7373 6642

SOCIETY OF BRITISH THEATRE DESIGNERS
*Professional body. Charity. Providing Advice and
Information.*
4th Floor, 55 Farringdon Road, London EC1M 3JB
Website: www.theatredesign.org.uk
e-mail: sbtd@ntu.ac.uk
Fax: 020-7242 9303   Tel: 020-7242 9200

SOCIETY OF LONDON THEATRE (SOLT)
32 Rose Street, London WC2E 9ET
e-mail: enquiries@solttma.co.uk
Fax: 020-7557 6799   Tel: 020-7557 6700

SOCIETY OF TEACHERS OF SPEECH & DRAMA The
Registered Office:
73 Berry Hill Road, Mansfield
Nottinghamshire NG18 4RU
Website: www.stsd.org.uk
e-mail: ann.k.jones@btinternet.com   Tel: 01623 627636

SOCIETY OF THEATRE CONSULTANTS
27 Old Gloucester Street
London WC1N 3AX
Website: www.theatreconsultants.org.uk
                                     Tel: 020-7419 8767

STAGE CRICKET CLUB
39-41 Hanover Steps
St George's Fields, Albion Street, London W2 2YG
Website: www.stagecc.co.uk
e-mail: brianjfilm@aol.com
Fax: 020-7262 5736   Tel: 020-7402 7543

STAGE GOLFING SOCIETY
Sudbrook Park,
Sudbrook Lane, Richmond
Surrey TW10 7AS   Tel: 020-8940 8861

WE CAN HELP ACTORS' CHILDREN

Are you:

- a professional actor?
- the parent of a child under 21?
- having trouble with finances?

Please get in touch for a confidential chat.

The Actors' Charitable Trust
020 7636 7868
robert@tactactors.org

TACT can help in many ways: with regular monthly payments, one-off grants, and long-term support and advice.
We help with clothing, child-care, music lessons, school trips, special equipment and adaptations, and in many other ways.

Our website has a link to a list of all the theatrical and entertainment charities which might be able to help you if you do not have children: www.tactactors.org

TACT, 58 Bloomsbury Street, London WC1B 3QT.
Registered charity number 206809.

TACT

STAGE MANAGEMENT ASSOCIATION
Providing Advice, Information & Support. Supports, represents & promotes stage management and all its practitioners
55 Farringdon Road
London EC1M 3JB
Website: www.stagemanagementassociation.co.uk
e-mail: admin@stagemanagementassociation.co.uk
Fax: 020-7242 9303   Tel: 020-7242 9250

STAGE ONE
(Operating Name of The Theatre Investment Fund Ltd)
32 Rose Street, London WC2E 9ET
Website: www.stageone.uk.com
e-mail: enquiries@stageone.uk.com
Fax: 020-7557 6799   Tel: 020-7557 6737

THEATRE MAD
(Theatre Making A Difference)
4th Floor
80-81 St Martin's Lane
London WC2N 4AA
Website: www.theatremad.org.uk
e-mail: office@theatremad.org.uk
Fax: 020-7395 7529   Tel: 020-7395 7528

THEATRE WRITING PARTNERSHIP
Nottingham Playhouse
Wellington Circus
Nottingham NG1 5AF
e-mail: info@theatrewritingpartnership.org.uk
Fax: 0115-947 5759   Tel: 0115-947 4361

THEATRES TRUST The
22 Charing Cross Road, London WC2H 0QL
Website: www.theatrestrust.org.uk
e-mail: info@theatrestrust.org.uk
Fax: 020-7836 3302   Tel: 020-7836 8591

THEATRICAL GUILD The
Charity for Backstage & Front of House Staff
PO Box 22712, London N22 5WQ
Website: www.ttg.org.uk
e-mail: admin@ttg.org.uk   Tel: 020-8889 7570

THEATRICAL MANAGEMENT ASSOCIATION
(See TMA)

TMA
(Theatrical Management Association)
32 Rose Street, London WC2E 9ET
Website: www.tmauk.org
e-mail: enquiries@solttma.co.uk
Fax: 020-7557 6799   Tel: 020-7557 6700

UK CHOREOGRAPHERS' DIRECTORY The
(See DANCE UK)

UK FILM COUNCIL
10 Little Portland Street, London W1W 7JG
Website: www.ukfilmcouncil.org.uk
e-mail: info@ukfilmcouncil.org.uk
Fax: 020-7861 7862   Tel: 020-7861 7861

UK THEATRE CLUBS
54 Swallow Drive, London NW10 8TG
e-mail: uktheatreclubs@aol.com   Tel/Fax: 020-8459 3972

UNITED KINGDOM COPYRIGHT BUREAU
110 Trafalgar Road, Portslade, East Sussex BN41 1GS
Website: www.copyrightbureau.co.uk
e-mail: info@copyrightbureau.co.uk
Fax: 01273 705451   Tel: 01273 277333

VARIETY & LIGHT ENTERTAINMENT COUNCIL
54 Keyes House, Dolphin Square, London SW1V 3NA
Fax: 020-7821 0261   Tel: 020-7798 5622

VARIETY CLUB CHILDREN'S CHARITY
Variety Club House
93 Bayham Street, London NW1 0AG
Website: www.varietyclub.org.uk
e-mail: info@varietyclub.org.uk
Fax: 020-7428 8111   Tel: 020-7428 8100

WOMEN IN FILM AND TELEVISION
Contact: Loretta Freeman
WFTV is the premier membership organisation for women working in the Film, Television and Digital Media industries in the UK. Provides Advice, Information, Social Membership & Support
Unit 2, Wedgewood Mews
12-13 Greek Street, London W1D 4BB
Website: www.wftv.org.uk
e-mail: info@wftv.org.uk
Fax: 020-7287 1500   Tel: 020-7287 1400

WRITERNET
Cabin V, Clarendon Buildings
25 Horsell Road, London N5 1XL
Website: www.writernet.org.uk
e-mail: info@writernet.org.uk
Fax: 020-7609 7557   Tel: 020-7609 7474

YOUTH MUSIC THEATRE: UK
40 Parkgate Road
Battersea, London SW11 4JH
Website: www.ymtuk.org
e-mail: mail@ymtuk.org   Tel: 0870 240 5057

PHOTOGRAPHERS

ACTORSHEADSHOTS.CO.UK
Website: www.actorsheadshots.co.uk
e-mail: info@actorsheadshots.co.uk
Mobile: 07740 507970

ACTOR'S ONE-STOP SHOP
Website: www.actorsonestopshop.com
e-mail: info@actorsonestopshop.com
Mobile: 07894 152651
Tel: 020-8888 7006

ALLEN Stuart
Website: www.stuartallenphotos.com
Mobile: 07776 258829

AM LONDON
Website: www.am-london.com
Mobile: 07974 188105
Tel: 020-7193 1868

ANKER Matt
e-mail: mattanker@onetel.com
Mobile: 07835 241835

ANNAND Simon
Website: www.simonannand.com
Mobile: 07884 446776
Tel: 020-7241 6725

ASCHA
Website: www.ascha.co.uk

BACON Ric
Website: www.ricbacon.co.uk
Mobile: 07970 970799

BAKER Chris
Website: www.chrisbakerphotographer.com
e-mail: chrisbaker@photos2000.demon.co.uk
Tel: 020-8441 3851

BAKER Sophie
Tel: 020-8340 3850

BALEHOUSE PHOTOGRAPHY
Website: www.balehousephotography.co.uk
e-mail: info@balehousephotography.co.uk
Mobile: 07947 804821 / 07876 350089

BARRASS Paul
Website: www.paulbarrass.co.uk
e-mail: paul@paulbarrass.co.uk
Mobile: 07973 265931

BARTLETT Pete
Website: www.petebartlett.com
e-mail: info@petebartlett.com
Mobile: 07971 653994

Photographers

Each photographer listed in this section has taken
an advertisement in this edition.
See Index to Advertisers pages to view each
advertisement.

Promotional Services
(CVs, Showreels, Websites etc)
Properties & Trades
Publications

[CONTACTS 2009]

How do I find a photographer?

Having a good quality, up-to-date promotional headshot is crucial for every performer. Make sure you choose your photographer very carefully: do some research and try to look at different examples. Photographers' adverts run throughout this book, featuring many sample shots, although to get a real feel for their work you should also try to see their portfolio or website since this will give a more accurate impression of the quality of their photography.

If you live in or around London, please feel free to visit the Spotlight offices and look through current editions of our directories to find a style you like. We also have nearly sixty photographers' portfolios available for you to browse, many of them from photographers listed over the next few pages. Our offices are open Monday - Friday, 10.00am - 5.30pm at 7 Leicester Place, London WC2H 7RJ (nearest tube is Leicester Square).

What should I expect from the photo shoot?

When it comes to your photo shoot, bear in mind that a casting director, agent or production company will want to see a photo of the 'real' you. Keep your appearance as neutral as possible so that they can imagine you in many different roles, rather than type-casting yourself from the outset and limiting your opportunities.

Your eyes are your most important feature, so make sure they are visible: face the camera straight-on and try not to smile too much because it makes them harder to see. Wear something simple and avoid jewellery, hats, scarves, glasses or props, since these will all add character. Do not wear clothes that detract from your face such as polo necks, big collars, busy patterns or logos. Always keep your hands out of the shot.

Also consider the background: some photographers like to do outdoor shots. A contrast between background and hair colour works well, whereas dark backgrounds work less well with dark hair, and the same goes for light hair on light backgrounds.

Which photograph should I choose?

When you get your contact sheet back from the photographer, make sure you choose a photo that looks like you - not how you would like to look. If you are unsure, ask friends or your agent for an honest opinion. Remember, you will be asked to attend meetings and auditions on the basis of your photograph, so if you turn up looking completely different you will be wasting everyone's time.

Due to copyright legislation, you must always credit the photographer when using the photo.

How should I submit my photo to Spotlight and to casting professionals?

All photographs submitted to Spotlight must be of the highest possible quality, otherwise casting professionals will not see you in the best possible light. If you are sending your photo by hard copy, we would expect a 10 x 8 sized print, which is the industry standard. It is not necessary to provide an original print: a high quality, clear focused repro is fine. If you are sending a digital image by email or disk, we have certain technical specifications which can be found on our website (see below). We would recommend that you follow similar guidelines when sending your headshot directly to casting professionals.

What are Spotlight portfolio photographs?

Every Spotlight performer can also add extra photographs onto their web page, in addition to their principal photograph. These are called portfolio photos, and they give you the opportunity to show yourself in a range of different shots and / or roles. Members can upload up to 15 photos free of charge using their update PIN.

For more information please visit www.spotlight.com/artists/appear/multimedia/photos

BENNETT Graham
Website: www.grahambennett.biz
Mobile: 020-8374 1697

BISHOP Brandon
Website: www.brandonbishopphotography.com
Mobile: 07931 383830
Tel: 020-7275 7468

BREAK A LEG PHOTOGRAPHY
Website: www.breakalegphotography.com
Mobile: 07770 760985
Tel: 020-8980 9067

BRITTON Anthony
Website: www.anthonybritton.co.uk
e-mail: anthony-britton@btconnect.com
Tel: 01784 488343

BURNETT Sheila
Website: www.sheilaburnett-photography.com
Tel: 020-7289 3058

CABLE Paul
Website: www.paulcable.com
e-mail: info@paulcable.com
Mobile: 07958 932764

CLARK John
Website: www.johnclarkphotography.com
e-mail: info@ johnclarkphotography.com
Mobile: 07702 627237
Tel: 020-8854 4069

CLARKE Rosy
Website: www.rosyclarkephotographer.com
e-mail: rosyphotographer@hotmail.com
Mobile: 07531 171074

CRAFER Ruth
Website: www.ruthcrafer.co.uk
e-mail: ruth@rutho.demon.co.uk
Mobile: 07974 088460

CROSBY Alex
Website: www.alexcrosby.co.uk
e-mail: info@alexcrosby.co.uk
Mobile: 07818 448019

CW PHOTOS (Clive Weeks)
Website: www.cwphotos.co.uk
Tel: 023-8073 2550

DANCE SCENE PHOTOGRAPHIC
Website: www.dancepics4u.co.uk
Tel: 01737 552874

DAVISON PICTURES
Website: www.davisonpictures.co.uk
e-mail: maggie@byronw7.freeserve.co.uk
Mobile: 07917 758754
Tel: 020-8579 7006

DEBAL
e-mail: debal@abeautifulimage.com
Tel: 020-8568 2122

DE SOUZA Ava
Website: www.avadesouza.co.uk
Tel: 020-8392 9093

DYE Debbie
Website: www.debbiedye.com
Mobile: 07957 653913

ELLIS Sean
Website: www.seanellis.co.uk
e-mail: sean@seanellis.co.uk
Mobile: 07702 381258

GAUDER Steven
Website: www.stevengauder.com
Mobile: 07779 588754

GREGAN Nick
Website: www.nickgregan.com
e-mail: info@nickgregan.com
Mobile: 07774 421878
Tel: 020-8533 3003

GROGAN Claire
Website: www.clairegrogan.co.uk
Mobile: 07932 635381
Tel: 020-7272 1845

HARWOOD-STAMPER Dan
Website: www.danharwoodstamper.co.uk
Tel: 07779 165777

HEADSHOT STUDIOS
Website: www.headshotstudios.co.uk
e-mail: info@headshotstudios.co.uk
Mobile: 07770 694686

HINDS Sean
Website: www.sean-hinds-photography.com
e-mail: seanhphotography@aol.com
Mobile: 07816 465809

HUGHES Jamie
Website: www.jamiehughesphotography.com
e-mail: jamie@jamiehughesphotography.com
Mobile: 07850 122977

HULL Anna
Website: www.annahullphotography.com
Tel: 020-7498 5023

HUNTER Remy
Website: www.remyhunter.co.uk
Mobile: 07766 760724
Tel: 020-7431 8055

I.N.C COLLECTIVE
Website: www.internationalcollective.com
e-mail: antoinette@internationalcollective.co.uk

JAMES Nick
Website: www.nickjamesphotography.co.uk
Mobile: 07961 122030

JAMIE Matt
Website: www.mattjamie.co.uk/portraits

JEFFERSON Paris
Website: www.parisjefferson.com
Mobile: 07876 586601

JONES Denis
Website: www.djpix.co.uk
Mobile: 07836 241158

KAMOTSKAIA Ksenia
Website: www.kseniakamotskaia.com
e-mail: kkamotskaia@hotmail.com
Mobile: 07751 233544

KEATES James
Website: www.jk-photography.net
Mobile: 07816 825578

LADENBURG Jack
Website: www.jackladenburg.co.uk
e-mail: info@jackladenburg.co.uk
Mobile: 07932 053743

LATIMER Carole
Website: www.carolelatimer.com
e-mail: carole.latimer@freenet.co.uk
Tel: 020-7727 9371

LAWTON Steve
Website: www.stevelawton.com
Mobile: 07973 307487

LE MAY Pete
Website: www.petelemay.co.uk
e-mail: pete@petelemay.co.uk
Mobile: 07703 649246

LENKA PHOTOGRAPHY
Website: www.galaxy-casting.com/photographer
e-mail: lenki13@yahoo.co.uk
Mobile: 07921 182055

LONEY Francis
e-mail: francisloney@talktalk.net
Mobile: 07753 634443
Tel: 020-7254 1199

McNEIL Oliver
Website: www.mcneildesigns.co.uk
Tel: 01424 430055

M.A.D. PHOTOGRAPHY
Website: www.mad-photography.co.uk
Mobile: 07949 581909
Tel: 020-8363 4182

MANN James
Website: www.j-mann.com
Mobile: 07742 814160

MARCUS Raymondo
Website: www.raymondomarcus.com
Mobile: 07831 649000

MARKS-PHILLIPS PHOTOGRAPHY
Website: www.marks-phillips-photography.com
e-mail: info@marks-phillips-photography.com
Mobile: 07976 239512
Tel: 020-8696 0248

MERCHANT-GREENBERG Natasha
Website: www.natashamerchant.com
Mobile: 07932 618111
Tel: 020-8653 5399

MITSIOS Socrates
Website: www.londonfaces.com
e-mail: email@londonfaces.com
Mobile: 07903 000017

MOUNT Gemma
Website: www.gemmamountphotography.com
Mobile: 07976 824923

MULHOLLAND Ruth
Website: www.ruthmulholland.com
Mobile: 07939 516987

NAMDAR Fatimah
Website: www.fatimahnamdar.com
e-mail: fnamdar@mac.com
Mobile: 07973 287535
Tel: 020-8341 1332

NEWMAN-WILLIAMS Claire
Website: www.clairenewmanwilliams.com
e-mail: claire@clairenewmanwilliams.com

PERKINS Christopher
Website: www.christopher-perkins.com
Mobile: 07803 507150

POLLARD Michael
Website: www.michaelpollard.co.uk
e-mail: info@michaelpollard.co.uk
Tel: 0161-456 7470

PRICE David
Website: www.davidpricephotography.co.uk
e-mail: info@ davidpricephotography.co.uk
Mobile: 07950 542494

PROCTOR Carl
Website: www.carlproctorphotography.com
e-mail: carlphotos@btconnect.com
Mobile: 07956 283340

PROFILE PHOTOGRAPHY
Website: www.profile-london.com
e-mail: info@profile-london.com
Mobile: 07971 431798

RAFIQUE Harry
Website: www.hr-photographer.co.uk
Mobile: 07986 679498
Tel: 020-7266 5398

RICHMOND Eric
Website: www.ericrichmond.net
e-mail: eric@ericrichmond.net
Mobile: 07866 766240
Tel: 020-8880 6909

ROSS Davey
Website: www.davixmedia.com
e-mail: davixuk@hotmail.com
Mobile: 07956 302894

SAVAGE Robin
Website: www.robinsavage.co.uk
e-mail: contact@robinsavage.co.uk
Mobile: 07901 927597

SAYER Howard
Website: www.howardsayer.com
e-mail: howard@howardsayer.com
Mobile: 07860 559891

SCOTT Karen
Website: www.karenscottphotography.com
e-mail: info@ karenscottphotography.com
Mobile: 07958 975950

SETARO Cristiana
Website: www.cristianasetaro.com
e-mail: info@cristianasetaro.com
Mobile: 07950 901492

SHAKESPEARE LANE Catherine
Website: www.csl-art.co.uk
Tel: 020-7226 7694

SIMPKIN Peter
Website: www.petersimpkin.co.uk
e-mail: petersimpkin@aol.com
Mobile: 07973 224084
Tel: 020-8883 2727

SMITH Lucy
Website: www.thatlucy.co.uk

STEDEFORD Matt
Website: www.stedeford.com/photography
e-mail: matt@stedeford.com
Mobile: 07793 741604

STILL Rosie
Website: www.rosiestillphotography.com
Tel: 020-8857 6920

SUGDEN Craig
Website: www.craigsugden.com
Mobile: 07967 380568

TM PHOTOGRAPHY
Website: www.tmphotography.co.uk
e-mail: info@tmphotography.co.uk
Mobile: 07931 755252
Tel: 020-7288 6846

ULLATHORNE Steve
Website: www.ullapix.xom
e-mail: steve@ullapix.com
Mobile: 07961 380969

URBAN ICON
Website: www.urbanicon.co.uk
e-mail: urbanicon@mac.com
Mobile: 07989 660459

VARLEY Luke
Website: www.lukevarley.com
Mobile: 07711 183631

VINCENZO PHOTOGRAPHY
Website: www.vincenzophotography.com
e-mail: info@vincenzophotography.com
Mobile: 07962 338289

WILKINSON Howard
Website: www.howardwilkinsonphotography.co.uk
Mobile: 07947 345305
Tel: 01706 645203

WILL C
Website: www.london-photographer.com
e-mail: billy_snapper@hotmail.com
Mobile: 07712 669953

WORKMAN Robert
Website: www.robertworkman.demon.co.uk
Tel: 020-7385 5442

SPOTLIGHT

Casting from start to finish

Spotlight Database

Whether online or through our books, browse over 30,000 actors, actresses, presenters, stunt artists, children and dancers

View CVs, photos, showreels, portfolios and contact details for every performer

Be confident that every performer featured either trained professionally or has relevant experience

Spotlight Website

Email casting briefs to hundreds of UK agents and performers, and receive reponses in minutes

Find exactly the right perfomer for the part, with our award-winning search engine

Search our database of behind-camera specialists

Spotlight Spaces

Audition in the heart of central London

Record onto any format, and post clips online free of charge

Cast live between the UK and any other country

www.spotlight.com   020-7440 5042   casting@spotlight.com

"Fantastic experience, fantastic result"

"Beautifully crafted Radio programmes"

"You feel loved"

"Our studio of choice for London ISDN"

"No wonder Vox is A1"

Sound Studios in Soho

Spoken Word specialists, for ISDN Links, Recordings, Production, Duplication & more
A1 VOX Ltd   Soho   London   020 7434 4404   info@a1vox.com   www.a1vox.com

A1 VOX Ltd
(Spoken Word Audio, ISDN Links, Demo CDs & Audio Clips)
20 Old Compton Street, London W1D 4TW
Website: www.a1vox.com
e-mail: info@a1vox.com   Tel: 020-7434 4404

ABBEY ROAD STUDIOS
3 Abbey Road, St John's Wood, London NW8 9AY
Website: www.abbeyroad.com
e-mail: bookings@abbeyroad.com
Fax: 020-7266 7250   Tel: 020-7266 7000

ACTOR SHOWREELS
(Showreel Service)
97B Central Hill, London SE19 1BY
Website: www.actorshowreels.co.uk
e-mail: post@actorshowreels.co.uk
Mobile: 07939 241377   Mobile: 07835 637965

ACTORS CV
(Print & Website Solutions)
17 Peabody Court, Martini Drive, Middlesex EN3 6GU
Website: www.actorscv.com   Tel: 01992 851082

ACTORS ILLUMINATED.COM
Contact: Kosha Engler (Websites for People in The
Performing Arts)
131 Glengall Road, London NW6 7HG
Website: www.actorsilluminated.com
e-mail: mail@actorsilluminated.com   Mobile: 07769 626074

ACTORS INTERACTIVE
(Web Design)
10 Frobisher Street, London SE10 9XB
Website: www.actorsinteractive.com
e-mail: office@actorsinteractive.com   Tel: 020-8465 5457

ACTOR'S ONE-STOP SHOP The
(Showreels for Performing Artists)
First Floor, Above The Gate Pub
Station Road, London N22 7SS
Website: www.actorsonestopshop.com
e-mail: info@actorsonestopshop.com   Tel: 020-8888 7006

ACTUALLYACTORS.COM
(Websites)
3 Milestone Road
London SE19 2LL
Website: www.actuallyactors.com
e-mail: mail@actuallyactors.co.uk   Tel: 020-8325 1946

AIR-EDEL RECORDING STUDIOS Ltd
18 Rodmarton Street
London W1U 8BJ
e-mail: trevorbest@air-edel.co.uk
Fax: 020-7224 0344   Tel: 020-7486 6466

ANGEL RECORDING STUDIOS Ltd
311 Upper Street
London N1 2TU
e-mail: angel@angelstudio.co.uk
Fax: 020-7226 9624   Tel: 020-7354 2525

ANT FARM STUDIOS VOICE-OVERS
Southend Farm
Southend Lane
Waltham Abbey EN9 3SE
Website: www.antfarmstudios.co.uk
e-mail: antfarmstudio@yahoo.co.uk   Tel: 01992 714664

ASCENT MEDIA Ltd
Film House
142 Wardour Street, London W1F 8DD
Website: www.ascentmedia.co.uk
Fax: 020-7878 7870   Tel: 020-7878 0000

ASPIRE PRODUCTIONS
34A Pollard Road
Morden
Surrey SM4 6EG
Website: www.aspirepresenting.com
e-mail: info@aspirepresenting.com   Tel: 020-8665 2275

BEWILDERING PICTURES
Contact: Graeme Kennedy (Showreel Service, Islington)
Website: www.bewildering.co.uk
e-mail: gk@bewildering.co.uk   Mobile: 07974 916258

What are promotional services?

This section contains listings for companies who provide practical services to help performers promote themselves. You might need to improve or create your CV; record a showreel or voicereel; design your own website; duplicate CDs; or print photographic repros, CVs or Z-cards: all essential ways to create a good impression with those that count in the industry.

Why do I need to promote myself?

Performers need to invest in marketing and promotion as much as any other self-employed businessperson. Even if you have trained at a leading drama school, have a well-known agent, or have just finished work on a popular TV series, you should never sit back and wait for your phone to ring or for the next job opportunity just to knock on your door. In such a competitive industry, successful performers are usually the ones who market themselves pro-actively and treat their careers as a 'business'.

Having up-to-date and well-produced promotional material makes a performer look professional and serious about their career: and hence a desirable person for a director or agent to work with.

Why is my CV important?

Poor presentation, punctuation and grammar create a bad first impression and you risk your CV being dismissed before it is even read. Make sure that you continually update your CV – you don't want it to look as if you haven't been working recently when you have, and you don't want to miss out on an audition because you haven't included skills you have put time and effort into achieving. Your CV should be kept to a maximum of one page and printed on good-quality paper.

Why is my covering letter important?

Always include a covering letter to introduce your CV and persuade casting professionals that it is worth reading. Remember that they receive hundreds each week. Keep your communication concise and be professional at all times. We also recommend that your letter has some kind of focus: perhaps you can tell them about your next showcase, or where they can see you currently appearing on stage. Ideally this should be addressed to an individual, not "Dear Sir or Madam".

Why is my headshot important?

Your CV should feature, or be accompanied by, a recent headshot which is an accurate current likeness. See the 'Photographers' section for more information about promotional photography. You may need to print copies of your headshot through a repro company, some of whom are listed over the following pages.

Why do I need a voicereel?

If you are interested in voice-over and/or radio work, you will need a professional-sounding voicereel to show agents, casting directors and potential employers what your voice is capable of. For commercial and corporate voice-over work this should be no more than two minutes long with a number of short clips demonstrating your range, but showcase the strengths of your natural voice as much as possible. It should contain a mixture of commercials and narrations.

A radio voicereel should be around eight minutes long, with four clips no longer than two minutes each, and read in your natural voice. To achieve a good balance of material, one clip should be 'classical', one 'contemporary', one 'comic' and one a poem. This is designed to give an overview of your suitability to various areas of radio work.

Record your voicereel in a professional studio to ensure a high-quality result, otherwise you are unlikely to be considered in this competitive industry. For further information please see the 'Agents – Voice-over' and 'Radio' sections.

Why do I need a showreel?

Some casting directors nowadays will only consider a performer for an audition if they have first seen them demonstrating their skills in a showreel. A CV and headshot give some indication of their potential, but can only provide a basic summary.

What should I do if I don't currently have anything on film?

Showreels are expensive to produce if you don't currently have any broadcasted material to use, but it is advisable to get one professionally recorded and edited if at all possible. Showreels help you to promote yourself, but a casting director may be put off by a poor quality one. You might want to consider a *Spotlight Intro* as a temporary alternative to a full showreel (see below). It may also be worth considering working unpaid on a student film. Students are usually willing to let you have a copy of their film in return and casting professionals would consider this an acceptable alternative. See 'Film & Television Schools' for further advice and listings.

How long should my showreel be?

We would recommend no more than three or four minutes. Casting professionals receive thousands of CVs and showreels and do not have time to watch every actor for ten minutes each. This is why we suggest you do not send your showreel out with your CV, but instead mention in your covering letter that one is available.

What should I use in my showreel?

Rather than one long excerpt, it is more beneficial to demonstrate your versatility with a number of 30 second clips. Focus on your strongest characters to enable the casting director to picture you in the roles you play best.

The first 30 seconds are the most important in your showreel, and can be the only part a busy casting director or agent has time to look at. You may wish to start with a brief montage summarising the clips that are to follow, or with a headshot of yourself so that they know who to watch out for.

The focus should be on you, not on the other actors, so close-up shots ought to be included. You should be speaking most if not all of the time. A visual contrast is good, whether this means filming in a different location or setting, or changing your outfit. You should avoid well-known scripts in order to prevent drawing comparisons between yourself and previous successful interpretations.

What is a Spotlight Intro?

If you are a Spotlight member, a *Spotlight Intro* is your opportunity to give casting professionals a quick introduction to you, your character and your voice with a one or two minute video as part of your Spotlight CV. Think of it as a video version of a covering letter you might enclose with a paper CV. It could also be used as a temporary alternative to a showreel, although ideally you should include both. Visit www.spotlight.com/spotlightintro for more information.

How should I use these listings?

If you are looking for a company to help you with any of these promotional items, browse through this section carefully and get quotes from a number of places to compare. If you are a Spotlight member, some companies offer a discount on their services. Always ask to see samples of a company's work, and ask friends in the industry for their own recommendations.

Charlie Lort-Phillips is an editor at Take Five, based in Soho, Central London. He has been editing showreels since 2003 for a wide range of actors, from newcomers to established names. Take Five has been established in the heart of London since 1993 as a casting studio, and an editing facility since 1998.

As more agents, directors, casting directors, and producers demand a quick and easy way of reviewing potential talent, so the showreel has begun to come into its own. Where previously a headshot and a CV would have done the job, now people are looking for something more informative that allows them to make decisions in the shortest possible time.

If you add a showreel to your portfolio it can go in a multitude of directions. On DVD it can be a high quality example of your work that can be watched in the comfort of an armchair or on the Internet – whether on Spotlight or on your own website – within a matter of minutes on the other side of the world.

I've now been editing showreels for over four years, and as a result have seen a great breadth of styles – and there lies the point. No one template can exactly fit everybody – each person has different material, a different persona, a different path they wish to tread. However, there are some basic building blocks that can help you to achieve your goal...

Firstly, remember that the people at the receiving end may not have a lot of time to watch it – either they are working on a project, or another twenty reels have also fallen on their doorstep. Keep your scenes to the point – get your characters across but don't leave them feeling that they have had to watch the entire programme! Also, make sure they know which actor is you – they're not there to watch someone else.

Secondly, play to your strengths – if you are a character actor play to that character, if not, try to show a wide range of skills.

Thirdly, consider the possibility of a montage of your various characters – if you don't have enough time to show all of your work, abridge your other projects into a short 'trailer' that shows your abilities in an even shorter time in addition to your longer clips.

When you are thinking of putting your showreel together it is also very important to collect all your potential work before booking an appointment – always go through your material to try and narrow down what you may wish to use as this will more than likely save you a great deal of money. Where possible, try to source your material on DVD as the quality is invariably much better. It may even be worth buying a DVD recorder in order to capture any TV work at high quality.

If you are thinking of filming additional material for your reel, or starting a reel from scratch, try to find a script or scripts that suit you, rather than a generic piece that may not reflect your skills accurately. Any piece should, again, be to the point – try to keep any individual scene to a minute, maximum.

If you're starting off with no material and want to film everything from scratch, remember that while a monologue is easy to film, it may not be the most effective way of getting your skills across. Try to gather a few pieces together that show your range, perhaps a monologue and a duologue or three, and again, make sure you know how you want to play them and what it is you wish to achieve.

A reel, while being a good showcase for your work, takes preparation and care. The more thought you can put into it beforehand – sourcing copies or scripts and thoroughly preparing them – the more time it will save on the day, and the better your reel will look. However, never be afraid to ask for advice as a showreel editor will have a fresh pair of eyes, and be able to see things that you may not. Even with very little material, a well thought out showreel can go a very long way.

Please visit www.takefivestudio.com for further information.

CHANNEL 2020 Ltd
The Clerkenwell Workshops (G15)
27-31 Clerkenwell Close, London EC1R 0AT
Website: www.channel2020.co.uk
e-mail: info@channel2020.co.uk   Tel: 0844 8402020

2020 House, 26-28 Talbot Lane, Leicester LE1 4LR
Fax: 0116-222 1113   Tel: 0844 8402020

CHASE Stephan PRODUCTIONS Ltd
(Director for Voice Overs and Showreels)
The Studio, 22 York Avenue
London SW14 7LG
Website: www.stephanchase.com
e-mail: stephan@stephanchase.com   Tel: 020-8878 9112

CLAW FILMS
Website: www.clawfilms.com
e-mail: info@clawfilms.com   Tel: 020-7193 2197

CLICKS
Media Studios, Grove Road
Rochester, Kent ME2 4BX
e-mail: info@clicksstudios.co.uk
Fax: 01634 726000   Tel: 01634 723838

CONCEPT
PO Box 192, Liverpool L69 1JA
Website: www.soundconcept.co.uk
e-mail: info@soundconcept.co.uk   Tel: 0151-522 9133

COURTWOOD PHOTOGRAPHIC Ltd
(Photographic Reproduction)
Profile Prints, Freepost T055
Penzance, Cornwall TR20 8DU
Website: www.courtwood.co.uk
e-mail: people@courtwood.co.uk
Fax: 01736 741255   Tel: 01736 741222

CROWE Ben
(Voice Clip Recording)
23 John Aird Court, London W2 1UY
e-mail: bencrowe@hotmail.co.uk
Mobile: 07952 784911   Tel/Fax: 020-7262 3543

CRYING OUT LOUD
(Voice-Over Specialists/Voice-Over Demo CDs)
Website: www.cryingoutloud.co.uk
e-mail: simon@cryingoutloud.co.uk
Mobile: 07796 266265   Tel: 020-8980 0124

CRYSTAL MEDIA
28 Castle Street, Edinburgh EH2 3HT
Website: www.crystal-media.co.uk
e-mail: hello@crystal-media.co.uk
Fax: 0131-240 0989   Tel: 0131-240 0988

CTS/LANSDOWNE RECORDING STUDIOS Ltd
PO Box 47189, London W6 6DA
Website: www.cts-lansdowne.co.uk
e-mail: info@cts-lansdowne.co.uk
Fax: 056-0115 5009   Tel: 020-8846 9444

CUT GLASS PRODUCTIONS
(Voice-over Showreels/Voice-over Production)
Studio 185,
181-187 Queens Crescent
Camden, London NW5 4DS
Website: www.cutglassproductions.com
e-mail: info@cutglassproductions.com   Tel: 020-7267 2339

DARK SIDE
(Photographic Repro Service)
4 Helmet Row, London EC1V 3QJ
Website: www.darksidephoto.co.uk
e-mail: info@darksidephoto.co.uk
Fax: 020-7250 1771   Tel: 020-7250 1200

DE LANE LEA SOUND
(Post-Production, Re-Recording Studios)
75 Dean Street, London W1D 3PU
Website: www.delanelea.com
e-mail: solutions@delanelea.com
Fax: 020-7432 3838   Tel: 020-7432 3800

DENBRY REPROS Ltd
(Photographic Reproduction)
57 High Street
Hemel Hempstead, Herts HP1 3AF
e-mail: info@denbryrepros.com   Tel: 01442 242411

DESIGN CREATIVES & OCTOPUS REACH
Contact: Anthony Rosato
(Artistic Promotions & Graphic/Web Design & Hosting)
Suite B, 5 South Bank Terrace
Surbiton, Surrey KT6 6DG
Website: www.octopusreach.com
e-mail: octopusreach1@aol.com
Mobile: 07787 995604   Tel/Fax: 020-8390 8535

ELMS STUDIOS
(Mac G5/Logic Pro 8/O2RV2/Composing/Scoring for
Film & TV)
Phil Lawrence, 10 Empress Avenue
London E12 5ES
Website: www.elmsstudios.com
e-mail: info@elmsstudios.com   Tel: 020-8518 8629

ESSENTIAL MUSIC
20 Great Chapel Street
London W1F 8FW
e-mail: info@essentialmusic.co.uk
Fax: 020-7287 3597   Tel: 020-7439 7113

EXECUTIVE AUDIO VISUAL
(Showreels for Actors & Presenters)
80 York Street
London W1H 1QW   Tel/Fax: 020-7723 4488

FARM DIGITAL POST-PRODUCTION The
27 Upper Mount Street, Dublin 2, Ireland
Website: www.thefarm.ie
e-mail: info@thefarm.ie
Fax: 00 353 1 676 8816   Tel: 00 353 1 676 8812

FLYING DUCKS GROUP Ltd The
(Conference, Multimedia & Video Production)
Oakridge, Weston Road
Staffordshire ST16 3RS
Website: www.flyingducks.biz
e-mail: enquiries@flyingducks.biz
Fax: 01785 252448   Tel: 0700 3401211

FREEDALE PRESS Ltd
(Printing)
36 Hedley Street
Maidstone, Kent ME14 5AD
e-mail: michael@freedale.co.uk
Fax: 01622 200131   Tel: 01622 200123

GENESIS UK.COM Ltd
18 Pendre Enterprise Park
Tywyn, Gwynedd LL36 9LW
Website: www.genesis-uk.com
e-mail: info@genesis-uk.com
Fax: 01654 712461   Tel: 01654 710137

HEAVY ENTERTAINMENT Ltd
111 Wardour Street, London W1F 0UH
Website: www.heavy-entertainment.com
e-mail: info@heavy-entertainment.com
Fax: 020-7494 1100   Tel: 020-7494 1000

HOTQS
(Showreels)
2nd Floor, 18 Kingsland Road
London E2 8DA
Website: www.houseofthequietstorm.com
e-mail: pat@houseofthequietstorm.com
                                      Mobile: 07903 017819

HOTREELS
(Voice and Showreels)
Website: www.hotreels.co.uk
e-mail: info@hotreels.co.uk
Mobile: 07793 394951   Tel: 020-7952 4362

HOUSE OF WEB
(Web Design)
16 Duncombe House
Windlesham Grove, London SW19 6AJ
Website: www.houseofweb.co.uk
e-mail: marte@houseofweb.co.uk   Mobile: 07962 471118

IMAGE PHOTOGRAPHIC
(Photographic Reproduction)
54 Shepherds Bush Road
London W6 7PH
Website: www.imagephotographic.com
e-mail: sales@imagephotographic.com
Fax: 020-7602 6219   Tel: 020-7602 1190

INIMITABLE
(Flash Website Design)
PO Box 147, Dewsbury WF12 0WZ
Website: www.inimitable.us
e-mail: info@inimitable.us   Tel: 01924 464049

JMS GROUP Ltd
(Multimedia Production)
3 Montagu Row, London W1U 6DY
Website: www.jms-group.com
e-mail: info@jms-group.com
Fax: 020-7224 4035   Tel: 020-7224 1031

Park Farm Studios, Norwich Road
Hethersett, Norfolk NR9 3DL
Fax: 01603 812255   Tel: 01603 811855

KONK STUDIOS
84-86 Tottenham Lane, London N8 7EE
e-mail: linda@konkstudios.com
Fax: 020-8348 3952   Tel: 020-8340 7873

LONDON FILM COMPANY Ltd
Suite B, 5 South Bank Terrace
Surbiton, Surrey KT6 6DG
Website: www.doncapo.com
e-mail: doncapoandco@aol.com
Mobile: 07787 995604   Tel/Fax: 020-8390 8535

MEDIAWEBS
(Graphic & Web Design)
20 Parker Road, Millbank Place
Colchester CO4 5BE
Website: www.mediawebs.co.uk
e-mail: jon@mediawebs.co.uk   Mobile: 07887 480241

MINAMON FILM
(Specialist in Showreels)
117 Downton Avenue, London SW2 3TX
e-mail: studio@minamonfilm.co.uk
Fax: 020-8674 1779   Tel: 020-8674 3957

MOTIVATION SOUND STUDIOS
35A Broadhurst Gardens
London NW6 3QT
Website: www.motivationsound.co.uk
e-mail: info@motivationsound.co.uk
Fax: 020-7624 4879   Tel: 020-7328 8305

MUSIC IN MOTION Ltd
1 Reubens Court, Chaseley Drive
Chiswick, London W4 4BD
Website: www.neilmyers.com
e-mail: neil@neilmyers.com
Mobile: 07813 070961   Tel: 020-8400 3706

MYCLIPS
Flat 1, 2 Blackdown Close
East Finchley, London N2 8JF
Website: www.myclipsdvd.com
e-mail: info@myclipsdvd.com   Tel: 020-8371 9526

PERFORMERS ONLINE Ltd
(Design, Web & Print)
18B High Street
London N8 7PB
Website: www.performersonline.co.uk
e-mail: info@performersonline.co.uk   Tel: 020-8347 0221

Make the final cut

High quality showreels for the entertainment industry

Contact
enquiries@tripleuproductions.com
020 7613 3632 / 077 6601 1340
www.tripleuproductions.com

tripleuproductions

PROFILE PRINTS
(Photographic Reproduction)
Unit 2, Plot 1A, Rospeath Industrial Estate
Crowlas TR20 8DU
Website: www.courtwood.co.uk
e-mail: sales@courtwood.co.uk
Fax: 01736 741255   Tel: 01736 741222

RED FACILITIES
61 Timberbush, Leith, Edinburgh EH6 6QH
Website: www.redfacilities.com
e-mail: doit@redfacilities.com
Fax: 0131-555 0088   Tel: 0131-555 2288

REEL McCOY The
(Showreel Editing Service)
4 Kirkdale, Sydenham, London SE26 4NE
Website: www.reelmccoy.notlong.com
e-mail: reelmccoyservice@aol.com   Mobile: 07708 626477

REPLAY Ltd
(Showreels & Performance Recording)
Museum House
25 Museum Street, London WC1A 1JT
Website: www.replayfilms.co.uk
e-mail: sales@replayfilms.co.uk   Tel: 020-7637 0473

ROUND ISLAND SHOWREELS
(Ben Warren)
Website: www.roundisland.net
e-mail: mail@roundisland.net   Mobile: 07701 093183

SARM WEST STUDIOS Ltd
8-10 Basing Street, London W11 1ET
Website: www.sarmstudios.com
e-mail: clare@spz.com
Fax: 020-7221 9247   Tel: 020-7229 1229

SCARLET INTERNET
Suite 4, 15 Market Square
Bishop's Stortford, Herts CM23 3UT
Website: www.scarletinternet.com
e-mail: info@scarletinternet.com
Fax: 0870 2241418   Tel: 0870 7771820

Claw Films
Music Video, Commercial & Viral Production
+44 (0)20 7193 2197
www.clawfilms.com - info@clawfilms.com

SHAW Bernard
(Specialist in Recording & Directing Voice Tapes)
Horton Manor, Canterbury CT4 7LG
Website: www.bernardshaw.co.uk
e-mail: bernard@bernardshaw.co.uk   Tel/Fax: 01227 730843

SHOWREEL The
(Voice-Over Workshops & Demo Production)
Knightsbridge House
229 Acton Lane, Chiswick, London W4 5DD
Website: www.theshowreel.com
e-mail: info@theshowreel.com
Fax: 020-8995 2144   Tel: 020-7043 8660

SHOWREELS 1
45-46 Poland Street, London W1F 7NA
Website: www.ukscreen.com/company/showreels1
e-mail: showreels1@aol.com
Fax: 020-7437 2830   Mobile: 07932 021232

SHOWREELZ
59 Church Street, St Albans, Herts AL3 5NG
Website: www.showreelz.com
e-mail: brad@showreelz.com
Mobile: 07885 253477   Tel: 01727 752960

SILVER-TONGUED PRODUCTIONS
(Specializing in the recording and production of Voicereels)
178 Ramillies Road, Sidcup DA15 9JH
Website: www.silver-tongued.co.uk
e-mail: contactus@silver-tongued.co.uk   Tel: 020-8309 0659

SMALL SCREEN SHOWREELS
The Production Office
17 Knole Road, Dartford, Kent DA1 3JN
Website: www.smallscreenshowreels.co.uk
e-mail: info@smallscreenshowreels.co.uk
    Tel: 020-8816 8896

SONICPOND STUDIO
(Specialising in Voicereels. Showreels & Websites)
70 Mildmay Grove South
Islington, London N1 4PJ
Website: www.sonicpond.co.uk
e-mail: info@sonicpond.co.uk   Tel: 020-7690 8561

SOUND COMPANY Ltd The
23 Gosfield Street, London W1W 6HG
Website: www.sound.co.uk
e-mail: info@sound.co.uk
Fax: 020-7580 6454   Tel: 020-7580 5880

SOUND CONCEPTION
Sound, 4 St Paul's Road
Clifton, Bristol BS8 1LT
Website: www.soundat4.com   Tel: 0117-973 4595

SOUND HOUSE POST PRODUCTION Ltd The
10th Floor, Astley House
Quay Street
Manchester M3 4AE
Website: www.thesoundhouse.tv
e-mail: mail@thesoundhouse.tv
Fax: 0161-832 7266   Tel: 0161-832 7299

SOUND MARKETING
Strattons House, Strattons Walk
Melksham, Wiltshire SN12 6JL
Website: www.soundm.com
e-mail: nicki@soundm.com
Fax: 01225 701601   Tel: 01225 701600

STAGES CAPTURE THE MOMENT
(Showreels)
31 Evensyde, Croxley Green
Watford, Herts WD18 8WN
Website: www.stagescapturethemoment.com/showreels
e-mail: info@stagescapturethemoment.com
    Tel: 020-7193 8519

STEDEFORD VOICE REELS
31 Cornwall Gardens
Gloucester Road, London SW7 4AP
Website: www.stedeford.com
e-mail: stedefordvoicereels@gmail.com
    Mobile: 07793 741604

STEDEFORD WEBSITE DESIGN
9 Belsize Avenue
London N13 4TL
Website: www.stedeford.com
e-mail: stedefordwebsitedesign@gmail.com
    Mobile: 07793 741604

SUPPORT ACT SERVICES
Contact: Ian McCracken (CD Duplication & Web Design)
243A Lynmouth Avenue
Morden, Surrey SM4 4RX
Website: www.supportact.co.uk
e-mail: info@supportact.co.uk   Tel: 0845 0940796

TAKE FIVE CASTING STUDIO
(Showreels)
37 Beak Street
London W1F 9RZ
Website: www.takefivestudio.com
e-mail: info@takefivestudio.com
Fax: 020-7287 3035   Tel: 020-7287 2120

TM DESIGN SERVICES
(Web Design, Model Cards, Actors CVs)
Website: www.tmphotography.co.uk
e-mail: info@tmphotography.co.uk   Tel: 020-7288 6846

TOP TV ACADEMY
(Showreels)
309 Kentish Town Road
London NW5 2TJ
Website: www.toptvacademy.co.uk
e-mail: liz@toptvacademy.co.uk
Fax: 020-7485 7536   Tel: 020-7267 3530

TOUCHWOOD AUDIO PRODUCTIONS
6 Hyde Park Terrace
Leeds
West Yorkshire LS6 1BJ
Website: www.touchwoodaudio.com
e-mail: bruce@touchwoodaudio.com   Tel: 0113-278 7180

TRIPLEU PRODUCTIONS
(Showreels)
17 Gainsborough Studios North
London N1 5EB
Website: www.tripleuproductions.com
e-mail: walt@tripleuproductions.com   Tel: 020-7613 3632

TWITCH FILMS
(Showreels)
22 Grove End Gardens, 18 Abbey Road, London NW8 9LL
Website: www.twitchfilms.co.uk
e-mail: post@twitchfilms.co.uk　　　Tel: 020-7266 0946

UNIVERSAL SOUND (JUST PLAY) Ltd
Old Farm Lane
London Road East, Amersham
Buckinghamshire HP7 9DH
Website: www.universalsound.co.uk
e-mail: foley@universalsound.co.uk
Fax: 01494 723500　　　Tel: 01494 723400

VISUALEYES IMAGING SERVICES
(Photographic Reproduction)
95 Mortimer Street, London W1W 7ST
Website: www.visphoto.co.uk
e-mail: sales@visimaging.co.uk
Fax: 020-7323 7438　　　Tel: 020-7323 7430

VOICE MASTER
(Specialized Training in the PSR Method - The World's only
Technique for Voice-Overs & Autocue)
88 Erskine Hill, London NW11 6HR
Website: www.voicemaster.co.uk
e-mail: stevehudson@voicemaster.co.uk　Tel: 020-8455 2211

VOICE TAPE SERVICES INTERNATIONAL
(Professional Management Voice-Over Direction & CDs)
80 Netherlands Road
New Barnet, Herts EN5 1BS
Website: www.vtsint.co.uk
e-mail: info@vtsint.co.uk
Fax: 020-8441 4828　　　Tel: 020-8440 4848

VSI - VOICE & SCRIPT INTERNATIONAL
(Foreign Language Specialists - Translation, Subtitling,
Casting, Dubbing, Recording Studios, Editing)
132 Cleveland Street
London W1T 6AB
Website: www.vsi.tv
e-mail: info@vsi.tv
Fax: 020-7692 7711　　　Tel: 020-7692 7700

WARWICK HALL OF SOUND
Warwick Hall, Off Banastre Avenue
Heath, Cardiff CF14 3NR
Website: www.myspace.com/cardiffswarwickhallrecordingstudio
e-mail: adamstangroom@btconnect.com
　　　　　　　　　　　Tel/Fax: 029-2069 4455

WARWICK SOUND
(Sound Transfer/Optical & Magnetic)
Warwick Sound
111A Wardour Street, London W1F 0UJ
Website: www.warwicksound.com
e-mail: studio@warwicksound.com
Fax: 020-7439 0372　　　Tel: 020-7437 5532

WORLDWIDE PICTURES Ltd
21-25 St Anne's Court
Soho, London W1F 0BJ
Website: www.worldwidepictures.tv
e-mail: reception@worldwidepictures.tv
Fax: 020-7734 0619　　　Tel: 020-7494 8000

XKYX DESIGNS
(Graphic Design Services)
398A Finchley Road, Golders Green, London NW2 2HR
e-mail: xkystarx@yahoo.com　　　Mobile: 07942 258951

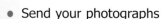

07000 BIG TOP
(Big Top, Seating, Circus)
The Arts Exchange, Congleton, Cheshire CW12 1JG
Website: www.arts-exchange.com
e-mail: phillipgandey@netcentral.co.uk
Fax: 01260 270777   Tel: 01260 276627

10 OUT OF 10 PRODUCTIONS Ltd
(Lighting, Sound, AV Hire, Sales & Installation)
5 Orchard Business Centre
Kangley Bridge Road, London SE26 5AQ
Website: www.10outof10.co.uk
e-mail: sales@10outof10.co.uk
Fax: 020-8778 9217   Tel: 0845 1235664

3D CREATIONS
(Production Design, Scenery Contractors, Prop Makers &
Scenic Artists)
9A Bells Road, Gorleston-on-Sea
Great Yarmouth, Norfolk NR31 6BB
Website: www.3dcreations.co.uk
e-mail: info@3dcreations.co.uk
Fax: 01493 443124   Tel: 01493 652055

ACROBAT PRODUCTIONS
(Artistes & Advisors)
12 Oaklands Court
Hempstead Road, Watford WD17 4LF
Website: www.acrobatproductions.com
e-mail: info@acrobatproductions.com   Tel: 01923 224938

ACTION CARS Ltd
Contact: Steven Royffe
Room 586, East Side Complex
Pinewood Studios, Pinewood Road
Iver Heath, Bucks SL0 0NH
Website: www.actioncars.co.uk
e-mail: info@actioncars.co.uk
Fax: 01753 652027   Tel: 01753 785690

ADAMS ENGRAVING
Unit G1A, The Mayford Centre
Mayford Green, Woking GU22 0PP
Website: www.adamsengraving.co.uk
e-mail: adamsengraving@pncl.co.uk
Fax: 01483 751787   Tel: 01483 725792

AIRBOURNE SYSTEMS INTERNATIONAL
(All Skydiving Requirements Arranged. Parachute Hire -
Period & Modern)
8 Burns Crescent, Chelmsford
Essex CM2 0TS   Tel: 01245 268772

ALCHEMICAL LABORATORIES ETC
(Medieval Science & Technology Recreated for Museums &
Films)
2 Stapleford Lane, Coddington
Newark, Nottinghamshire NG24 2QZ
Website: www.jackgreene.co.uk   Tel: 01636 707836

ALL SCENE ALL PROPS
(Props, Masks, Painting & Scenery Makers)
Units 2 & 3, Spelmonden Farm
Goudhurst, Kent TN17 1HE
Website: www.allscene.net
e-mail: info@allscene.net
Fax: 01580 211131   Tel: 01580 211121

ALL STARS
Fieldgate, Station Road, Northiam, Rye TN31 6QT
Website: www.allstarsamericanlimo.co.uk
e-mail: twtg@aol.com   Tel: 01797 252528

AMERICAN DREAMS
(Vehicle Supply)
47 Wilsons Lane
Mark's Tey, Essex CO6 1HP
Website: www.americandreams.co.uk
e-mail: tphj47@aol.com   Tel: 0800 8488032

ANELLO & DAVIDE
(Handmade Shoes)
15 St Albans Grove, London W8 5BP
Website: www.handmadeshoes.co.uk   Tel: 020-7938 2255

ANGLO PACIFIC INTERNATIONAL Plc
(Freight Forwarders & Removal Services)
5-9 Willenfield Road
Park Row, London NW10 7BQ
Website: www.anglopacific.co.uk
e-mail: info@anglopacific.co.uk
Fax: 020-8965 4945   Tel: 020-8965 1234

ANIMAL ARK
(Animals & Natural History Props)
The Studio, 29 Somerset Road
Brentford, Middlesex TW8 8BT
Website: www.animal-ark.co.uk
e-mail: info@animal-ark.co.uk
Fax: 020-8560 5762   Tel: 020-8560 3029

ANNUAL CLOWNS DIRECTORY The
(Salvo The Clown)
13 Second Avenue, Kingsleigh Park
Thundersley, Essex SS7 3QD
Website: www.annualclownsdirectory.com
e-mail: salvo@annualclownsdirectory.com
                                     Tel: 01268 745791

AQUARIUS
(Film & TV Stills Library)
PO Box 5, Hastings TN34 1HR
Website: www.aquariuscollection.com
e-mail: aquarius.lib@clara.net
Fax: 01424 717704 Tel: 01424 721196

AQUATECH
(Camera Boats)
2 Cobbies Rock, Epney
Gloucestershire GL2 7LN
Website: www.aquatech-uk.com
e-mail: office@aquatech-uk.com
Fax: 01452 741958 Tel: 01452 740559

ARCHERY CENTRE The
PO Box 39, Battle
East Sussex TN33 0ZT Tel: 01424 777183

ARMS & ARCHERY
(Armour, Weaponry, Chainmail, X-bows, Longbows, Tents)
Thrift Lane, off Common Road
London Road, Ware, Herts SG12 9QS
e-mail: armsandarchery@btconnect.com
Tel: 01920 460335

ART
(Art Consultant, Supplier of Paintings & Sculpture)
89 Spencer Road, Mitcham CR4 1SJ
Website: www.artstar.clara.net
e-mail: h_artstar@hotmail.com Mobile: 07967 294985

ART DIRECTORS & TRIP PHOTO LIBRARY
(Digital Scans, Colour Slides - All Subjects)
57 Burdon Lane, Cheam, Surrey SM2 7BY
Website: www.artdirectors.co.uk
e-mail: images@artdirectors.co.uk
Fax: 020-8395 7230 Tel: 020-8642 3593

A. S. DESIGNS
(Theatrical Designer, Sets, Costumes, Heads, Masks,
Puppets etc)
Website: www.astheatricaldesign.co.uk
e-mail: maryannscadding@btinternet.com
Fax: 01279 435642 Tel: 01279 722416

ASH Riky
(Equity Registered Stunt Performer/Co-ordinator)
8 Balmoral Drive, Grantham NG31 8SY
Website: www.fallingforyou.tv
Mobile: 07850 471227 Tel: 01476 407383

AUTOMOTIVE ACTION
(Suppliers of H1 Hummers)
Flat 4, 2 Park Road, Hampton Hill
Middlesex TW12 1BW
Website: www.carstunts.co.uk
e-mail: carstunts@hotmail.co.uk Mobile: 07974 919589

AWESOME
(Bespoke Custom Upholstery Specialists)
The Stables, Grange Farm, Green End
Great Stukeley, Huntingdon
Cambridgeshire PE28 4AE
Website: www.awesome.eu.com
e-mail: glenn@awesome.eu.com
Fax: 01480 464879 Tel: 01480 457007

BAPTY 2000 Ltd
(Weapons, Dressing, Props etc)
Witley Works, Witley Gardens
Norwood Green, Middlesex UB2 4ES
e-mail: hire@bapty.demon.co.uk
Fax: 020-8571 5700 Tel: 020-8574 7700

BARNES CATERERS Ltd
9 Ripley Drive, Normanton, Wakefield
West Yorkshire WF6 1QT Tel/Fax: 01924 892332

BARTON Joe
(Puppeteer, Model & Prop Maker)
7 Brands Hill Avenue, High Wycombe
Buckinghamshire Tel: 01494 439056

BEAT ABOUT THE BUSH Ltd
(Musical Instrument Hire)
Unit 23, Enterprise Way, Triangle Business Centre
Salter Street (Off Hythe Road), London NW10 6UG
Website: www.beataboutthebush.com
e-mail: info@beataboutthebush.com
Fax: 020-8969 2281 Tel: 020-8960 2087

BEAVEROCK PRODUCTIONS Ltd
(Location & Transport services)
39 Orangefield Drive, Prestwick, Ayrshire KA9 1HF
e-mail: dayoot@aol.com
Mobile: 07979 818915 Tel: 01292 479577

BIANCHI AVIATION FILM SERVICES
(Historic & Other Aircraft)
Wycombe Air Park, Booker Marlow
Buckinghamshire SL7 3DP
Website: www.bianchiaviation.com
e-mail: info@bianchiaviation.com
Fax: 01494 461236 Tel: 01494 449810

BIDDLES Ltd
(Quality Book Manufacturers)
24 Rollesby Road, Hardwick Industrial Estate
King's Lynn, Norfolk PE30 4LS
Website: www.biddles.co.uk
e-mail: enquiries@biddles.co.uk
Fax: 01553 766820 Tel: 01553 764728

BIG BREAK CARDS
(Theatrical greetings cards featuring Hamlet the Pig, made
by actors for actors)
PO Box 45, Chipping Campden GL55 6WH
Website: www.bigbreakcards.co.uk
e-mail: info@bigbreakcards.co.uk Tel: 01386 438952

BLUEBELL RAILWAY Plc
(Steam Locomotives, Pullman Coaches, Period Stations,
Much Film Experience)
Sheffield Park Station
East Sussex TN22 3QL
Website: www.bluebell-railway.co.uk
e-mail: info@bluebell-railway.co.uk
Fax: 01825 720804 Tel: 01825 720800

BLUE MILL Ltd
(Dyers & Finishers)
84 Halstead Street, Leicester LE5 3RD
Website: www.bluemill.co.uk
e-mail: tom@bluemill.co.uk
Fax: 0116-253 7633 Tel: 0116-248 8130

BOLD BLUE DESIGN Ltd
(Design, Web & Print)
18B High Street, London N8 7PB
Website: www.boldblue.co.uk
e-mail: info@boldblue.co.uk
Mobile: 07985 245971 Tel: 020-8347 0221

BOLDGATE COMMERCIAL SERVICES Ltd
The Crossbow Centre, 40 Liverpool Road
Slough, Berkshire SL1 4QZ
Fax: 01753 610587 Tel: 01753 610525

BOSCO LIGHTING
(Design/Technical Consultancy)
47 Woodbourne Avenue, London SW16 1UX
e-mail: boscolx@lineone.net   Tel: 020-8769 3470

BOUNCY CASTLES BY P. A. LEISURE
(Specialists in Amusements & Fairground Equipment)
Delph House, Park Bridge Road
Towneley Park, Burnley, Lancs BB10 4SD
Website: www.paleisure.com
e-mail: paleisure@btconnect.com
Fax: 01282 420467   Tel: 01282 453939

BRISTOL (UK) Ltd
(Scenic Paint & StageFloor Duo Suppliers, VFX Solutions)
Unit 3, Sutherland Court
Tolpits Lane, Watford WD18 9SP
Website: www.bristolpaint.com
Fax: 01923 779666   Tel: 01923 779333

BRODIE & MIDDLETON Ltd
(Theatrical Suppliers, Paints, Powders, Glitter etc)
68 Drury Lane, London WC2B 5SP
Website: www.brodies.net
e-mail: info@brodies.net
Fax: 020-7497 0554   Tel: 020-7836 3289

BRUNEL'S THEATRICAL SERVICES
(Removal Services)
Unit 8, Pucklechurch
Bristol, Bristol BS16 9QH
Website: www.brunelsremovalservices.co.uk
e-mail: enquiries@brunelsremovalervices.co.uk
Fax: 0117-907 7856   Tel: 0117-907 7855

BULL Richard OCEANAIRE DIVING SERVICES Ltd
14 Townsend, Lower Almondsbury
South Gloucestershire BS32 4EN
e-mail: richard.bull6@btopenworld.com
Mobile: 07766 674356   Tel/Fax: 01454 613357

CAMDEN ATTIC
(Period Prop Hire & Making)
Location House, 5 Dove Lane, Bristol BS2 9HP
Website: www.camdenattic.co.uk
e-mail: genie@camdenattic.co.uk
Fax: 0117-955 2480   Tel: 0117-941 1969

CANDLE MAKERS SUPPLIES
The Wax & Dyecraft Centre
28 Blythe Road, London W14 0HA
Website: www.candlemakers.co.uk
e-mail: candles@candlemakers.co.uk
Fax: 020-7602 2796   Tel: 020-7602 4031

CARLINE & CREW TRANSPORTATION
(Celebrity Services)
12A Bridge Industrial Estate
Balcombe Road
West Sussex RH6 9HU
Website: www.carlineprivatehire.co.uk
e-mail: carlinehire@btconnect.com
Fax: 01293 430432   Tel: 01293 400505

CHALFONT CLEANERS & DYERS Ltd
(Dry Cleaners, Launderers & Dyers, Stage Curtains & Costumes)
222 Baker Street
London NW1 5RT   Tel: 020-7935 7316

CHRISANNE Ltd
(Specialist Fabrics & Accessories for Theatre & Dance)
Chrisanne House
14 Locks Lane, Mitcham, Surrey CR4 2JX
Website: www.chrisanne.com
e-mail: sales@chrisanne.co.uk
Fax: 020-8640 2106   Tel: 020-8640 5921

CIRCUS MANIACS
(Circus Equipment, Rigging & Training)
Office 8A
The Kingswood Foundation
Britannia Road, Kingswood, Bristol BS15 8DB
Website: www.circusmaniacs.com
e-mail: info@circusmaniacs.com
Mobile: 07977 247287   Tel/Fax: 0117-947 7042

CIRCUS PROMOTIONS
(Entertainers)
36 St Lukes Road, Tunbridge Wells
Kent TN4 9JH   Tel: 01892 537964

CLASSIC CAR AGENCY The
(Film, Promotional, Advertising, Publicity)
PO Box 427
Dorking, Surrey RH5 6WP
Website: www.theclassiccaragency.com
e-mail: theclassiccaragency@btopenworld.com
Mobile: 07788 977655   Tel: 01306 731052

CLASSIC CAR HIRE
(Over 30 Classic and Vintage Vehicles in our private
collection)
Unit 2 Hampton Court Estate
Summer Road, Thames Ditton KT7 0RG
Website: www.classic-hire.com
e-mail: info@classic-hire.co.uk
Fax: 020-8398 9234   Tel: 020-8398 8304

CLASSIC OMNIBUS
(Vintage Open-Top Buses & Coaches)
44 Welson Road
Folkestone, Kent CT20 2NP
Website: www.opentopbus.co.uk
Fax: 01303 241245   Tel: 01303 248999

COBO MEDIA Ltd
(Performing Arts, Entertainment & Leisure Marketing)
43A Garthorne Road, London SE23 1EP
Website: www.cobomedia.com
e-mail: admin@cobomedia.com
Fax: 020-8291 4969   Tel: 020-8291 7079

COMPTON Mike & Rosi
(Costumes, Props & Models)
11 Woodstock Road, Croydon, Surrey CR0 1JS
e-mail: mikeandrosicompton@btopenworld.com
Fax: 020-8681 3126   Tel: 020-8680 4364

CONCEPT ENGINEERING Ltd
(Smoke, Fog, Snow etc)
7 Woodlands Business Park
Woodlands Park Avenue
Maidenhead, Berkshire SL6 3UA
Website: www.concept-smoke.co.uk
Fax: 01628 826261   Tel: 01628 825555

COOK Sheila TEXTILES
(Textiles, Costumes & Accessories for Hire/Sale)
105-107 Portobello Road, London W11 2QB
Website: www.sheilacook.co.uk
e-mail: sheilacook@sheilacook.co.uk   Tel: 020-7792 8001

COSTUMES & SHOWS UNLIMITED
(Ice Rink Rental, Costume Rental & Design, Show
Production)
PO Box 57
Poulton-le-Fylde, Lancs FY6 8GN
Website: www.ice-shows-and-costumes-unlimited.co.uk
e-mail: iceshowpro@aol.com   Tel: 01253 827092

CREATIVE WORKS
(Floral Design)
Unit 1, The Stable Block, Brewer Street
Bletchingley, Surrey RH1 4QP
Website: www.ckworks.net
e-mail: info@ckworks.net   Tel: 01883 742999

CRESTA BLINDS Ltd
(Supplier of Vertical Blinds)
Crown Works, Tetnall Street
Dudley DY2 8SA
Website: www.crestablindsltd.co.uk
e-mail: info@crestablindsltd.co.uk
Fax: 01384 457675   Tel: 01384 255523

CROCKSHARD FARMHOUSE
Contact: Nicola Ellen (Bed & Breakfast)
Wingham, Canterbury, Kent CT3 1NY
Website: www.crockshard.com
e-mail: crockshard_bnb@yahoo.com   Tel: 01227 720464

CROFTS Andrew
(Book Writing Services)
Westlands Grange, West Grinstead
Horsham, West Sussex RH13 8LZ
Website: www.andrewcrofts.com   Tel/Fax: 01403 864518

CUE ACTION POOL PROMOTIONS
(Advice for UK & US Pool, Snooker, Trick Shots)
PO Box 3941, Colchester, Essex CO2 8HN
Website: www.stevedaking.com
e-mail: sales@cueaction.com
Fax: 01206 729480   Tel: 07000 868689

CURTAIN TRACKS & DRAPES
28 The Street, Brettenham
Ipswich, Suffolk IP7 7QP
Website: www.suffolkscenery.info
e-mail: piehatch@aol.com
Fax: 01449 737620   Tel: 01449 736679

DAVEY Brian
(See NOSTALGIA AMUSEMENTS)

DAWSON Mr N.
(Former Coach House Barn Conversion set in 4 Acres of
Land & Landscaped Gardens overlooking Rolling
Countryside)
Holbrook View, Birchwood Farm
Portway, Coxbench, Derby DE21 5BE
e-mail: dawsonj34@aol.com   Tel: 01332 781011

DESIGN ASYLUM
(Design, Web & Print)
Unit 2, 6 Chase Road
Park Royal, London NW1 6HZ
Website: www.designasylum.co.uk
e-mail: info@designasylum.co.uk   Tel: 020-8838 3555

DESIGN PROJECTS
Perrysfield Farm, Broadham Green
Old Oxted, Surrey RH8 9PG
Website: www.designprojects.co.uk
Fax: 01883 723707   Tel: 01883 730262

DEVEREUX DEVELOPMENTS Ltd
(Removals, Haulage, Trucking)
Daimler Drive
Cowpen Industrial Estate
Billingham, Cleveland TS23 4JD
e-mail: mike.bell@kdevereux.co.uk
Fax: 01642 566664
Tel: 01642 560854

DORANS PROPMAKERS/SET BUILDERS
53 Derby Road, Ashbourne, Derbyshire DE6 1BH
Website: www.doransprops.com
e-mail: info@doransprops.com
Tel/Fax: 01335 300064

DREAM DESTINATIONS
(Corporate & Stretch Limousines)
PO Box 6990, Mansfield, Nottinghamshire NG19 9EW
Website: www.dreamdestinationsonline.co.uk
e-mail: info@dreamdestinationsonline.co.uk
Tel: 0800 0191345

DURRENT Peter
(Audition & Rehearsal Pianist, Cocktail Pianist, Composer, Vocalist)
Blacksmiths Cottage
Bures Road, Little Cornard, Sudbury
Suffolk CO10 0NR
Tel: 01787 373483

EAT TO THE BEAT
(Production & Location Caterers)
Studio 4-5, Garnett Close, Watford, Herts WD24 7GN
Website: www.eattothebeat.com
e-mail: enquiries@eattothebeat.com
Fax: 01923 211704
Tel: 01923 211702

ELECTRO SIGNS Ltd
97 Vallentin Road, London E17 3JJ
e-mail: info@electrosigns.co.uk
Fax: 020-8520 8127
Tel: 020-8521 8066

ELMS LESTERS PAINTING ROOMS
(Scenic Painting)
1-3-5 Flitcroft Street, London WC2H 8DH
e-mail: office@elmslesters.co.uk
Fax: 020-7379 0789
Tel: 020-7836 6747

ESCORT GUNLEATHER
(Custom Leathercraft)
602 High Road, Benfleet, Essex SS7 5RW
Website: www.escortgunleather.com
e-mail: info@escortgunleather.com
Fax: 01268 566775
Tel: 0870 7515957

EST Ltd
(Trucking - Every Size & Country)
Bell Lane, Off North Woolwich Road, London E16 2AB
Website: www.yourockweroll.com
e-mail: delr@est-uk.com
Fax: 020-7055 7201
Tel: 020-7055 7200

EVANS Peter STUDIOS Ltd
(Scenic Embellishment, Vacuum Forming)
12-14 Tavistock Street, Dunstable, Bedfordshire LU6 1NE
e-mail: sales@peterevansstudios.co.uk
Fax: 01582 481329
Tel: 01582 725730

EXL CARS / LAIT Nick
29 The Gluyas, Falmouth, Cornwall TR11 4SE
Website: www.exlcars.com
e-mail: exlcars@aol.com
Tel: 01326 210306

FACADE
(Musical Production Services)
43A Garthorne Road, London SE23 1EP
e-mail: facade@cobomedia.com
Tel: 020-8291 7079

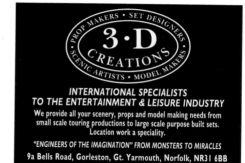

FAIRGROUNDS TRADITIONAL
Halstead, Fovant
Salisbury, Wiltshire SP3 5NL
Website: www.pozzy.co.uk
e-mail: sv@pozzy.co.uk
Mobile: 07710 287251
Tel: 01722 714786

FELLOWES Mark TRANSPORT SERVICES
(Transport/Storage)
59 Sherbrooke Road, London SW6 7QL
Website: www.fellowesproductions.com
Mobile: 07850 332818
Tel: 020-7386 7005

FILM MEDICAL SERVICES
Units 5 & 7, Commercial Way
Park Royal, London NW10 7XF
Website: www.filmmedical.co.uk
e-mail: filmmed@aol.com
Fax: 020-8961 7427
Tel: 020-8961 3222

FIREBRAND
(Flambeaux Hire & Sales)
Leac Na Ban, Tayvallich
By Lochgilphead, Argyll PA31 8PF
e-mail: firebrand.props@btinternet.com
Tel/Fax: 01546 870310

FLAME RETARDING Ltd
Grove Farm, Grove Farm Road
Tolleshunt Major
Maldon, Essex CM4 8LR
Website: www.flameretarding.co.uk
e-mail: email@flameretarding.co.uk
Fax: 07092 036931
Tel: 01621 818477

FLAMENCO PRODUCTIONS
(Entertainers)
Sevilla 4 Cormorant Rise, Lower Wick
Worcester WR2 4BA
Tel: 01905 424083

FLINT HIRE & SUPPLY Ltd
Queen's Row, London SE17 2PX
Website: www.flints.co.uk
e-mail: sales@flints.co.uk
Fax: 020-7708 4189
Tel: 020-7703 9786

FLYING BY FOY
(Flying Effects for Theatre, TV, Corporate Events etc)
Unit 4, Borehamwood Enterprise Centre
Theobald Street
Borehamwood, Herts WD6 4RQ
Website: www.flyingbyfoy.co.uk
e-mail: mail@flyingbyfoy.co.uk
Fax: 020-8236 0235
Tel: 020-8236 0234

FOXTROT PRODUCTIONS Ltd
(Armoury Services, Firearms, Weapons & Costume Hire)
Unit 46 Canalot Production Studios
222 Kensal Road, London W10 5BN
Website: www.foxtrot-productions.co.uk
                                        Tel: 020-8964 3555

FRANKIE'S YANKEES
(Classic 1950s American Cars, Memorabilia & New
Superstretch Limos)
283 Old Birmingham Road
Bromsgrove B60 1HQ
Mobile: 07970 062142   Tel: 0121-445 5522

FREEDALE PRESS Ltd
(Printing)
36 Hedley Street, Maidstone, Kent ME14 5AD
e-mail: michael@freedale.co.uk
Fax: 01622 200131   Tel: 01622 200123

FROST John NEWSPAPERS
(Historical Newspaper Service)
22B Rosemary Avenue
Enfield, Middlesex EN2 0SS
Website: www.johnfrostnewspapers.com
e-mail: andrew@johnfrostnewspapers.com
                                        Tel: 020-8366 1392

GARRATT Jonathan FRSA
(Suppliers of Traditional & Unusual Garden Pots &
Installations. Glazed Tableware)
Hare Lane Farmhouse, Cranborne, Dorset BH21 5QT
Website: www.jonathangarratt.com
e-mail: jonathan.garratt@talk21.com   Tel: 01725 517700

GAV NICOLA THEATRICAL FOOTWEAR
West Wick, Marshes
Burnham-on-Crouch, Essex CMO 8NE
e-mail: sale@gavnicola.freeserve.co.uk
Mobile: 07961 974278   Tel/Fax: 01621 785623

GET STUFFED
(Taxidermy)
105 Essex Road, London N1 2SL
Website: www.thegetstuffed.co.uk
e-mail: taxidermy@thegetstuffed.co.uk
Fax: 020-7359 8253   Tel: 020-7226 1364

GHOSTWRITER/AUTHOR
Contact: John Parker
21 Hindsleys Place, London SE23 2NF
e-mail: parkerwrite@aol.com   Tel: 020-8244 5816

GORGEOUS GOURMETS Ltd
(Caterers & Equipment Hire)
Gresham Way, Wimbledon SW19 8ED
Website: www.gorgeousgourmets.co.uk
e-mail: hire@gorgeousgourmets.co.uk
Fax: 020-8946 1639   Tel: 020-8944 7771

GOULD Gillian ANTIQUES
(Scientific & Marine Antiques & Collectables)
18A Belsize Park Gardens
Belsize Park, London NW3 4LH
Website: www.gilliangouldantiques.co.uk
e-mail: gillgould@dealwith.com
Mobile: 07831 150060   Tel: 020-7419 0500

GRADAV HIRE & SALES Ltd
(Lighting & Sound Hire/Sales)
Units C6 & C9 Hastingwood Trading Estate
Harbet Road, Edmonton, London N18 3HU
e-mail: office@gradav.co.uk
Fax: 020-8803 5060   Tel: 020-8803 7400

GRAY Robin COMMENTARIES
(Saddles, Bridles, Racing Colours & Hunting Attire)
Comptons, Isington, Alton
Hampshire GU34 4PL
e-mail: gray@isington.fsnet.co.uk
Mobile: 07831 828424   Tel/Fax: 01420 23347

GREENPROPS
(Prop Suppliers, Artificial Trees, Plants, Flowers, Fruit,
Grass etc)
West Bovey Farm, Waterrow, Somerset TA4 2BA
Website: www.greenprops.com
e-mail: trevor@greenprops.com   Tel: 01398 361531

GREENSOURCE SOLUTIONS Ltd
(Providers of Mobile Phone Props)
14 Kingsland Trading Estate
St Phillips Road, Bristol BS2 0JZ
Website: www.greensource.co.uk
e-mail: props@greensource.co.uk
Fax: 0117-304 2391   Tel: 0845 3100200

HAMPTON COURT HOUSE
(1757 Country House & Grounds)
East Molesey KT8 9BS
Website: www.hamptoncourthouse.co.uk
Fax: 020-8977 5357   Tel: 020-8943 0889

HANDS UP PUPPETS
c/o Peter Charlesworth & Associates
68 Old Brompton Road, London SW7 3LD
Website: www.handsuppuppets.com
e-mail: handsuppuppets@btinternet.com
                                        Tel: 020-7581 2478

HARLEQUIN (BRITISH HARLEQUIN Plc)
(Floors for Stage, Opera, Dance, Concert, Shows & Events)
Festival House, Chapman Way
Tunbridge Wells, Kent TN2 3EF
Website: www.harlequinfloors.com
e-mail: sales@harlequinfloors.co.uk
Fax: 01892 514222   Tel: 01892 514888

HAWES Joanne
(Children's Administrator for Theatre, Film & TV)
21 Westfield Road, Maidenhead, Berkshire SL6 5AU
e-mail: jo.hawes@virgin.net
Fax: 01628 672884   Tel: 01628 773048

HERON & DRIVER
(Scenic Furniture & Prop Makers)
Unit 7, Dockley Road Industrial Estate
Rotherhithe, London SE16 3SF
Website: www.herondriver.co.uk
e-mail: mail@herondriver.co.uk
Fax: 020-7394 8680   Tel: 020-7394 8688

HI-FLI (Flying Effects)
2 Boland Drive, Manchester M14 6DS
e-mail: mikefrost@hi-fli.co.uk   Tel/Fax: 0161-224 6082

HISTORICAL INTERPRETER & ROLE PLAYING
Contact: Donald Clarke
80 Warden Avenue, Rayners Lane
Harrow, Middlesex HA2 9LW
Website: www.historicalinterpretations.co.uk
e-mail: info@historicalinterpretations.co.uk
Mobile: 07811 606285   Tel: 020-8866 2997

HISTORY IN THE MAKING Ltd
(Weapon & Costume Hire)
4A Aysgarth Road, Waterlooville, Hampshire PO7 7UG
Website: www.history-making.com   Tel: 023-9225 3175

KENSINGTON EYE CENTRE Ltd
(Special Eye Effects)
37 Kensington Church Street
London W8 4LL   Tel/Fax: 020-7937 8282

KEW BRIDGE STEAM MUSEUM
Green Dragon Lane, Brentford
Middlesex TW8 0EN
Website: www.kbsm.org
e-mail: jo@kbsm.org
Fax: 020-8569 9978   Tel: 020-8568 4757

KIRBY'S AFX Ltd
8 Greenford Avenue, Hanwell, London W7 3QP
Website: www.kirbysflying.co.uk
e-mail: mail@afxuk.com
Mobile: 07958 285608   Tel/Fax: 020-8723 8552

KNEBWORTH HOUSE, GARDENS & PARK
(Knebworth)
Herts SG3 6PY   Tel: 01438 812661

LAREDO Alex
(Expert with Ropes, Bullwhips, Shooting, Riding)
29 Lincoln Road, Dorking, Surrey RH4 1TE
Mobile: 07906 271766   Tel: 01306 889423

LAREDO WILD WEST TOWN
(Wild West Entertainment)
1 Bower Walk, Staplehurst
Tonbridge, Kent TN12 0LU
Website: www.laredo.org.uk
e-mail: enquiries@laredo.org.uk
Mobile: 07947 652771   Tel: 01580 891790

LEES-NEWSOME Ltd
(Manufacturers of Flame Retardant Fabrics)
Ashley Works, Unit 2
Rule Business Park, Grimshaw Lane
Middleton, Manchester M24 2AE
e-mail: info@leesnewsome.co.uk
Fax: 0845 0708006   Tel: 0845 0708005

LEIGHTON HALL
(Historic House)
Carnforth, Lancashire LA5 9ST
Website: www.leightonhall.co.uk
e-mail: info@leightonhall.co.uk
Fax: 01524 720357   Tel: 01524 734474

LEVRANT Stephen - HERITAGE ARCHITECTURE Ltd
(Architects & Historic Building Consultants)
62 British Grove, Chiswick, London W4 2NL
e-mail: info@heritagearchitecture.co.uk
Fax: 020-8748 4992   Tel: 020-8748 5501

LONDON BUSINESS EQUIPMENT
(Authorised Canon Dealer)
527-529 High Road, Leytonstone, London E11 4PB
Website: www.londonbusinessequipment.com
e-mail: sales@londonbusinessequipment.com
Fax: 020-8556 4865   Tel: 020-8558 0024

LONO DRINKS COMPANY The
The Hawthorns, Driffield, Cirencester
Gloucestershire GL7 5PY
Website: www.lono.co.uk
e-mail: info@lono.co.uk
Fax: 01285 850455   Tel: 01285 850682

LOS KAOS
(Street Theatre, Circus, Puppetry & Animatronics)
Crown Lodge, Tintern, Chepstow, Wales NP16 6TF
Website: www.loskaos.co.uk   Tel/Fax: 01291 680074

LUCKINGS
(Transporters/Storage/Stage Hands)
63 Kew Green, Richmond, Surrey TW9 3AH
Website: www.luckings.co.uk
e-mail: enquiries@luckings.co.uk
Fax: 020-8332 3000   Tel: 020-8332 2000

LUCKINGS SCREEN SERVICES
(Artists' Trailers/Splits/2-3 Ways)
63 Kew Green, Richmond, Surrey TW9 3AH
Website: www.luckings.co.uk
e-mail: enquiries@luckings.co.uk
Fax: 020-8332 3000   Tel: 020-8332 2000

LYON EQUIPMENT
(Petzl & Beal Rope Access Equipment (PPE) for Industrial &
Theatrical Work)
Rise Hill Mill, Dent, Sedbergh, Cumbria LA10 5QL
Website: www.lyon.co.uk
e-mail: info@lyon.co.uk
Fax: 01539 625454   Tel: 01539 625493

M A C
(Sound Hire)
1-2 Attenburys Park, Park Road
Altrincham, Cheshire WA14 5QE
Website: www.macsound.co.uk
e-mail: hire@macsound.co.uk
Fax: 0161-962 9423   Tel: 0161-969 8311

MACKIE Sally LOCATIONS
(Location Finding & Management)
Cownham Farm, Broadwell
Moreton-in-Marsh, Gloucestershire GL56 0TT
Website: www.sallymackie-locations.com
e-mail: sally@mackie.biz   Tel: 01451 830294

MADDERMARKET THEATRE
Contact Rhett Davies: (Resident Stage Manager)
St John's Alley, Norwich NR2 1DR
Website: www.maddermarket.co.uk
e-mail: mmtheatre@btconnect.com
Fax: 01603 661357   Tel: 01603 626560

MAGICAL MART
(Magic, Ventriloquists' Dolls, Punch & Judy, Hire & Advising.
Callers by Appointment)
42 Christchurch Road, Sidcup, Kent DA15 7HQ
Website: www.johnstylesentertainer.co.uk
                               Tel/Fax: 020-8300 3579

MAINSTREAM LEISURE GROUP
(Riverboat/Canal Boat Hire)
5 The Mews, 6 Putney Common, London SW15 1HL
Website: www.mainstreamleisure.co.uk
Fax: 020-8788 0073   Tel: 020-8788 2669

MARCUS HALL PROPS
80 Malyons Road, Ladywell, London SE13 7XG
Website: www.marcushallprops.com
e-mail: info@marcushallprops.com   Mobile: 07802 873127

MARKSON PIANOS
8 Chester Court, Albany Street, London NW1 4BU
Website: www.marksonpianos.com
e-mail: info@marksonpianos.com
Fax: 020-7224 0957   Tel: 020-7935 8682

MATTLX Ltd
Signal Cottage, 4 Station Mews
Robertsbridge, East Sussex TN32 5DD
Website: www.mattlx.com
e-mail: admin@mattlx.com
Fax: 0560 1505452   Tel: 01580 880303

McNEILL Brian
(Vintage Truck & Coaches)
Hawk Mount, Kebcote
Todmorden, Lancashire OL14 8SB
Website: www.rollingpast.com
e-mail: autotrans@uk2.net   Tel: 01706 812291

MIDNIGHT ELECTRONICS
(Sound Hire)
Off Quay Building, Foundry Lane
Newcastle upon Tyne NE6 1LH
Website: www.midnightelectronics.co.uk
e-mail: info@midnightelectronics.co.uk
Fax: 0191-224 0080   Tel: 0191-224 0088

MILITARY, MODELS & MINATURES
(Model Figures)
38A Horsell Road, London N5 1XP
e-mail: figsculpt@aol.com
Fax: 020-7700 4624   Tel: 020-7700 7036

MODDED MOTORS AGENCY
(Suppliers of Modified Cars)
38 Williamson Way
Rickmansworth, Hertfordshire WD3 8GL
Website: www.moddedmotorsagency.com
e-mail: danielle@moddedmotorsagency.com
     Mobile: 07989 128131

MODEL BOX
(Computer Aided Design & Design Services)
2 Saddlers Way, Okehampton, Devon EX20 1TL
Website: www.modelbox.co.uk
e-mail: info@modelbox.co.uk   Tel: 01837 54026

MODERNEON LONDON Ltd
(Lighting & Signs)
Cromwell House
27 Brabourne Rise, Park Langley
Beckenham, Kent BR3 6SQ
Website: www.moderneon.co.uk
e-mail: moderneon@tiscali.co.uk
Fax: 020-8658 2770   Tel: 020-8650 9690

MOORFIELDS PHOTOGRAPHIC Ltd
2 Old Hall Street
Liverpool L3 9RQ
Website: www.moorfieldsphoto.com
e-mail: info@moorfieldsphoto.com   Tel: 0151-236 1611

MORTON G & L
(Horses/Farming)
Hashome Carr, Holme-on-Spalding Moor
Yorkshire YO43 4BD   Tel: 01430 860393

MOTORHOUSE HIRE Ltd
(Action Vehicles) (Contact: Michael Geary)
Weston Underwood, Olney, Buckinghamshire MK46 5LD
e-mail: michael@motorhouseltd.co.uk
Fax: 01234 240393   Tel: 020-7495 1618

M V DIXIE QUEEN
(Thames Luxury Charters)
5 The Mews, 6 Putney Common, London SW15 1HL
Website: www.thamesluxurycharters.co.uk
e-mail: sales@thamesluxurycharters.co.uk
Fax: 020-8788 0072   Tel: 020-8780 1562

NATIONAL MOTOR MUSEUM
John Montagu Building, Beaulieu
Brockenhurst, Hampshire SO42 7ZN
Website: www.beaulieu.co.uk
e-mail: info@beaulieu.co.uk
Fax: 01590 612624   Tel: 01590 612345

NEWMAN HIRE COMPANY
(Lighting Hire)
16 The Vale, Acton, London W3 7SB
e-mail: info@newmanhire.com   Tel: 020-8743 0741

NINE-NINE CARS Ltd
Hyde Meadow Farm, Hyde Lane
Hemel Hempstead HP3 8SA
e-mail: david@nineninecars.com   Tel: 01923 266373

NORTHERN LIGHT
Assembly Street, Leith, Edinburgh EH6 7RG
Website: www.northernlight.co.uk
e-mail: enquiries@northernlight.co.uk
Fax: 0131-622 9101   Tel: 0131-622 9100

NOSTALGIA AMUSEMENTS
Contact: Brian Davey
22 Greenwood Close, Thames Ditton, Surrey KT7 0BG
Mobile: 07973 506869   Tel: 020-8398 2141

NOTTINGHAM JOUSTING ASSOCIATION SCHOOL OF NATIONAL EQUITATION Ltd
(Jousting & Medieval Tournaments, Horses & Riders for Films & TV)
Bunny Hill Top, Costock, Loughborough
Leicestershire LE12 6XE
Website: www.bunnyhill.co.uk
e-mail: info@bunnyhill.co.uk
Fax: 01509 856067   Tel: 01509 852366

OCEAN LEISURE
(Scuba Diving, Watersports Retail)
11-14 Northumberland Avenue, London WC2N 5AQ
Website: www.oceanleisure.co.uk
e-mail: info@oceanleisure.co.uk
Fax: 020-7930 3032   Tel: 020-7930 5050

OFFSTAGE
(Theatre & Film Bookshop)
34 Tavistock Street, London WC2E 7PB
e-mail: offstagebookshop@aol.com   Tel: 020-7240 3883

PAPERFLOW Plc
(Stationery & Office Equipment)
Units 5 & 6, Meridian Trading Estate
20 Bugsbys Way, Charlton, London SE7 7SJ
e-mail: info@paperflowgroup.com
Fax: 020-8331 2007   Tel: 020-8331 2000

PATCHETTS EQUESTRIAN CENTRE
(Location)
Hillfield Lane, Aldenham, Watford, Herts WD25 8PE
Website: www.patchetts.co.uk
e-mail: info@patchetts.co.uk
Fax: 01923 859289   Tel: 01923 852255

PATERSON Helen
(Typing Services)
40 Whitelands House, London SW3 4QY
e-mail: pater@waitrose.com   Tel: 020-7730 6428

PERIOD PETROL PUMP COLLECTION
c/o Diss Ironworks, 7 St Nicholas Street
Diss, Norfolk IP22 4LB
Website: www.periodpetrolpump.co.uk   Tel: 01379 643978

PHOSPHENE
(Lighting & Sound. Design, Sales, Hire)
Milton Road South, Stowmarket, Suffolk IP14 1EZ
Website: www.phosphene.co.uk
e-mail: cliff@phosphene.freeserve.co.uk   Tel: 01449 770011

PIANO PEOPLE The
(Piano Hire & Transport)
74 Playford Road, London N4 3PH
Website: www.pianopeople.co.uk
e-mail: info@pianopeople.co.uk   Tel: 0845 6076713

PICKFORDS Ltd
Heritage House, 345 Southbury Road, Enfield EN1 1UP
Website: www.pickfords.com
Fax: 020-8362 4219   Tel: 020-8219 8000

PICKFORDS REMOVALS Ltd
Heritage House, 345 Southbury Road
Enfield, Middlesex EN1 1UP
Website: www.pickfords.com
e-mail: enquiries@pickfords.com
Fax: 020-8219 8001   Tel: 020-8219 8000

PICTURES PROPS CO Ltd
(TV, Film & Stage Hire)
12-16 Brunel Road, London W3 7XR
Fax: 020-8740 5846   Tel: 020-8749 2433

PINK POINTES DANCEWEAR
1A Suttons Lane
Hornchurch, Essex RM12 6RD
e-mail: pink.pointes@btconnect.com Tel/Fax: 01708 438584

PLAYHOUSE ENTERTAINMENT GROUP The
Playhouse Studios
2 Brampton Business Park
Eastbourne BN27 9AF
Website: www.playhousecostumes.co.uk
e-mail: enquiries@playhousecostumes.co.uk
Tel/Fax: 01323 501511

PLUS FILM Ltd
(All Periods Vehicle Hire)
1 Mill House Cottages, Winchester Road
Bishop's Waltham SO32 1AH
e-mail: stephen@plusfilms7.freeserve.co.uk
Tel/Fax: 01489 895559

POLAND Anna: SCULPTOR AND MODELMAKER
(Sculpture, Models, Puppets, Masks etc)
Salterns, Old Bursledon, Southampton
Hampshire SO31 8DH
e-mail: polandanna@hotmail.com   Tel: 023-8040 5166

POLLEX PROPS / FIREBRAND
(Prop Makers)
Leac Na Ban, Tayvallich, Lochgilphead, Argyll PA31 8PF
e-mail: firebrand.props@btinternet.com
Tel/Fax: 01546 870310

PRAETORIAN ASSOCIATES/PROCUREMENT SERVICES - SA
(Personal Safety & Anti-Stalking Consultancy & Services for Film/TV industry within South Africa)
Suite 501, 2 Old Brompton Road, London SW7 3DG
Website: www.praetorianasc.com
e-mail: martin.beale@praetorianasc.com
Tel/Fax: 020-7096 1827

PROBLOOD
11 Mount Pleasant, Framlingham
Suffolk IP13 9HQ   Tel/Fax: 01728 723865

PROFESSOR PATTEN'S PUNCH & JUDY
(Hire & Performances/Advice on Traditional Show)
14 The Crest, Goffs Oak, Hertfordshire EN7 5NP
Website: www.dennispatten.co.uk   Tel: 01707 873262

PROP FARM Ltd
Contact: Pat Ward
Grange Farm, Elmton, Nr Creswell
North Derbyshire S80 4LX
e-mail: pat/les@propfarm.co.uk
Fax: 01909 721465   Tel: 01909 723100

PROPS GALORE
(Period Textiles/Jewellery)
15 Brunel Road, London W3 7XR
e-mail: propsgalore@farley.co.uk
Fax: 020-8354 1866   Tel: 020-8746 1222

PROPS STUDIOS Ltd
Unit 3, Old Kiln Works
Ditchling Common Industrial Estate
Hassocks, East Sussex BN6 8SG
Website: www.propsstudios.co.uk
e-mail: info@propsstudios.co.uk
Fax: 0870 7700961   Tel: 0870 7700960

GREENPROPS
Foliage * Flowers * Fruit & Veg
Importers of Raffia Grass Matting

The Artificial STAGE SUPPLIERS, serving The West End, The UK and Europe
T: 01398 361531   trevor@greenprops.com   www.greenprops.com

‖‖‖

PUNCH & JUDY PUPPETS & BOOTHS
(Hire & Advisory Service, Callers by Appointment)
42 Christchurch Road, Sidcup, Kent DA15 7HQ
Website: www.johnstylesentertainer.co.uk
Tel/Fax: 020-8300 3579

Q2Q Ltd
(Production Solutions)
Lyric Theatre, Shaftesbury Avenue, London W1D 7ES
Website: www.q2qgroup.com
e-mail: solutions@q2qgroup.com
Fax: 0870 9506727
Tel: 0870 9505727

RAINBOW PRODUCTIONS Ltd
(Creation & Appearances of Costume Characters/Stage Shows)
Unit 3, Greenlea Park
Prince George's Road, London SW19 2JD
Website: www.rainbowproductions.co.uk
e-mail: info@rainbowproductions.co.uk
Fax: 020-8254 5306
Tel: 020-8254 5300

RENT-A-CLOWN
Contact: Mattie Faint
37 Sekeforde Street, Clerkenwell
London EC1R 0HA
Tel/Fax: 020-7608 0312

REPLAY Ltd
(Showreels & TV Facilities Hire)
Museum House, 25 Museum Street, London WC1A 1JT
Website: www.replayfilms.co.uk
e-mail: sales@replayfilms.co.uk
Tel: 020-7637 0473

ROBERTS Chris INTERIORS
(Film Set & Property Maintenance & Tiling)
117 Colebrook Lane
Loughton IG10 2HP
Mobile: 07956 512074

ROOTSTEIN Adel Ltd
(Mannequin Manufacturer)
9 Beaumont Avenue, London W14 9LP
Fax: 020-7381 3263
Tel: 020-7381 1447

ROYAL HORTICULTURAL HALLS & CONFERENCE CENTRE
(Film Location: Art Deco & Edwardian Buildings)
80 Vincent Square, London SW1P 2PE
Website: www.horticultural-halls.co.uk
e-mail: horthalls@rhs.org.uk
Fax: 020-7834 2072
Tel: 020-7828 4125

RUDKIN DESIGN
(Design Consultants, Brochures, Advertising, Corporate etc)
10 Cottesbrooke Park
Heartlands Business Park, Daventry
Northamptonshire NN11 8YL
Website: www.rudkindesign.com
e-mail: studio@rudkindesign.com
Fax: 01327 872728
Tel: 01327 301770

RUMBLE Jane
(Props to Order, No Hire)
121 Elmstead Avenue, Wembley
Middlesex HA9 8NT
Tel: 020-8904 6462

SABAH STYLIST
(Wardrobe, Sets, Props)
2841 N. Ocean Blvd, Apt 501
Fort Lauderdale, Florida 33308 USA
e-mail: sabah561@aol.com
Mobile: (954) 383-2179
Tel/Fax: (954) 566-6219

SAPEX SCRIPTS
The Maxwell Building
Elstree Film Studios
Shenley Road
Borehamwood, Herts WD6 1JG
Website: www.sapex.co.uk
e-mail: scripts@sapex.co.uk
Fax: 020-8324 2771
Tel: 020-8236 1600

SCHULTZ & WIREMU FABRIC EFFECTS Ltd
(Dyeing/Printing/Distressing)
Unit B202 Faircharm Studios
8-12 Creekside, London SE8 3DX
Website: www.schultz-wiremufabricfx.co.uk
e-mail: swfabricfx@hotmail.co.uk
Tel/Fax: 020-8469 0151

SCRIPTRIGHT
(S.C. Hill - Script/Manuscript Typing Services/Script Reading Services)
6 Valetta Road, London W3 7TN
e-mail: samc.hill@virgin.net
Tel: 020-8740 7303

SCRIPTS BY ARGYLE
(Play, Film & Book. Word Processing, Copying & Binding)
St John's Buildings
43 Clerkenwell Road, London EC1M 5RS
Website: www.scriptsbyargyle.co.uk
e-mail: info@scriptsbyargyle.co.uk
Fax: 0871 4336130
Tel: 020-7608 2095

SFD
Ground Floor, Sunningdale, The Belfry
Colonial Way, Watford, Herts WD24 4WH
Website: www.sfd.co.uk
e-mail: sales@sfd.co.uk
Fax: 01923 232326
Tel: 01923 232425

SHAOLIN WAY
(Martial Arts Supplies, Lion Dance & Kung Fu Instruction)
10 Little Newport Street
London WC2H 7JJ
Website: www.shaolinway.com
e-mail: shaolinway@btconnect.com
Fax: 020-7287 6548 Tel: 020-7734 6391

21 Baron Street
Angel, London N1 9EX Tel: 020-7833 8388

SHIRLEY LEAF & PETAL COMPANY Ltd
(Flower Makers Museum)
58A High Street, Old Town, Hastings
East Sussex TN34 3EN Tel/Fax: 01424 427793

SIDE EFFECTS
(Props, Models & FX)
92 Fentiman Road
London SW8 1LA
e-mail: sfx@lineone.net
Fax: 020-7207 0062 Tel: 020-7587 1116

SNOW BUSINESS
(Snow/Winter Effects on Any Scale)
The Snow Mill, Bridge Road
Ebley, Stroud, Gloucestershire GL5 4TR
Website: www.snowfx.com
e-mail: snow@snowbusiness.com Tel/Fax: 01453 840077

SOFT PROPS
(Costume & Modelmakers)
92 Fentiman Road
London SW8 1LA
e-mail: jackie@softprops.co.uk
Fax: 020-7207 0062 Tel: 020-7587 1116

SPUR CREATIVE WORKSHOP
Unit 1A, North Yard, Pennybridge Lane
Mayfield, East Sussex TN20 6QB
Website: www.spurcreative.co.uk
e-mail: info@spurcreative.co.uk
Mobile: 07970 805871 Tel: 01435 873755

STEELDECK RENTALS/SALES Ltd
(Stage Equipment Hire & Modular Staging)
Unit 58, T Marchant Trading Estate
42-72 Verney Road
London SE16 3DH
Website: www.steeldeck.co.uk
e-mail: rentals@steeldeck.co.uk
Fax: 020-7232 1780 Tel: 020-7833 2031

STEVENSON Scott
(Prop Maker)
60 Ripley Road, Sawmills
Belper, Derbyshire DE56 2JQ
Website: www.bodymechprops.co.uk
e-mail: scott@bodymechprops.co.uk Mobile: 07739 378579

STOKE BRUERNE BOAT COMPANY Ltd
(Passenger & Commercial Boats)
29 Main Road
Shutlanger
Northamptonshire NN12 7RU
Website: www.stokebruerneboats.co.uk
Fax: 01604 864098 Tel: 01604 862107

SUFFOLK SCENERY
(Curtain Tracks & Drapes Only)
Pie Hatch Farm, Brettenham Road
Buxall, Stowmarket, Suffolk IP14 3DZ
Website: www.suffolkscenery.info
e-mail: piehatch@aol.com
Fax: 01449 737620 Tel: 01449 736679

SUPERHIRE GROUP
(Prop Hire Specialist Victorian - Present Day)
55 Chase Road, London NW10 6LU
Website: www.superhire.com
e-mail: enquiries@superhire.com
Fax: 020-8965 8107 Tel: 020-8453 3900

SUPERSCRIPTS
51 Buckingham Gardens, West Moseley, Surrey KT8 1TJ
e-mail: super_scripts@sky.com
Mobile: 07793 160138 Tel: 020-8979 8048

SUPERSCRIPTS
(Audio Typing, Rushes, Post-Prod Scripts)
56 New Road, Hanworth, Middlesex TW13 6TQ
e-mail: jackie@supercripts.fsnet.co.uk
Mobile: 07971 671011 Tel: 020-8898 7933

TALK TO THE HAND PUPPETS
(Custom Puppets for Film, Television & Theatre)
Studio 277, Wimbledon Art Studios, Riverside Yard
Riverside Road, Earlsfield, London SW17 0BB
Website: www.talktothehandproductions.com
e-mail: info@talktothehandproductions.com
Mobile: 07813 682293 Mobile: 07855 421454

TAYLOR Charlotte
(Stylist/Props Buyer)
18 Eleanor Grove, Barnes, London SW13 0JN
e-mail: charlottetaylor1@blueyonder.co.uk
Mobile: 07836 708904 Tel/Fax: 020-8876 9085

THAMES LUXURY CHARTERS Ltd
5 The Mews, 6 Putney Common, London SW15 1HL
Website: www.thamesluxurycharters.co.uk
e-mail: sales@thamesluxurycharters.co.uk
Fax: 020-8788 0072 Tel: 020-8780 1562

THEATRESEARCH
(Theatre Consultants)
Dacre Hall, Dacre, North Yorkshire HG3 4ET
Website: www.theatresearch.co.uk
e-mail: info@theatresearch.co.uk
Fax: 01423 781957 Tel: 01423 780497

THEATRICAL SHOEMAKERS Ltd
(Footwear)
Unit 7A, Thames Road Industrial Estate
Thames Road, Silvertown, London E16 2EZ
Website: www.shoemaking.co.uk
e-mail: ts@shoemaking.co.uk
Fax: 020-7476 5220 Tel: 020-7474 0500

THEME TRADERS Ltd
(Props)
The Stadium, Oaklands Road, London NW2 6DL
Website: www.themetraders.com
e-mail: mailroom@themetraders.com
Fax: 020-8450 7322 Tel: 020-8452 8518

TOP SHOW
(Props & Scenery, Conference Specialists)
North Lane, Huntington
Yorks YO32 9SU Tel/Fax: 01904 750022

TOTAL LOGISTICS MANAGEMENT
Unit 1, 42 Hanworth Road, Sunbury, Middlesex TW16 5LN
Website: www.tlmltd.co.uk
e-mail: sales@tlmltd.co.uk
Fax: 01932 733009 Tel: 01932 733000

TRACK THAT
(Tracking Vehicle/Camera Car Supplier)
Wandsworth, London SW18
Website: www.trackthat.co.uk
e-mail: info@trackthat.co.uk Mobile: 07941 234254

TRANSCRIPTS
(I/Vs, Scripts, Conferences & Trailers from Audio, DVD or
Downloads)
#2, 6 Cornwall Gardens
London SW7 4AL
e-mail: lucy@transcripts.demon.co.uk
Mobile: 07973 200197　　　　　　　　Tel: 020-7584 9758

TRAPEZE & AERIAL COACH/CHOREOGRAPHER
Contact: Jacqueline Welbourne
c/o Circus Maniacs Agency
Office 8A, The Kingswood Foundation
Britannia Road
Kingswood, Bristol BS15 8DB
Website: www.circusmaniacs.com
e-mail: jackie@circusmaniacs.com
Mobile: 07977 247287　　　　　　　Tel/Fax: 0117-947 7042

TRYFONOS Mary MASKS
(Mask, Headdress & Puppet Specialist)
59 Shaftesbury Road, London N19 4QW
e-mail: marytryfonos@aol.com
Mobile: 07764 587433　　　　　　　　Tel: 020-7561 9880

TURN ON LIGHTING
(Antique Lighting c1850-1950)
11 Camden Passage
London N1 8EA　　　　　　　　Tel/Fax: 020-7359 7616

UK SAME DAY DELIVERY SERVICE
Contact: Philip Collings
18 Billingshurst Road, Broadbridge Heath
West Sussex RH12 3LW
Fax: 01403 266059　　　　　　　　Mobile: 07785 717179

UPBEAT EVENT DESIGN
(Corporate Hospitality Caterers)
Studio 4-5, Garnett Close, Watford, Herts WD24 7GN
Website: www.upbeateventdesign.com
e-mail: enquiries@upbeateventdesign.com
Fax: 01923 211704　　　　　　　　Tel: 01923 211703

UPSTAGE
(Live Communications Agency)
Studio A, 7 Maidstone Buildings Mews
72-76 Borough High Street, London SE1 1GD
Website: www.upstagelivecom.co.uk
e-mail: post@upstagelivecom.co.uk
Fax: 020-7403 6511　　　　　　　　Tel: 020-7403 6510

VENTRILOQUIST DOLLS HOME
(Hire & Helpful Hints, Callers by Appointment)
42 Christchurch Road, Sidcup, Kent DA15 7HQ
Website: www.johnstylesentertainer.co.uk
　　　　　　　　　　　　　　Tel/Fax: 020-8300 3579

VENTRILOQUIST DUMMY HIRE
Contact: Dennis Patten (Hire & Advice)
14 The Crest, Goffs Oak, Herts EN7 5NP
Website: www.dennispatten.co.uk　　　　Tel: 01707 873262

VINMAG ARCHIVE Ltd
84-90 Digby Road, London E9 6HX
Website: www.vinmagarchive.com
e-mail: piclib@vinmag.com
Fax: 020-8985 9810　　　　　　　　Tel: 020-8533 7588

VINTAGE CARRIAGES TRUST
(Owners of the Museum of Rail Travel at Ingrow Railway
Centre)
Keighley, West Yorkshire BD22 8NJ
Website: www.vintagecarriagestrust.org
e-mail: admin@vintagecarriagestrust.org
Fax: 01535 610796　　　　　　　　Tel: 01535 680425

VOCALEYES
(Providers of Audio Description for Theatrical Performance)
1st Floor, 54 Commercial Street
London E1 6LT
Website: www.vocaleyes.co.uk
e-mail: enquiries@vocaleyes.co.uk
Fax: 020-7247 5622　　　　　　　　Tel: 020-7375 1043

WALK YOUR DOG
(Dog Walking Service for South East London)
92 Wricklemarsh Road
London SE3 8DS
Website: www.walkyourdog.co.uk
e-mail: info@walkyourdog.co.uk
Mobile: 07867 502333　　　　　　Tel/Fax: 020-8319 1806

WEBBER Peter HIRE/RITZ STUDIOS
(Music Equipment Hire, Rehearsal Studios)
110-112 Disraeli Road, London SW15 2DX
e-mail: ben@peterwebberhire.com
Fax: 020-8877 1036　　　　　　　　Tel: 020-8870 1335

WESTED LEATHERS COMPANY
(Suede & Leather Suppliers/Manufacturers)
Little Wested House
Wested Lane, Swanley, Kent BR8 8EF
e-mail: wested@wested.com
Fax: 01322 667039　　　　　　　　Tel: 01322 660654

WESTWARD Lynn BLINDS
(Window Blind Specialist)
458 Chiswick High Road, London W4 5TT
Website: www.lynnwestward.com
Fax: 020-8742 8444　　　　　　　　Tel: 020-8742 8333

WILLIAMS Frank
(Bottles, Jars, Footwarmers, Flagons, Spitoons, Poisons,
Milk, Beers & Inks 1870-1940)
33 Enstone Road
Ickenham, Uxbridge, Middlesex
e-mail: wllmsfrn4@aol.com　　　　　　Tel: 01895 672495

WILTSHIRE A. F. LLP
(Agricultural Vehicle Engineers, Repairs, etc)
The Agricultural Centre, Alfold Road
Dunsfold, Surrey GU8 4NP
e-mail: team@afwiltshire.co.uk
Fax: 01483 200491　　　　　　　　Tel: 01483 200516

WORBEY Darryl STUDIOS
(Specialist Puppet Design)
Ground Floor
33 York Grove, London SE15 2NY
e-mail: info@darrylworbeystudios.com
Fax: 020-7635 6397　　　　　　　　Tel: 020-7639 8090

A & C BLACK (Publicity Dept)
38 Soho Square, London W1D 3HB
e-mail: publicity@acblack.com
Fax: 020-7758 0222 Tel: 020-7758 0200

ACADEMY PLAYERS DIRECTORY
(See PLAYERS DIRECTORY)

A C I D PUBLICATIONS
The Office Suite, Minus One House
Lyttelton Road, London E10 5NQ
e-mail: acidnews@aol.com Tel/Fax: 07050 205206

ACTING: A DRAMA STUDIO SOURCE BOOK
(Peter Owen Publishers)
73 Kenway Road, London SW5 0RE
Website: www.peterowen.com
e-mail: admin@peterowen.com Tel: 020-7373 5628

ACTIONS: THE ACTORS' THESAURUS
(By Marina Caldarone & Maggie Lloyd-Williams)
Nick Hern Books
The Glasshouse
49A Goldhawk Road
London W12 8QP
Website: www.nickhernbooks.co.uk
e-mail: info@nickhernbooks.demon.co.uk
Fax: 020-8735 0250 Tel: 020-8749 4953

ACTORS' YEARBOOK 2009
(A & C Black Publishers)
38 Soho Square, London W1D 3HB
Website: www.acblack.com
e-mail: performing@acblack.com
Fax: 020-7758 0222 Tel: 020-7758 0200

AMATEUR STAGE MAGAZINE & COMMUNITY ARTS DIRECTORY
(Platform Publications Ltd)
Hampden House
2 Weymouth Street, London W1W 5BT
e-mail: admin@platformpublications.com
Fax: 020-7636 2323 Tel: 020-7636 4343

ANNUAIRE DU CINEMA BELLEFAYE
(French Actors' Directory, Production, Technicians & All
Technical Industries & Suppliers)
30 rue Saint Marc, 75002 Paris
Website: www.bellefaye.com
e-mail: contact@bellefaye.com
Fax: 00 331 42 33 39 00 Tel: 00 331 42 33 52 52

ARTISTES & AGENTS
(Richmond House Publishing Co Ltd)
70-76 Bell Street
Marylebone, London NW1 6SP
Website: www.rhpco.co.uk
e-mail: sales@rhpco.co.uk
Fax: 020-7224 9688 Tel: 020-7224 9666

AUDITIONS: A PRACTICAL GUIDE
Website: www.auditionsapracticalguide.com

AURORA METRO PRESS (1989)
(Drama, Fiction, Reference & International Literature in
English Translation)
67 Grove Avenue
Twickenham TW2 4HX
Website: www.aurorametro.com
e-mail: info@aurorametro.com Tel/Fax: 020-3261 0000

BIG BREAK CARDS Ltd
(Theatrical greetings cards featuring Hamlet the pig, made
by actors for actors)
PO Box 45
Chipping Campden GL55 6WH
Website: www.bigbreakcards.co.uk
e-mail: info@bigbreakcards.co.uk Tel: 01386 438952

BIRTH OF THEATRE The - STAGE BY STAGE
(Drama/Theatre Studies/History/Reference)
(Peter Owen Publishers)
73 Kenway Road, London SW5 0RE
Website: www.peterowen.com
e-mail: admin@peterowen.com
Fax: 020-7373 6760 Tel: 020-7373 5628

BRITISH PERFORMING ARTS YEARBOOK
(Rhinegold Publishing)
241 Shaftesbury Avenue
London WC2H 8TF
Website: www.rhinegold.co.uk
e-mail: bpay@rhinegold.co.uk Tel: 020-7333 1720

BRITISH THEATRE DIRECTORY
(Richmond House Publishing Co Ltd)
70-76 Bell Street
Marylebone, London NW1 6SP
Website: www.rhpco.co.uk
e-mail: sales@rhpco.co.uk
Fax: 020-7224 9688 Tel: 020-7224 9666

BROADCAST
Greater London House
Hampstead Road, London NW1 7EJ
Website: www.broadcastnow.co.uk
Fax: 020-7728 5555 Tel: 020-7728 5542

CASTCALL & CASTFAX
(Casting Information Services)
106 Wilsden Avenue
Luton LU1 5HR
Website: www.castcall.co.uk
e-mail: admin@castcall.co.uk
Fax: 01582 480736 Tel: 01582 456213

CASTWEB
7 St Luke's Avenue
London SW4 7LG
Website: www.castweb.co.uk
e-mail: info@castweb.co.uk Tel: 020-7720 9002

CELEBRITY BULLETIN The
10 Wiseton Road, London SW17 7EE
e-mail: enquiries@celebrity-bulletin.co.uk
Fax: 020-8672 2282 Tel: 020-8672 3191

CHAPPELL OF BOND STREET
(Sheet Music, Musical Instruments, Pianos, Synthesizers,
Keyboards)
152-160 Wardour Street
London W1F 8YA
Website: www.chappellofbondstreet.co.uk
Fax: 020-7432 4410 Tel: 020-7432 4400

CONFERENCE & INCENTIVE TRAVEL MAGAZINE
174 Hammersmith Road, London W6 7JP
Website: www.citmagazine.com
e-mail: cit@haymarket.com
Fax: 020-8267 4192 Tel: 020-8267 4307

CREATIVE HANDBOOK
(Centaur Media Plc)
50 Poland Street, London W1F 7AX
Website: www.creativehandbook.co.uk   Tel: 020-7770 6713

DANCE EXPRESSION
(A. E. Morgan Publications Ltd)
8A High Street, Epsom, Surrey KT19 8AD
Website: www.danceexpression.co.uk
e-mail: catalina@globalnet.co.uk   Tel: 01372 741411

DANCERS SPOTLIGHT
7 Leicester Place
London WC2H 7RJ
Website: www.spotlight.com
e-mail: info@spotlight.com
Fax: 020-7437 5881   Tel: 020-7437 7631

DIRECTING DRAMA
(Peter Owen Publishers)
73 Kenway Road, London SW5 0RE
Website: www.peterowen.com
e-mail: admin@peterowen.com   Tel: 020-7373 5628

EQUITY MAGAZINE
Guild House, Upper St Martin's Lane
London WC2H 9EG
Website: www.equity.org.uk
e-mail: mmcgrath@equity.org.uk
Fax: 020-7379 6074   Tel: 020-7670 0211

FILMLOG
(Subscriptions)
PO Box 100, Broadstairs, Kent CT10 1UJ
Website: www.pcrnewsletter.com
Tel: 01843 860885   Tel: 01843 866538

FORESIGHT-NEWS
(The Profile Group (UK) Ltd)
Dragon Court
27-29 Macklin Street
London WC2B 5LX
Website: www.profilegroup.co.uk
Fax: 020-7190 7858   Tel: 020-7190 7777

HERN Nick BOOKS
(Plays, Theatrebooks, Screenplays & Performing Rights)
The Glasshouse
49A Goldhawk Road
London W12 8QP
Website: www.nickhernbooks.co.uk
e-mail: info@nickhernbooks.demon.co.uk
Fax: 020-8735 0250   Tel: 020-8749 4953

HOLLYWOOD REPORTER The
5th Floor, Endeavour House
189 Shaftesbury Avenue
London WC2H 8TJ
Website: www.hollywoodreporter.com
e-mail: london_one@eu.hollywoodreporter.com
Fax: 020-7420 6014   Tel: 020-7420 6000

KAY'S UK & EUROPEAN PRODUCTION MANUALS
Pinewood Studios
Pinewood Road
Iver Heath, Bucks SL0 0NH
Website: www.kays.co.uk
e-mail: info@kays.co.uk
Fax: 020-8960 6700   Tel: 020-8960 6900

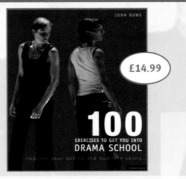
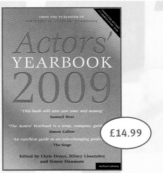

KEMP'S FILM, TV & VIDEO
(Reed Business Information)
East Grinstead House
East Grinstead, West Sussex RH19 1XA
Website: www.kftv.com
e-mail: kemps@reedinfo.co.uk
Fax: 01342 336113   Tel: 01342 335779

KNOWLEDGE The
Paulton House
8 Shepherdess Walk, London N1 7LB
Website: www.theknowledgeonline.com
e-mail: knowledge@hollis-publishing.com
Fax: 020-7549 2505   Tel: 020-7549 8666

LIMELIGHT The
(Limelight Publications, Contacts & Casting Directory)
Postal Address: PO Box 760
Randpark Ridge
2156, Gauteng, South Africa
Website: www.limelight.co.za
e-mail: info@limelight.co.za   Tel/Fax: 00 27 11 793 7231

MAKING OF THE PROFESSIONAL ACTOR The
(Peter Owen Publishers)
73 Kenway Road, London SW5 0RE
Website: www.peterowen.com
e-mail: admin@peterowen.com   Tel: 020-7373 5628

METHUEN DRAMA
A & C Black
38 Soho Square, London W1D 3HB
e-mail: methuendrama@acblack.com
Fax: 020-7758 0222   Tel: 020-7758 0200

MOVIE MEMORIES MAGAZINE
(Devoted to Films & Stars of the 40s, 50s & 60s)
10 Russett Close
Scunthorpe, N. Lincs DN15 8YJ
e-mail: crob.mvm@ntlworld.com

MUSIC WEEK DIRECTORY/MUSIC WEEK
CPMi
8th Floor, Ludgate House
245 Blackfriars Road, London SE1 9UY
Website: www.musicweek.com
e-mail: enquiries@musicweek.com   Tel: 020-7921 8320

MUSICAL STAGES
(Musical Theatre Magazine)
Box 8365, London W14 0GL
Website: www.musicalstages.co.uk
e-mail: editor@musicalstages.co.uk   Tel/Fax: 020-7603 2221

OFFICIAL LONDON SEATING PLAN GUIDE The
(Richmond House Publishing Co Ltd)
70-76 Bell Street
Marylebone, London NW1 6SP
Website: www.rhpco.co.uk
e-mail: sales@rhpco.co.uk
Fax: 020-7224 9668   Tel: 020-7224 9666

PA ENTERTAINMENT
292 Vauxhall Bridge Road
Victoria, London SW1V 1AE
Website: www.pa-entertainment.co.uk
e-mail: events@pa-entertainment.co.uk
Fax: 020-7963 7805   Tel: 020-7963 7707

PANTOMIME BOOK The
(Peter Owen Publishers)
73 Kenway Road, London SW5 0RE
Website: www.peterowen.com
e-mail: admin@peterowen.com   Tel: 020-7373 5628

PCR
(See PRODUCTION & CASTING REPORT)

PLAYERS DIRECTORY
2210 W. Olive Avenue
Suite 320, Burbank, California 91506
Website: www.playersdirectory.com
e-mail: info@playersdirectory.com   Tel: (310) 247-3058

PLAYS INTERNATIONAL
33A Lurline Gardens, London SW11 4DD
Website: www.playsinternational.org.uk   Tel: 020-7720 1950

PRESENTERS CLUB The
Presenter Promotions
123 Corporation Road, Gillingham, Kent ME7 1RG
Website: www.presenterpromotions.com
e-mail: info@presenterpromotions.com
                                Tel/Fax: 01634 851077

PRESENTERS SPOTLIGHT
7 Leicester Place, London WC2H 7RJ
Website: www.spotlight.com
e-mail: info@spotlight.com
Fax: 020-7437 5881   Tel: 020-7437 7631

PRESENTING FOR TV & VIDEO
(Joanne Zorian-Lynn, published by A & C Black)
A & C Black Customer Services
c/o Robert Smith Literacy Agency
12 Bridge Wharf, 156 Caledonian Road
London N1 9UU
e-mail: mdl@macmillan.co.uk   Tel: 01256 302692

PRODUCTION & CASTING REPORT
(Editorial)
PO Box 11, London N1 7JZ
Website: www.pcrnewsletter.com
e-mail: info@pcrnewsletter.com
Fax: 020-7566 8284   Tel: 020-7566 8282

PRODUCTION & CASTING REPORT
(Subscriptions)
PO Box 100, Broadstairs, Kent CT10 1UJ
Website: www.pcrnewsletter.com
Tel: 01843 860885   Tel: 01843 866538

RADIO TIMES
80 Wood Lane, London W12 0TT
e-mail: radio.times@bbc.com
Fax: 020-8433 3160   Tel: 020-8433 3400

RICHMOND HOUSE PUBLISHING COMPANY Ltd
70-76 Bell Street, Marylebone, London NW1 6SP
Website: www.rhpco.co.uk
e-mail: sales@rhpco.co.uk
Fax: 020-7224 9688   Tel: 020-7224 9666

ROGUES & VAGABONDS
(On-line Theatre Magazine)
13 Elm Road, London SW14 7JL
Website: www.roguesandvagabonds.co.uk
e-mail: contact@roguesandvagabonds.co.uk
                                Tel: 020-8876 1175

SBS Ltd
Suite 204
254 Belsize Road, London NW6 4BT
e-mail: office@sbscasting.co.uk
Fax: 020-7372 1992   Tel: 020-7372 6337

SCREEN INTERNATIONAL
Greater London House
Hampstead Road, London NW1 7EJ
Website: www.screendaily.com
e-mail: mai.le@emap.com
Fax: 020-7728 5555   Tel: 020-7728 5605

SHOWBIZ FRIENDS
(Community Website for Showbiz people)
Website: www.showbizfriends.com

SHOWCALL
47 Bermondsey Street, London SE1 3XT
Website: www.showcall.co.uk
e-mail: marcus@thestage.co.uk
Fax: 020-7378 0480   Tel: 020-7403 1818

SHOWCAST
PO Box 2001, Leumeah
NSW 2560 Australia
Website: www.showcast.com.au
e-mail: danelle@showcast.com.au
Fax: 02 4647 4167   Tel: 02 4647 4166

SHOWDIGS.CO.UK
Website: www.showdigs.co.uk
e-mail: info@showdigs.co.uk   Mobile: 07984 422353

SIGHT & SOUND
(British Film Institute)
21 Stephen Street, London W1T 1LN
Website: www.bfi.org.uk/sightandsound
e-mail: s&s@bfi.org.uk
Fax: 020-7436 2327   Tel: 020-7255 1444

SO YOU WANT TO BE AN ACTOR?
(By Timothy West & Prunella Scales)
Nick Hern Books
The Glasshouse
49A Goldhawk Road, London W12 8QP
Website: www.nickhernbooks.co.uk
e-mail: info@nickhernbooks.demon.co.uk
Fax: 020-8735 0250   Tel: 020-8749 4953

SO YOU WANT TO BE A THEATRE DIRECTOR?
(By Stephen Unwin)
Nick Hern Books
The Glasshouse
49A Goldhawk Road, London W12 8QP
Website: www.nickhernbooks.co.uk
e-mail: info@nickhernbooks.demon.co.uk
Fax: 020-8735 0250   Tel: 020-8749 4953

SPEECH FOR THE SPEAKER
(Peter Owen Publishers)
73 Kenway Road, London SW5 0RE
Website: www.peterowen.com
e-mail: admin@peterowen.com   Tel: 020-7373 5628

SPOTLIGHT
7 Leicester Place, London WC2H 7RJ
Website: www.spotlight.com
e-mail: info@spotlight.com
Fax: 020-7437 5881   Tel: 020-7437 7631

STAGE NEWSPAPER Ltd The
47 Bermondsey Street
London SE1 3XT
Website: www.thestage.co.uk
e-mail: editor@thestage.co.uk
Fax: 020-7939 8478   Tel: 020-7403 1818

TELEVISUAL MEDIA UK Ltd
48 Charlotte Street, London W1T 2NS
Website: www.televisual.com
Fax: 020-3008 5784   Tel: 020-3008 5750

THEATRE RECORD
131 Sherringham Avenue
London N17 9RU
Website: www.theatrerecord.com
e-mail: editor@theatrerecord.com   Tel/Fax: 01243 539437

THEATRE REPORT
(Subscriptions)
PO Box 100, Broadstairs
Kent CT10 1UJ
Website: www.pcrnewsletter.com
Tel: 01843 860885   Tel: 01843 866538

TIME OUT GROUP Ltd
Universal House
251 Tottenham Court Road
London W1T 7AB
Website: www.timeout.com
Fax: 020-7813 6001   Tel: 020-7813 3000

TV TIMES
IPC Media
Blue Fin Building
110 Southwark Street, London SE1 0SU
Fax: 020-3148 8115   Tel: 020-3148 5615

VARIETY NEWSPAPER
Procter House
Procter Street, London WC1V 6EU
Website: www.variety.com
Fax: 020-7911 1922   Tel: 020-7911 1701

WHITE BOOK The
Bank House
23 Warwick Road
Coventry CV1 2EW
Website: www.whitebook.co.uk
e-mail: admin@whitebook.co.uk
Fax: 024-7657 1172   Tel: 024-7657 1171

So you want to tread the boards...
...the everything-you-need-to-know insider's guide to a career in the Performing Arts

Musical Theatre
Choosing an Agent
Cover Letters
Photos
Touring
Television and Film
Living in London
Singing Repertoire
Dance Issues
Song Lists
Drama School & Other Training
Auditions: How to Prepare, What to Expect

JENNIFER REISCHEL

'Contains a wealth of useful information… an essential read for beginners for many years to come'

The Stage

Published in paperback at £16.99 by JR Books

ARTHUR Leone PR
The Ground Floor
3 Charlotte Mews, London W1T 4DZ
Website: www.arthurleone.com
e-mail: name@arthurleone.com
Fax: 020-7637 2984   Tel: 020-7637 2994

AVALON PUBLIC RELATIONS
(Marketing/Arts)
4A Exmoor Street, London W10 6BD
e-mail: markj@avalonuk.com
Fax: 020-7598 7223   Tel: 020-7598 7222

BARLOW Tony ASSOCIATES
(Press & Marketing for Music, Dance & Theatre)
13 Burns Court
Park Hill Road
Wallington SM6 0SF
e-mail: artspublicity@hotmail.com
Mobile: 07711 929170   Tel: 020-8773 1919

BOLTON Erica & QUINN Jane Ltd
10 Pottery Lane, London W11 4LZ
e-mail: name@boltonquinn.com
Fax: 020-7221 8100   Tel: 020-7221 5000

BORKOWSKI Mark PR & IMPROPERGANDA Ltd
65 Clerkenwell Road
London EC1R 5BL
Website: www.borkowski.co.uk
e-mail: larry@borkowski.co.uk
Fax: 020-7404 5000   Tel: 020-7404 3000

CAHOOTS PRODUCTION & PR
Contact: Denise Silvey
Suite 1803, 16-19 Southampton Place, London WC1A 1AJ
Website: www.cahootstheatre.co.uk
e-mail: denise@silveyassociates.co.uk   Tel: 020-7745 7181

CENTRESTAGE PUBLIC RELATIONS
Yeates Cottage
27 Wellington Terrace
Woking, Surrey GU21 2AP
Website: www.centrestage.com
e-mail: centrestagepr@dsl.pipex.com
Fax: 0870 2882398   Mobile: 07838 995736

CHESTON Judith PUBLICITY
30 Telegraph Street, Shipston-on-Stour
Warwickshire CV36 4DA
e-mail: jcheston@tiscali.co.uk
Fax: 01608 663772   Tel: 01608 661198

CLOUT COMMUNICATIONS Ltd
79 Wardour Street, London W1D 6QD
Website: www.cloutcom.co.uk
e-mail: info@cloutcom.co.uk   Tel: 020-7851 8625

DAVEY Christine ASSOCIATES
29 Victoria Road, Eton Wick
Windsor, Berkshire SL4 6LY
Fax: 01753 851123   Tel: 01753 852619

DDA PUBLIC RELATIONS Ltd
192-198 Vauxhall Bridge Road
London SW1V 1DX
Website: www.ddapr.com
e-mail: info@ddapr.com
Fax: 020-7932 4950   Tel: 020-7932 9800

ELSON Howard PROMOTIONS
(Marketing & Management)
16 Penn Avenue, Chesham
Buckinghamshire HP5 2HS
e-mail: helson1029@aol.com
Fax: 01494 784760   Tel: 01494 785873

EMPICA Ltd
1 Lyons Court, Long Ashton Business Park
Yanley Lane, Bristol BS41 9LB
Fax: 01275 393933   Tel: 01275 394400

GADABOUTS Ltd
(Theatre Marketing & Promotions)
54 Friary Road, London N12 9PB
Website: www.gadabouts.co.uk
e-mail: info@gadabouts.co.uk
Fax: 0870 7059140   Tel: 020-8445 5450

GAYNOR Avril ASSOCIATES
126 Brudenell Road
London SW17 8DE   Mobile: 07958 623013

GOODMAN Deborah PUBLICITY
25 Glenmere Avenue, London NW7 2LT
Website: www.dgpr.co.uk
e-mail: publicity@dgpr.co.uk
Fax: 020-8959 7875   Tel: 020-8959 9980

HYMAN Sue ASSOCIATES Ltd
St Martin's House
59 Martin's Lane, London WC2N 4JS
Website: www.suehyman.com
e-mail: sue.hyman@btinternet.com
Fax: 020-7379 4944   Tel: 020-7379 8420

IMPACT AGENCY The
3 Bloomsbury Place
London WC1A 2QL
e-mail: mail@impactagency.co.uk
Fax: 020-7580 7200   Tel: 020-7580 1770

KEAN LANYON Ltd
Contact: Sharon Kean
Rose Cottage, The Aberdeen Centre
22 Highbury Grove, London N5 2EA
Website: www.keanlanyon.com
e-mail: sharon@keanlanyon.com
Fax: 020-7359 0199   Tel: 020-7354 3574

KELLER Don ARTS MARKETING
65 Glenwood Road
Harringay, London N15 3JS
e-mail: info@dakam.org.uk
Fax: 020-8809 6825   Tel: 020-8800 4882

LAKE-SMITH GRIFFIN ASSOCIATES
Walter House
418 Strand, London WC2R 0PT
e-mail: info@lakesmithgriffin.co.uk
Fax: 020-7836 1040   Tel: 020-7836 1020

LEEP MARKETING & PR
(Marketing, Press and Publicity)
5 Nassau House
122 Shaftesbury Avenue
London W1D 5ER
e-mail: philip@leep.biz
Fax: 020-7439 8833   Tel: 020-7439 9777

MATTHEWS Liz PR
83 Charlotte Street, London W1T 4PR
Website: www.lizmatthewspr.com
e-mail: liz@lizmatthewspr.com   Tel: 020-7436 4433

MAYER Anne PR
82 Mortimer Road, London N1 4LH
e-mail: annemayer@btopenworld.com
Fax: 020-7254 8227   Tel: 020-7254 7391

McAULEY ARTS MARKETING
118 Broxholm Road, London SE27 0BT
Website: www.mcauleyartsmarketing.co.uk
e-mail: sam@mcauleyartsmarketing.co.uk
        Tel: 020-8676 4773

MITCHELL Jackie
(JM Communications)
4 Sims Cottages, The Green, Claygate, Surrey KT10 0JH
Website: www.jackiem.com
e-mail: pr@jackiem.com
Fax: 01372 471073   Tel: 01372 465041

MOBIUS
8A Great Newport Street, London WC2H 7JB
Website: www.mobiusindustries.com
e-mail: info@mobiusindustries.com   Tel: 020-7836 3864

MORGAN Jane ASSOCIATES (JMA)
(Marketing & Media)
8 Heathville Road, London N19 3AJ
e-mail: jma@janemorganassociates.com
Fax: 020-7263 9877   Tel: 020-7263 9867

NELSON BOSTOCK COMMUNICATIONS
Compass House, 22 Redan Place, London W2 4SA
Website: www.nelsonbostock.com
e-mail: info@nelsonbostock.com
Fax: 020-7727 2025   Tel: 020-7229 4400

NEWLEY Patrick ASSOCIATES
45 Kingscourt Road, London SW16 1JA
e-mail: patricknewley@yahoo.com   Tel/Fax: 020-8677 0477

PARKER James ASSOCIATES
67 Richmond Park Road, London SW14 8JY
e-mail: jimparkerjpa@hotmail.com   Tel/Fax: 020-8876 1918

PR PEOPLE The
1 St James Drive, Sale, Cheshire M33 7QX
Website: www.pr-people.uk.com
e-mail: graham@pr-people.uk.com   Tel: 0161-976 2729

PREMIER PR
91 Berwick Street, London W1F 0NE
Website: www.premierpr.com
Fax: 020-7734 2024   Tel: 020-7292 8330

PUBLIC EYE COMMUNICATIONS Ltd
Suite 313, Plaza, 535 Kings Road, London SW10 0SZ
e-mail: ciara@publiceye.co.uk
Fax: 020-7351 1010   Tel: 020-7351 1555

RICHMOND TOWERS COMMUNICATIONS Ltd
26 Fitzroy Square, London W1T 6BT
Fax: 020-7388 7761   Tel: 020-7388 7421

RKM COMMUNICATIONS Ltd
(London. Los Angeles)
19B Grosvenor Gardens, London SW1W 0BD
Website: www.rkmp.com
e-mail: info@rkmpr.com
Fax: 020-7821 1369   Tel: 020-7856 2233

S & X MEDIA
Contact: Roulla Xenides
411B The Big Peg
Vyse Street, Birmingham B18 6NF
Website: www.sx-media.com
e-mail: roulla@sx-media.com
Fax: 0121-694 6494   Tel: 0121-604 6366

SAVIDENT Paul
(Marketing & Press Management)
The Office
27 St Dunstan's Road, London W7 2EY
Website: www.savident.com
e-mail: info@savident.com
Fax: 0870 0516418   Tel: 020-8567 2089

SHIPPEN Martin MARKETING & MEDIA
88 Purves Road
London NW10 5TB
e-mail: m.shippen@virgin.net
Mobile: 07956 879165   Tel: 020-8968 1943

SNELL Helen Ltd
4th Floor
80-81 St Martin's Lane, London WC2N 4AA
e-mail: info@helensnell.com
Fax: 020-7240 2947   Tel: 020-7240 5537

STOTT Barbara
20 Sunbury Lane, London SW11 3NP
e-mail: b-stott@talktalk.net   Tel: 020-7350 1159

TARGET LIVE Ltd
(Marketing & Press Support)
Fitzroy House
11 Chenies Street, London WC1E 7EY
e-mail: admin@target-live.co.uk
Fax: 020-7907 1751   Tel: 020-7907 1777

TAYLOR HERRING PUBLIC RELATIONS
11 Westway Centre
69 St Marks Road, London W10 6JG
Website: www.taylorherring.com
e-mail: james.herring@taylorherring.com
Fax: 020-8206 5155   Tel: 020-8206 5151

THOMPSON Peter ASSOCIATES
Flat One
12 Bourchier Street, London W1V 5HN
Fax: 020-7439 1202   Tel: 020-7439 1210

TRE-VETT Eddie
Brink House, Avon Castle, Ringwood
Hampshire BH24 2BL   Tel: 01425 475544

WILLIAMS Tei PRESS & ARTS MARKETING
Post Office Cottage
Clifton, Oxon OX15 0PD
e-mail: artsmarketing@btconnect.com
Mobile: 07957 664116   Tel: 01869 337940

WILSON Stella PUBLICITY & PERSONAL MANAGEMENT
293 Faversham Road
Seasalter, Whitstable, Kent CT5 4BN
e-mail: stella@stellawilson.com   Mobile: 07860 174301

WINGHAM Maureen PRESS & PUBLIC RELATIONS
PO Box 125
Stowmarket, Suffolk IP14 1PB
e-mail: maureen.wingham@mwmedia.uk.com
        Tel: 01449 771200

Radio
  BBC Radio
  BBC Local Radio Stations
  Independent Local Radio
Rehearsal Rooms & Casting Suites
Role Play Companies/Theatre Skills
  in Business

BBC RADIO, Broadcasting House
London W1A 1AA
Tel: 020-7580 4468 (Main Switchboard)

• DRAMA

BBC Radio Drama
Bush House
The Aldwych, London WC2B 4PH
Tel: 020-7580 4468 (Main Switchboard)

Production

Head	Alison Hindell
Production Executive	Rebecca Wilmshurst
Administrator Radio Drama Company	Cynthia Fagan

Executive Producers

World Service	Marion Nancarrow
London	Sally Avens
	David Hunter
	Jeremy Mortimer
Manchester	Sue Roberts
Birmingham	Vanessa Whitburn

Producers - London

Marc Beeby	Peter Kavanagh
Steven Canny	Pam Marshall
Jessica Dromgoole	Duncan Minshull
Claire Grove	Tracey Neale
Gemma Jenkins	Jonquil Panting
	Toby Swift

Producers - Manchester

Gary Brown	Nadia Molinari
Pauline Harris	

Producers - Birmingham

Naylah Ahmed (Silver Street)	James Peries (Silver Street)
Julie Beckett (Archers)	Deborah Sathe (Silver Street)
Kate Oates (Archers)	Peter Wild

Development Producers

Charlotte Riches (Manchester)	Faith Collingwood
Fiona Kelcher (Birmingham)	Abigail Le Fleming

Writersroom

Director	Kate Rowland

Why should I work in radio?

To make a smooth transition from stage or camera to radio acting, everything that would otherwise be conveyed through body language and facial expressions must all be focused into the tone and pitch of the actor's voice.

If you have only ever considered visual acting work before, pursuing radio work would certainly enable you to expand your horizons and add additional skills to your CV. It is an opportunity to work in a different way and meet new requirements. Rehearsal and recording time is reduced in radio, which may allow you to pursue visual and radio acting alongside each other. Time constraints can be a pressure, and you have to get used to working without props (just sound effects), but this 'back to basics' existence is appealing to a lot of actors.

How can I become a radio presenter?

Presenting work in any medium comes under a different category as this is not classed as acting. It is a skill in its own right. Please refer to the 'Agents – Presenters' section for more information.

Do I need a voicereel?

This has to be your first and most important step into getting work as a radio actor. Your CV is not enough to get you a job without a professional-sounding voicereel. Voice-over work in commercial and corporate sectors requires a different type of reel. Please see the 'Promotional Services' section for more detailed voicereel advice.

Do I need an agent?

It is not strictly necessary to have an agent for radio work. The BBC is by far the main producer of radio drama and welcomes applications directly from actors, but some independent radio stations prefer using agents to put actors forward. It might be worth doing some research on your local radio stations and finding out their preferred method of contact and making a decision from there. If you are looking for a new agent and are interested in radio work as well as straight acting work, find out whether they deal with this area of the industry before signing up. If you only want to pursue radio and/or voice-over work, or are looking for a specialist agent in addition to your main agent, please see the 'Agents – Voice-over' section for further advice and listings.

How do I find work in radio?

You can send your CV and voicereel directly out to producers of radio drama, but make sure you target your search. Listen to radio plays and make a note of any producers whose work you particularly liked. This may also help you to identify what types of dramas you feel your voice would be most suited to. Once you have done your research and made a shortlist, send your voicereel with a personalised letter. Mention the plays you liked and explain that you feel he or she will be able to use your voice in productions like these. This method is likely to be much more effective than sending out a generic covering letter en masse, and will make you stand out. You don't need to send a headshot with your CV, but you could incorporate your photo in the body of your CV. It would be a good idea to have your name and contact details professionally printed onto the CD in case it becomes separated from your CV – see 'Promotional Services' for listings of companies that can do this for you.

BROADCAST

Radio Drama – BBC Scotland
Head	Patrick Rayner
Editor, Radio Drama	Bruce Young
Management Assistant	Sue Meek

Producers
Gaynor Macfarlane	David Jackson Young
Lu Kemp	

Radio Drama – BBC Wales
Kate McAll

Radio Drama – BBC Northern Ireland
All enquiries to Anne Simpson

• RADIO COMEDY/RADIO PRODUCTION

Head, Radio Comedy	Paul Schlesinger
Executive Producers	Alison Vernon-Smith, Katie Tyrrell

Producers
Colin Anderson	Katie Marsden
Dawn Ellis	Ed Morrish
Tilusha Ghelani	Pamela Norris
Claire Jones	Ben Walker
Victoria Lloyd	

Production Executive	Sophie Butler
Production Manager	Mel Almond

SPOTLIGHT PRESENTERS

The industry's leading directory of professional presenters.

Full page colour photos, credits and agent details.

To join, call 020 7437 7631 or visit www.spotlight.com

• NEWS AND CURRENT AFFAIRS

BBC News (Television & Radio)
Television Centre
Wood Lane, London W12 7RJ
Tel: 020-8743 8000 (Main Switchboard)

Director of News	Helen Boaden
Head Newsroom	Peter Horrocks
Head of Multimedia Programmes & Deputy Director of News	Stephen Mitchell
Head of News Gathering	Fran Unsworth
Executive Editor & Commissioning Editor for TV Current Affairs	Clive Edwards
Head of Political Programmes	Sue Inglish
Head of Radio Current Affairs	Nicola Meyrick
Acting Head of MC&A Journalism	Chris Gottlieb
Controller of Operations & Technology	Peter Coles
Head of Editorial Development, Multi-media Journalism	Pete Clifton

• RADIO SPORT
Head of Sport	Gordon Turnbull

• CONTROLLERS
Director of Audio & Music	Tim Davie

RADIO 1
Controller	Andy Parfitt

RADIO 2
Controller	Lesley Douglas

RADIO 3
Controller	Roger Wright

RADIO 4
Controller	Mark Damazer

RADIO 5 LIVE
Controller	Adrian Van Klaveren

• BBC NEW WRITING

BBC Writersroom
Grafton House
379-381 Euston Road
London NW1 3AU   Tel: 020-7765 2703
e-mail: writersroom@bbc.co.uk
Website: www.bbc.co.uk/writersroom

Creative Director	Kate Rowland
Development Manager	Paul Ashton

BBC BEDFORDSHIRE, HERTFORDSHIRE & BUCKINGHAMSHIRE THREE COUNTIES RADIO
1 Hastings Street
Luton LU1 5XL
Website: www.bbc.co.uk/threecounties
e-mail: 3cr@bbc.co.uk
Fax: 01582 401467   Tel: 01582 637400
Managing Editor: Mark Norman

BBC RADIO BRISTOL
PO Box 194, Bristol BS99 7QT
Website: www.bbc.co.uk/bristol
e-mail: radio.bristol@bbc.co.uk
Fax: 0117-923 8323   Tel: 0117-974 1111
Managing Editor: Tim Pemberton
News Editor: Charlotte Callen

BBC RADIO CAMBRIDGESHIRE
Broadcasting House
104 Hills Road, Cambridge CB2 1LQ
Website: www.bbc.co.uk/cambridgeshire
e-mail: cambs@bbc.co.uk   Tel: 01223 259696
Managing Editor: Jason Horton
Acting Assistant Editor: Will Chambers

BBC TEES
PO Box 95 FM
Broadcasting House
Newport Road
Middlesbrough TS1 5DG
Website: www.bbc.co.uk/tees
Fax: 01642 211356   Tel: 01642 225211
Managing Editor: Matthew Barraclough

BBC RADIO CORNWALL
Phoenix Wharf
Truro, Cornwall TR1 1UA
Website: www.bbc.co.uk/cornwall
Fax: 01872 240679   Tel: 01872 275421
Managing Editor: Pauline Causey

BBC COVENTRY & WARWICKSHIRE
Priory Place
Coventry CV1 5SQ
Website: www.bbc.co.uk/coventryandwarwickshire
e-mail: coventry.warwickshire@bbc.co.uk
Fax: 024-7655 2000   Tel: 024-7655 1000
Senior Broadcast Journalist: Tim Atkinson

BBC RADIO CUMBRIA
Annetwell Street
Carlisle, Cumbria CA3 8BB
Website: www.bbc.co.uk/radiocumbria
Fax: 01228 511195   Tel: 01228 592444
Managing Editor: Nigel Dyson

BBC RADIO DERBY
PO Box 104.5, Derby DE1 3HL
Website: www.bbc.co.uk/derby   Tel: 01332 361111
Managing Editor: Simon Cornes

BBC RADIO DEVON
PO Box 1034, Plymouth PL3 5YQ
Website: www.bbc.co.uk/devon
Fax: 01752 234564   Tel: 01752 260323
Managing Editor: Robert Wallace

BBC ESSEX
PO Box 765, Chelmsford, Essex CM2 9AB
Website: www.bbc.co.uk/essex
e-mail: essex@bbc.co.uk   Tel: 01245 616000
Managing Editor: Gerald Main

BBC RADIO GLOUCESTERSHIRE
London Road, Gloucester GL1 1SW
Website: www.bbc.co.uk/gloucestershire   Tel: 01452 308585
Managing Editor: Mark Hurrell

BBC GUERNSEY
Broadcasting House, Bulwer Avenue
St Sampsons, Channel Islands GY2 4LA
Website: www.bbc.co.uk/guernsey
e-mail: bbcguernsey@bbc.co.uk
Fax: 01481 200361   Tel: 01481 200600
Managing Editor: David Martin
Senior Broadcast Journalist: Simon Alexander

BBC HEREFORD & WORCESTER
Hylton Road, Worcester WR2 5WW
Website: www.bbc.co.uk/herefordandworcester
Managing Editor: James Coghill   Tel: 01905 748485

BBC RADIO HUMBERSIDE
Queens Court, Queens Gardens, Hull HU1 3RH
Website: www.bbc.co.uk/humber
e-mail: radio.humberside@bbc.co.uk
Fax: 01482 226409   Tel: 01482 323232
Editor: Simon Pattern

BBC RADIO JERSEY
18 & 21 Parade Road
St Helier, Jersey JE2 3PL
Website: www.bbc.co.uk/jersey
Fax: 01534 732569   Tel: 01534 870000
Editor: Denzil Dudley
Assistant Editor: Matthew Price

BBC RADIO KENT
The Great Hall, Mount Pleasant Road
Tunbridge Wells, Kent TN1 1QQ
Website: www.bbc.co.uk/kent
e-mail: radio.kent@bbc.co.uk   Tel: 01892 670000
Managing Editor: Paul Leaper

BBC RADIO LANCASHIRE
20-26 Darwen Street
Blackburn, Lancashire BB2 2EA
Website: www.bbc.co.uk/lancashire   Tel: 01254 262411
Editor: John Clayton

BBC RADIO LEEDS
BBC Broadcasting Centre
2 St Peter's Square, Leeds LS9 8AH
Website: www.bbc.co.uk/leeds
Fax: 0113-224 7316   Tel: 0113-244 2131
Managing Editor: Phil Squire

BBC RADIO LEICESTER
9 St Nicholas Place, Leicester LE1 5LB
Website: www.bbc.co.uk/leicester
e-mail: leicester@bbc.co.uk
Fax: 0116-251 1463   Tel: 0116-251 6688
Managing Editor: Kate Squire

BBC RADIO LINCOLNSHIRE
Newport, Lincoln LN1 3XY
Website: www.bbc.co.uk/lincolnshire
Fax: 01522 511058   Tel: 01522 511411
Managing Editor: Charlie Partridge

BBC LONDON 94.9 FM
35C Marylebone High Street
London W1U 4AA
Website: www.bbc.co.uk/london   Tel: 020-7224 2424
Managing Editor: David Robey

BBC RADIO MANCHESTER
PO Box 951
Oxford Road, Manchester M60 1SD
Website: www.bbc.co.uk/manchester   Tel: 0161-200 2000
Managing Editor: John Ryan

BBC RADIO MERSEYSIDE
PO Box 95.8
Liverpool L69 1ZJ
Website: www.bbc.co.uk/liverpool
e-mail: radio.merseyside@bbc.co.uk   Tel: 0151-708 5500
Managing Editor: Mick Ord

BBC RADIO NEWCASTLE
Broadcasting Centre
Barrack Road
Newcastle upon Tyne NE99 1RN
Website: www.bbc.co.uk/tyne
Fax: 0191-232 5082   Tel: 0191-232 4141
Editor: Andrew Robson

BBC RADIO NORFOLK
The Forum
Millennium Plain, Norwich NR2 1BH
Website: www.bbc.co.uk/norfolk
e-mail: radionorfolk@bbc.co.uk
Fax: 01603 284488   Tel: 01603 617411
Managing Editor: David Clayton

BBC NORTHAMPTON
Broadcasting House
Abington Street
Northampton NN1 2BH
Website: www.bbc.co.uk/northamptonshire
e-mail: northampton@bbc.co.uk
Fax: 01604 230709   Tel: 01604 239100
Manager: Laura Moss

BBC RADIO NOTTINGHAM
London Road
Nottingham NG2 4UU
Website: www.bbc.co.uk/nottingham
Fax: 0115-902 1984   Tel: 0115-955 0500
Editor: Sophie Stewart
Editor News Gathering: Emma Agnew

BBC RADIO SHEFFIELD
54 Shoreham Street
Sheffield S1 4RS
Website: www.bbc.co.uk/southyorkshire
e-mail: radio.sheffield@bbc.co.uk
Fax: 0114-267 5454   Tel: 0114-273 1177
Managing Editor: Gary Keown

BBC RADIO SHROPSHIRE
2-4 Boscobel Drive
Shrewsbury, Shropshire SY1 3TT
Website: www.bbc.co.uk/shropshire
e-mail: radio.shropshire@bbc.co.uk
Fax: 01743 271702   Tel: 01743 248484
Editor: Tim Beech
Senior Broadcast Journalist News: Sharon Simcock

BBC RADIO SOLENT
Broadcasting House
Havelock Road
Southampton SO14 7PW
Website: www.bbc.co.uk/hampshire
e-mail: radio.solent@bbc.co.uk
Fax: 023-8033 9648   Tel: 023-8063 1311
Managing Editor: Mia Costello

BBC RADIO STOKE
Cheapside, Hanley
Stoke-on-Trent, Staffordshire ST1 1JJ
Website: www.bbc.co.uk/stoke
e-mail: radio.stoke@bbc.co.uk
Fax: 01782 289115   Tel: 01782 208080
Managing Editor: Sue Owen

BBC RADIO SUFFOLK
Broadcasting House
St Matthews Street
Ipswich IP1 3EP
Website: www.bbc.co.uk/radiosuffolk
e-mail: radiosuffolk@bbc.co.uk   Tel: 01473 250000
Editor: Peter Cook

BBC SOUTHERN COUNTIES RADIO
Broadcasting Centre
Guildford, Surrey GU2 7AP
Website: www.bbc.co.uk/southerncounties
e-mail: southern.counties.radio@bbc.co.uk
Fax: 01483 304952   Tel: 01483 306306
Managing Editor: Nicci Holliday
Assistant Editor: Sara David

BBC RADIO SWINDON & BBC RADIO WILTSHIRE
Broadcasting House
56-58 Prospect Place
Swindon SN1 3RW
Website: www.bbc.co.uk/wiltshire
e-mail: radio.wiltshire@bbc.co.uk   Tel: 01793 513626
Manager: Tony Worgan

BBC WEST MIDLANDS
The Mailbox
Birmingham B1 1RF
Website: www.bbc.co.uk/westmidlands
e-mail: bbcwm@bbc.co.uk   Tel: 0845 3009956
Editor Local Services: Keith Beech

BBC RADIO YORK
20 Bootham Row, York YO30 7BR
Website: www.bbc.co.uk/northyorkshire
e-mail: radio.york@bbc.co.uk
Fax: 01904 540339   Tel: 01904 641351
Managing Editor: Sarah Drummond

ABERDEEN
Northsound Radio
Abbotswell Road, West Tullos
Aberdeen AB12 3AG
Website: www.northsound1.com   Tel: 01224 337000

AYR
West Sound FM
Radio House, 54A Holmston Road, Ayr KA7 3BE
Website: www.westsound.co.uk   Tel: 01292 283662

BELFAST
City Beat 96.7 FM & 102.5 FM
2nd Floor, Arena Building, 85 Ormeau Road, Belfast BT7 1SH
Website: www.citybeat.co.uk
e-mail: news@citybeat.co.uk
Fax: 028-9089 0100   Tel: 028-9023 4967

BELFAST
Cool FM
PO Box 974, Belfast BT1 1RT
Website: www.coolfm.co.uk
e-mail: music@coolfm.co.uk   Tel: 028-9181 7181

BELFAST
Downtown Radio
Newtownards, Co Down BT23 4ES
e-mail: programmes@downtown.co.uk   Tel: 028-9181 5555

BERKSHIRE & NORTH HAMPSHIRE
2-Ten FM
PO Box 2020, Reading
Berkshire RG31 7FG
Website: www.2tenfm.co.uk   Tel: 0118-945 4400

BIRMINGHAM
96.4 BRMB & Capital Gold
Nine Brindley Place, 4 Oozells Square, Birmingham B1 2DJ
Website: www.brmb.co.uk   Tel: 0121-226 9964

BORDERS The
Radio Borders Ltd
Tweedside Park, Galashiels TD1 3TD
Website: www.radioborders.com
e-mail: info@radioborders.com
Fax: 0845 3457080   Tel: 01896 759444

BRADFORD
Sunrise Radio
55 Leeds Road, Bradford BD1 5AF
Website: www.sunriseradio.fm
Fax: 01274 728534   Tel: 01274 735043

BRADFORD, HUDDERSFIELD, HALIFAX, KEIGHLEY, DEWSBURY
Pulse Gold
Forster Square, Bradford BD1 5NE
e-mail: general@pulse.co.uk   Tel: 01274 203040

BRIGHTON, EASTBOURNE & HASTINGS
Southern FM
Radio House, Franklin Road
PO Box 2000, Brighton BN41 2SS
Website: www.southernfm.com
Fax: 01273 316909   Tel: 01273 430111

BRISTOL
GWR FM & Classic Gold 1260
1 Passage Street, PO Box 2000, Bristol BS99 7SN
Website: www.gwrfm.co.uk
Fax: 0117-984 3202   Tel: 0117-984 3200

CAMBRIDGE & NEWMARKET
Q103 FM
Q103, The Vision Park, Chivers Way
Histon, Cambridge CB4 9WW
Website: www.q103.co.uk   Tel: 01223 235255

CARDIFF & NEWPORT
Red Dragon FM & Capital Gold
Atlantic Wharf, Cardiff Bay
Cardiff CF10 4DJ
Website: www.reddragonfm.co.uk   Tel: 029-2066 2066

CHESTER, NORTH WALES & WIRRAL
Marcher Group & Classic Gold
The Studios, Mold Road
Wrexham LL11 4AF
Website: www.marchersound.co.uk
e-mail: news@marchersound.co.uk   Tel: 01978 752202
Programme Controller: Lisa Marley

COVENTRY
Mercia
Hertford Place, Coventry CV1 3TT
Website: www.mercia.co.uk
Fax: 024-7686 8209   Tel: 024-7686 8200

DERBY
Ram FM
35-36 Irongate, Derby DE1 3GA
Website: www.ramfm.co.uk   Tel: 01332 324000

DUMFRIES
South West Sound FM
Unit 40, The Loreburn Centre
High Street, Dumfries DG1 2BD
Website: www.southwestsound.co.uk
Fax: 01387 265629   Tel: 01387 250999

DUNDEE & PERTH
Tay FM & Radio Tay AM
PO Box 123, 6 North Isla Street
Dundee DD3 7JQ
Website: www.radiotay.co.uk
e-mail: tayfm@radiotay.co.uk   Tel: 01382 200800

EDINBURGH
Radio Forth Ltd
Forth House, Forth Street, Edinburgh EH1 3LE
Website: www.radioforth.com
e-mail: info@radioforth.com   Tel: 0131-556 9255

EXETER & TORBAY
Gemini FM
Hawthorn House
Exeter Business Park, Exeter EX1 3QS
Website: www.geminifm.co.uk
Fax: 01392 354249   Tel: 01392 444444

FALKIRK
Central FM
201-203 High Street, Falkirk FK1 1DU
Website: www.centralfm.co.uk
Fax: 01324 611168   Tel: 01324 611164

GLASGOW
Radio Clyde 1 & Clyde 2
3 South Avenue,
Clydebank Business Park, Glasgow G81 2RX
Website: www.clyde1.com / www.clyde2.com
Fax: 0141-565 2265   Tel: 0141-565 2200

GLOUCESTER & CHELTENHAM
Severn Sound, FM & Gold
Bridge Studios
Eastgate Centre
Gloucester GL1 1SS
Website: www.severnsound.co.uk
Fax: 01452 572409   Tel: 01452 572400

GREAT YARMOUTH & NORWICH
Radio Broadland & Classic Gold Amber
St Georges Plain
47-49 Colegate, Norwich NR3 1DB
Website: www.radiobroadland.co.uk
Fax: 01603 671189   Tel: 01603 630621

GUILDFORD
96.4 Eagle Radio
Eagle Radio Ltd, Dolphin House
3 North Street, Guildford, Surrey GU1 4AA
Website: www.964eagle.co.uk
e-mail: onair@964eagle.co.uk   Tel: 01483 300964

HEREFORD & WORCESTER
Wyvern FM
1st Floor, Kirkham House
John Comyn Drive, Worcester WR3 7NS
Website: www.wyvernfm.co.uk   Tel: 01905 612212

INVERNESS
Moray Firth Radio
PO Box 271, Scorguie Place, Inverness IV3 8UJ
Website: www.mfr.co.uk
e-mail: mfr@mfr.co.uk
Fax: 01463 243224   Tel: 01463 224433

IPSWICH
SGR-FM
Radio House, Alpha Business Park
Whitehouse Road, Ipswich IP1 5LT
Website: www.sgrfm.co.uk
Fax: 01473 467549   Tel: 01473 461000

ISLE OF WIGHT
Isle of Wight Radio
Dodnor Park, Newport
Isle of Wight PO30 5XE
Website: www.iwradio.co.uk
e-mail: admin@iwradio.co.uk
Fax: 01983 821690   Tel: 01983 822557

KENT
Invicta FM & Capital Gold
Radio House
John Wilson Business Park
Whitstable, Kent CT5 3QX
Website: www.invictafm.com   Tel: 01227 772004

LEEDS
96.3 Radio Aire & Magic 828
51 Burley Road, Leeds LS3 1LR
Website: www.radioaire.com
Fax: 0113-283 5501   Tel: 0113-283 5500

LEICESTER
Leicester Sound
6 Dominus Way, Meridian Way Business Park
Leicester LE19 1RP
Website: www.leicestersound.co.uk
Fax: 0116-256 1309   Tel: 0116-256 1300

LEICESTER, NOTTINGHAM & DERBY
96 Trent FM & Gold GEM
Chapel Quarter, Maid Marian Way
Nottingham NG1 6JR
Website: www.trentfm.co.uk
Fax: 0115-873 1569   Tel: 0115-873 1500

LIVERPOOL
Radio City
St Johns Beacon
1 Houghton Street, Liverpool L1 1RL
Website: www.radiocity.co.uk   Tel: 0151-472 6800

LONDON
102.2 Smooth Radio
26-27 Castlereagh Street
London W1H 5DL
Website: www.smoothradio.com
e-mail: info@smoothradio.com   Tel: 020-7706 4100

LONDON
Capital Gold - London
(GCap Media Plc)
30 Leicester Square, London WC2H 7LA
Website: www.gcapmedia.com
Fax: 020-7766 6100   Tel: 020-7766 6810

LONDON
Choice FM
(GCap Media Plc)
30 Leicester Square, London WC2H 7LA
Website: www.gcapmedia.com
Fax: 020-7766 6100   Tel: 020-7766 6810

LONDON
Classic FM
(GCap Media Plc)
30 Leicester Square, London WC2H 7LA
Website: www.gcapmedia.com
Fax: 020-7344 2700   Tel: 020-7343 9000

LONDON
Heart 106.2 FM
The Chrysalis Building
Bramley Road, London W10 6SP
Website: www.heart1062.co.uk
Fax: 020-7470 1066   Tel: 020-7468 1062

LONDON
(Independent Radio News) ITN Radio
200 Gray's Inn Road, London WC1X 8XZ
Website: www.irn.co.uk
e-mail: irn@itn.co.uk   Tel: 020-7430 4814

LONDON
London Greek Radio
437 High Road, Finchley
London N12 0AP
Website: www.lgr.co.uk   Tel: 020-8349 6950

LONDON
Magic 105.4 FM
Mappin House, 4 Winsley Street
London W1W 8HF
Website: www.magic.co.uk   Tel: 020-7182 8233

LONDON
Time 106.8 FM/South 107.3 FM
2-6 Basildon Road
London SE2 0EW   Tel: 020-8311 3112

LONDON
Virgin Radio
1 Golden Square, London W1F 9DJ
Website: www.virginradio.co.uk
Fax: 020-7434 1197   Tel: 020-7434 1215

LUTON & BEDFORD
97.6 Chiltern Radio & Gold
Broadcast Centre
Chiltern Road
Dunstable LU6 1HQ
Website: www.mychilternradio.co.uk
Fax: 01582 676209   Tel: 01582 676200

MANCHESTER
Key 103 FM & Magic 1152
Piccadilly Radio Ltd, Castle Quay
Castle Field, Manchester M15 4PR
Website: www.key103.co.uk
Fax: 0161-288 5151   Tel: 0161-288 5000

MILTON KEYNES
Horizon Radio
14 Vincent Avenue
Milton Keynes Broadcast Centre
Crownhill, Milton Keynes MK8 0AB
Website: www.horizonmk.co.uk   Tel: 01908 269111

NORTHAMPTON
Northhants 96/Classic Gold 1557
19-21 St Edmunds Road
Northampton NN1 5DT
Website: www.northants96.co.uk   Tel: 01604 795600

NORTHAMPTONSHIRE
Connect FM 97.2 & 107.4 FM
2nd Floor, 5 Church Street
Peterborough PE1 1XB
Website: www.connectfm.com
Fax: 01733 898107   Tel: 0844 8001769

NOTTINGHAM
Gold
Level 6, Chapel Quarter
Maid Marian Way, Nottingham NG1 6JR
Website: www.musicradio.com
Fax: 0115-873 1509   Tel: 0115-873 1500

NOTTINGHAM & DERBY
96 Trent FM
Chapel Quarter, Maid Marian Way
Nottingham NG1 6JR
Website: www.trentfm.co.uk   Tel: 0115-873 1500

OXFORD & BANBURY
Fox FM
Brush House, Pony Road
Oxford OX4 2XR
Website: www.foxfm.co.uk   Tel: 01865 871000

PETERBOROUGH
102.7 Hereward FM & Classic Gold
PO Box 225, Queensgate Centre
Peterborough PE1 1XJ
Website: www.hereward.co.uk   Tel: 01733 460460

PLYMOUTH
Plymouth Sound & Gold
Earl's Acre, Alma Road, Plymouth PL3 4HX
Website: www.plymouthsound.com   Tel: 01752 275600

PORTSMOUTH & SOUTHAMPTON
Power FM, Ocean FM & Capital Gold
(GCap Media Plc)
Radio House, Whittle Avenue
Segensworth West, Fareham
Hampshire PO15 5SH
Website: www.powerfm.com   Tel: 01489 589911

SOMERSET
Orchard FM
Haygrove House, Shoreditch Road, Taunton TA3 7BT
Website: www.orchardfm.co.uk   Tel: 01823 338448

SOUTH MANCHESTER
Imagine FM (104.9)
Regent House, Heaton Lane
Stockport, Cheshire SK4 1BX
Website: www.imaginefm.net
e-mail: info@imaginefm.net
Fax: 0161-609 1401   Tel: 0161-609 1400

STOKE-ON-TRENT
Focal Radio
Studio 15, Initiative House
Campbell Road, Stoke-on-Trent ST4 4DE
Website: www.focalradio.com
e-mail: verity.hilton@focalradio.com   Tel: 01782 415333

STOKE-ON-TRENT & STAFFORD
Signal Radio
Stoke Road, Stoke-on-Trent
Staffordshire ST4 2SR
Website: www.signalone.co.uk
e-mail: info@signalradio.com   Tel: 01782 441300

SWANSEA
96.4 FM The Wave
Victoria Road,, Gowerton, Swansea SA4 3AB
Website: www.thewave.co.uk   Tel: 01792 511964

TEESSIDE
TFM 96.6 & Magic 1170
Yale Crescent, Teesdale
Thornaby, Stockton on Tees TS17 6AA
Website: www.tfmradio.com   Tel: 01642 888222

TYNE & WEAR & NORTHUMBERLAND & DURHAM
Metro Radio
55 Degrees North, Pilgrim Street
Newcastle upon Tyne NE1 6BF
Website: www.metroradio.co.uk   Tel: 0191-230 6100

WOLVERHAMPTON & BLACK COUNTRY/SHREWSBURY & TELFORD
West Midlands Beacon Radio
267 Tettenhall Road
Wolverhampton WV6 0DE
Website: www.beaconradio.co.uk   Tel: 01902 461200

YORKSHIRE
Hallam FM & Magic AM
Radio House, 900 Herries Road
Hillsborough, Sheffield S6 1RH
Website: www.hallamfm.co.uk   Tel: 0114-209 1000

YORKSHIRE & LINCOLNSHIRE
96.9 Viking FM & Magic 1161 AM
Commercial Road
Hull HU1 2SG
Website: www.vikingfm.co.uk   Tel: 01482 325141

3 MILLS STUDIOS
Three Mill Lane, London E3 3DU
Website: www.3mills.com
e-mail: info@3mills.com
Fax: 08715 944028   Tel: 020-7363 3336

ACTORS CENTRE The (LONDON)
(Audition Space Only)
1A Tower Street, London WC2H 9NP
Website: www.actorscentre.co.uk
e-mail: roomhire@actorscentre.co.uk
Fax: 020-7240 3896   Tel: 020-7632 8011

ACTOR'S TEMPLE The
13 Warren Street, London W1T 5LG
Website: www.actorstemple.com
e-mail: info@actorstemple.com
Mobile: 07771 734670   Tel: 020-3004 4537

ADI The
218 Lambeth Road, London SE1 7JY
e-mail: playltd@btconnect.com   Tel: 020-7928 6160

ALFORD HOUSE
Aveline Street, London SE11 5DQ
Website: www.alfordhouse.org.uk
e-mail: tim@alfordhouse.org.uk   Tel: 020-7735 1519

ALL TALENT UK
Central Chambers, 93 Hope Street, Glasgow G2 6LD
Website: www.alltalentuk.co.uk
e-mail: enquiries@alltalentuk.co.uk
Fax: 0141-221 8883   Tel: 0141-221 8887

ALRA (Academy of Live and Recorded Arts)
The Royal Victoria Patriotic Building
John Archer Way, London SW18 3SX
Website: www.alra.co.uk
e-mail: info@alra.co.uk
Fax: 020-8875 0789   Tel: 020-8870 6475

AMADEUS CENTRE The
50 Shirland Road, London W9 2JA
Website: www.amadeuscentre.co.uk
e-mail: info@amadeuscentre.co.uk
Fax: 020-7266 1225   Tel: 020-7286 1686

AMERICAN CHURCH IN LONDON The
Whitefield Memorial Church
79A Tottenham Court Road
London W1T 4TD
Website: www.latchcourt.com
e-mail: latchcourt@amchurch.co.uk
Fax: 020-7580 5013   Tel: 020-7580 2791

ARCH 468 THEATRE STUDIO
Arch 468, 209A Coldharbour Lane, London SW9 8RU
Website: www.arch468.com   Mobile: 07973 302908

ARTSADMIN
Toynbee Studios
28 Commercial Street, London E1 6AB
Website: www.artsadmin.co.uk
e-mail: admin@artsadmin.co.uk
Fax: 020-7247 5103   Tel: 020-7247 5102

AVIV DANCE STUDIOS
Wren House, 1st Floor
19-23 Exchange Road, Watford WD18 6JD
Website: www.avivdance.com
e-mail: nikkiavron@btconnect.com   Tel/Fax: 01923 250000

BAC
Lavender Hill, London SW11 5TN
Website: www.bac.org.uk
e-mail: mailbox@bac.org.uk
Fax: 020-7978 5207   Tel: 020-7223 6557

BELSIZE MUSIC ROOMS
(Casting, Auditioning, Filming)
67 Belsize Lane
Hampstead, London NW3 5AX
Website: www.belsize-music-rooms.co.uk
e-mail: info@belsize-music-rooms.co.uk
Fax: 020-7916 0222   Tel: 020-7916 0111

BIG CITY STUDIOS
Montgomery House
159-161 Balls Pond Road
Islington, London N1 4BG
Website: www.pineappleagency.com
Fax: 020-7241 3006   Tel: 020-7241 6655

How should I prepare for an audition?

When you are called to a casting you should make sure you are fully prepared with accurate information about the audition time, venue and format. Research the casting director too: look on his or her website and pay attention to media news. What productions have they worked on previously? What do they seem to look for and expect from the actors they cast?

For most auditions you will be given a script to learn, but you could be provided with a brief in advance and asked to find something suitable yourself. It would be advisable to have about five or six pieces ready to choose from that demonstrate your range before you are even called to a casting. You should select two relevant but contrasting pieces of about two to three minutes each for your audition, with the others as backups. If you can, read the whole play in addition to your speech.

It is generally best not to use 'popular' or very well-known pieces and instead to use original modern speeches, as this prevents the likelihood of the casting director comparing you, perhaps unfavourably, with anyone else. Having said this, however, you should still rehearse at least one Shakespeare piece. To find suitable speeches you should read widely for inspiration, or you could search online. If you are still struggling, think about who your favourite playwrights are and find out if they have written anything that is not too well-known.

What should I expect when I arrive at the audition?

Arrive early for your audition, but be prepared to wait! Time slots are allocated but auditions can overrun for various reasons. Be presentable and think about how your character might choose to dress, but overall you will feel more comfortable and confident if you don't differ too much from what you would normally wear. Don't come in costume unless specifically asked.

When you enter the audition room, you may have just the casting director in the room, or you could be confronted with a panel including the director and/or producer, and an editor and cameraman if you are being filmed. Don't let this disconcert you. Nerves are to be expected, but try to be positive and enjoy yourself. Remember, the casting director doesn't want to spend several days auditioning – they want you to get the job!

Take a few moments to work out where you should stand and where everything is. Don't ask too many questions as this can be irritating but you could ask whether to address your monologue to the casting director / camera, or whether to speak into the 'middle distance'. Make sure that your face, and in particular your eyes, can be seen as much as possible.

Once you have performed your monologue, pause and wait for the casting director to speak to you. Don't ask if they want to see a second speech. If they want another one, and if there's time, they will ask you. You may be asked your opinion on the speech so be prepared with possible answers. Never criticise previous productions you have worked on. At the end of the casting, remember to take your script away unless you are asked to leave it, otherwise it can look as if you're not interested.

Auditions are never a waste of time, even if you don't get the part. You may have performed well but you might not have been quite right for that particular role. Every audition is great practice and experience, and the casting director may very well keep you in mind for future productions.

Should I attend a casting in a house or flat?

Professional auditions are rarely held anywhere other than an official casting studio or venue. Be very wary if you are asked to go elsewhere. Trust your instincts. If something doesn't seem right to you, it probably isn't. Always take someone with you if you are in any doubt.

BLACK BOX MERSEYSIDE Ltd
The Black Box, 21 Hutchinson Walk, Liverpool L6 1JW
Website: www.blackboxmerseyside.co.uk
e-mail: admin@blackboxmerseyside.co.uk
Fax: 0151-260 3001   Tel: 0151-260 3000

BLOOMSBURY THEATRE The
15 Gordon Street, London WC1H 0AH
Website: www.thebloomsbury.com
e-mail: blooms.theatre@ucl.ac.uk   Tel: 020-7679 2777

BRIXTON COMMUNITY SPACE
(Formerly Brixton St Vincent's Community Centre)
Talma Road, London SW2 1AS
Website: www.bsvcc.org
e-mail: carofunnell@bsvcc.org   Tel: 020-7326 4417

BRIXTON ST VINCENT'S COMMUNITY CENTRE
(See BRIXTON COMMUNITY SPACE)

CARDINBROOK Ltd
32 Barkston Gardens, London SW5 0EN
Website: www.ycbc.co.uk/roomhire.htm
e-mail: info@ycbc.co.uk   Tel: 020-7373 1665

CAST IN SPACE
27 Little Russell Street, London WC1A 2HN
Website: www.castinspace.com
e-mail: castinspace@btconnect.com   Tel: 020-7404 9637

CASTING AT SWEET
Sweet Entertainments Ltd
42 Theobalds Road, London WC1X 8NW
e-mail: casting@sweet-uk.net
Fax: 07092 863782   Tel: 020-7404 6411

CASTING STUDIOS INTERNATIONAL Ltd
Ramillies House, 1-2 Ramillies Street, London W1F 7LN
Website: www.castingstudios.com
e-mail: info@castingstudios.com
Fax: 020-7437 2080   Tel: 020-7437 2070

CASTING SUITE The
8-10 Lower James Street, London W1F 9EL
Website: www.thecastingsuite.com
e-mail: info@thecastingsuite.com
Fax: 020-7494 0803   Tel: 020-7534 5757

CECIL SHARP HOUSE
2 Regent's Park Road, London NW1 7AY
Website: www.efdss.org
e-mail: hire@efdss.org
Fax: 020-7284 0534   Tel: 020-7485 2206

CENTRAL LONDON GOLF CENTRE
Burntwood Lane, London SW17 0AT
Website: www.clgc.co.uk
Fax: 020-8874 7447   Tel: 020-8871 2468

CENTRAL STUDIOS
470 Bromley Road, Bromley, Kent BR1 4PN
Website: www.dandbperformingarts.co.uk
e-mail: bonnie@dandbmanagement.com
Fax: 020-8697 8100   Tel: 020-8698 8880

CHATS PALACE ARTS CENTRE
42-44 Brooksby's Walk, Hackney, London E9 6DF
Website: www.chatspalace.com
e-mail: info@chatspalace.com   Tel: 020-8533 0227

CHELSEA THEATRE
Contact: James Tilston
World's End Place, King's Road
London SW10 0DR
Website: www.chelseatheatre.org.uk
e-mail: admin@chelseatheatre.org.uk
Fax: 020-7352 2024   Tel: 020-7349 7811

CIRCUS MANIACS SCHOOL OF CIRCUS ARTS
(Circus Skills Rehearsal & Casting Facilities)
Office 8A, The Kingswood Foundation
Britannia Road
Kingswood, Bristol BS15 8DB
Website: www.circusmaniacs.com
e-mail: info@circusmaniacs.com
Mobile: 07977 247287   Tel/Fax: 0117-947 7042

CLAPHAM COMMUNITY PROJECT
St Anne's Hall
31-33 Bromells Road, London SW4 0BN
Website: www.rehearseatccp.co.uk
e-mail: admin@claphamcommunityproject.org.uk
    Tel/Fax: 020-7720 8731

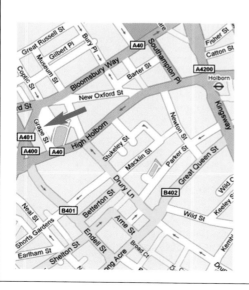

CLEAN BREAK
2 Patshull Road, London NW5 2LB
Website: www.cleanbreak.org.uk
e-mail: general@cleanbreak.org.uk
Fax: 020-7482 8611　　　　　Tel: 020-7482 8600

CLUB FOR ACTS & ACTORS
(Incorporating Concert Artistes Association)
20 Bedford Street, London WC2E 9HP
Website: www.thecaa.org
e-mail: office@thecaa.org　　　Tel: 020-7836 3172

COLOMBO CENTRE The
(Rehearsal & Audition Space)
34-68 Colombo Street, London SE1 8DP
Website: www.colombocentre.org
e-mail: clubmanager@colombo-centre.org
　　　　　　　　　　　　　　Tel: 020-7261 1658

COPTIC STREET STUDIO Ltd
9 Coptic Street, London WC1A 1NH
e-mail: andrew@copticstreet.com　Tel: 020-7636 2030

CRAGRATS Ltd
The Mill, Dunford Road, Holmfirth, Huddersfield HD9 2AR
Website: www.cragrats.com
e-mail: chrislunn@cragrats.com
Fax: 01484 686212　　　　　Tel: 01484 686451

CUSTARD FACTORY The
Gibb Street, Digbeth, Birmingham B9 4AA
Website: www.custardfactory.co.uk
e-mail: dave.peebles@custardfactory.co.uk
Fax: 0121-604 8888　　　　　Tel: 0121-224 7777

DANCE ATTIC STUDIOS
368 North End Road
London SW6　　　　　　　　Tel: 020-7610 2055

DANCE COMPANY STUDIOS
76 High Street, Beckenham BR3 1ED
Website: www.dancecompanystudios.co.uk
e-mail: hire@dancecompanystudios.co.uk
　　　　　　　　　　　　　　Tel: 020-8402 2424

DANCEWORKS
16 Balderton Street, London W1K 6TN
Website: www.danceworks.net
Fax: 020-7629 2909　　　　　Tel: 020-7318 4100

DAVIES Siobhan STUDIOS
85 St George's Road, London SE1 6ER
Website: www.siobhandavies.com
e-mail: info@siobhandavies.com
Fax: 020-7091 9669　　　　　Tel: 020-7091 9650

DIORAMA ARTS
1 Euston Centre, London NW1 3JG
Website: www.diorama-arts.org.uk
e-mail: admin@diorama-arts.org.uk　Tel: 020-7916 5467

DRILL HALL The
16 Chenies Street, London WC1E 7EX
Website: www.drillhall.co.uk
e-mail: box.office@drillhall.co.uk
Fax: 020-7307 5062　　　　　Tel: 020-7307 5060

EALING STUDIOS
Ealing Green, London W5 5EP
Website: www.ealingstudios.com
e-mail: bookings@ealingstudios.com
Fax: 020-8758 8658　　　　　Tel: 020-8567 6655

ELMS LESTERS PAINTING ROOMS
1-3-5 Flitcroft Street, London WC2H 8DH
e-mail: info@elmslesters.co.uk
Fax: 020-7379 0789　　　　　Tel: 020-7836 6747

ENGLISH FOLK DANCE & SONG SOCIETY
Cecil Sharp House, 2 Regent's Park Road, London NW1 7AY
Website: www.efdss.org
e-mail: hire@efdss.org
Fax: 020-7284 0534   Tel: 020-7485 2206

ENGLISH NATIONAL OPERA
Lilian Baylis House
165 Broadhurst Gardens, London NW6 3AX
Website: www.eno.org
e-mail: receptionlbh@eno.org
Fax: 020-7625 3398   Tel: 020-7624 7711

ENGLISH TOURING THEATRE
25 Short Street, Waterloo, London SE1 8LJ
Website: www.ett.org.uk
e-mail: admin@ett.org.uk
Fax: 020-7633 0188   Tel: 020-7450 1990

ET-NIK-A CASTING STUDIO
30 Great Portland Street, London W1W 8QU
Website: www.etnikastudios.com
e-mail: info@etnikastudios.com
Fax: 020-7299 3558   Tel: 020-7193 4230

ETCETERA THEATRE
265 Camden High Street, London NW1 7BU
Website: www.etceteratheatre.com
e-mail: etc@etceteratheatre.com
Fax: 020-7482 0378   Tel: 020-7482 4857

EUROKIDS & EKA CASTING STUDIOS
The Warehouse Studios, Glaziers Lane, Culcheth
Warrington, Cheshire WA3 4AQ
Website: www.eka-agency.com
e-mail: castings@eka-agency.com
Fax: 01925 767563   Tel: 01925 761088

EXCHANGE The
Old Market Hill, Sturminster Newton DT10 1QU
Website: www.stur-exchange.co.uk
e-mail: info@stur-exchange.co.uk   Tel: 01258 475137

EXPRESSIONS STUDIOS
Linton House, 39-51 Highgate Road, London NW5 1RT
Website: www.expressionsstudios.com
e-mail: info@expressionsstudios.com
Fax: 020-7813 1582   Tel: 020-7813 1580

FACTORY DANCE CENTRE
407 Hornsey Road, London N19 4DX
e-mail: info@tangolondon.com   Tel: 020-7272 1122

FACTORY FITNESS & DANCE CENTRE The
407 Hornsey Road, London N19 4DX
e-mail: info@tangolondon.com   Tel: 020-7272 1122

FOX CASTING STUDIOS & REHEARSAL SPACE
Pinewood Studios, Pinewood Road
Iver Heath, Bucks SL0 0NH
e-mail: info@actorsstudio.co.uk   Tel: 01753 656848

Unit 10, 21 Wren Street, London WC1 0HX

FSU LONDON STUDY CENTRE
98-104 Great Russell Street, London WC1B 3LA
Fax: 020-7813 3270   Tel: 020-7813 3223

FUNK PHYSICS Ltd
Unit 5, Bernie Grant Enterprise Building
Town Hall, Approach Road, London N15 4RX
Website: www.funkphysics.com
e-mail: info@funkphysics.com   Tel: 020-8885 0500

32 Cubitt Street

32 Cubitt Street, London WC1X 0LR between Kings Cross and Holborn, is a former Baptist church with seating for 220 in the main hall and balcony. The hall measures 13m X 11.5m (42' X 37'). It has an upright piano, a Bose audio system and sound desk, an adaptable Steeldeck stage, wooden floors and wall mirrors. Downstairs at Cubitt Street is a large studio space and a full catering kitchen.

Cubitt Street is available for rehearsals, auditions, recitals, film shoots and private parties.

For bookings, prices or more information please call 0845 370 7990 or email info@onlyconnectuk.org

HAMPSTEAD THEATRE
Eton Avenue, Swiss Cottage, London NW3 3EU
Website: www.hampsteadtheatre.com
e-mail: info@hampsteadtheatre.com
Fax: 020-7449 4201   Tel: 020-7449 4200

HOLY INNOCENTS CHURCH
Paddenswick Road, London W6 0UB
Website: www.hisj.co.uk
e-mail: innocent@fish.co.uk
Fax: 020-8563 8735   Tel: 020-8748 2286

HOPE STREET Ltd
13A Hope Street, Liverpool L1 9BQ
Website: www.hope-street.org
e-mail: arts@hope-street.org
Fax: 0151-709 3242   Tel: 0151-708 8007

HOXTON HALL THEATRE & YOUTH ARTS CENTRE
130 Hoxton Street, London N1 6SH
Website: www.hoxtonhall.co.uk
e-mail: carolyn@hoxtonhall.co.uk
Fax: 020-7729 3815   Tel: 020-7684 0060

HUB The @ TOOTING & MITCHAM
Imperial Fields, Bishops Ford Road
Morden, Surrey SM4 6BF
Website: www.thehubattmufc.co.uk
e-mail: maren.dallman@visitthehub.co.uk
Fax: 020-8685 6190   Tel: 020-8685 6193

IMT SPACE Ltd
Unit 2, 210 Cambridge Heath Road, London E2 9NQ
Website: www.imagemusictext.com
e-mail: mail@imagemusictext.com   Tel: 020-8980 5475

INC SPACE
9-13 Grape Street, London WC2
Website: www.inc-space.com
e-mail: studiohire@inc-space.com

ISLINGTON ARTS FACTORY
2 Parkhurst Road, London N7 0SF
Website: www.islingtonartsfactory.org.uk
e-mail: iaf@islingtonartsfactory.fsnet.co.uk
Fax: 020-7700 7229   Tel: 020-7607 0561

JACKSONS LANE
(Various Spaces incl Rehearsal Rooms & Theatre Hire)
269A Archway Road, London N6 5AA
Website: www.jacksonslane.org.uk
e-mail: reception@jacksonslane.org.uk
Tel: 020-8340 5226   Tel: 020-8340 8902

Rehearsal Space for hire
Very close to Clapham Common tube (1min)

Main Hall
Wooden floor
Dimensions: 12.19 x 13.4m,
stage: 8.19 x 4.44m approx
• piano • toilets • kitchen area
• adjoining green room & separate
  lower hall also available.

New additional space
Ideal for auditions/production meetings
or as a small rehearsal space
Dimensions: 8 x 4.5m approx
• Harlequin floor • Roland keyboard
• water machine.

Facilities: • telephone • fax • photocopying • tv & dvd • wi-fi.

clapham community project
St Anne's Hall, 31-33 Bromells Road, London SW4 0BN
Tel/Fax: 0207 720 8731 www.rehearseatccp.co.uk
Clapham Community Project is a registered charity, number 299072

RADA
ROYAL ACADEMY OF DRAMATIC ART

three theatres
fifteen multi-purpose rehearsal rooms
one mirrored dance studio
one audio recording studio
one bar and cabaret space
construction workshops and paintframe

All available for hire at RADA
62-64 Gower Street, London WC1E 6ED and
18-22 Chenies Street, London WC1E 7PA

Contact Nick De Courcy, 0207 908 4754
bookings@rada.ac.uk, www.rada.org

JERWOOD SPACE
171 Union Street, London SE1 0LN
Website: www.jerwoodspace.co.uk
e-mail: space@jerwoodspace.co.uk
Fax: 020-7654 0172   Tel: 020-7654 0171

LIVE THEATRE
27 Broad Chare, Quayside
Newcastle upon Tyne NE1 3DQ
Website: www.live.org.uk
e-mail: info@live.org.uk   Tel: 0191-261 2694

LONDON BUBBLE THEATRE COMPANY Ltd
5 Elephant Lane
London SE16 4JD
Website: www.londonbubble.org.uk
e-mail: admin@londonbubble.org.uk
Fax: 020-7231 2366   Tel: 020-7237 4434

LONDON SCHOOL OF CAPOEIRA
Units 1 & 2 Leeds Place
Tollington Park
London N4 3RF
Website: www.londonschoolofcapoeira.co.uk
e-mail: info@londonschoolofcapoeira.co.uk
    Tel: 020-7281 2020

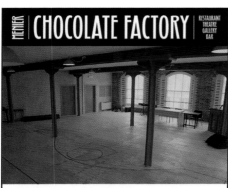

MENIER CHOCOLATE FACTORY | RESTAURANT THEATRE GALLERY BAR

Self-contained rehearsal room
with production office (incl. tel / fax / internet
facilities) 2 X WC, kitchenette. Playing area is
approx. 30 sqm with additional space
for production desk / props etc.
Contact **020 7378 1712** for availability and prices.

Menier
Chocolate Factory
53 Southwark Street
London SE1 1RU

Tel: 020 7378 1712
office@menierchocolatefactory.com
www.menierchocolatefactory.com

LONDON STUDIO CENTRE
42-50 York Way, London N1 9AB
e-mail: info@london-studio-centre.co.uk
Fax: 020-7837 3248   Tel: 020-7837 7741

LONDON WELSH TRUST Ltd
157-163 Gray's Inn Road, London WC1X 8UE
Fax: 020-7837 6268   Tel: 020-7837 3722

LYRIC HAMMERSMITH
King Street, London W6 0QL
Website: www.lyric.co.uk
e-mail: enquiries@lyric.co.uk
Fax: 020-8741 5965   Tel: 0871 2211722

MACKINTOSH Cameron REHEARSAL STUDIO
The Tricycle, 269 Kilburn High Road, London NW6 7JR
Website: www.tricycle.co.uk
e-mail: admin@tricycle.co.uk
Fax: 020-7328 0795   Tel: 020-7372 6611

MADDERMARKET THEATRE
St John's Alley, Norwich, Norfolk NR2 1DR
Website: www.maddermarket.co.uk
e-mail: mmtheatre@btconnect.com
Fax: 01603 661357   Tel: 01603 626560

MARIA ASSUMPTA CENTRE
23 Kensington Square, London W8 5HN
Website: www.maria-assumpta.org.uk
e-mail: conf@maria-assumpta.org.uk   Tel: 020-7361 4704

MENIER CHOCOLATE FACTORY
53 Southwark Street, London SE1 1RU
Website: www.menierchocolatefactory.com
e-mail: office@menierchocolatefactory.com
Fax: 020-7378 1713   Tel: 020-7378 1712

MOBERLY SPORTS & EDUCATION CENTRE
Kilburn Lane, London W10 4AH
Fax: 020-7641 5878   Tel: 020-7641 4807

MOUNTVIEW
Academy of Theatre Arts
Ralph Richardson Memorial Studios, Kingfisher Place
Clarendon Road, London N22 6XF
Website: www.mountview.org.uk
e-mail: enquiries@mountview.org.uk
Fax: 020-8829 0034   Tel: 020-8881 2201

MUSIC ROOM AT COLE KITCHENN The
212 Strand, London WC2R 1AP
e-mail: info@colekitchenn.com   Tel: 020-7427 5680

NATIONAL YOUTH THEATRE OF GREAT BRITAIN
443-445 Holloway Road, London N7 6LW
Website: www.nyt.org.uk
e-mail: info@nyt.org.uk
Fax: 020-7281 8246   Tel: 020-7281 3863

NEALS YARD MEETING ROOMS
14 Neals Yard, Covent Garden, London WC2H 9DP
Website: www.meetingrooms.org.uk
e-mail: info@walkinbackrub.co.uk   Tel/Fax: 020-7436 9875

SPOTLIGHT SPACES

Spacious casting rooms and studios in the heart of the West End

- Free receptionist service
- Large waiting room
- Wireless Internet
- Video conference facilities
- Post free audition clips online
- Competitive rates

www.spotlight.com/spaces
For bookings: 020 7440 5030 email: spaces@spotlight.com
7 Leicester Place London WC2H 7RJ

DANCE COMPANY STUDIOS
Rehearsal spaces available

Dance Company's top-quality professional studios are available 7 days a week for rehearsals, auditions, workshops, photo shoots and other functions. The studios are on the High Street surrounded by cafés & shops. 10 minutes from London Victoria to Beckenham Junction. Wimbledon/Croydon to Beckenham via Tram link.

Studio 1: 60/40 feet 18m/6m.
Studio 2: 30/30 feet 9m/9m **Studio 3:** 30/20 feet 9m/6m
Sprung maple floors, mirrors, barres & pianos.
Reception/waiting area. Hot & cold drinks available.

Contact 020 8402 2424
hire@dancecompanystudios.co.uk
76 High St, Beckenham. BR3 1ED
www.dancecompanystudios.co.uk

BLOOMSBURY THEATRE

REHEARSAL STUDIO

Attractive and modern, 11m x 8m (36ft x 26ft 4in)
Sprung dance floor, mirrored wall, piano,
kitchenette, adjustable lighting.
Shop and café on site.

Easily accessible central location

Available Mon through Sat, daytime and evening

Contact the Administration Officer
on **020 7679 2777**

15 Gordon Street, London WC1H 0AH
www.thebloomsbury.com

NETTLEFOLD The
West Norwood Library Centre
1 Norwood High Street, London SE27 9JX
e-mail: thenettlefold@lambeth.gov.uk   Tel: 020-7926 8070

NEW PLAYERS THEATRE
The Arches, Off Villiers Street, London WC2N 6NG
Website: www.newplayerstheatre.com
e-mail: info@newplayerstheatre.com
Fax: 0845 6382102   Tel: 020-7930 5868

NLPAC PERFORMING ARTS
(Production & Casting Office Facilities)
76 St James Lane
Muswell Hill, London N10 3DF
Website: www.nlpac.co.uk
e-mail: nlpac@aol.com
Fax: 020-8444 4040   Tel: 020-8444 4544

OBSERVATORY STUDIOS The
45-46 Poland Street, London W1F 7NA
e-mail: info@theobservatorystudios.com
Fax: 020-7437 2830   Tel: 020-7437 2823

OCTOBER GALLERY
24 Old Gloucester Street
London WC1N 3AL
Website: www.octobergallery.co.uk
e-mail: rentals@octobergallery.co.uk
Fax: 020-7405 1851   Tel: 020-7831 1618

OLD VIC THEATRE The
The Cut, London SE1 8NB
Website: www.oldvictheatre.com   Tel: 020-7928 2651

ONLY CONNECT UK
32 Cubitt Street, London WC1X 0LR
Website: www.cubittstreetth.com
e-mail: info@onlyconnectuk.org   Tel: 0845 3707990

OPEN DOOR COMMUNITY CENTRE
Beaumont Road, Wimbledon SW19 6TF
Website: www.wandsworth.gov.uk
e-mail: opendoor@wandsworth.gov.uk
Tel/Fax: 020-8871 8174

OUT OF JOINT
7 Thane Works, Thane Villas, London N7 7NU
Website: www.outofjoint.co.uk
e-mail: ojo@outofjoint.co.uk
Fax: 020-7609 0203   Tel: 020-7609 0207

OVAL HOUSE
52-54 Kennington Oval, London SE11 5SW
Website: www.ovalhouse.com
e-mail: info@ovalhouse.com   Tel: 020-7582 0080

PAINES PLOUGH REHEARSAL & AUDITION SPACE
4th Floor, 43 Aldwych, London WC2B 4DN
Website: www.painesplough.com
e-mail: office@painesplough.com
Fax: 020-7240 4534   Tel: 020-7240 4533

PEOPLE SHOW
(3 Rehearsal Rooms, Set Building Workshop, Casting Suites,
Sound & Lighting Equipment for Hire)
People Show Studios, Pollard Row, London E2 6NB
Website: www.peopleshow.co.uk
e-mail: people@peopleshow.co.uk
Fax: 020-7739 0203   Tel: 020-7729 1841

PHA
Tanzaro House, Ardwick Green North
Manchester M12 6FZ
Website: www.pha-agency.co.uk
e-mail: info@pha-agency.co.uk
Fax: 0161-273 4567   Tel: 0161-273 4444

PINEAPPLE DANCE STUDIOS
7 Langley Street, London WC2H 9JA
Website: www.pineapple.uk.com
e-mail: studios@pineapple.uk.com
Fax: 020-7836 0803   Tel: 020-7836 4004

PLACE The
Robin Howard Dance Theatre
17 Duke's Road, London WC1H 9PY
Website: www.theplace.org.uk
e-mail: info@theplace.org.uk
Fax: 020-7121 1142   Tel: 020-7121 1100

Spacious Rehearsal Rooms / Casting Suites convenient for SW London and Surrey

We have 2 spacious rehearsal rooms / casting suites, both with their own PA / music system and adjustable lighting. One has a sprung dance floor and mirrored walls. Catering can be arranged upon request. There is ample parking and we are within easy reach of Morden tube station and Mitcham tram stop.

Please contact us for further details: maren.dallmann@thehubattmufc.co.uk
The Hub @ Tooting & Mitcham, Imperial Fields, Bishopsford Rd, Morden
Surrey, SM4 6BF, Tel: 020 8685 6193, Fax: 020 8685 6190 www.thehubattmufc.co.uk

PLAYGROUND STUDIO The
Unit 8, Latimer Road
London W10 6RQ
Website: www.the-playground.co.uk
e-mail: info@the-playground.co.uk   Tel/Fax: 020-8960 0110

POOR SCHOOL The
242 Pentonville Road, London N1 9JY
Website: www.thepoorschool.com
e-mail: acting@thepoorschool.com   Tel: 020-7837 6030

PRECINCT THEATRE The
Units 2/3 The Precinct
Packington Square, London N1 7UP
Website: www.breakalegman.com
e-mail: reima@breakalegman.com
Fax: 020-7359 3660   Tel: 020-7359 3594

PUPPET CENTRE TRUST
BAC Lavender Hill, London SW11 5TN
Website: www.puppetcentre.org.uk
e-mail: space@puppetcentre.org.uk   Tel: 020-7228 5335

QUESTORS THEATRE EALING The
12 Mattock Lane, London W5 5BQ
Website: www.questors.org.uk
e-mail: alice@questors.org.uk
Fax: 020-8567 2275   Tel: 020-8567 0011

QUICKSILVER THEATRE
The Glasshouse
4 Enfield Road, London N1 5AZ
Website: www.quicksilvertheatre.org
e-mail: talktous@quicksilvertheatre.org
Fax: 020-7254 3119   Tel: 020-7241 2942

RAG FACTORY The
16-18 Heneage Street, London E1 5LJ
Website: www.ragfactory.org.uk
e-mail: hello@ragfactory.org.uk
Fax: 020-7092 9099   Tel: 020-7650 8749

RAMBERT DANCE COMPANY
94 Chiswick High Road, London W4 1SH
Website: www.rambert.org.uk
e-mail: rdc@rambert.org.uk
Fax: 020-8747 8323   Tel: 020-8630 0600

REALLY USEFUL GROUP THEATRES
(Michael Townsend)
22 Tower Street, London WC2H 9TW
Website: www.reallyuseful.com
e-mail: mike.townsend@reallyuseful.co.uk
Fax: 020-7240 1292   Tel: 020-7240 0880

RED ONION DANCE STUDIO
26-28 Hatherley Mews, London E17 4QP
Website: www.redonion.uk.com
e-mail: info@redonion.uk.com   Tel: 020-8520 3975

RIDGEWAY STUDIOS
Fairley House, Andrews Lane
Cheshunt, Herts EN7 6LB
Fax: 01992 633844   Tel: 01992 633775

RITZ STUDIOS
110-112 Disraeli Road, London SW15 2DX
e-mail: lee@ritzstudios.com
Fax: 020-8877 1036   Tel: 020-8870 1335

RIVERSIDE STUDIOS
Crisp Road, Hammersmith, London W6 9RL
Website: www.riversidestudios.co.uk
e-mail: info@riversidestudios.co.uk
Fax: 020-8237 1001   Tel: 020-8237 1000

ROOFTOP STUDIO THEATRE
Rooftop Studio, Somerfield Arcade
Stone, Staffordshire ST15 8AU
Website: www.rooftopstudio.co.uk
Fax: 01785 818176   Tel: 01785 761233

ROOMS ABOVE The
Westheath Yard (Opposite The Emmanuel School)
174 Mill Lane, West Hampstead, London NW6 1TB
Website: www.theroomsabove.org.uk
e-mail: info@theroomsabove.org.uk
Fax: 020-8201 9464   Tel: 0845 6860802

ROSE STUDIO
Rose Theatre, Kingston
24-26 High Street
Kingston upon Thames
Surrey KT1 1HL
Website: www.rosetheatrekingston.org
e-mail: eventsandhires@rosetheatrekingston.org
Fax: 020-8546 8783   Tel: 020-8546 6983

ROTHERHITHE STUDIOS
119 Rotherhithe Street
London SE16 4NF
Website: www.sandsfilms.co.uk
e-mail: ostockman@sandsfilms.co.uk
Fax: 020-7231 2119   Tel: 020-7231 2209

ROYAL ACADEMY OF DANCE
36 Battersea Square, London SW11 3RA
Website: www.rad.org.uk
e-mail: info@rad.org.uk
Fax: 020-7924 3129   Tel: 020-7326 8000

ROYAL ACADEMY OF DRAMATIC ART
62-64 Gower Street, London WC1E 6ED
e-mail: bookings@rada.ac.uk   Tel: 020-7908 4754

ROYAL SHAKESPEARE COMPANY
35 Clapham High Street, London SW4 7TW
Website: www.rsc.org.uk
e-mail: london@rsc.org.uk
Fax: 020-7845 0505   Tel: 020-7845 0500

SADLER'S WELLS
Rosebery Avenue, London EC1R 4TN
Website: www.sadlerswells.com
e-mail: events@sadlerswells.com
Fax: 020-7863 8061   Tel: 020-7863 8065

SMA CENTRE
Vicarage Gate
Kensington
London W8 4HN
Website: www.smacentre.com
e-mail: manager@smacentre.com
Fax: 020-7368 6505   Tel: 020-7937 8885

SOHO GYMS
Clapham Common Gym
95-97 Clapham High Street, London SW4 7TB
Website: www.sohogyms.com
Fax: 020-7720 6510   Tel: 020-7720 0321

Covent Garden Gym
12 Macklin Street
London WC2B 5NF
Fax: 020-7242 0899   Tel: 020-7242 1290

Earl's Court Gym
254 Earl's Court Road
London SW5 9AD
Fax: 020-7244 6893   Tel: 020-7370 1402

Camden Town Gym
193-199 Camden High Street
London NW1 7BT
Fax: 020-7267 0500   Tel: 020-7482 4524

SOHO THEATRE
21 Dean Street, London W1D 3NE
Website: www.sohotheatre.com
e-mail: jenny@sohotheatre.com
Fax: 020-7287 5061   Tel: 020-7478 0117

SPACE @ CLARENCE MEWS
40 Clarence Mews, London E5 8HL
e-mail: frith.salem@virgin.net   Tel: 020-8986 5260

SPACE ARTS CENTRE The
269 Westferry Road, London E14 3RS
Website: www.space.org.uk
e-mail: info@space.org.uk   Tel: 020-7515 7799

SPACE CITY STUDIOS
77 Blythe Road, London W14 0HP
Website: www.spacecity.co.uk
e-mail: info@spacecity.co.uk
Fax: 020-7371 4001   Tel: 020-7371 4000

S.P.A.C.E. The
(Studio for Performing Arts & Creative Enterprise)
34 Argyle Arcade Chambers
Buchanan Street
Glasgow G2 8BD
Website: www.glasgowactingacademy.com
e-mail: info@glasgowactingacademy.com
Tel: 0141-222 2942

SPOTLIGHT
7 Leicester Place
London WC2H 7RJ
Website: www.spotlight.com/rooms
e-mail: info@spotlight.com
Fax: 020-7437 5881   Tel: 020-7437 7631

ST GEORGE'S CHURCH BLOOMSBURY
Vestry Hall
6 Little Russell Street, London WC1A 2HR
Website: www.stgeorgesbloomsbury.org.uk
e-mail: hiring@stgeorgesbloomsbury.org.uk
Tel: 020-7242 1979

ST JAMES'S CHURCH PICCADILLY
197 Piccadilly, London W1J 9LL
Website: www.st-james-piccadilly.org
e-mail: roomhire@st-james-piccadilly.org
Fax: 020-7734 7449   Tel: 020-7734 4511

ST JOHN'S CHURCH
Waterloo Road
Southbank, London SE1 8TY
Fax: 020-7928 4470   Tel: 020-7633 9819

ST MARTINS-IN-THE-FIELDS
6 St Martins Place
London WC2N 4JJ
Website: www.smitf.org
e-mail: jennifer.lang@smitf.org   Tel: 020-7766 1130

ST MARY'S CHURCH HALL PADDINGTON
c/o Bill Kenwright Ltd
1 Venice Walk, London W2 1RR
e-mail: julia.redican@kenwright.com
Fax: 020-7446 6222   Tel: 020-7446 6200

ST MARY NEWINGTON CHURCH HALL
The Parish Office
57 Kennington Park Road
London SE11 4JQ   Tel: 020-7735 1894

STUDIO 326
Royal Exchange
St Ann's Square, Manchester M2 7BR
Website: www.emmastafford.tv
e-mail: info@emmastafford.tv
Fax: 0161-833 4264   Tel: 0161-833 4263

SUMMERS Mark STUDIOS
137 Freston Road
London W10 6TH
Website: www.marksummers.com
e-mail: info@marksummers.com
Fax: 020-7243 1987   Tel: 020-7299 8413

TAKE FIVE CASTING STUDIO
(Casting Suite)
37 Beak Street, London W1F 9RZ
Website: www.takefivestudio.com
e-mail: info@takefivestudio.com
Fax: 020-7287 3035   Tel: 020-7287 2120

TREADWELL'S
34 Tavistock Street, London WC2E 7PB
Website: www.treadwells-london.com/rehearsal.asp
e-mail: info@treadwells-london.com   Tel: 020-7240 8906

TRESTLE ARTS BASE
(Home of Trestle Theatre Company)
Russet Drive, St Albans, Herts AL4 0JQ
Website: www.trestle.org.uk
e-mail: admin@trestle.org.uk
Fax: 01727 855558   Tel: 01727 850950

TRICYCLE The
269 Kilburn High Road
London NW6 7JR
Website: www.tricycle.co.uk
e-mail: info@tricycle.co.uk
Fax: 020-7328 0795   Tel: 020-7372 6611

TWICKENHAM SEA CADETS
Fairways, Off Broom Road
Teddington
Middlesex TW11 9PL   Tel: 01784 241020

UNION CHAPEL PROJECT
Compton Avenue
London N1 2XD
Website: www.unionchapel.org.uk
e-mail: spacehire@unionchapel.org.uk
Fax: 020-7354 8343   Tel: 020-7226 3750

URDANG ACADEMY The
Finsbury Town Hall
Rosebery Avenue
London EC1
Website: www.theurdangacademy.com
e-mail: info@theurdangacademy.com
Fax: 020-7278 6727   Tel: 020-7713 7710

WALKING FORWARD Ltd
Studio 1
35 Britannia Row
London N1 8QH
Website: www.walkingforward.co.uk
e-mail: info@walkingforward.co.uk
Fax: 020-7359 5091   Tel: 020-7359 5249

WATERMANS
40 High Street
Brentford TW8 0DS
Website: www.watermans.org.uk
e-mail: info@watermans.org.uk
Fax: 020-8232 1030   Tel: 020-8232 1020

YOUNG ACTORS THEATRE
70-72 Barnsbury Road, London N1 0ES
Website: www.yati.org.uk
e-mail: info@yati.org.uk
Fax: 020-7833 9467   Tel: 020-7278 2101

YOUNG Sylvia THEATRE SCHOOL
Rossmore Road
Marylebone, London NW1 6NJ
e-mail: info@sylviayoungtheatreschool.co.uk
Fax: 020-7723 1040   Tel: 020-7723 0037

Y TOURING THEATRE COMPANY
One KX
120 Cromer Street
London WC1H 8BS
Website: www.ytouring.org.uk
e-mail: info@ytouring.org.uk   Tel: 020-7520 3090

ACTIVATION
Riverside House
Feltham Avenue
Hampton Court
Surrey KT8 9BJ
Website: www.activation.co.uk
e-mail: info@activation.co.uk
Fax: 020-8783 9345   Tel: 020-8783 9494

ACT UP
Unit 88, 99-109 Lavender Hill
London SW11 5QL
Website: www.act-up.co.uk
e-mail: info@act-up.co.uk
Fax: 020-7924 6606   Tel: 020-7924 7701

APROPOS PRODUCTIONS Ltd
2nd Floor
91A Rivington Street
London EC2A 3AY
Website: www.aproposltd.com
e-mail: info@aproposltd.com
Fax: 020-7739 3852   Tel: 020-7739 2857

BARKING PRODUCTIONS/INSTANT WIT
(Comedy Improvisation Show/Corporate Entertainment & Drama Based Training)
Regus, 1 Friary, Temple Quay, Bristol BS1 6EA
Website: www.barkingproductions.co.uk
e-mail: info@barkingproductions.co.uk
Tel/Fax: 0117-908 5384

BROWNE Michael ASSOCIATES Ltd
The Cloisters, 168C Station Road
Lower Stondon, Bedfordshire SG16 6JQ
Website: www.mba-roleplay.co.uk
e-mail: enquiries@mba-roleplay.co.uk
Tel/Fax: 01462 812483

BUZZWORD FILMS
(Role Play, Film Training Dramas)
Website: www.buzzword-films.co.uk
e-mail: mike.ferrand@buzzword-films.co.uk
Mobile: 07974 355885   Tel: 01395 446895

CRAGRATS Ltd
Cragrats Mill, Dunford Road
Holmfirth, Huddersfield HD9 2AR
Website: www.cragrats.com
e-mail: info@cragrats.com
Fax: 01484 686212   Tel: 01484 686451

DRAMA FOR TRAINING
Impact Universal, Hopebank House, Woodhead Road
Honley, Huddersfield HD9 6PF
Website: www.impactonlearning.com
e-mail: sharon.taylor@impactonlearning.com
Fax: 01484 660088   Tel: 01484 668881

INTERACT
Bowden House, 14 Bowden Street, London SE11 4DS
Website: www.interact.eu.com
e-mail: info@interact.eu.com
Fax: 020-7793 7755   Tel: 020-7793 7744

NV MANAGEMENT Ltd
Central Office, 4 Carters Leaze, Great Wolford
Warwickshire CV36 5NS
Website: www.nvmanagement.co.uk
e-mail: hello@nvmanagement.co.uk

PERFORMANCE BUSINESS The
78 Oatlands Drive,, Weybridge, Surrey KT13 9HT
Website: www.theperformance.biz
e-mail: michael@theperformance.biz   Tel: 01932 888885

ROLEPLAY UK
2 St Mary's Hill, Stamford PE9 2DW
Website: www.roleplayuk.com
Fax: 01780 764436   Tel: 01780 761960

STEPS DRAMA LEARNING DEVELOPMENT
Unit 4.1.1, The Leathermarket
Weston Street, London SE1 3ER
Website: www.stepsdrama.com
e-mail: mail@stepsdrama.com
Fax: 020-7403 0909   Tel: 020-7403 9000

THEATRE AND
Church Hall, St James Road
Marsh, Huddersfield HD1 4QA
Website: www.theatreand.com
e-mail: clare@theatreand.com
Fax: 01484 532962   Tel: 01484 532967

WEST END WORKSHOPS
(Audition Coaching/Arts Workshops)
Website: www.westendworkshops.co.uk
e-mail: info@westendworkshops.co.uk
Mobile: 07989 422808

3D SET COMPANY
(Sets, Scenery Design & Construction)
Unit 8 Temperance Street, Manchester M12 6HR
Website: www.3dsetco.com   e-mail: twalsh@3dsetco.com
Fax: 0161-273 6786   Tel: 0161-273 8831

ALBEMARLE SCENIC STUDIOS
(Suppliers of Scenery & Costumes Construction/Hire)
PO Box 240, Rotherfield TN6 9BN
Website: www.albemarleproductions.com
e-mail: albemarle.productions@virgin.net
Fax: 01435 867854   Tel: 0845 6447021

ALL SCENE ALL PROPS
(Scenery, Props, Painting Contractors)
Units 2 & 3, Spelmonden Farm, Goudhurst, Kent TN17 1HE
Website: www.allscene.net   e-mail: info@allscene.net
Fax: 01580 211131   Tel: 01580 211121

BRISTOL (UK) Ltd
(Scenic Paint)
Unit 3, Southerland Court, Tolpits Lane, Watford WD18 9SP
Website: www.bristolpaint.com
e-mail: tech.sales@bristolpaint.com
Fax: 01923 779666   Tel: 01923 779333

CCT LIGHTING UK Ltd
(Lighting, Dimmers, Sound & Stage Machinery)
Unit 3, Ellesmere Business Park, Haydn Road
Sherwood, Nottingham NG5 1DX
Website: www.cctlighting.com
e-mail: office@cctlighting.co.uk
Fax: 0115-985 7091   Tel: 0115-985 8919

COD STEAKS
(Set Construction, Design, Model Making, Exhibitions,
Costume)
2 Cole Road, Bristol BS2 0UG
Website: www.codsteaks.com
e-mail: info@codsteaks.com   Tel: 0117-980 3910

CREW CO
(Stage & Technical Crew for London & Midlands)
55 Main Street, Long Compton, Warwickshire CV36 5JS
Website: www.crewco.net   e-mail: contactus@crewco.net
Fax: 0845 4589411   Tel: 0845 4589400

DAP STUDIO
94 Kenley Road, Merton Park, London SW19 3DS
Website: www.dapstudio.co.uk
e-mail: james@dapstudio.co.uk   Tel/Fax: 01892 730897

DISPLAY MAINTENANCE Ltd
Unit 1, Calder Trading Estate
Lower Quarry Road, Bradley, Huddersfield HD5 0RR
Website: www.dmnsolutions.co.uk
e-mail: enquiries@dmnsolutions.co.uk   Tel: 0870 8508500

DOBSON SOUND PRODUCTION Ltd
(Sound Hire, Design & Installation)
66 Windsor Avenue, Merton, London SW19 2RR
e-mail: enquiries@dobsonsound.co.uk
Fax: 020-8543 3636   Tel: 020-8545 0202

DOVETAIL SPECIALIST SCENERY
(Scenery, Prop & Furniture Builders)
42-50 York Way, London N1 9AB
e-mail: dovetail.ss@btopenworld.com Tel/Fax: 020-7278 7379

FUTURIST SOUND & LIGHT Ltd
Clayton Wood Road, Ringroad West Park, Leeds LS16 6RA
Website: www.futurist.co.uk
Fax: 0113-230 5233   Tel: 0113-230 5222

HALL STAGE Ltd
Unit 4, Cosgrove Way, Luton, Beds LU1 1XL
Website: www.hallstage.com   e-mail: sales@hallstage.com
Fax: 0845 3454256   Tel: 0845 3454255

HARLEQUIN (British Harlequin Plc)
Festival Hse, Chapman Way, Tunbridge Wells, Kent TN2 3EF
Website: www.harlequinfloors.com
e-mail: sales@harlequinfloors.com
Fax: 01892 514222   Tel: 01892 514888

S

**Set Construction, Lighting,
Sound & Scenery**

[CONTACTS 2009]

HENSHALL John
(Director of Lighting & Photography)
68 High Street, Stanford in the Vale, Oxfordshire SN7 8NL
e-mail: john@epi-centre.com   Tel: 01367 710191

HERON & DRIVER
(Scenic Furniture & Structural Prop Makers)
Unit 7, Dockley Road Industrial Estate
Rotherhithe, London SE16 3SF
Website: www.herondriver.co.uk
e-mail: mail@herondriver.co.uk
Fax: 020-7394 8680   Tel: 020-7394 8688

LIGHT WORKS Ltd
2A Greenwood Road, London E8 1AB
Fax: 020-7254 0306   Tel: 020-7249 3627

LIVERPOOL SCENIC WORKSHOP Ltd
Baltic Road, Bootle, Liverpool L20 1AW
Website: www.liverpoolscenicworkshop.co.uk
e-mail: scenic@liverpoolscenicworkshop.co.uk
Fax: 0151-933 6699   Tel: 0151-933 6677

MALTBURY STAGING
(Portable Staging Sales & Consultancy)
Unit 9, Level 5 (South), New England House
New England Street, Brighton BN1 4GH
Website: www.maltbury.com
e-mail: info@maltbury.com
Fax: 0845 1308882   Tel: 0845 1308881

MASSEY Bob ASSOCIATES
(Electrical & Mechanical Stage Consultants)
9 Worrall Avenue, Arnold, Nottinghamshire NG5 7GN
e-mail: bm.associates@virgin.net   Tel/Fax: 0115-967 3969

MATTLX Ltd
Signal Cottage, 4 Station Mews
Robertsbridge, East Sussex TN32 5DD
Website: www.mattlx.com   e-mail: admin@mattlx.com
Fax: 0560 1505452   Tel: 01580 880303

MODELBOX
(Computer Aided Design & Design Services)
2 Saddlers Way, Okehampton, Devon EX20 1TL
Website: www.modelbox.co.uk
e-mail: info@modelbox.co.uk   Tel/Fax: 01837 54026

MOUNSEY Matthew
(Scenic Artist)
16 White Cliff House, Vermont Road, London SW18 2LH
e-mail: matthewmounsey@hotmail.com
                         Mobile: 07941 355450

NEED Paul J
(Lighting Designer)
5 Orchard Business Centre
Kangley Bridge Road, London SE26 5AQ
Website: www.10outof10.co.uk
e-mail: paul@10outof10.co.uk
Fax: 020-8778 9217   Tel: 020-8291 6885

NORTHERN LIGHT
(Lighting, Sound, Communications & Stage Equipment)
Assembly Street, Leith, Edinburgh EH6 7RG
Website: www.northernlight.co.uk
e-mail: info@northernlight.co.uk
Fax: 0131-622 9101   Tel: 0131-622 9100

ORBITAL
(Sound Hire & Design)
57 Acre Lane, Brixton, London SW2 5TN
Website: www.orbitalsound.co.uk
e-mail: hire@orbitalsound.co.uk
Fax: 020-7501 6869   Tel: 020-7501 6868

PANALUX
12 Waxlow Road, London NW10 7NU
Website: www.panalux.biz   e-mail: info@panalux.biz
Fax: 020-8233 7001   Tel: 020-8233 7000

PMB THEATRE & EXHIBITION SERVICES Ltd
The Barn, Kingston Wood Manor
Arrington, Royston, Herts SG8 0AP
Website: www.pmbltd.co.uk
Fax: 01954 718032   Tel: 01954 718227

RE VAMP EVENTS & ENTERTAINMENT
(Cabaret, Decor, Event Management & Entertainment)
Ealing House, 33 Hanger Lane, London W5 3HJ
e-mail: revampevents@aol.com   Tel: 020-8997 3355

REVOLVING STAGE COMPANY Ltd The
Unit F5, Little Heath Industrial Estate, Old Church Road
Coventry, Warwickshire CV6 7ND
Website: www.therevolvingstagecompany.co.uk
e-mail: enquiries@therevolvingstagecompany.co.uk
Fax: 024-7668 9355   Tel: 024-7668 7055

RK RESOURCE
2 Wyvern Way, Henwood, Ashford, Kent TN24 8DW
Fax: 01233 750133   Tel: 01233 750180

RWS ELECTRICAL & AUDIO CONTRACTORS Ltd
(All Aspects of Electrical Services including Installation,
Design & Consultancy)
1 Spinners Close, Biddenden, Kent TN27 8AY
Website: www.rwselectrical.com   Tel: 01580 291764

S + H TECHNICAL SUPPORT Ltd
(Starcloths, Drapes)
Starcloth Way, Mullacott Industrial Estate
Ilfracombe, Devon EX34 8PL
Website: www.starcloth.co.uk   e-mail: shtsg@aol.com
Fax: 01271 865423   Tel: 01271 866832

S2 EVENTS
(Production - Lighting, Set Construction & Scenery)
3-5 Valentine Place, London SE1 8QH
Website: www.s2events.co.uk
Fax: 020-7928 6082   Tel: 020-7928 5474

SCENA PROJECTS Ltd
(Set Construction)
240 Camberwell Road, London SE5 0DP
Website: www.scenapro.com
e-mail: info@scenapro.com
Fax: 020-7703 7012   Tel: 020-7703 4444

SCOTT FLEARY PRODUCTIONS Ltd
Unit 1-4 Block A, Vale Industrial Park
170 Rowan Road, London SW16 5BN
e-mail: info@scottflearyltd.com
Fax: 0870 4448322   Tel: 0870 4441787

SCOTT MYERS
(Sound Design & Original Music for Theatre)
36 Madras Road, Cambridge CB1 3PX
e-mail: scott.myers100@gmail.com
Mobile: 07875 547412   Tel: 01223 413791

SETS IN THE CITY Ltd
Location House, 5 Dove Lane, Bristol BS2 9HP
Website: www.setsinthecity.co.uk
e-mail: info@setsinthecity.co.uk
Fax: 0117-955 2480   Tel: 0117-955 5538

SMITH Paul Don
(Scenery, Graphics, Artist)
11A Cadogan Road, Surbiton, Surrey KT6 4DQ
e-mail: firedon_1@hotmail.com   Mobile: 07949 710306

STAGE MANAGEMENT COMPANY
36 Oak Avenue, Bingley, West Yorkshire BD16 1ES
Website: www.stagemanagementcompany.co.uk
e-mail: peter@stagemanagementcompany.co.uk
Mobile: 07731 429544

STAGE SYSTEMS
(Designers & Suppliers of Modular Staging, Tiering &
Auditorium Seating)
Stage House, Prince William Rd, Loughborough LE11 5GU
Website: www.stagesystems.co.uk
e-mail: info@stagesystems.co.uk
Fax: 01509 233146   Tel: 01509 611021

STAGECRAFT Ltd
(Hire & Sales of Lighting, Sound, Audio Visual & Staging for
Conference & Live Events)
Ashfield Trading Estate, Salisbury, Wiltshire SP2 7HL
Website: www.stagecraft.co.uk
e-mail: hire@stagecraft.co.uk
Fax: 01722 414076   Tel: 01722 326055

STAGEWORKS WORLDWIDE PRODUCTIONS
(Scenery, Props, Lighting & Sound)
525 Ocean Boulevard, Blackpool, FY4 1EZ
Website: www.stageworkswwp.com
e-mail: info@stageworkswwp.com
Fax: 01253 342702   Tel: 01253 342426

STEWART Helen
(Theatre Designer)
45 Quernmore Road, London N4 4QP
Website: www.helenstewart.co.uk
e-mail: design@helenstewart.co.uk   Mobile: 07887 682186

STORM LIGHTING Ltd
Unit 6 Wintonlea Industrial Estate
Monument Way West
Woking, Surrey GU21 5EN
Website: www.stormlighting.co.uk
e-mail: hire@stormlighting.co.uk
Fax: 01483 757710   Tel: 01483 757211

STRAND LIGHTING EUROPE Ltd
(Lighting Equipment for Stage, Studio, Film & TV)
Unit 2 Royce Road, Fleming Way
Crawley, West Sussex RH10 9JY
Website: www.strandlighting.com
Fax: 01293 554019   Tel: 01293 554010

TMS INTERNATIONAL Ltd
(Terry Murphy Scenery) (Set Construction & Painting)
306 St James's Road, London SE1 5JX
Website: www.terrymurphy.co.uk
e-mail: admin@tmsi.co.uk
Fax: 020-7232 2347   Tel: 020-7394 9519

TOP SHOW
(Props, Scenery, Conference Specialists)
North Lane, Huntington, York YO32 9SU   Tel: 01904 750022

WEST John ASSOCIATES
(Painting & Design)
103 Abbotswood Close, Winyates Green
Redditch, Worcestershire B98 0QF
Website: www.johnwestartist.co.uk
e-mail: johnwest@blueyonder.co.uk
Mobile: 07753 637451   Tel/Fax: 01527 516771

WHITE LIGHT Ltd
(Stage & TV Lighting)
20 Merton Industrial Park, Jubilee Way, London SW19 3WL
Website: www.whitelight.ltd.uk
e-mail: info@whitelight.ltd.uk
Fax: 020-8254 4801   Tel: 020-8254 4800

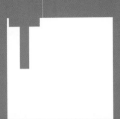

Television
Television (BBC London)
BBC Television & Sound (Regional)
Independent

Theatre Producers

Theatre
Alternative & Community
Children's, Young People's & TIE
English Speaking in Europe
London
Outer London, Fringe & Venues
Provincial/Touring
Puppet Theatre Companies
Repertory (Regional)

Where appropriate, Rep periods are indicated,
e.g. (4 Weekly) and matinee times e.g. Th 2.30 for
Thursday 2.30pm.
SD Stage Door
BO Box Office
TIE Theatre in Education (For further details of
TIE/YPT
              See Theatre - Children's, Young People's & TIE

BBC Television
Wood Lane, London W12 7RJ
Tel: 020-8743 8000

• TALENT & RIGHTS NEGOTIATION GROUP
Room 3400
201 Wood Lane
White City
London W12 7TS

Head of Talent Rights & Negotiation	Simon Hayward-Tapp
Head of Copyright Contracting	Rob Kirkham
Head of Performance Contracting	Annie Thomas
Literary Copyright Manager	Neil Hunt

Executives
Nigel Crow	Alistair Murray
Michael Finlay	Madeleine Pow
Julieann May	Christian Zante

LITERARY COPYRIGHT
Room 395-396 Drama Building
BBC Television Centre, London W12 7RJ

Music Copyright Manager	Nicky Bignell

Executives
Laura Amphlett	Debbie Rogerson
Sally Dunsford	Celine Palavioux
Kate Fawcett	Charlie Pickup

MUSIC COPYRIGHT
Room 201 EBX Building
BBC Television Centre, London W12 7RJ

News & Current Affairs Rights Manager	Tessa Beckett

LONDON FACTUAL
Executives
Chris Dabbs	Stuart Krelle
Selena Harvey	Jonathan Slack

FICTION
Executives
Mike Bickerdike	Jemma McGee
Lorraine Clark	Annie Pollard
Teresa Cordall	Thalia Reynolds
	Colette Robertson

Classical Music Rights Manager	Simon Brown

Executives
Naomi Anderson	Selena Harvey
Penelope Davies	John Hunter
Hilary Dodds	Pamela Wise

BRISTOL
Executives

Jane Armstrong	Sophie Clark

BIRMINGHAM
Executives

Rachel Amos	Andrea Coles
	Jill Ridley

MANCHESTER
Executives

Colleen Burrows	Sarah McHugh
	Collette Tanner

• DRAMA
Room 265, Drama Room
Wood Lane, London W12 7RJ   Tel: 020-8743 8000

Controller, Drama Production & New Talent	John Yorke
Director, Drama Production	Nicolas Brown
Controller, Series & Serials	Kate Harwood
Executive Producer, EastEnders	Diederick Santer
Creative Director	Manda Levin
Head of Production	Susy Liddell
Head of Development	Emma Broughton

Executive Producers, Drama Production

Ruth Caleb	Sue Hogg
Belinda Campbell	Jessica Pope
Phillippa Giles	Hilary Salmon
Kate Harwood	Diederick Santer
	Will Trotter

Producers, Drama Production

Sarah Brown	George Ormond
Ben Evans	Sally Stokes
Mike Hobson	Annie Tricklebank
Kate Lewis	Pier Wilkie
Peter Lloyd	Colin Wratten

• COMMISSIONING

Controller, BBC Knowledge	George Entwistle
Controller, Entertainment Commissioning	Elaine Bedell
Controller, Fiction	Jane Tranter
Commissioning Editor, Independent	Polly Hill
	Lucy Richer
Head of Drama Commisssioning, Development	Sarah Brandist
Controller, Drama Production Studios	John Yorke
Arts Commissioner	Adam Kemp
Head of Documentaries	Richard Klein
Head of Knowledge Mutlimedia Commissioning	Emma Swain
Head of Drama Series & Serials	Kate Harwood
Head of Drama Commissioning	Ben Stephenson

• NEWS AND CURRENT AFFAIRS

BBC News (Television & Radio)
Television Centre, Wood Lane, London W12 7RJ
Tel: 020-8743 8000 (Main Switchboard)

Director News	Helen Boaden
Deputy Director, News & Head of News Programmes	Steve Mitchell
Head of Newsgathering	Fran Unsworth
Head of Political Programmes Research & Analysis	Sue Inglish
Head of Radio News	Steve Mitchell
Head of Newsroom	Peter Horrocks
Director of Sport	Roger Mosey
Controller of Children's	Richard Deverell
Head of TV Current Affairs	Peter Horrocks
Controller, Operations & Technology, News	Peter Coles
Acting Head of MC & A (Marketing, Communications & Audiences), BBC Journalism	Chris Gottlieb
Executive Editor & Commissioner, Current Affairs	Clive Edwards

London Factual Executive Producers
Tel main switchboard: 020-8743 8000
All based in the Media Centre at White City Media Village.

Arts	Basil Comely
Documentaries	Jane Aldus
Consumer	Lisa Ausden
Science	John Lynch
Horizon Editor	Andrew Cohen
Science	Michael Mosley
	Kim Shillinglaw
	Anne Laking
	Dinah Lord
	Nick Mirsky
The Money Programme	Dominic Crossley-Holland
	Clare Sillery
	Gary Hunter
	Tina Fletcher
The Culture Show	Eddie Morgan
Series Editor, Imagine	Janet Lee

• CHILDREN

Controller	Richard Deverell
Controller, CBBC	Anne Gilchrist
Controller, CBeebies	Michael Carrington
Head of Entertainment (inc on-air talent management)	Joe Godwin
Head of Drama	Jon East
Head of Children's Programmes, Scotland	Simon Parsons
Head of News, Factual & Learning	Reem Nouss
Head of Interactive and On-Demand	Marc Goodchild

• MUSIC

Head of Television	
Classical Music & Performance	Peter Maniura
Managing Editor, Classical Music,	
Television	Caroline Speed
Editor Music Programmes - Television,	
Classical Music & Performance	Oliver Macfarlane
Programme Development Manager	Toby Jones

Executive Producers

Sue Judd	Celina Parker

Producers/Directors

Jonathan Haswell	Andy King-Dabbs
Francesca Kemp	Helen Mansfield

Production Executive   Rachel Wright

• SPORT

Director of Sport	Roger Mosey
Head of Major Events	Dave Gordon
Head of Sport Production	Barbara Slater
Head of Football	Niall Sloane
H.R. & Development Partner	Pam Sikora
Head of Radio	Gordon Turnbull
Head of TV Sport Editorial	Philip Bernie

• NEW WRITING

BBC Writersroom
Grafton House, 379-381 Euston Road
London NW1 3AU   Tel: 020-7765 2703
e-mail: writersroom@bbc.co.uk
Website: www.bbc.co.uk/writersroom

Creative Director	Kate Rowland
Development Manager	Paul Ashton

• BBC BRISTOL

Broadcasting House
Whiteladies Road
Bristol BS8 2LR — Tel: 0117-973 2211

NETWORK TELEVISION FEATURES AND DOCUMENTARIES

Head of Programmes	Tom Archer

Executive Producers

Mob Dar	Julian Mercer
Pete Lawrence	Michael Poole
	Simon Shaw

Series Producers

Lynn Barlow	Alastair Laurence
Kate Broome	Kimberley Littlemore
Michele Burgess	Peter Smith
Chris Hutchins	Ben Southwell

Producers/Directors

Robert Bayley	Colin Napthine
Georgina Harvey	David Olusoga
Louise Hibbins	Tuppence Stone
	Jonny Young

NETWORK RADIO

Unit Manager, Radio 4	Kate Chaney
Editor, Radio 4	Clare McGinn

Producers

John Byrne	Chris Ledgard
Sara Davies	Mary Ward Lowery
Tim Dee	Mark Smalley
Jolyon Jenkins	Miles Warde

NATURAL HISTORY UNIT

Head of Natural History Unit	Neil Nightingale
Executive Editor, Natural World	Tim Martin
Managing Editor, NHU Radio	Julian Hector
Project Executive	Mark Jacobs

Executive Producers

Sara Ford	Mike Gunton
Alastair Fothergill	Tim Scoones

Senior Producers

Paul Appleby	Miles Barton

Series Producers

Karen Bass	Huw Cordey
Phil Chapman	Patrick Morris
	Stephen Moss

Television Producers

Vanessa Berlowitz	Hilary Jeffkins
Mark Brownlow	Mark Linfield
Mary Colwell	Mary Summerhill

• BBC WEST

Whiteladies Road
Bristol BS8 2LR — Tel: 0117-973 2211

Head of Regional & Local Programmes,
including BBC West, Radio Bristol
BBC Somerset, BBC Gloucestershire

BBC Wiltshire	Lucio Mesquita
Editor, Output	Stephanie Marshall
News Gathering	Neil Bennett

• BBC SOUTH WEST

Seymour Road
Mannamead
Plymouth PL3 5BD — Tel: 01752 229201

Head of BBC South West	John Lilley
Editor TV Current Affairs	Simon Willis
Output Editor	Simon Read

• BBC SOUTH

Havelock Road
Southampton SO14 7PU — Tel: 023-8022 6201

Head of Regional & Local Programmes	Mike Hapgood
TV News Editor	Lee Desty
Managing Editor, BBC Oxford	Steve Taschini
Managing Editor, Radio Solent	Mia Costello
Managing Editor, Radio Berkshire	Marianne Bell

• BBC LONDON

35C Marylebone High Street
London W1M 4AA — Tel: 020-7224 2424

BBC London News:
TV: *The Politics Show*
Radio: *BBC London Radio 94.9FM*
Online: *BBC London online*

Head of BBC London	Michael MacFarlane
News/Output Editor	Antony Dore
Editor, Inside Out	Dippy Chaudhary
Managing Editor, BBC Radio London 94.9FM	David Robey
Political Editor	Tim Donovan
Editor, BBC London Online	Claire Timms

• BBC SOUTH EAST

The Great Hall Arcade
Mount Pleasant Road
Tunbridge Wells
Kent TN1 1QQ — Tel: 01892 670000

Head of Regional & Local Programmes BBC South East	Michael Rawsthorne

Managing Editor BBC Radio Kent	Paul Leaper
Managing Editor BBC Southern Counties	Nicki Holliday
Editor BBC South East Today	Quentin Smith
Editor Inside Out	Linda Bell
Editor Politics Show	Dan Fineman

• BBC NORTH WEST

New Broadcasting House
Oxford Road
Manchester M60 1SJ   Tel: 0161-200 2020
Website: www.bbc.co.uk/manchester

Entertainment & Features

Editor, Entertainment & Features	Helen Bullough

Religion & Ethics

Head of Religion & Ethics	Michael Wakelin

Network News & Current Affairs

Editor, Network News & Current Affairs	Liz Molyneux

Regional & Local Programmes

Head of Regional & Local Programmes North West	Tamsin O'Brien
Head of Regional & Local Programmes North East & Cumbria	Phil Roberts

• BBC BIRMINGHAM

BBC Birmingham
The Mailbox
Birmingham B1 1RF
Fax: 0121-567 6875   Tel: 0121-567 6767

English Regions

Controller, English Regions. Head of Centre (Birmingham)	Andy Griffee
Head of New Services, English Regions	John Allen
Chief Operating Officer, English Regions	Ian Hughes
Senior Officer, Press & PR	Becky Jones-Owen
Secretary, BBC Trust	Louise Hall
Head of Regional & Local Programmes West Midlands	David Holdsworth

Factual & Learning
BBC Birmingham

Head of Studios	Nick Patten

Managing Editor, BBC Vision, Birmingham & Manchester	Jane Booth

Network Radio

Executive Editor, Audio & Music Factual	Andrew Thorman
Head of Specialist, Radio 2 Music & Compliance	David Barber

Drama

BBC Brimingham TV Drama Village
Archibald House
1059 Bristol Road, Selly Oak
Birmingham B29 6LT   Tel: 0121-567 7350

Executive Producer	Will Trotter

• BBC SCOTLAND

40 Pacific Quay
Glasgow G51 1DA   Tel: 0141-422 6000
Website: www.bbc.co.uk/scotland

Scottish Executive Board

Controller, Scotland	Ken MacQuarrie
Heads of Programmes & Services	Donalda MacKinnon
	Maggie Cunningham
Head of Public Policy	Ian Small
Chief Operating Officer	Bruce Malcolm
Head of Talent Division	Donald-Iain Brown
Head of HR & Development	Wendy Aslett
Head of Marketing, Communications & Audiences	Mairead Ferguson

Genre Heads

Commissioning Editor, Television & Head of Sport	Ewan Angus
Head of News & Current Affairs	Atholl Duncan
Head of Radio	Jeff Zycinski
Head of Gaelic Digital Service	Margaret Mary Murray
Managing Editor, Gaelic	Marion MacKinnon
Head Factual	Andrea Miller
Head of Drama, Television	Anne Mensah
Head of Drama, Radio	Patrick Rayner
Head of Children's	Simon Parsons
Head of Comedy & Entertainment	Alan Tyler
Executive Editor, Learning	Nick Simons
Executive Editor, Cross Media	Matthew Lee
Director, BBC Scottish Symphony Orchestra	Gavin Reid

BBC Scotland provides television and radio programmes for Scotland and the UK networks as well as online and interactive content. Based in the new digital headquarters in Glasgow since 2007, there are also centres throughout Scotland which include the home of the BBC Scottish Symphony Orchestra.

Aberdeen
Broadcasting House, Beechgrove Terrace
Aberdeen AB15 5ZT　　Tel: 01224 625233

Dumbarton
Strathleven Bottling Plant, Dumbarton
Dumbartonshire G82 2AP　　Tel: 01389 736666

Dumfries
Elmbank, Lover's Walk
Dumfries DG1 1NZ　　Tel: 01387 268008

Dundee
Nethergate Centre, 4th Floor, 66 Nethergate
Dundee DD1 4ER　　Tel: 01382 202481

Edinburgh
The Tun, 4 Jackson's Entry, 111 Holyrood Road
Edinburgh EH8 8PJ　　Tel: 0131-557 5888

Glasgow
Glasgow City Halls (BBC Scottish Symphony Orchestra)
87 Albion Street, Glasgow G1 1NQ　　Tel: 0141-552 0909

Inverness
7 Culduthel Road, Inverness IV2 4AD　　Tel: 01463 720720

Orkney
Castle Street, Kirkwall
Orkney KW15 1DF　　Tel: 01856 873939

Portree
Clydesdale Bank Buildings, Somerled Square, Portree
Isle of Skye IV51 9BT　　Tel: 01478 612005

Selkirk
Unit 1, Ettrick Riverside
Dunsdale Road, Selkirk TD7 5EB　　Tel: 01750 724567

Shetland
Pitt Lane, Lerwick
Shetland ZE1 0DW　　Tel: 01595 694747

Stornoway
Radio nan Gaidheal, Rosebank, 52 Church Street
Stornoway, Isle of Lewis HS1 2LS　　Tel: 01851 705000

• BBC WALES

Broadcasting House
Llandaff
Cardiff CF5 2YQ　　**Tel: 029-2032 2000**

Controller	Menna Richards
Head of Programmes (Welsh)	Keith Jones
Head of Programmes (English)	Clare Hudson
Head of Marketing, Communications & Audiences	Rhodri Talfan Davies
Head of News & Current Affairs	Mark O'Callaghan
Head of HR & Development	Jude Gray
Chief Operating Officer	Gareth Powell
Head of Drama	Piers Wenger
Head of Broadcast Development	Cathryn Allen
Head of Sport	Nigel Walker
Head of North Wales	Marian Wyn Jones
Head of Factual & Music	Adrian Davies
Head of Education & Learning	Eleri Wyn-Williams
Editor Radio Wales	Sali Collins
Editor Radio Cymru	Sian Gwynedd
Editor New Media	Iain Tweedale

• BBC NORTHERN IRELAND

Belfast
Ormeau Avenue
Belfast BT2 8HQ　　**Tel: 028-9033 8000**

Controller	Peter Johnston
Head of Programmes	Ailsa Orr
Head of Public Policy, Corporate & Community Affairs	Mark Adair
Head of Drama	Patrick Spence
Chief Operating Officer	Mark Taylor
Head of HR & Development	Lawrence Jackson
Head of Marketing, Communications & Audiences	Kathy Martin
Head of News & Current Affairs	Andrew Colman
Head of TV Current Affairs	Jeremy Adams
Head of Entertainment & Events	Mike Edgar
Head of Factual	Paul McGuigan
Head of Radio	Susan Lovell

Londonderry
BBC Radio Foyle　　Tel: 028-7137 8600
Editor Foyle　　Paul McCauley

itv Anglia

ITV ANGLIA
Head Office
Anglia House
Norwich NR1 3JG
Fax: 01603 631032　　　　　　　Tel: 01603 615151
East of England: Weekday & Weekend

Regional News Centres

Cambridge
Link House
Station Road
Great Shelford
Cambridge CB2 5LT　　　　　News: 08448 816985

Chelmsford
64-68 New London Road
Chelmsford CM1 0YU
Fax: 01245 267228　　　　　　Tel: 01245 357676

Northampton
77B Abington Street
Northampton NN1 2BH
Fax: 01604 629856　　　　　　Tel: 01604 624343

Peterborough
6 Bretton Green Village
Rightwell, Bretton PE3 8DY
Fax: 01733 269424　　　　　　Tel: 01733 269440

Ipswich
Hubbard House
Civic Drive, Ipswich IP1 2QA
Fax: 01473 233279　　　　　　Tel: 01473 226157

Luton
Unit D20
Basepoint Business and Innovation Centre
110 Butterfield
Great Marlings
Luton, Beds LU2 8DL　　　　　Tel: 08448 816990

itv Border

ITV BORDER
Head Office & Studios
The Television Centre
Carlisle CA1 3NT　　　　　　Tel: 08448 815850
Cumbria, South West Scotland,
Scottish Border Region
North Northumberland and the Isle of Man;
Weekday and Weekend

Executive Director　　　　　　　Paddy Merrall
Regional Director　　　　　　Graeme Thompson
Production Manager　　　　　　　Livvy Ellis

itv Channel Television

CHANNEL TELEVISION Ltd
Registered Office
The Television Centre, La Pouquelaye
St Helier, Jersey JE1 3ZD, Channel Islands
Fax: 01534 816817　　　　　　Tel: 01534 816816
Website: www.channelonline.tv
Channel Islands: Weekday and Weekend

Managing Director (Broadcast)　　　Karen Rankine
Head of News and Content　　　　Allan Watts
Managing Director (Commercial)　　Mike Elsey
Director of Resource & Transmission　Kevin Banner
News Editor　　　　　　　　Russell Hookey

Producers
Melissa Goguelin　　　　　　Russell Hookey

CHANNEL FOUR TELEVISION CORPORATION

London Office
124 Horseferry Road
London SW1P 2TX
Textphone: 020-7396 8691　　　Tel: 020-7396 4444

Members of the Board
Chairman　　　　　　　　　Luke Johnson
Deputy Chairman　　　　　Lord David Puttnam
Chief Executive　　　　　　Andy Duncan
Director of Television　　　　Kevin Lygo
Group Finance Director　　　　Anne Bulford
Sales Director　　　　　　Andy Barnes
New Business Director　　　　Rod Henwood

Non-Executive Directors
Sue Ashtiany　　　　　　Martha Lane Fox
Karren Brady　　　　　　Andy Mollett
Tony Hall　　　　　　　Stephen Hill

Heads of Department
Head of Features　　　　　Sue Murphy
Head of E4 and Big Brother　　　Angela Jain
Head of Factual Entertainment　Andrew Mackenzie
Head of Specialist Factual　　　Ralph Lee
Head of History, Science & Religion　Hamish Mykura
Controller of Broadcasting　　Rosemary Newell
Head of Scheduling and T4　　Julie Oldroyd
Head of More 4　　　　　Peter Dale
Head of News & Current Affairs　Dorothy Byrne
Head of Entertainment　　　Andrew Newman

CHANNEL FOUR TELEVISION CORPORATION Cont'd

Head of Drama and FilmFour	Tessa Ross
Head of Documentaries	Hamish Mykura
Head of Comedy and Film	Caroline Leddy
Head of Education	
& Managing Editor Commissioning	Janey Walker
Head of Information Systems	Ian Dobb
Head of Channel Operations	Stephen White
Controller of Legal & Compliance	Jan Tomalin
Managing Director, New Media	Andy Taylor
Head of Commercial Affairs	vacant
Director of Nations & Regions	Stuart Cosgrove
Director of Corporate Relations	Nick Toon
Head of Corporate Development	Michael Hodgson
Director of Strategy & Research	Jonathan Thompson
Controller of Research & Insight	Claire Grimmond
Director of Human Resources	Diane Herbert
Head of Facilities Management	Julie Kortens
Director of Acquisitions	Jeff Ford
Director of Marketing	Polly Cochrane
Head of Media Planning	Greg Smith
Head of Press & Publicity	Matt Baker
Network Creative Director	Brett Foraker
Head of Marketing	Rufus Radcliffe
Head of Sponsorship	David Charlesworth
Head of Airtime Management	Merlin Inkley
Head of Agency Sales	Matt Shreeve
Head of Strategic Sales	Mike Parker
Head of Channel 4	Julian Bellamy

CHANNEL 5 BROADCASTING

22 Long Acre
London WC2E 9LY
Fax: 020-7550 5554   Tel: 020-7550 5555
Website: www.five.tv

Acting Chief Executive	Mark White
Director of Programmes	Ben Gale
Director of Strategy	Charles Constable
Director of Sales	Mark White
Director of Finance	Grant Murray
Head of Legal	Paul Chinnery
Director of Broadcasting	Richard Brent
Senior Programme Controller	
News & Current Affairs	Chris Shaw
Head of Factual Entertainment	
& Multi Channel Commissioner	Steve Gowans
Controller of Sport	Robert Charles
Controller Children's	Nick Wilson

GMTV

London Television Centre, Upper Ground, London SE1 9TT
Fax: 020-7827 7001   Tel: 020-7827 7000
Website: www.gm.tv

Chairman	Clive Jones
Acting Chief Operating Officer	Clive Crouch
Director of Programmes	Peter McHugh
Sales & Marketing Controller	Simon Poole
Finance Director	Rhian Walker
Editor	Martin Frizell
Deputy Editor	Malcolm Douglas
Deputy Editor (Presentation)	Emma Gormley
Operations Director	Di Holmes
Avid Project Manager	Henry Clark
Head of Futures	Annemarie Leahy
Deputy Head of Futures	Caroline Sigley
Head of Entertainment	Corine Bishop
Deputy Head of Entertainment	Amy Vosburgh
Head of Press	Nikki Johnceline

INDEPENDENT TELEVISION NEWS

200 Gray's Inn Rd
London WC1X 8XZ   Tel: 020-7833 3000

Chief Executive	Mark Wood
Editor-in-Chief, ITV News	David Mannion
Editor, ITV Network News	Deborah Turness
Editor, Channel 4 News	Jim Gray

ITV Plc Registered Office

200 Gray's Inn Road, London WC1V 8HF
Fax: 08448 816355   Tel: 08448 818000
Contact your regional ITV comany at itv.com/local

Executive Board:

Executive Chairman, ITV Plc	Michael Grade
Chief Operating Officer	
& Finance Director, ITV Plc	John Cresswell
Director of Television, ITV	Peter Fincham
Director of ITV Productions	John Whiston
MD, ITV Consumer	Jeff Henry
Director of Group Development	
& Strategy	Carolyn Fairburn
Deputy Group Finance Director	Mike Green
Group HR Director	Philippa Hird
Chief Operating Officer	Ben McOwen Wilson
Legal Director	Kyla Mullins

ITV Plc Cont'd

Director of Regulatory Affairs & Managing Director of ITV London	Christy Swords
Company Secretary	James Tibbets
Director of Communications, Channels & Commercials	Ruth Settle
Director of Group Corporate Affairs	Mark Gallagher

Casting Directors at ITV Productions

Manchester

Gennie Radcliffe, Coronation Street
June West, Casting Director
Rick Laxton, Casting Assistant (to Gennie Radcliffe)
Katy Belshaw, Casting Assistant (to June West)
Elaine Brunskill, Casting Assistant

Leeds

Faye Styring, Emmerdale
Rebecca Scott, Casting Assistant (to Faye Styring)
Louise Bennett, Casting Assistant

London

Janie Frazer, Casting Director
Stephanie Dawes, Assistant Casting Director
David Wheal, Casting Assistant (to Janie Frazer)

If you would like one of the casting teams to cover your performance in a stage production, please email casting@itv.com including your name, the theatre and dates.

 Meridian

ITV MERIDIAN
ITV Meridian is part of ITV BROADCASTING Ltd

Forum One
Solent Business Park
Whiteley
Hants PO15 7PA
Fax: 0844 881207   Tel: 0844 8812000

Meridian Board

Executive Chairman, ITV plc	Michael Grade
Director of Regional Sales	David Croft
Regional Director, ITV Meridian & ITV London	Mark Southgate

Executives

Head of Personnel	Elaine Austin
Finance Manager	Dan Spencer
Head of News	Robin Britton

itv Wales

ITV WALES

Television Centre
Culverhouse Cross
Cardiff CF5 6XJ   Tel: 0844 8810101

Television Centre
Bath Road
Bristol BS4 3HG   Tel: 0844 8812345

Wales/West of England: All week

National Director, Wales	Elis Owen
Director, ITV West	Jane McCloskey
ITV Wales Head of Drama Development	Peter Edwards

S4/C

S4C - THE WELSH FOURTH CHANNEL

Parc Tŷ Glas
Llanishen
Cardiff CF14 5DU
Fax: 029-2075 4444   Tel: 029-2074 7444
e-mail: s4c@s4c.co.uk

The Welsh Fourth Channel Authority

Chair	John Walter Jones OBE
Bill Davies	Sir Roger Jones OBE
Elra Davies	Dr Chris Llewelyn
Carys Howell	Winston Roddick CB QC
Cenwyn Jones	Rheon Tomos

Senior Staff

Chief Executive	Iona Jones
Director of Commissioning	Rhian Gibson
Director of Communications	Huw Rossiter
Director of Finance & Human Resources	Kathryn Morris
Director of Broadcast & Distribution	Arshad Rasul
Director of Business Affairs	Delyth Wynne Griffiths
Director of Commercial & Corporate Policy	Nerys Hopkins

STV CENTRAL

Pacific Quay, Glasgow G51 1PQ
Tel: 0141-300 3000   Website: www.stv.tv

STV NORTH

Television Centre
Craigshaw Business Park
West Tullos
Aberdeen AB12 3QH
Tel: 01224 848848   Website: www.stv.tv

Managing Director	Bobby Hain
Head of News & Current Affairs	Gordon MacMillan

SMG TV PRODUCTIONS
Glasgow Office
Pacific Quay
Glasgow G51 1PQ
Fax: 0141-300 3030 — Tel: 0141-300 3000
Managing Director — Elizabeth Partyka
Head of Drama — Eric Coulter

London Office
1st Floor
3 Waterhouse Square
138-142 Holborn
London EC1N 2NY — Tel: 020-7882 1010

 Tyne Tees

ITV TYNE TEES
ITV Tyne Tees
Television House
The Watermark,
Gateshead NE11 9SZ
Fax: 0844 8815010 — Tel: 0844 8815000

Teesside News Gathering
20 Manor Way
Belasis Hall Technology Park
Billingham
Cleveland TS23 4HN
Fax: 08448 815330 — Tel: 08448 815320

North East and North Yorkshire:
Weekday and Weekend

Executive Chair ITV — Michael Grade
Regional Director, ITV North — Graeme Thompson
Head of News — Catherine Houlihan
Managing Director, SignPost — Malcolm Wright

UTV Plc
Ormeau Road
Belfast BT7 1EB
Fax: 028-9024 6695 — Tel: 028-9032 8122
Northern Ireland: Weekday and Weekend

Chairman — J B McGuckian BSc (Econ)
Group Chief Executive — J McCann BSc, FCA
Group Financial Director — Jim Downey
Managing Director, Television — Michael Wilson
Head of Communications — Orla McKibbin
Head of News & Current Affairs — Rob Morrison
Sales Director — Paul Hutchinson

 **Yorkshire**

ITV YORKSHIRE
The Television Centre, Leeds LS3 1JS
Fax: 0113-244 5107 — Tel: 0113-222 7000

London Office
London Television Centre
Upperground, London SE1 9LT — Tel: 020-7620 1620

Hull Office
23 Brook Street
The Prospect Centre
Hull HU2 8PN — Tel: 01482 324488

Sheffield Office
Charter Square, Sheffield S1 3EJ — Tel: 0114-272 7772

Lincoln Office
88 Bailgate, Lincoln LN1 3AR — Tel: 01522 530738

Grimsby Office
Margaret Street, Immingham
North East Lincs DN40 1LE — Tel: 01469 515151

York Office
8 Coppergate, York YO1 1NR — Tel: 01904 610066

Executives
Managing Director — David M B Croft
Director of Business Affairs — Filip Cieslik
Head of News — Will Venters
Controller of Comedy Drama
  & Drama Features — David Reynolds
Controller of Drama, Leeds — Keith Richardson
Director of Finance — Ian Roe
Director of ITV Productions — John Whiston
Producer of Regional Features — Mark Witty

SKY Satellite Television
BRITISH SKY BROADCASTING LIMITED (BSkyB)
6 Centaurs Business Park
Grant Way, Isleworth, Middlesex TW7 5QD
Fax: 0870 240 3060 — Tel: 0870 240 3000

Chief Executive — Jeremy Darroch
Chief Financial Officer — Andrew Griffith
Managing Director, Sky Networks — Sophie Turner-Laing
Director for People — Deborah Baker
Group Commercial and Strategy Director — Mike Darcey
Group Director for Communications — Matthew Anderson
Managing Director, Customer Group — Brian Sullivan
Group Director for IT & Strategy — Jeff Hughes
General Counsel — James Conyers
Managing Director, Sky Media — Nick Milligan
Head of Regulatory Affairs — Vicky Sandy
Managing Director, Sky Sports — Vic Wakeling
Group Director of Engineering
  & Platform Technology — Alun Webber

30 BIRD PRODUCTIONS
17 Emery Street, Cambridge CB1 2AX
Website: www.30birdproductions.org
e-mail: info@30birdproductions.org   Mobile: 07970 960995

ACORN ENTERTAINMENTS Ltd
PO Box 64, Cirencester, Glos GL7 5YD
Website: www.acornents.co.uk
e-mail: info@acornents.co.uk
Fax: 01285 642291   Tel: 01285 644622

ACT PRODUCTIONS Ltd
20-22 Stukeley Street, London WC2B 5LR
Website: www.actproductions.co.uk
e-mail: info@actproductions.co.uk
Fax: 020-7242 3548   Tel: 020-7438 9520

ACTING PRODUCTIONS
Unit 88, Battersea Business Centre
99-109 Lavender Hill, London SW11 5QL
Website: www.acting-productions.co.uk
e-mail: info@acting-productions.co.uk
Fax: 020-7924 6606   Tel: 020-7924 7701

ACTOR'S TEMPLE The
13 Warren Street, London W1T 5LG
Website: www.actorstemple.com
e-mail: info@actorstemple.com
Mobile: 07771 734670   Tel: 020-3004 4537

AJTC THEATRE COMPANY
28 Rydes Hill Crescent
Guildford, Surrey GU2 9UH
Website: www.ajtctheatre.co.uk   Tel/Fax: 01483 232795

ALGERNON Ltd
24B Cleveleys Road, London E5 9JN
Website: www.algernonproductions.com
e-mail: info@algernonproductions.com
Fax: 0870 1388516   Tel: 07092 805026

AMBASSADOR THEATRE GROUP
39-41 Charing Cross Road, London WC2H 0AR
e-mail: atglondon@theambassadors.com
Fax: 020-7534 6109   Tel: 020-7534 6100

ANTIC DISPOSITION
4A Oval Road, London NW1 7EB
Website: www.anticdisposition.co.uk
e-mail: info@anticdisposition.co.uk   Tel: 020-7284 0760

AOD - ACTORS OF DIONYSUS
14 Cuthbert Road, Brighton BN2 0EN
Website: www.actorsofdionysus.com
e-mail: info@actorsofdionysus.com   Tel/Fax: 01273 692604

ARDEN ENTERTAINMENT
2nd Floor, 23 Tavistock Street, London WC2E 7NX
Website: www.arden-entertainment.co.uk
e-mail: info@arden-entertainment.co.uk
Fax: 020-7420 7748   Tel: 020-7420 7730

ARTS MANAGEMENT (Redroofs Associates)
Contact: By Post
Novello Theatre, High Street, Sunninghill, Ascot SL5 9NE

ASHTON GROUP THEATRE The
The Old Fire Station, Abbey Road
Barrow-in-Furness, Cumbria LA14 1XH
Website: www.ashtongroup.co.uk
e-mail: info@ashtongroup.co.uk   Tel/Fax: 01229 430636

ATC
Malvern House, 15-16 Nassau Street, London W1W 7AB
Website: www.atc-online.com
e-mail: atc@atc-online.com
Fax: 020-7580 7724   Tel: 020-7580 7723

ATTIC THEATRE COMPANY (LONDON) Ltd
Mitcham Library
157 London Road, Mitcham CR4 2YR
Website: www.attictheatrecompany.com
e-mail: info@attictheatrecompany.com   Tel: 020-8640 6800

BACKGROUND Ltd
44 Carnaby Street, London W1F 9PP
e-mail: insight@background.co.uk
Fax: 020-7479 4710   Tel: 020-7479 4700

BARKING PRODUCTIONS/INSTANT WIT
(Comedy Improvisation Show/Corporate Entertainment &
Drama Based Training)
Regus, 1 Friary, Temple Quay, Bristol BS1 6EA
Website: www.barkingproductions.co.uk
e-mail: info@barkingproductions.co.uk
                                     Tel/Fax: 0117-908 5384

BARNES Andy PRODUCTIONS
Ambassadors Theatre
West Street, London WC2H 9ND
Website: www.andybarnesproductions.com
e-mail: andybarnes@ukonline.co.uk   Mobile: 07957 313666

BEE & BUSTLE ENTERPRISES
32 Exeter Road, London NW2 4SB
Website: www.beeandbustle.co.uk
e-mail: info@beeandbustle.co.uk
Fax: 020-8450 1057   Tel: 020-8450 0371

BIRMINGHAM STAGE COMPANY The
Suite 228, The Linen Hall
162 Regent Street, London W1B 5TB
Website: www.birminghamstage.net
e-mail: info@birminghamstage.net
Fax: 020-7437 3395   Tel: 020-7437 3391

BLUE BOX ENTERTAINMENT Ltd
Top Floor
80-81 St Martin's Lane, London WC2N 4AA
Website: www.blue-box.biz
e-mail: info@blue-box.biz
Fax: 020-7240 2947   Tel: 020-7240 7520

BORDER CROSSINGS
13 Bankside, Enfield EN2 8BN
Website: www.bordercrossings.org.uk
e-mail: info@bordercrossings.org.uk
Fax: 020-8366 5239   Tel: 020-8829 8928

BORDERLINE THEATRE COMPANY
North Harbour Street, Ayr KA8 8AA
e-mail: enquiries@borderlinetheatre.co.uk
                                          Tel: 01292 281010

BOTELLO Catalina
48 New Cavendish Street, London W1G 8TG
Website: www.catalinabotello.com
e-mail: contact@catalinabotello.com
                                     Tel/Fax: 020-7935 1360

BRIT-POL THEATRE Ltd
10 Bristol Gardens, London W9 2JG
Website: www.britpoltheatre.com
e-mail: admin@britpoltheatre.com   Tel: 020-7266 0323

What is a theatre producer?

A theatre producer is someone who oversees and organises a theatre show. He or she will find, or arrange for other professionals to find, a suitable script, design, director and cast for each production, while also managing all finances and marketing.

How should I use these listings?

Theatre producers tend to use casting directors to put forward suitable actors for the parts in forthcoming productions, but you could also try approaching them yourself. Rather than sending your CV and headshot to every producer listed, it would be best to do some research first in order to target your search. Find out what each company has produced in the past, what they are currently working on, and if possible what they are considering producing in the future, and only send your CV to those most relevant to the roles you want to play. Don't forget to include a covering letter which states why you are contacting this producer in particular. Personalising and targeting your correspondence in this way gives you the best chance of your CV being considered in a favourable light.

How should I approach theatre producers?

You should contact theatre producers by post or email only. We would advise against calling them, especially when approaching them for the first time. If you are unsure as to the best method of applying to them, as with other casting professionals it is safest to post your CV and headshot in the traditional way rather than emailing it. Do not enclose your showreel but you can mention that you have one available in your covering letter.

When should I approach theatre producers?

Listen to industry news and have a look at theatre producers' websites for forthcoming production details. The casting process usually takes place around 3 months prior to rehearsals, so bear this in mind when you are writing your covering letter.

Anthony Field Associates Ltd is a production company which brings together 150 years of West End theatre experience enjoyed by John Causebrook, Elizabeth Lomas and Anthony Field. From the original London productions of plays such as *A View from the Bridge, Cat on a Hot Tin Roof* and *I'm not Rappaport* to the first West End productions of Sondheim's *Company, A Little Night Music* and *A Funny Thing Happened on the Way to the Forum,* this company has pioneered drama and musicals since the 1950's. Currently it is involved in some ten new productions in 2008/9.

Oh dear! As a producer daily going through the mail it is simply depressing to receive a pile of unsolicited well-thumbed scripts of plays, scores of musicals complete with DVDs, and biogs of performers with expensive glossy photographs. Each section of Contacts, whether listing agents, casting directors, festivals, theatres, press representatives, or producers, screams out "do your homework first!" It is simply a waste of money and time for an actor wanting to play Hamlet to write to Sir Cameron Mackintosh or a singer wanting to sing in Carousel sending a CD to Michael Codron. It is also a waste of money to produce an expensive DVD of a whole musical production with orchestra and chorus. One can tell by one voice and a piano whether a score (music and lyrics) is sufficiently captivating to hear it more extensively.

But more than that, performers should know the whole background of their profession. This is why performing arts schools not only teach acting and diction and how to project a personality eight times a week for months on end in a large auditorium, but also set their work in historic perspective. Read the show business press constantly, the daily reviews in newspapers, the weekly pages about forthcoming productions in London, in the UK, in the US and all over the world, what dramatists are writing, directors are planning and producers thinking about so that when you come to meet a producer you can show that you know what you are about.

An initial approach to a producer could be hinged on what you know that production office might have in mind over the next few years. Latch on to what a director might be eating his heart out to get launched. Muscle in to what is happening in the show business world and do not, whatever you do, reveal you are ignorant about a dramatist's recent work, or a producer's favourite subject, or the last time a certain play or musical was produced.

Thus, a constructive approach to a producer might catch attention: if, for example, a couple of actors link up with a dramatist and a director and together evolve a project, this might capture a producer's attention much better than a simple CV and photo saying "I want work!"

Bear in mind that, frustrating as it is when one needs to eat, many productions take years to gestate. Producers acquire rights of plays which might take up to ten years to come together – that is, with the right director, the correct artists and the appropriate theatre. Hence, a production office can have a couple of dozen 'projects' in the pipeline out of which only a few each year might come to the surface. So a performer has to be in the right place at the right time and this takes research as much as luck.

Further, as a producer, I would urge a dramatist who spends years attempting to get one play produced instead to continue writing and writing and writing just as a performer must not spend every day trying to land the one right role. Just think how many times Irving Berlin, George Gershwin or Rodgers and Hart reached into a bottom drawer and brought out an old score which suddenly saw the light of day at an appropriate moment. So keep on creating work, get out and do other jobs and acquire other skills which can be used to extend one's experience as well as one's bank balance.

Cleo Laine was once surprised to find her regular waitress at a local Broadway restaurant arriving at the theatre as her understudy in *The Mystery of Edwin Drood!*

BRITISH SHAKESPEARE COMPANY
8 Adelaide Grove, London W12 0JJ
Website: www.britishshakespearecompany.com
e-mail: info@britishshakespearecompany.com
Mobile: 07502 245540

BRITISH STAGE PRODUCTIONS
455 Waterloo Road, Blackpool FY4 4BW
e-mail: britstage@aol.com
Tel/Fax: 01253 692289

BRITISH THEATRE SEASON IN MONACO
Theatre Princesse Grace, Monaco
1 Hogarth Hill, London NW11 6AY
Website: www.montecarlotheatre.co.uk
e-mail: mail@montecarlotheatre.co.uk
Tel: 020-8455 3278

BROADHOUSE PRODUCTIONS Ltd
Lodge Rocks House, Bilbrook
Minehead, Somerset TA24 6RD
e-mail: admin@broadhouse.co.uk
Fax: 01984 641027
Tel: 01984 640773

BROOKE Nick Ltd
2nd Floor, 80-81 St Martin's Lane, London WC2N 4AA
e-mail: nick@nickbrooke.com
Fax: 020-7240 2947
Tel: 020-7240 3901

BUSH THEATRE
Shepherd's Bush Green, London W12 8QD
Website: www.bushtheatre.co.uk
e-mail: info@bushtheatre.co.uk
Tel: 020-8743 3584

BYAM SHAW Matthew for ST ELMO PRODUCTIONS
2nd Floor, 20-22 Stukeley Street, London WC2B 5LR
Fax: 020-7242 3548
Tel: 020-7438 9520

CAHOOTS THEATRE COMPANY
Contact: Denise Silvey
Suite 1803, 16-19 Southampton Place, London WC1A 1AJ
Website: www.cahootstheatre.co.uk
e-mail: denise@silveyassociates.co.uk
Tel: 020-7745 7181

CAP PRODUCTION SOLUTIONS Ltd
20 Merton Industrial Park
Jubilee Way, Wimbledon, London SW19 3WL
e-mail: leigh@leighporter.com
Fax: 07970 763480
Tel: 020-8544 8668

CAPRICORN STAGE (& SCREEN) DIRECTIONS
9 Spencer House, Vale of Health
Hampstead, London NW3 1AS
Tel: 020-7794 5843

CELEBRATION
(Theatre Company for the Young)
48 Chiswick Staithe, London W4 3TP
e-mail: wortman.speakwell@btinternet.com
Mobile: 07976 805976
Tel: 020-8994 8886

CENTRELINE PRODUCTIONS
293 Lea Bridge Road, London E10 7NE
Website: www.centrelinenet.com
e-mail: jenny@centrelinenet.com
Mobile: 07710 522438

CHAIN REACTION THEATRE COMPANY
Three Mills Studios
Sugar House Yard, Sugar House Lane, London E15 2QS
Website: www.chainreactiontheatre.co.uk
e-mail: mail@chainreactiontheatre.co.uk
Tel/Fax: 020-8534 0007

CHANNEL THEATRE PRODUCTIONS
Central Studios, 36 Park Place, Margate, Kent CT9 1LE
Website: www.channel-theatre.co.uk
e-mail: info@channel-theatre.co.uk
Fax: 01843 280088
Tel: 01843 280077

Richard Jordan Productions Ltd

- Producing
- General Management
  UK and International Productions,
  and International Festivals
- Consultancy

Richard Jordan Productions Ltd
Mews Studios, 16 Vernon Yard
London W11 2DX

Tel: 020 7243 9001
Fax: 020 7313 9667
e-mail: richard.jordan@virgin.net

CHAPMAN Duggie ASSOCIATES
(Concerts, Musicals, Pantomimes)
The Old Coach House
202 Common Edge Road, Blackpool FY4 5DG
Website: www.duggiechapman.co.uk
e-mail: duggie@chapmanassociates.fsnet.co.uk
Tel/Fax: 01253 691823

CHEEK BY JOWL
Contact: Declan Donnellan, Nick Ormerod
Stage Door, Barbican Centre, Silk Street, London EC2Y 8DS
Website: www.cheekbyjowl.com
Tel: 020-7382 7281

CHEEKY MAGGOT PRODUCTIONS
Website: www.cheekymaggot.co.uk
e-mail: info@cheekymaggot.co.uk

CHICHESTER FESTIVAL THEATRE
Oaklands Park, Chichester, West Sussex PO19 6AP
Website: www.cft.org.uk
e-mail: admin@cft.org.uk
Fax: 01243 787288
Tel: 01243 784437

CHICKENSHED
Chase Side, Southgate, London N14 4PE
Website: www.chickenshed.org.uk
e-mail: info@chickenshed.org.uk
Minicom: 020-8350 0676
Tel: 020-8351 6161

CHURCHILL THEATRE BROMLEY Ltd
The Churchill, High Street, Bromley, Kent BR1 1HA
Website: www.churchilltheatre.co.uk
Fax: 020-8290 6968
Tel: 020-8464 7131

CLEAN BREAK
(Theatre Education, New Writing)
2 Patshull Road, London NW5 2LB
Website: www.cleanbreak.org.uk
e-mail: general@cleanbreak.org.uk
Fax: 020-7482 8611
Tel: 020-7482 8600

CLUBWEST PRODUCTIONS
Arundel Town Hall, Arundel, West Sussex BN18 9AP
Website: www.clubwest.co.uk
e-mail: admin@clubwest.co.uk
Tel/Fax: 01903 889821

CODRON Michael PLAYS Ltd
Aldwych Theatre Offices, London WC2B 4DF
Fax: 020-7240 8467
Tel: 020-7240 8291

COLE KITCHENN Ltd
212 Strand, London WC2R 1AP
Website: www.colekitchenn.com
e-mail: info@colekitchenn.com
Fax: 020-7353 9639
Tel: 020-7427 5682

COMPASS THEATRE COMPANY
St Jude's Parish Hall, 175 Gibraltar Street, Sheffield S3 8UA
Website: www.compasstheatrecompany.com
e-mail: info@compasstheatrecompany.com
Fax: 0114-278 6931   Tel: 0114-275 5328

COMPLICITE
14 Anglers Lane, London NW5 3DG
Website: www.complicite.org
e-mail: email@complicite.org
Fax: 020-7485 7701   Tel: 020-7485 7700

CONCORDANCE
Contact: Neil McPherson
Finborough Theatre
118 Finborough Road, London SW10 9ED
Website: www.concordance.org.uk
e-mail: admin@concordance.org.uk
Fax: 020-7835 1853   Tel: 020-7244 7439

CONTEMPO THEATRE COMPANY
37 White House, Vicarage Crescent, London SW11 3LJ
Website: www.contempotheatrecompany.com
e-mail: contemp1@mac.com   Mobile: 07906 348741

CONTEMPORARY STAGE COMPANY
Etchingham Park Road, Finchley, London N3 2DU
Website: www.contemporarystage.co.uk
e-mail: contemp.stage@hotmail.co.uk
Fax: 020-8349 2458   Tel: 020-8349 4402

CONWAY Clive CELEBRITY PRODUCTIONS Ltd
32 Grove Street, Oxford OX2 7JT
e-mail: info@celebrityproductions.org
Fax: 01865 514409   Tel: 01865 514830

CREATIVE MANAGEMENT & PRODUCTIONS (CMP) Ltd
1st Floor, 24 Litchfield Street, London WC2H 9NJ
Website: www.cmplimited.com
e-mail: mail@cmplimited.com
Fax: 020-7240 3037   Tel: 020-7240 3033

CRISP THEATRE
8 Cornwallis Crescent
Clifton, Bristol BS8 4PL
Website: www.crisptheatre.co.uk
e-mail: crisptheatre@btconnect.com   Tel: 0117-973 7106

DEAD EARNEST THEATRE
The Quadrant, 99 Parkway Avenue, Sheffield S9 4WG
Website: www.deadearnest.co.uk
e-mail: info@deadearnest.co.uk   Tel: 0114-227 0085

DEAN Lee
PO Box 10703, London WC2H 9ED
e-mail: admin@leedean.co.uk
Fax: 020-7836 6968   Tel: 020-7497 5111

DEBUT PRODUCTIONS
(Actor Showcases in London's West End & Manchester)
65 Norton Way North, Letchworth, Herts SG6 1BH
Website: www.debutproductions.co.uk
e-mail: enquiries@debutproductions.co.uk
                              Mobile: 07505 677994

DISNEY THEATRICAL PRODUCTIONS (UK)
Lyceum Theatre, 21 Wellington Street, London WC2E 7RQ
Fax: 020-7845 0999   Tel: 020-7845 0900

DONEGAN David Ltd
PO Box LB689, London W1A 9LB
e-mail: daviddonegan@hotmail.co.uk
                              Mobile: 07957 358909

DOODAH THEATRE
5 Broomans Terrace, Broomans Lane, Lewes
East Sussex BN7 2BH
e-mail: doodahtc@aol.com   Tel: 01273 477738

DOWNTOWN PRODUCTIONS Ltd
8 Scott Park Road, Burnley BB11 4JN
Website: www.downtownproductions.co.uk
e-mail: enquiries@downtownproductions.co.uk
                              Tel: 01282 703972

DRAMATIS PERSONAE Ltd
Contact: Nathan Silver, Nicolas Kent
19 Regency Street, London SW1P 4BY
e-mail: ns@nathansilver.com   Tel: 020-7834 9300

DUAL CONTROL THEATRE COMPANY
The Admiral's Offices
The Historic Dockyard, Chatham, Kent ME4 4TZ
Website: www.ellenkent.com
e-mail: info@ellenkentinternational.co.uk
Fax: 01634 819149   Tel: 01634 819141

EASTERN ANGLES THEATRE COMPANY
(Touring)
Sir John Mills Theatre
Gatacre Road, Ipswich, Suffolk IP1 2LQ
Website: www.easternangles.co.uk
e-mail: admin@easternangles.co.uk
Fax: 01473 384999   Tel: 01473 218202

ELLIOTT Paul Ltd
1st Floor, 18 Exeter Street, London WC2E 7DU
e-mail: pre@paulelliott.ltd.uk
Fax: 020-7379 4860   Tel: 020-7379 4870

ENGLISH CHAMBER THEATRE The
(No Drama School Applicants)
Flat 3, 6 St Simon's Avenue, London SW15 6DU
Website: www.englishchambertheatre.co.uk
e-mail: jane@janemcculloch.com
Mobile: 07951 912425   Tel: 020-8789 2424

ENGLISH NATIONAL OPERA
London Coliseum, St Martin's Lane, London WC2N 4ES
Website: www.eno.org
Fax: 020-7845 9277   Tel: 020-7836 0111

ENGLISH STAGE COMPANY Ltd
Royal Court, Sloane Square, London SW1W 8AS
Website: www.royalcourttheatre.com
e-mail: info@royalcourttheatre.com
Fax: 020-7565 5001   Tel: 020-7565 5050

ENGLISH THEATRE COMPANY Ltd The
(TMA Member)
Nybrogatan 35, 114 39 Stockholm, Sweden
Website: www.englishtheatre.se
e-mail: etc.ltd@telia.com
Fax: 00 46 8660 1159   Tel: 00 46 8662 4133

ENGLISH TOURING THEATRE (ETT)
25 Short Street, London SE1 8LJ
Website: www.ett.org.uk
e-mail: admin@ett.org.uk
Fax: 020-7633 0188   Tel: 020-7450 1990

EUROPEAN THEATRE COMPANY The
39 Oxford Avenue, London SW20 8LS
Website: www.europeantheatre.co.uk
e-mail: admin@europeantheatre.co.uk
Fax: 020-8544 1999   Tel: 020-8544 1994

FACADE
(Musicals)
43A Garthorne Road, London SE23 1EP
e-mail: facade@cobomedia.com   Tel: 020-8291 7079

FAIRBANK PRODUCTIONS
Contact: Gerald Armin
27 Harcourt Road, London E15 3DX
Website: www.fairbankproductions.co.uk
e-mail: fairbank@fpuk.freeserve.co.uk
                    Tel/Fax: 020-8555 3085

FEATHER PRODUCTIONS Ltd
The Studio, 137 Sheen Road
Richmond, Surrey TW9 1YJ
Website: www.featherproductions.com
e-mail: info@featherproductions.com
Fax: 020-8940 2335   Tel: 020-8439 9848

FELL Andrew Ltd
4 Ching Court, 49-51 Monmouth Street, London WC2H 9EY
e-mail: hq@andrewfell.co.uk
Fax: 020-7240 2499   Tel: 020-7240 2420

FIELD Anthony ASSOCIATES Ltd
Top Floor, 80-81 St Martin's Lane, London WC2N 4AA
e-mail: tony@afatheatre.com
Fax: 020-7240 2947   Tel: 020-7240 5453

FIELDER Simon Ltd
The Theatre, 7 Church Street
Leatherhead, Surrey KT22 8DN
e-mail: enquiries@simonfielder.com
Fax: 01372 365135   Tel: 01372 365134

FIERY ANGEL Ltd
22-24 Torrington Place, London WC1E 7HJ
Website: www.fiery-angel.com
e-mail: mail@fiery-angel.com
Fax: 020-7436 6287   Tel: 020-7907 7012

FORBIDDEN THEATRE COMPANY
18 Rupert Street, London W1D 6DE
Website: www.forbidden.org.uk
e-mail: info@forbidden.org.uk   Tel: 0845 0093084

FORD Vanessa PRODUCTIONS Ltd
Upper House Farm, Upper House Lane
Shamley Green, Surrey GU5 0SX
Website: www.vfpltd.com
e-mail: vfpltd@btinternet.com   Tel: 01483 278203

FOX Robert Ltd
6 Beauchamp Place, London SW3 1NG
Website: www.robertfoxltd.com
e-mail: info@robertfoxltd.com
Fax: 020-7225 1638   Tel: 020-7584 6855

FREEDMAN Bill Ltd
Colebrooke House, 10-12 Gaskin Street
London N1 2RY   Tel: 020-7288 8080

FRESH GLORY PRODUCTIONS
59 St Martin's Lane, London WC2N 4JS
Website: www.freshglory.com
e-mail: info@freshglory.com   Tel: 020-7240 1941

FRICKER Ian (THEATRE) Ltd
3rd Floor, 146 Strand, London WC2R 1JD
Website: www.ianfricker.com
e-mail: mail@ianfricker.com
Fax: 020-7836 3078   Tel: 020-7836 3090

FRIEDMAN Sonia PRODUCTIONS
Duke of York's Theatre
104 St Martin's Lane, London WC2N 4BG
Website: www.soniafriedman.com
e-mail: mail@soniafriedman.com
Fax: 020-7845 8759   Tel: 020-7845 8750

FUTURA MUSIC (PRODUCTIONS) Ltd
Contact: By Post
29 Emanuel House, Rochester Row
London SW1P 1BS

GALLEON THEATRE COMPANY Ltd
Contact: Alice De Sousa
Greenwich Playhouse
Greenwich BR Station Forecourt
189 Greenwich High Road, London SE10 8JA
Website: www.galleontheatre.co.uk
e-mail: boxoffice@galleontheatre.co.uk
Fax: 020-8310 7276   Tel: 020-8858 9256

GBM PRODUCTIONS Ltd
Bidlake Toft, Roadford Lake, Germansweek, Devon EX21 5BD
Website: www.musicaltheatrecreations.com
e-mail: gbm@bidlaketoft.com
Fax: 01837 871123   Tel: 01837 871522

GIANT STEPS Ltd
41 Parfrey Street, London W6 9EW
Website: www.rolandjaquarello.com
e-mail: roland@jaquarello.freeserve.co.uk
Mobile: 07808 742307   Tel/Fax: 020-8741 2446

GLASS David ENSEMBLE
96 Teesdale Street, London E2 6PU
Website: www.davidglassensemble.com
e-mail: info@davidglassensemble.com
                    Tel/Fax: 020-7729 9993

GODOT COMPANY
51 The Cut, London SE1 8LF
e-mail: godot@calderpublications.com   Tel: 020-7633 0599

GOODNIGHTS ENTERTAINMENT Ltd
74 Pannier Place, Milton Keynes MK14 7QP
Website: www.goodnights.org
e-mail: goodnights@talk21.com   Tel: 01908 672077

GOUCHER Mark Ltd
3rd Floor, 20-22 Stukeley Street, London WC2B 5LR
e-mail: jess@markgoucher.com
Fax: 020-7438 9577   Tel: 020-7438 9570

GRAEAE THEATRE COMPANY
LVS Resource Centre
356 Holloway Road, London N7 6PA
Website: www.graeae.org
e-mail: info@graeae.org
Fax: 020-7609 7324   Tel: 020-7700 2455

GRAHAM David ENTERTAINMENT Ltd
72 New Bond Street, London W1S 1RR
Website: www.davidgrahamentertainment.com
e-mail: info@davidgraham.co.uk
Fax: 0870 3211700   Tel: 0870 3211600

HAMPSTEAD THEATRE PRODUCTIONS Ltd
Eton Avenue, Swiss Cottage, London NW3 3EU
Website: www.hampsteadtheatre.com
e-mail: info@hampsteadtheatre.com
Fax: 020-7449 4201   Tel: 020-7449 4200

HANDSTAND PRODUCTIONS
13 Hope Street, Liverpool L1 9BH
Website: www.handstand-uk.com
e-mail: info@handstand-uk.com
Fax: 0151-709 3515   Tel: 0151-708 7441

HARLEY PRODUCTIONS
68 New Cavendish Street, London W1G 8TE
e-mail: harleyprods@aol.com
Fax: 020-8202 8863   Tel: 020-7580 3247

HAYMARKET The
c/o The Anvil Trust, Wote Street
Basingstoke, Hampshire RG21 7NW
Website: www.anvilarts.org.uk
Fax: 01256 357130   Tel: 01256 819797

HEADLONG THEATRE Ltd
Chertsey Chambers, 12 Mercer Street, London WC2H 9QD
Website: www.headlongtheatre.co.uk
e-mail: info@headlongtheatre.co.uk
Fax: 020-7438 9941   Tel: 020-7438 9940

HENDERSON Glynis PRODUCTIONS Ltd
69 Charlotte Street, London W1T 4PJ
Website: www.ghmp.co.uk
e-mail: info@ghmp.co.uk
Fax: 020-7436 1489   Tel: 020-7580 9644

HESTER John PRODUCTIONS
(Intimate Mysteries Theatre Company)
105 Stoneleigh Park Road, Epsom, Surrey KT19 0RF
e-mail: hjohnhester@aol.com   Tel/Fax: 020-8393 5705

HISS & BOO COMPANY Ltd The
Contact: Ian Liston
Nyes Hill, Wineham Lane, Bolney
West Sussex RH17 5SD
Website: www.hissboo.co.uk
e-mail: email@hissboo.co.uk
Fax: 01444 882057   Tel: 01444 881707

HISTORIA THEATRE COMPANY
8 Cloudesley Square, London N1 0HT
Website: www.historiatheatre.com
e-mail: kateprice@lineone.net
Fax: 020-7278 4733   Tel: 020-7837 8008

HOIPOLLOI
Office F, Dale's Brewery, Gwydir Street, Cambridge CB1 2LJ
Website: www.hoipolloi.org.uk
e-mail: info@hoipolloi.org.uk   Tel: 01223 322748

HOLLOW CROWN PRODUCTIONS
2 Norfolk Road, London E17 5QS
Website: www.hollowcrown.co.uk
e-mail: enquiries@hollowcrown.co.uk
                                   Mobile: 07930 530948

HOLMAN Paul ASSOCIATES Ltd
Morritt House, 58 Station Approach
South Ruislip, Middlesex HA4 6SA
Website: www.paulholmanassociates.co.uk
e-mail: enquiries@paulholmanassociates.co.uk
Fax: 020-8839 3124   Tel: 020-8845 9408

HOLT Thelma Ltd
Noel Coward Theatre
85 St Martin's Lane, London WC2N 4AU
Website: www.thelmaholt.co.uk
e-mail: thelma@dircon.co.uk
Fax: 020-7812 7550   Tel: 020-7812 7455

HOUSE OF GULLIVER Ltd
Contact: By Post
60 Beaconsfield Road, Tring, Herts HP23 4DW

HUGHES Steve
Oakwood, 4 Armitage Road, Armitage Bridge HD4 7PG
Website: www.hughes-productions.co.uk
e-mail: steve@hughes-productions.co.uk
                                   Mobile: 07816 844024

HULL TRUCK THEATRE
Spring Street, Hull HU2 8RW
Website: www.hulltruck.co.uk
e-mail: admin@hulltruck.co.uk
Fax: 01482 581182   Tel: 01482 224800

IAN David PRODUCTIONS
Third Floor, 33 Henrietta Street, London WC2E 8NA
Fax: 020-7257 6381   Tel: 020-7257 6380

IBSEN STAGE COMPANY
434B Hornsey Road, London N19 4EB
Website: www.ibsenstagecompany.co.uk
e-mail: info@ibsenstagecompany.co.uk   Tel: 020-7281 4322

ICARUS THEATRE COLLECTIVE
105 Bell Street, London NW1 6TL
Website: www.icarustheatre.co.uk
e-mail: info@icarustheatre.co.uk   Tel: 020-3239 7033

IMAGE MUSICAL THEATRE
23 Sedgeford Road, Shepherd's Bush, London W12 0NA
Website: www.imagemusicaltheatre.co.uk
e-mail: brian@imagemusicaltheatre.co.uk
Fax: 020-8749 9294   Tel: 020-8743 9380

INCISOR
Flat 1, 5 York Avenue, Hove BN3 1RJ
Website: www.theatre-company-incisor.com
e-mail: sarahmann7@hotmail.co.uk
Fax: 020-8830 4992   Mobile: 07979 498450

INDIGO ENTERTAINMENTS
Tynymynydd, Bryneglwys
Corwen, Denbighshire LL21 9NP
e-mail: indigoentertain@btinternet.com   Tel: 01978 790211

INGRAM Colin Ltd
Suite 526, Linen Hall
162-168 Regent Street, London W1B 5TE
Website: www.coliningramltd.com
e-mail: info@coliningramltd.com
Fax: 020-7038 3907   Tel: 020-7038 3906

INSIDE INTELLIGENCE
(Theatre, Contemporary Opera & Music)
13 Athlone Close, London E5 8HD
Website: www.inside-intelligence.org.uk
e-mail: admin@inside-intelligence.org.uk
Fax: 020-8985 7211   Tel: 020-8986 8013

INTERNATIONAL THEATRE & MUSIC Ltd
Contact: Piers Chater Robinson
Garden Studios, 11-15 Betterton Street
Covent Garden, London WC2H 9BP
Website: www.it-m.co.uk
e-mail: info@it-m.co.uk
Fax: 020-7379 0801   Tel: 020-7470 8786

ISLEWORTH ACTORS COMPANY
38 Eve Road, Isleworth
Middlesex TW7 7HS   Tel/Fax: 020-8891 1073

JAM THEATRE COMPANY
21 Beechtree Avenue, Marlow, Bucks SL7 3NH
Website: www.jamtheatre.co.uk
e-mail: office@jamtheatre.co.uk　　Tel: 01628 487773

JAMES Bruce PRODUCTIONS Ltd
68 St Georges Park Avenue
Westcliff-on-Sea, Essex SS0 9UD
Website: www.brucejamesproductions.co.uk
e-mail: info@brucejamesproductions.co.uk
Mobile: 07850 369018　　Tel/Fax: 01702 335970

JENKINS Andrew Ltd
63 Kidbrooke Park Road, London SE3 0EE
Website: www.andrewjenkinsltd.com
e-mail: info@andrewjenkinsltd.com
Fax: 020-8856 7106　　Tel: 020-8319 3657

JOHNSON David
85B Torriano Avenue, London NW5 2RX
e-mail: david@johnsontemple.co.uk　　Tel: 020-7284 3733

JOHNSON Gareth Ltd
Plas Hafren, Eglwyswrw, Crymych
Pembrokeshire SA41 3UL
e-mail: gjltd@mac.com
Fax: 07779 007845　　Mobile: 07770 225227

JORDAN Andy PRODUCTIONS Ltd
Studio D, 413 Harrow Road
Maida Vale, London W9 3QJ
e-mail: ANDYJAndyjordan@aol.com　　Mobile: 07775 615205

JORDAN PRODUCTIONS Ltd
Dyke House, 110 South Street
Eastbourne, East Sussex BN21 4LB
e-mail: info@jordanproductionsltd.co.uk
Fax: 01323 417766　　Tel: 01323 417745

JORDAN Richard PRODUCTIONS Ltd
Mews Studios, 16 Vernon Yard, London W11 2DX
e-mail: richard.jordan@virgin.net
Fax: 020-7313 9667　　Tel: 020-7243 9001

KELLY Robert C Ltd
The Alhambra Suite
82 Mitchell Street, Glasgow G1 3NA
Website: www.robertckelly.co.uk
e-mail: robert@robertckelly.co.uk
Fax: 0141-229 1441　　Tel: 0141-229 1444

KENWRIGHT Bill Ltd
BKL House, 1 Venice Walk, London W2 1RR
e-mail: info@kenwright.com
Fax: 020-7446 6222　　Tel: 020-7446 6200

KING'S HEAD THEATRE PRODUCTIONS Ltd
115 Upper Street, London N1 1QN
Website: www.kingsheadtheatre.org　　Tel: 020-7226 8561

LAIDLAW Neil PRODUCTIONS
14 Spectrum Tower
20 Hainault Street, Ilford IG1 4GZ
e-mail: info@neillaidlaw.co.uk
Fax: 0870 4601483　　Tel: 020-8911 9276

LATCHMERE THEATRE
Contact: Chris Fisher
Unit 5A, Imex Business Centre
Ingate Place, London SW8 3NS
e-mail: latchmere@fishers.org.uk
Fax: 020-7978 2631　　Tel: 020-7978 2620

LHP Ltd
PO Box 60231, London EC1P 1FL
e-mail: lhpltd@msn.com　　Mobile: 07973 938634

LINNIT PRODUCTIONS Ltd
123A King's Road, London SW3 4PL
Fax: 020-7352 3450　　Tel: 020-7352 7722

LIVE THEATRE
Broad Chare, Quayside
Newcastle upon Tyne NE1 3DQ
Website: www.live.org.uk　　Tel: 0191-261 2694

LONDON BUBBLE THEATRE COMPANY Ltd
5 Elephant Lane, London SE16 4JD
Website: www.londonbubble.org.uk
e-mail: admin@londonbubble.org.uk
Fax: 020-7231 2366　　Tel: 020-7237 4434

LONDON CLASSIC THEATRE
The Production Office
63 Shirley Avenue, Sutton, Surrey SM1 3QT
Website: www.londonclassictheatre.co.uk
e-mail: admin@londonclassictheatre.co.uk
　　Tel/Fax: 020-8395 2095

LONDON PRODUCTIONS Ltd
PO Box 10703, London WC2H 9ED
e-mail: admin@leedean.co.uk
Fax: 020-7836 6968　　Tel: 020-7497 5111

LONDON REPERTORY COMPANY
27 Old Gloucester Street, London WC1N 3XX
Website: www.londonrepertorycompany.com
e-mail: info@londonrepertorycompany.com
　　Tel/Fax: 020-7258 1944

LOUDER THAN WORDS Ltd
75 Church Walk, London N16 8QR
e-mail: giles@louderthanwords.info
Fax: 0870 1333085　　Mobile: 07851 729078

MACKINTOSH Cameron Ltd
1 Bedford Square, London WC1B 3RB
Fax: 020-7436 2683　　Tel: 020-7637 8866

MACNAGHTEN PRODUCTIONS Ltd
Dundarave, Bushmills, Co. Antrim
Northern Ireland BT57 8ST
Fax: 028-2073 2575　　Tel: 028-2073 1215

MALCOLM Christopher PRODUCTIONS Ltd
11 Claremont Walk, Bath BA1 6HB
Website: www.christophermalcolm.co.uk
e-mail: cm@christophermalcolm.co.uk
Fax: 01225 480077　　Tel: 01225 445459

MANS Johnny PRODUCTIONS Ltd
PO Box 196, Hoddesdon, Herts EN10 7WG
Website: www.johnnymansproductions.co.uk
e-mail: johnnymansagent@aol.com
Fax: 01992 470516　　Tel: 01992 470907

MASTERSON Guy PRODUCTIONS
Millfield Theatre, Silver Street, Edmonton N18 1PJ
Website: www.theatretoursinternational.com
e-mail: admin@theatretoursinternational.com
　　Tel/Fax: 020-8807 5770

MCM LIMELIGHT Ltd
The Gateway, 2A Rathmore Road, London SE7 7QW
e-mail: enquiries@limelightents.co.uk
Fax: 020-8305 2684　　Tel: 020-8858 6141

MEADOW Jeremy Ltd
73 Great Titchfield Street, London W1W 6RD
e-mail: info@jeremymeadow.com
Fax: 0870 7627882   Tel: 020-7436 2244

MENZIES Lee Ltd
118-120 Wardour Street, London W1F 0TU
Website: www.leemenzies.co.uk
e-mail: leemenzies@leemenzies.co.uk
Fax: 020-7734 4224   Tel: 020-7734 9559

MIDDLE GROUND THEATRE CO Ltd
3 Gordon Terrace, Malvern Wells
Malvern, Worcestershire WR14 4ER
Website: www.middlegroundtheatre.co.uk
e-mail: middleground@middlegroundtheatre.co.uk
Fax: 01684 574472   Tel: 01684 577231

MITCHELL Matthew Ltd
New Barn Farm, London Road
Hassocks, West Sussex BN6 9ND
e-mail: matthew@matthewmitchell.org
      Tel/Fax: 01273 842572

MJE PRODUCTIONS Ltd
Contact: Carole Winter, Michael Edwards
Amadeus House, Floral Street
Covent Garden, London WC2E 9DP
Website: www.mjeproductions.com
e-mail: info@mjeproductions.com
Fax: 020-7812 6495   Tel: 020-7812 7290

MONSTAR PRODUCTIONS
65A Huddleston Road, London N7 0AE
Website: www.monstarproductions.co.uk
e-mail: monstar@fsmail.net   Mobile: 07900 864694

MONSTER PRODUCTIONS
Buddle Arts Centre
258B Station Road, Wallsend, Tyne & Wear NE28 8RG
Website: www.monsterproductions.co.uk
e-mail: info@monsterproductions.co.uk
Fax: 0191-240 4016   Tel: 0191-240 4011

MOVING THEATRE
16 Laughton Lodge
Nr Lewes, East Sussex BN8 6BY
Website: www.movingtheatre.com
e-mail: info@movingtheatre.com
Fax: 01323 815737   Tel: 01323 815726

MUSIC THEATRE LONDON
Chertsey Chambers
12 Mercer Street, London WC2H 9QD
Website: www.capriolfilms.co.uk
e-mail: musictheatre.london@virgin.net   Tel: 07831 243942

NATIONAL ANGELS
123A Kings Road, London SW3 4PL
e-mail: admin@nationalangels.com
Fax: 020-7352 3450   Tel: 020-7376 4878

NATIONAL THEATRE
South Bank, London SE1 9PX
Website: www.nationaltheatre.org.uk
Fax: 020-7452 3344   Tel: 020-7452 3333

NEAL STREET PRODUCTIONS Ltd
1st Floor, 26-28 Neal Street, London WC2H 9QQ
e-mail: post@nealstreetproductions.com
Fax: 020-7240 7099   Tel: 020-7240 8890

NEW GODS AND HEROES
1 Lyndale House, Puttenham Lane
Shackleford, Surrey GU8 6AU
Website: www.loveanddeath.co.uk
e-mail: info@loveanddeath.co.uk   Mobile: 07813 615878

NEW SHAKESPEARE COMPANY Ltd The
Open Air Theatre, The Iron Works
Inner Circle, Regent's Park, London NW1 4NR
Website: www.openairtheatre.org
Fax: 020-7487 4562   Tel: 020-7935 5756

NEWPALM PRODUCTIONS
26 Cavendish Avenue, London N3 3QN
e-mail: newpalm@btopenworld.com
Fax: 020-8346 8257   Tel: 020-8349 0802

NICHOLAS Paul & IAN David ASSOCIATES Ltd
c/o Third Floor, 33 Henrietta Street, London WC2E 8NA
Fax: 020-7257 6381   Tel: 020-7257 6380

NITRO
(Formerly Black Theatre Co-operative)
6 Brewery Road, London N7 9NH
Website: www.nitro.co.uk
e-mail: info@nitro.co.uk
Fax: 020-7609 1221   Tel: 020-7609 1331

NORDIC NOMAD PRODUCTIONS
64 Tulse Hill, London SW2 2PT
Website: www.nordicnomad.com
e-mail: info@nordicnomad.com   Mobile: 07980 619165

NORTHERN BROADSIDES THEATRE COMPANY
Dean Clough, Halifax HX3 5AX
Website: www.northern-broadsides.co.uk
e-mail: sue@northern-broadsides.co.uk
Fax: 01422 383175   Tel: 01422 369704

NORTHERN STAGE (THEATRICAL PRODUCTIONS) Ltd
Barras Bridge, Newcastle upon Tyne NE1 7RH
Website: www.northernstage.co.uk
e-mail: info@northernstage.co.uk
Fax: 0191-261 8093   Tel: 0191-232 3366

NORTHUMBERLAND THEATRE COMPANY (NTC)
The Playhouse, Bondgate Without, Alnwick
Northumberland NE66 1PQ
Website: www.ntc-touringtheatre.co.uk
e-mail: admin@ntc-touringtheatre.co.uk
Fax: 01665 605837   Tel: 01665 602586

NOT THE NATIONAL THEATRE
Contact: By Post
(Small/Mid-Scale Touring - UK & Abroad)
116 Dalberg Road, London SW2 1AW

NOTIONAL THEATRE Ltd
PO Box 130, Hexham NE46 4WA
Website: www.notionaltheatre.com
e-mail: notional.theatre@virgin.net   Mobile: 07766 661795

O'BRIEN Barry (1968) Ltd
26 Cavendish Avenue, London N3 3QN
Fax: 020-8346 8257   Tel: 020-8346 8011

OFF THE CUFF THEATRE COMPANY
2nd Floor, 91A Rivington Street, London EC2A 3AY
Website: www.otctheatre.co.uk
e-mail: otctheatre@aol.com
Fax: 020-7739 3852   Tel: 020-7739 2857

OLD VIC PRODUCTIONS Plc
The Old Vic Theatre, The Cut, Waterloo, London SE1 8NB
e-mail: becky.barber@oldvictheatre.com
Fax: 020-7981 0946   Tel: 020-7928 2651

ONE NIGHT BOOKING COMPANY The
1 Hogarth Hill, London NW11 6AY
Website: www.onenightbooking.com
e-mail: mail@onenightbooking.com   Tel: 020-8455 3278

OPEN AIR THEATRE
(See NEW SHAKESPEARE COMPANY Ltd The)

OPERATING THEATRE COMPANY
22 Burghley Road, London NW5 1UE
Website: www.operating-theatre.co.uk
e-mail: info@operating-theatre.co.uk   Tel: 020-7419 2476

OUT OF JOINT
7 Thane Works
Thane Villas, London N7 7NU
Website: www.outofjoint.co.uk
e-mail: ojo@outofjoint.co.uk
Fax: 020-7609 0203   Tel: 020-7609 0207

OVATION
Upstairs at The Gatehouse
The Gatehouse, Highgate Village, London N6 4BD
Website: www.ovationtheatres.com
e-mail: events@ovationproductions.com
Fax: 020-8340 3466   Tel: 020-8340 4256

P&S PRODUCTIONS
Top Flat, 51 Norroy Road
London SW15 1PQ
e-mail: timsawers@msn.com   Tel: 020-8788 8521

PAINES PLOUGH
Fourth Floor, 43 Aldwych, London WC2B 4DN
Website: www.painesplough.com
e-mail: office@painesplough.com
Fax: 020-7240 4534   Tel: 020-7240 4533

PASSWORD PRODUCTIONS Ltd
Contact: John Mackay
85B Torriano Avenue, London NW5 2RX
e-mail: johnmackay2001@aol.com   Tel: 020-7284 3733

PENDLE PRODUCTIONS
Bridge Farm, 249 Hawes Side Lane
Blackpool FY4 4AA
Website: www.pendleproductions.co.uk
e-mail: admin@pendleproductions.co.uk
Fax: 01253 792930   Tel: 01253 839375

PENTABUS
(National Touring Company for New Writing)
Bromfield, Ludlow, Shropshire SY8 2JU
Website: www.pentabus.co.uk
e-mail: john@pentabus.co.uk   Tel: 01584 856564

PEOPLE SHOW
People Show Studios, Pollard Row, London E2 6NB
Website: www.peopleshow.co.uk
e-mail: people@peopleshow.co.uk
Fax: 020-7739 0203   Tel: 020-7729 1841

PERFORMANCE BUSINESS The
78 Oatlands Drive, Weybridge, Surrey KT13 9HT
Website: www.theperformance.biz
e-mail: info@theperformance.biz   Tel: 01932 888885

PILOT THEATRE
(New Writing & Multimedia YPT)
York Theatre Royal, St Leonard's Place, York YO1 7HD
Website: www.pilot-theatre.com
e-mail: info@pilot-theatre.com
Fax: 01904 656378   Tel: 01904 635755

PLANTAGENET PRODUCTIONS
Westridge (Open Centre), (Drawing Room Recitals)
Star Lane, Highclere
Nr Newbury RG20 9PJ   Tel: 01635 253322

PLUTO PRODUCTIONS Ltd
New End Theatre, 27 New End, Hampstead, London NW3 1JD
Website: www.newendtheatre.co.uk
e-mail: briandaniels@newendtheatre.co.uk
Fax: 020-7794 4044   Tel: 020-7472 5800

POLKA THEATRE
240 The Broadway, Wimbledon SW19 1SB
Website: www.polkatheatre.com
e-mail: admin@polkatheatre.com
Fax: 020-8545 8365   Tel: 020-8545 8320

POPULAR PRODUCTIONS Ltd
18B High Street, London N8 7PB
Website: www.popularproductions.com
e-mail: info@popularproductions.com
Mobile: 07812 859767   Tel: 020-8347 0221

POSTER Kim
4th Floor, 80-81 St Martin's Lane
London WC2N 4AA
e-mail: admin@stanhopeprod.com
Fax: 020-7504 8656   Tel: 020-7240 3098

PREMIER SHOWS Ltd
PO Box 638, Chichester
West Sussex PO19 9HB
Website: www.premiershows.co.uk
e-mail: mail@premiershows.co.uk   Mobile: 07071 888990

PROMENADE PRODUCTIONS
6 Russell Grove, London SW9 6HS
Website: www.promenadeproductions.com
e-mail: info@promenadeproductions.com
          Tel: 020-7582 9354

PUGH David & ROGERS Dafydd
Wyndhams Theatre, Charing Cross Road
London WC2H 0DA
e-mail: dpl@davidpughltd.com
Fax: 020-7292 0399   Tel: 020-7292 0390

PURSUED BY A BEAR PRODUCTIONS
Farnham Maltings
Bridge Square, Farnham GU9 7QR
Website: www.pursuedbyabear.co.uk
e-mail: pursuedbyabear@yahoo.co.uk   Tel: 01252 745445

PW PRODUCTIONS Ltd
2nd Floor, 80-81 St Martin's Lane, London WC2N 4AA
Website: www.pwprods.co.uk
Fax: 020-7240 2947   Tel: 020-7395 7580

QDOS ENTERTAINMENT
Qdos House, Queen Margaret's Road
Scarborough, North Yorkshire YO11 2YH
Website: www.qdosentertainment.com
e-mail: info@qdosentertainment.co.uk
Fax: 01723 361958   Tel: 01723 500038

QUANTUM THEATRE
The Old Button Factory
1-11 Bannockburn Road, Plumstead, London SE18 1ET
Website: www.quantumtheatre.co.uk
e-mail: office@quantumtheatre.co.uk   Tel: 020-8317 9000

RAGS & FEATHERS THEATRE COMPANY
80 Summer Road, Thames Ditton, Surrey KT7 0QP
e-mail: jill@ragsandfeathers.freeserve.co.uk
Mobile: 07958 724374   Tel: 020-8224 2203

RAIN OR SHINE THEATRE COMPANY
25 Paddock Gardens, Longlevens, Gloucester GL2 0ED
Website: www.rainorshine.co.uk
e-mail: theatre@rainorshine.co.uk   Tel/Fax: 01452 521575

REAL CIRCUMSTANCE THEATRE COMPANY
100 Lexden Road, West Bergholt, Colchester CO6 3BW
Website: www.realcircumstance.com
e-mail: info@realcircumstance.com

REALLY USEFUL GROUP Ltd The
22 Tower Street, London WC2H 9TW
Fax: 020-7240 1204   Tel: 020-7240 0880

RED ROOM The
Oval House, 52-54 Kennington Oval, London SE11 5SW
Website: www.theredroom.org.uk
e-mail: info@theredroom.org.uk   Tel: 020-7735 7797

RED ROSE CHAIN
1 Fore Hamlet, Ipswich IP3 8AA
Website: www.redrosechain.co.uk
e-mail: info@redrosechain.co.uk   Tel: 01473 288886

RED SHIFT THEATRE COMPANY
PO Box 60151, London SW19 2TB
Website: www.redshifttheatreco.co.uk
e-mail: jane@redshifttheatreco.co.uk
    Tel/Fax: 020-8540 1271

REVEAL THEATRE COMPANY
40 Pirehill Lane, Walton, Stone, Staffs ST15 0JN
Website: www.revealtheatre.co.uk
e-mail: robert.marsden@revealtheatre.co.uk
    Tel/Fax: 0115-878 0651

RGC PRODUCTIONS Ltd
260 Kings Road, Kingston, Surrey KT2 5HX
Website: www.rgcproductions.com
e-mail: roger@rgcproductions.com   Tel: 020-3093 5718

RHO DELTA Ltd
Contact: Greg Ripley-Duggan
26 Goodge Street, London W1T 2QG
e-mail: info@ripleyduggan.com   Tel: 020-7436 1392

ROCKET THEATRE
245 Broadfield Road, Manchester M14 7JT
Website: www.rockettheatre.co.uk
e-mail: martin@rockettheatre.co.uk
Mobile: 07788 723570   Tel: 0161-226 8788

ROSE Michael Ltd
The Old Dairy, Throop Road
Holdenhurst, Bournemouth, Dorset BH8 0DL
e-mail: firstname@michaelroseltd.com
Fax: 01202 522311   Tel: 01202 522711

ROSENTHAL Suzanna Ltd
PO Box 40001, London N6 4YA
e-mail: admin@suzannarosenthal.com
    Tel/Fax: 020-8340 4421

ROYAL COURT THEATRE PRODUCTIONS Ltd
Sloane Square, London SW1W 8AS
Website: www.royalcourttheatre.com
e-mail: info@royalcourttheatre.com
Fax: 020-7565 5001   Tel: 020-7565 5050

ROYAL EXCHANGE THEATRE
St Ann's Square, Manchester M2 7DH
Website: www.royalexchange.co.uk   Tel: 0161-833 9333

ROYAL SHAKESPEARE COMPANY
1 Earlham Street, London WC2H 9LL
Website: www.rsc.org.uk
Fax: 020-7845 0505   Tel: 020-7845 0500

Waterside
Stratford-upon-Avon CV37 6BB
Fax: 01789 294810   Tel: 01789 296655

RUBINSTEIN Mark Ltd
25 Short Street, London SE1 8LJ
e-mail: info@mrluk.com
Fax: 0870 7059731   Tel: 020-7021 0787

SALBERG & STEPHENSON Ltd
18 Soho Square, London W1D 3QL
e-mail: soholondon@aol.com
Fax: 020-7025 8100   Tel: 020-7025 8701

SANDIS PRODUCTIONS
Office 423, 266 Banbury Road
Summertown, Oxford OX2 7DL
Website: www.sandisproductions.com
e-mail: info@sandisproductions.com
Mobile: 07775 520906   Tel/Fax: 01865 514327

SANDPIPER PRODUCTIONS Ltd
49A Ossington Street, London W2 4LY
e-mail: harold@sanditen.fsworld.co.uk
Fax: 0871 7333998   Tel: 020-7229 6708

SCAMP
(Sutherland Callow Arts Management & Production)
44 Church Lane, Arlesley, Beds SG15 6UX
Website: www.scamptheatre.com
e-mail: admin@scamptheatre.com
Mobile: 07710 491111   Tel: 01462 734843

SCARLET THEATRE
Studio 4, The Bull, 68 High Street
Barnet, Herts EN5 5SJ
Website: www.scarlettheatre.co.uk
e-mail: admin@scarlettheatre.co.uk   Tel: 020-8441 9779

SEABRIGHT James
3rd Floor, 118-120 Wardour Street, London W1F 0TU
Website: www.seabright.info
e-mail: contacts@seabright.info
Fax: 08701 255706   Tel: 020-7439 1173

SHAKESPEARE'S MEN
10 Dee Close, Upminster, Essex RM14 1QD
Website: www.terencemustoo.com
e-mail: terence@terencemustoo.com   Tel: 01708 222938

SHARED EXPERIENCE
(National/International Touring)
13 Riverside House, 27-29 Vauxhall Grove, London SW8 1SY
Website: www.sharedexperience.org.uk
e-mail: admin@sharedexperience.org.uk
Fax: 020-7735 0374   Tel: 020-7587 1596

SHOW OF STRENGTH
74 Chessel Street, Bedminster, Bristol BS3 3DN
Website: www.showofstrength.org.uk
Fax: 0117-902 0196   Tel: 0117-902 0235

SHOWCASE ENTERTAINMENTS PRODUCTIONS
2 Lumley Close, Newton Aycliffe, Co Durham DL5 5PA
Website: www.showcaseproductions.co.uk
e-mail: gjl@showcaseproductions.co.uk   Tel: 01325 316224

SIMPLY THEATRE
Chemin des Coeuvres 8B, 1295 Tannay, Switzerland 1295
Website: www.simplytheatre.com
e-mail: info@simplytheatre.com   Tel: 00 41 22 8600518

SINDEN Marc PRODUCTIONS
1 Hogarth Hill, London NW11 6AY
Website: www.sindenproductions.com
e-mail: mail@sindenproductions.com   Tel: 020-8455 3278

SOHO THEATRE COMPANY
21 Dean Street, London W1D 3NE
Website: www.sohotheatre.com
Fax: 020-7287 5061   Tel: 020-7287 5060

SPHINX THEATRE COMPANY
25 Short Street, London SE1 8LJ
Website: www.sphinxtheatre.co.uk
e-mail: info@sphinxtheatre.co.uk   Tel: 020-7401 9993

SPINNING WHEEL THEATRE
5 Haughmond, Woodside Grange Road
Finchley, London N12 8ST
Website: www.spinningwheeltheatre.com
e-mail: info@spinningwheeltheatre.com
       Mobile: 07990 575496

SPLATS ENTERTAINMENT
5 Denmark Street, London WC2H 8LP
Website: www.splatsentertainment.co.uk
e-mail: admin@splatsentertainment.co.uk
Fax: 020-7240 8409   Tel: 020-7240 8400

SPLITMOON THEATRE
Flat 1, 17 Westgrove Lane, London SE10 8QP
Website: www.splitmoontheatre.org
e-mail: info@splitmoontheatre.org   Tel: 020-8694 3703

SQUAREDEAL PRODUCTIONS Ltd
Contact: Jenny Topper
24 De Beauvoir Square, London N1 4LE
e-mail: jenny@jennytopper.com
Fax: 020-7275 7553   Tel: 020-7249 5966

SQUIRES & JOHNS PRODUCTIONS Ltd
Sullon Lodge, Sullon Side Lane, Garstang PR3 1GH
Website: www.trendsgroup.co.uk
e-mail: info@trendsgroup.co.uk
Fax: 01253 407715   Tel: 0871 2003343

STACEY Barrie UK PRODUCTIONS Ltd
Flat 8, 132 Charing Cross Road, London WC2H 0LA
Website: www.barriestacey.com
e-mail: hopkinstacey@aol.com
Fax: 020-7836 2949   Tel: 020-7836 6220

STAGE ENTERTAINMENT UK Ltd
6th Floor, Swan House, 52 Poland Street, London W1F 7NQ
Fax: 020-7025 6971   Tel: 020-7025 6970

STAGE FURTHER PRODUCTIONS Ltd
Westgate House, Stansted Road
Eastbourne, East Sussex BN22 8LG
e-mail: davidsfp@hotmail.com
Fax: 01323 736127   Tel: 01323 739478

STAND UP DRAMA Ltd
Unit 8, 8 Balmes Road, London N1 5TQ
Website: www.standupdrama.com
e-mail: info@standupdrama.com   Tel: 020-7923 2295

STANHOPE PRODUCTIONS Ltd
4th Floor
80-81 St Martin's Lane
London WC2N 4AA
e-mail: admin@stanhopeprod.com
Fax: 020-7504 8656   Tel: 020-7240 3098

STRAIGHT LINE PRODUCTIONS
58 Castle Avenue
Epsom, Surrey KT17 2PH
e-mail: mary@straightlinemanagement.co.uk
Fax: 020-8393 8079   Tel: 020-8393 4220

SUPPORT ACT PRODUCTIONS
Contact: Ian McCracken
243A Lynmouth Avenue
Morden, Surrey SM4 4RX
Website: www.supportact.co.uk
e-mail: info@supportact.co.uk   Tel: 0845 0940796

SUSPECT CULTURE
CCA, 350 Sauchiehall Street
Glasgow G2 3JD
Website: www.suspectculture.com
e-mail: info@suspectculture.com
Fax: 0141-332 8823   Tel: 0141-332 9775

TABS PRODUCTIONS
57 Chamberlain Place
Higham Street
Walthamstow, London E17 6AZ
Website: www.tabsproductions.co.uk
e-mail: adrianmljames@aol.com
Fax: 08714 332938   Tel: 020-8527 9255

TALAWA THEATRE COMPANY
Ground Floor, 53-55 East Road
London N1 6AH
Website: www.talawa.com
e-mail: hq@talawa.com
Fax: 020-7251 5969   Tel: 020-7251 6644

TAMASHA THEATRE COMPANY
Unit 220, Great Guildford Business Square
30 Great Guildford Street, London SE1 0HS
Website: www.tamasha.org.uk
e-mail: info@tamasha.org.uk
Fax: 020-7021 0421   Tel: 020-7633 2270

TBA MUSIC
1 St Gabriels Road, London NW2 4DS
e-mail: peter@tbagroup.co.uk
Fax: 0700 607 0808   Tel: 0845 1203722

TEG PRODUCTIONS Ltd
73 Great Titchfield Street, London W1W 6RD
e-mail: info@tegproductions.com
Fax: 0870 7627882   Tel: 020-7436 2244

TENTH PLANET PRODUCTIONS
75 Woodland Gardens, London N10 3UD
Website: www.10thplanetproductions.com
e-mail: admin@10thplanetproductions.com
Fax: 020-8883 1708   Tel: 020-8442 2659

Medius House
2 Sheraton Street, London W1F 8BH
Fax: 020-7439 3584   Tel: 020-7297 9474

THAT'S ENTERTAINMENT PRODUCTIONS
8 Ellis Avenue, High Salvington, Worthing BN13 3DY
Website: www.thatsentertainmentproductions.co.uk
e-mail: info@thatsentertainmentproductions.co.uk
Tel: 01903 263454

THEATRE ABSOLUTE
I.C.E., Parkside, Coventry CV1 2QR
Website: www.theatreabsolute.co.uk
e-mail: info@theatreabsolute.co.uk   Tel: 024-7615 8340

THEATRE ALIVE!
c/o Menier Chocolate Factory
4 O'Meara Street, London SE1 1TE
Website: www.theatrealive.org.uk
e-mail: theatrealiveinfo@tiscali.co.uk
Tel/Fax: 020-7403 4405

THEATRE BABEL
PO Box 5103, Glasgow G78 9AR
Website: www.theatrebabel.co.uk
e-mail: admin@theatrebabel.co.uk   Tel: 0141-416 0051

THEATRE NORTH
Woodlands, The Mains, Giggleswick
Settle, North Yorkshire BD24 0AX
Website: www.theatrenorth.co.uk
e-mail: info@theatrenorth.co.uk   Tel/Fax: 01729 822058

THEATRE OF COMEDY COMPANY Ltd
Shaftesbury Theatre
210 Shaftesbury Avenue, London WC2H 8DP
Fax: 020-7836 8181   Tel: 020-7379 3345

THEATRE PARTNERS Ltd
21 Catherine Street, Covent Garden, London WC2B 5JS
Website: www.theatrepartners.com
e-mail: info@theatrepartners.com
Fax: 020-7240 4282   Tel: 020-7240 9941

THEATRE ROYAL HAYMARKET PRODUCTIONS
Theatre Royal Haymarket
18 Suffolk Street, London SW1Y 4HT
e-mail: nigel.everett@trh.co.uk
Fax: 020-7389 9698   Tel: 020-7389 9669

THEATRE ROYAL STRATFORD EAST
Gerry Raffles Square, Stratford, London E15 1BN
Website: www.stratfordeast.com
e-mail: theatreroyal@stratfordeast.com
Fax: 020-8534 8381   Tel: 020-8534 7374

THEATRE SANS FRONTIERES
The Queen's Hall Arts Centre
Beaumont Street, Hexham NE46 3LS
Website: www.tsf.org.uk
e-mail: admin@tsf.org.uk
Fax: 01434 607206   Tel: 01434 652484

THEATRE SET-UP
12 Fairlawn Close, Southgate, London N14 4JX
Website: www.ts-u.co.uk   Tel: 020-8886 9572

THEATRE TOURS INTERNATIONAL
Contact: Guy Masterson, Rebecca Vaughan
Millfield Theatre, Silver Street, Edmonton N18 1PJ
Website: www.theatretoursinternational.com
e-mail: mail@theatretoursinternational.com
Tel: 020-8807 5770

THEATRE WORKOUT Ltd
13A Stratheden Road, Blackheath, London SE3 7TH
Website: www.theatreworkout.co.uk
e-mail: enquiries@theatreworkout.co.uk
Tel: 020-8144 2290

THEATREWORKS
2 Hanley Road, Malvern Wells, Worcs WR14 4PQ
Website: www.theatreworks.info
e-mail: info@theatreworks.info   Tel: 01684 578342

TIATA FAHODZI
AH 112 Aberdeen Centre
22-24 Highbury Grove, London N5 2EA
Website: www.tiatafahodzi.com
e-mail: info@tiatafahodzi.com   Tel/Fax: 020-7226 3800

TOLD BY AN IDIOT
Unit LF 1.7 Lafone House
The Leathermarket
11-13 Weston Street, London SE1 3ER
Website: www.toldbyanidiot.org
e-mail: info@toldbyanidiot.org
Fax: 020-7407 9002   Tel: 020-7407 4123

TOPPER Jenny
(Squaredeal Productions Ltd)
24 De Beauvoir Square, London N1 4LE
e-mail: jenny@jennytopper.com
Fax: 020-7275 7553   Tel: 020-7249 5966

TOURING TALES THEATRE COMPANY Ltd
Suite 228, The Linen Hall
162 Regent Street, London W1B 5TB
Website: www.birminghamstage.net
e-mail: info@birminghamstage.net
Fax: 020-7437 3395   Tel: 020-7437 3391

TOWER THEATRE COMPANY
(Full-time non-professional)
St Bride Foundation, Bride Lane, London EC4Y 8EQ
Website: www.towertheatre.org.uk
e-mail: info@towertheatre.freeserve.co.uk
Tel/Fax: 020-7353 5700

TREAGUS Andrew ASSOCIATES Ltd
5th Floor, 35 Soho Square, London W1D 3QX
e-mail: admin@at-assoc.co.uk
Fax: 020-7851 0151   Tel: 020-7851 0150

TREAGUS STONEMAN ASSOCIATES Ltd
5th Floor, 35 Soho Square, London W1D 3QX
Website: www.treagusstoneman.com
e-mail: info@treagusstoneman.com
Fax: 020-7851 0151   Tel: 020-7851 0150

TRESTLE THEATRE COMPANY
(Visual/Physical Theatre, Music, Choreography,
New Writing)
Trestle Arts Base, Russet Drive
Herts, St Albans AL4 0JQ
Website: www.trestle.org.uk
e-mail: admin@trestle.org.uk
Fax: 01727 855558   Tel: 01727 850950

TRICYCLE LONDON PRODUCTIONS
269 Kilburn High Road, London NW6 7JR
Website: www.tricycle.co.uk
e-mail: admin@tricycle.co.uk
Fax: 020-7328 0795   Tel: 020-7372 6611

TRIUMPH PROSCENIUM PRODUCTIONS Ltd
1 Lumley Court, Off 402 The Strand
London WC2R 0NB   Tel: 020-7836 0186

TURTLE KEY ARTS
Ladbroke Hall, 79 Barlby Road, London W10 6AZ
Website: www.turtlekeyarts.org.uk
e-mail: admin@turtlekeyarts.org.uk
Fax: 020-8964 4080   Tel: 020-8964 5060

TWIST & CHEETHAM
39 Rosslyn Crescent
Edinburgh EH6 5AT
e-mail: ben.twist@blueyonder.co.uk   Tel/Fax: 0131-477 7425

TWO'S COMPANY
244 Upland Road
London SE22 0DN
e-mail: graham@2scompanytheatre.co.uk
Fax: 020-8299 3714   Tel: 020-8299 4593

UK ARTS INTERNATIONAL
First Floor, 6 Shaw Street
Worcester WR1 3QQ
Website: www.ukarts.com
e-mail: janryan@ukarts.com
Fax: 01905 22868   Tel: 01905 26424

UK PRODUCTIONS Ltd
Churchmill House, Ockford Road
Godalming, Surrey GU7 1QY
Website: www.ukproductions.co.uk
e-mail: mail@ukproductions.co.uk
Fax: 01483 418486   Tel: 01483 423600

UNRESTRICTED VIEW
Above Hen & Chickens Theatre Bar
109 St Paul's Road, London N1 2NA
Website: www.henandchickens.com
e-mail: james@henandchickens.com   Tel: 020-7704 2001

VANCE Charles PRODUCTIONS
(CV Productions Ltd)
Hampden House
2 Weymouth Street, London W1W 5BT
e-mail: cvpersonal@aol.com
Fax: 020-7636 2323   Tel: 020-7636 4343

VANDER ELST Anthony PRODUCTIONS
The Studio, 14 College Road
Bromley, Kent BR1 3NS
Fax: 020-8313 0443   Tel: 020-8466 5580

VAYU NAIDU COMPANY
Unit LFB2, Lafone House
The Leathermarket
11-13 Leathermarket Street, London SE1 3HN
Website: www.vayunaiducompany.org.uk
e-mail: info@vayunaiducompany.org.uk
       Tel/Fax: 020-7378 0739

VOLCANO THEATRE COMPANY Ltd
Swansea Metropolitan University
Townhill Road
Swansea SA2 0UT
Website: www.volcanotheatre.co.uk
e-mail: volcano.tc@virgin.net
Fax: 01792 281282   Tel: 01792 281280

WALKING FORWARD Ltd
Studio 1, 35 Britannia Row
London N1 8QH
Website: www.walkingforward.co.uk
e-mail: info@walkingforward.co.uk
Fax: 020-7359 5091   Tel: 020-7359 5249

WALLACE Kevin Ltd
10 (H) St Martin's Place
London WC2N 4JL
e-mail: enquiries@kevinwallace.co.uk
Fax: 020-7836 9587   Tel: 020-7836 9586

WAREHOUSE THEATRE COMPANY
Dingwall Road, Croydon CR0 2NF
Website: www.warehousetheatre.co.uk
e-mail: info@warehousetheatre.co.uk
Fax: 020-8688 6699   Tel: 020-8681 1257

WAX Kenny Ltd
3rd Floor, 25 Lexington Street, London W1F 9AG
Website: www.kennywax.com
Fax: 020-3214 6063   Tel: 020-7437 1736

WEAVER HUGHES ENSEMBLE
12B Carholme Road, London SE23 2HS
Website: www.weaverhughesensemble.co.uk
e-mail: ensemble@weaverhughesensemble.co.uk
       Tel/Fax: 020-8291 0514

WELDON Duncan C PRODUCTIONS Ltd
1 Lumley Court, Off 402 The Strand
London WC2R 0NB   Tel: 020-7836 0186

WEST END PROPERTY PRODUCTIONS
29 Creek Road, Hayling Island, Hampshire PO11 9QZ
Website: www.soultraders-themusical.com
e-mail: terry@angelsandkings.com
Fax: 023-9263 7264   Tel: 023-9263 7067

WEYLAND Valerie
29 Darby Crescent
Lower Sunbury TW16 5LB
e-mail: valweyland@hotmail.com   Tel: 01932 886413

WHITALL Keith
25 Solway, Hailsham
East Sussex BN27 3HB   Tel: 01323 844882

WHITEHALL Michael
10 Lower Common South, London SW15 1BP
e-mail: mwhitehall@msn.com
Fax: 020-8788 2340   Tel: 020-8785 3737

WILDCARD THEATRE COMPANY
Suite A, Swan House
White Hart Street
High Wycombe, Bucks HP11 2HL
Website: www.wildcardtheatre.org.uk
e-mail: admin@wildcardtheatre.org.uk
Fax: 07092 024967   Tel: 0870 7606158

WILLS Newton MANAGEMENT
The Studio, 29 Springvale Avenue
Brentford, Middlesex TW8 9QH
e-mail: newtoncttg@aol.com
Fax: 00 33 468 218685   Mobile: 07989 398381

WRESTLING SCHOOL The
(The Howard Baker Company)
42 Durlston Road, London E5 8RR
Website: www.thewrestlingschool.co.uk
       Tel/Fax: 020-8442 4229

YELLOW EARTH THEATRE
18 Rupert Street, London W1D 6DE
Website: www.yellowearth.org
e-mail: admin@yellowearth.org
Fax: 020-7287 3141   Tel: 020-7734 5988

YOUNG VIC THEATRE
66 The Cut, London SE1 8LZ
Website: www.youngvic.org
e-mail: info@youngvic.org
Fax: 020-7922 2802   Tel: 020-7922 2800

7:84 THEATRE COMPANY (SCOTLAND) Ltd
Film City Glasgow
No. 4 Summertown Road, Glasgow G51 2LY
Website: www.784theatre.com
e-mail: admin@784theatre.com   Tel: 0141-445 7245

ABERYSTWYTH ARTS CENTRE
Penglais Campus, Aberystwyth, Ceredigion SY23 3DE
Website: www.aber.ac.uk/artscentre
e-mail: ggo@aber.ac.uk
Fax: 01970 622883   Tel: 01970 621512

ADMIRATION THEATRE
PO Box 50255, London EC3A 5WA
Website: www.admirationtheatre.com
e-mail: admiration@admirationtheatre.com
                                      Tel: 0870 7651584

AGE EXCHANGE THEATRE TRUST
Contact: Suzanne Lockett (Administrator)
The Reminiscence Centre
11 Blackheath Village, London SE3 9LA
Website: www.age-exchange.org.uk
e-mail: administrator@age-exchange.org.uk
Fax: 020-8318 0060   Tel: 020-8318 9105

ALTERNATIVE ARTS
Top Studio, Montefiore Centre
Hanbury Street, London E1 5HZ
Website: www.alternativearts.co.uk
e-mail: info@alternativearts.co.uk
Fax: 020-7375 0484   Tel: 020-7375 0441

ANGLES THEATRE The
Alexandra Road, Wisbech, Cambridgeshire PE13 1HQ
e-mail: astromanis@anglestheatre.co.uk
Fax: 01945 581967   Tel: 01945 585587

ASHTON GROUP THEATRE The
The Old Fire Station, Abbey Road
Barrow-in-Furness, Cumbria LA14 1XH
Website: www.ashtongroup.co.uk
e-mail: theashtongroup@btconnect.com
                                 Tel/Fax: 01229 430636

ATTIC THEATRE COMPANY
Mitcham Library, 157 London Road, Mitcham CR4 2YR
Website: www.attictheatrecompany.com
e-mail: info@attictheatrecompany.com Tel: 020-8640 6800

BANNER THEATRE
Oaklands New Church Centre
Winleigh Road, Handsworth Wood, Birmingham B20 2HN
e-mail: info@bannertheatre.co.uk   Tel: 0845 4581909

BECK THEATRE
Grange Road, Hayes, Middlesex UB3 2UE
Website: www.becktheatre.org.uk   Tel: 020-8561 7506

BENT BACK TULIPS THEATRE COMPANY
4 Connolly House, 65 North Road, Wimbledon SW19 1XA
Website: www.bentbacktulips.com
e-mail: info@bentbacktulips.com   Mobile: 07971 159940

BLUEYED THEATRE PRODUCTIONS
76 Barcombe Avenue, London SW2 3AZ
Website: www.blueyedtheatreproductions.co.uk
e-mail: info@blueyedtheatreproductions.co.uk
                                  Mobile: 07957 215965

BLUNDERBUS THEATRE COMPANY Ltd
The Studio, Ollerton Primary School, Whinney Lane
New Ollerton, Newark, Notts NG22 9TH
Website: www.blunderbus.co.uk
e-mail: admin@blunderbus.co.uk
Fax: 01623 869559   Tel: 01623 835888

BORDERLINE THEATRE COMPANY
Contact: Eddie Jackson
North Harbour Street, Ayr KA8 8AA
Website: www.borderlinetheatre.co.uk
e-mail: enquiries@borderlinetheatre.co.uk
Fax: 01292 618685   Tel: 01292 281010

BRUVVERS THEATRE COMPANY
36 Lime Street, Ouseburn, Newcastle upon Tyne NE1 2PQ
Website: www.bruvvers.co.uk
e-mail: mikeofbruvvers@hotmail.com   Tel: 0191-261 9230

CAPITAL ARTS YOUTH THEATRE
Wyllyotts Centre, Darkes Lane, Potters Bar, Herts EN6 2HN
e-mail: capitalarts@btconnect.com
Mobile: 07885 232414   Tel/Fax: 020-8449 2342

CARIB THEATRE COMPANY
73 Lancelot Road, Wembley, Middlesex HA0 2AN
e-mail: antoncarib@yahoo.co.uk   Tel/Fax: 020-8903 4592

CENTRE FOR PERFORMANCE RESEARCH
The Foundry, Parry Williams, Penglais Campus SY23 3AJ
Website: www.thecpr.org.uk
e-mail: cprwww@aber.ac.uk
Fax: 01970 622132   Tel: 01970 622133

CHAIN REACTION THEATRE COMPANY
Three Mills Studios, Sugar House Yard
Sugar House Lane, London E15 2QS
Website: www.chainreactiontheatre.co.uk
e-mail: mail@chainreactiontheatre.co.uk
                                 Tel/Fax: 020-8534 0007

CHALKFOOT THEATRE ARTS
Central Studios, 36 Park Place, Margate, Kent CT9 1LE
Website: www.chalkfoot.org.uk
e-mail: info@chalkfoot.org.uk
Fax: 01843 280088   Tel: 01843 280077

CHATS PALACE ARTS CENTRE
42-44 Brooksby's Walk, Hackney, London E9 6DF
Website: www.chatspalace.com
e-mail: info@chatspalace.com   Tel: 020-8533 0227

CHEEKY MAGGOT PRODUCTIONS
Website: www.cheekymaggot.co.uk
e-mail: info@cheekymaggot.co.uk

CHERUB COMPANY LONDON The
Office: 9 Park Hill, London W5 2JS
Website: www.cherub.org.uk
e-mail: casting@cherub.org.uk
Fax: 020-8248 0318   Tel/Fax: 020-8723 4358

CHICKENSHED
Chase Side, Southgate, London N14 4PE
Website: www.chickenshed.org.uk
e-mail: info@chickenshed.org.uk
Minicom: 020-8350 0676   Tel: 020-8351 6161

CLOSE FOR COMFORT THEATRE COMPANY
34 Boleyn Walk, Leatherhead, Surrey KT22 7HU
Website: www.hometown.aol.com/close4comf
e-mail: close4comf@aol.com
Mobile: 07710 258290   Tel: 01372 378613

COLLUSION THEATRE COMPANY
131 Renfrew Street, Glasgow G3 6QZ
Website: www.collusiontheatre.co.uk
e-mail: admin@collusiontheatre.co.uk
Fax: 0141-644 4163   Tel: 0141-332 7001

COMPLETE WORKS CREATIVE COMPANY Ltd The
The Old Truman Brewery, 91 Brick Lane, London E1 6QL
Website: www.tcw.org.uk
e-mail: info@tcw.org.uk
Fax: 0870 1431979   Tel: 0870 1431969

There are hundreds of theatres in the UK, varying dramatically in size and type.
The theatre sections are organised under headings which best indicate a theatre's principal area of work. A summary of each of these is below.

Alternative and Community
Many of these companies tour to Arts Centres, small and middle-scale theatres, and non-theatrical venues which do not have a resident company, or they may be commissioned to develop site specific projects. The term 'alternative' is sometimes used to describe work that is more experimental in style and execution.

Children's, Young People's and TIE
The primary focus of these theatre companies is to reach younger audiences. They often tour to smaller theatres, schools and non-theatrical venues. Interactive teaching - through audience participation and workshops - is often a feature of their work.

English Speaking Theatre Companies in Europe
These work principally outside of the UK. Some are based in one venue whilst others are touring companies. Their work varies enormously and includes Young People's Theatre, large scale musicals, revivals of classics and dinner theatre. Actors are employed either for an individual production or a 'season' of several plays.

London Theatres
Larger theatres situated in the West End and Central London. A few are producing houses, but most are leased to Theatre Producers who take responsibility for putting together a company for a run of a single show. In such cases it is they and not the venue who cast productions (often with the help of Casting Directors). Alternatively, a production will open outside London and tour to Provincial Theatres. Then subsequently, if successful, transfer to a London venue.

Outer London, Fringe and Venues
Small and middle-scale theatres in Outer London and around the country. Some are producing houses, others are only available for hire. Many of the London venues have provided useful directions on how they may be reached by public transport.

Provincial / Touring
Theatre Producers and other companies sell their ready-made productions to the Provincial/Touring Theatres, a list of larger venues outside London. A run in each theatre varies between a night and several weeks, but a week per venue for tours of plays is usual. Even if a venue is not usually a producing house, most Provincial Theatres and Arts Centres put on a family show at Christmas.

Puppet Theatre Companies
Some Puppet Theatres are one-performer companies who literally create their own work from scratch. The content and style of productions varies enormously. For example, not all are aimed at children, and some are more interactive than others. Although we list a few theatres with Puppet Companies in permanent residence, this kind of work often involves touring. As with all small and middle scale touring, performers who are willing, and have the skills, to involve themselves with all aspects of company life are always more valuable.

Repertory (Regional) Theatres
Theatres situated outside London which employ a resident company of actors (i.e. the 'repertory company') on a play-by-play basis or for a season of several plays. In addition to the main auditorium (usually the largest acting space) these theatres may have a smaller studio theatre attached, which will be home to an additional company whose focus is education or the production of new plays (see Children's, Young People's and TIE). In recent years the length of repertory seasons has become shorter; this means that a number of productions are no longer in-house. It is common for gaps in the performance calendar to be filled by tours mounted by Theatre Producers, other Repertory (Regional) Theatres and non-venue based production companies.

CORNELIUS & JONES ORIGINAL PRODUCTIONS
49 Carters Close, Sherington
Newport Pagnell, Buckinghamshire MK16 9NW
Website: www.corneliusjones.com
e-mail: admin@corneliusjones.com   Tel/Fax: 01908 612593

CRAGRATS THEATRE
The Mill, Dunford Road, Holmfirth, Huddersfield HD9 2AR
Website: www.cragrats.com
e-mail: info@cragrats.com
Fax: 01484 686212   Tel: 01484 686451

CUT-CLOTH THEATRE
41 Beresford Road, Highbury
London N5 2HR   Tel: 020-7503 4393

DRAMA ZONE
Arundel Town Hall, Arundel, West Sussex BN18 9AP
Website: www.dramazone.net
e-mail: admin@dramazone.net   Tel/Fax: 01903 889821

ELAN WALES
(European Live Arts Network)
17 Douglas Buildings, Royal Stuart Lane, Cardiff CF10 5EL
Website: www.elanwales.org
e-mail: david@elanwales.org   Tel/Fax: 029-2019 0077

ELECTRIC CABARET
107 High Street, Brackley, Northants NN13 7BN
Website: www.electricccabaret.co.uk
e-mail: richard@electriccabaret.co.uk
Mobile: 07714 089763   Tel: 01280 700956

EUROPEAN THEATRE COMPANY The
39 Oxford Avenue, London SW20 8LS
Website: www.europeantheatre.co.uk
e-mail: admin@europeantheatre.co.uk
Fax: 020-8544 1999   Tel: 020-8544 1994

FOREST FORGE THEATRE COMPANY
The Theatre Centre, Endeavour Park
Crow Arch Lane, Ringwood, Hampshire BH24 1SF
Website: www.forestforge.co.uk
e-mail: forestforge@btconnect.com
Fax: 01425 471158   Tel: 01425 470188

FOUND THEATRE
c/o Packhorse Cottage, Crowdecote, Buxton SK17 0DB
Website: www.foundtheatre.org.uk
e-mail: found_theatre@yahoo.co.uk   Tel: 01298 83167

FOURSIGHT THEATRE Ltd
Newhampton Arts Centre
Dunkley Street, Wolverhampton WV1 4AN
Website: www.foursighttheatre.co.uk
e-mail: admin@foursighttheatre.co.uk
Fax: 01902 428413   Tel: 01902 714257

FRANTIC THEATRE COMPANY
32 Woodlane, Falmouth TR11 4RF
Website: www.frantictheatre.com
e-mail: info@frantictheatre.com   Tel/Fax: 0870 1657350

GALLEON THEATRE COMPANY Ltd
Greenwich Playhouse, Greenwich BR Station Forecourt
189 Greenwich High Road, London SE10 8JA
Website: www.galleontheatre.co.uk
e-mail: alice@galleontheatre.co.uk
Fax: 020-8310 7276   Tel: 020-8858 9256

GRANGE ARTS CENTRE
Rochdale Road, Oldham, Greater Manchester OL9 6EA
Website: www.grangeartsoldham.co.uk
e-mail: grangearts@oldham.ac.uk
Fax: 0161-785 4263   Tel: 0161-785 4239

GREASEPAINT ANONYMOUS
4 Gallus Close
Winchmore Hill, London N21 1JR
e-mail: info@greasepaintanonymous.co.uk
Fax: 020-8882 9189   Tel: 020-8886 2263

HALL FOR CORNWALL
Contact: Anna Coombs (Community & Education)
Back Quay, Truro, Cornwall TR1 2LL
Website: www.hallforcornwall.co.uk
e-mail: annac@hallforcornwall.org.uk
Fax: 01872 260246   Tel: 01872 321964

HIJINX THEATRE
(Adults with Learning Disabilities, Community)
Wales Millennium Centre, Bute Place, Cardiff CF10 5AL
Website: www.hijinx.org.uk
e-mail: info@hijinx.org.uk
Fax: 029-2063 5621   Tel: 029-2030 0331

HISTORIA THEATRE COMPANY
8 Cloudesley Square, London N1 0HT
Website: www.historiatheatre.com
e-mail: kateprice@lineone.net
Fax: 020-7278 4733   Tel: 020-7837 8008

ICON THEATRE
The Print House, 18 Ashlin Street, London E8 3DL
Website: www.icontheatre.org.uk
e-mail: sally@icontheatre.org.uk   Tel/Fax: 020-3051 8620

IMAGE MUSICAL THEATRE
23 Sedgeford Road, Shepherd's Bush, London W12 0NA
Website: www.imagemusicaltheatre.co.uk
e-mail: brian@imagemusicaltheatre.co.uk
Fax: 020-8749 9294   Tel: 020-8743 9380

IMMEDIATE THEATRE
1.2 Hoxton Works
128 Hoxton Street, London N1 6SH
Website: www.immediate-theatre.com
e-mail: info@immediate-theatre.com
Fax: 020-7012 1682   Tel: 020-7012 1677

INOCENTE ART & FILM Ltd
(Film, Multimedia, Music Videos & two Rock 'n' Roll
Musicals)
5 Denmans Lane, Haywards Heath
West Sussex RH16 2LA
e-mail: tarascas@btopenworld.com   Mobile: 07973 518132

ISOSCELES
7 Amity Grove, Raynes Park
London SW20 0LQ
Website: www.isosceles.freeserve.co.uk
e-mail: patanddave@isosceles.freeserve.co.uk
                                      Tel: 020-8946 3905

KOMEDIA
44-47 Gardner Street, Brighton BN1 1UN
Website: www.komedia.co.uk
e-mail: info@komedia.co.uk
Fax: 01273 647102   Tel: 01273 647101

KORU THEATRE
11 Clovelly Road, London W5 5HF
Website: www.korutheatre.com
e-mail: info@korutheatre.com   Tel: 020-8579 1029

LADDER TO THE MOON ENTERTAINMENT
Unit 105, Battersea Business Centre
99-109 Lavender Hill, London SW11 5QL
e-mail: enquiries@laddertothemoon.co.uk
                                      Tel: 020-7228 9700

LIVE THEATRE
(New Writing)
Broad Chare, Quayside
Newcastle upon Tyne NE1 3DQ
Website: www.live.org.uk
e-mail: info@live.org.uk
Fax: 0191-232 2224   Tel: 0191-261 2694

LONDON ACTORS THEATRE COMPANY
Unit 5A, Imex Business Centre
Ingate Place, London SW8 3NS
e-mail: latchmere@fishers.org.uk
Fax: 020-7978 2631   Tel: 020-7978 2620

LONDON BUBBLE THEATRE COMPANY Ltd
5 Elephant Lane, London SE16 4JD
Website: www.londonbubble.org.uk
e-mail: admin@londonbubble.org.uk
Fax: 020-7231 2366   Tel: 020-7237 4434

LSW JUNIOR INTER-ACT
PO Box 31855, London SE17 3XP
Website: www.londonshakespeare.org.uk
e-mail: londonswo@hotmail.com   Tel/Fax: 020-7793 9755

LSW PRISON PROJECT
PO Box 31855, London SE17 3XP
Website: www.londonshakespeare.org.uk
e-mail: londonswo@hotmail.com   Tel/Fax: 020-7793 9755

LSW SENIOR RE-ACTION
PO Box 31855, London SE17 3XP
Website: www.londonshakespeare.org.uk
e-mail: londonswo@hotmail.com   Tel/Fax: 020-7793 9755

LUNG HA'S THEATRE COMPANY
Eric Liddell Centre
15 Morningside Road,
Edinburgh EH10 4DP
Website: www.lunghas.co.uk
e-mail: info@lunghas.co.uk
Fax: 0131-447 3290   Tel: 0131-447 8496

M6 THEATRE COMPANY
Studio Theatre, Hamer CP School
Albert Royds Street, Rochdale OL16 2SU
Website: www.m6theatre.co.uk
e-mail: info@m6theatre.co.uk
Fax: 01706 712601   Tel: 01706 355898

MADDERMARKET THEATRE
(Resident Community Theatre Company & Small-Scale
Producing & Receiving House)
St John's Alley, Norwich NR2 1DR
Website: www.maddermarket.co.uk
e-mail: mmtheatre@btconnect.com
Fax: 01603 661357   Tel: 01603 626560

MAGIC HAT PRODUCTIONS
Brookslee, Brookshill Drive, Harrow HA3 6SB
Website: www.magichat-productions.com
e-mail: general@magichat-productions.com
                        Mobile: 07769 560991

MANCHESTER ACTORS COMPANY
PO Box 54, Manchester M60 7AB
Website: www.manactco.org.uk
e-mail: s.s.boyes@btinternet.com   Tel: 0161-227 8702

MAYA PRODUCTIONS Ltd
156 Richmond Road
London E8 3HN
Website: www.mayaproductions.co.uk
e-mail: mayachris@aol.com   Tel/Fax: 020-7923 0675

MIKRON THEATRE COMPANY Ltd
Marsden Mechanics
Peel Street, Marsden, Huddersfield HD7 6BW
Website: www.mikron.org.uk
e-mail: admin@mikron.org.uk   Tel: 01484 843701

MONTAGE THEATRE ARTS
Contact: Judy Gordon (Artistic Director)
The Albany, Douglas Way, London SE8 4AG
Website: www.montagetheatre.com
e-mail: admin@montagetheatre.com   Tel: 020-8692 7007

NATURAL THEATRE COMPANY
(Street Theatre & Touring)
Widcombe Institute, Widcombe Hill, Bath BA2 6AA
Website: www.naturaltheatre.co.uk
e-mail: info@naturaltheatre.co.uk
Fax: 01225 442555   Tel: 01225 469131

NET CURTAINS THEATRE COMPANY
Contact: Claire Farrington (Artisitc Director)
The Bath House, 96 Dean Street, London W1D 3TD
Website: www.netcurtains.org
e-mail: claire@netcurtains.org   Mobile: 07968 564687

NETTLEFOLD The
West Norwood Library Centre
1 Norwood High Street, London SE27 9JX
e-mail: thenettlefold@lambeth.gov.uk   Tel: 020-7926 8070

NEWFOUND THEATRE COMPANY
18 India House, 73 Whitworth Street, Manchester M1 6LG
Website: www.newfoundtheatre.co.uk
e-mail: newfoundtheatre@gmail.com

NEW PERSPECTIVES THEATRE COMPANY
(Regional/National New Writing Touring Theatre)
Park Lane Business Centre
Park Lane, Basford, Nottinghamshire NG6 0DW
Website: www.newperspectives.co.uk
e-mail: info@newperspectives.co.uk   Tel: 0115-927 2334

NORTHERN STAGE (THEATRICAL PRODUCTIONS) Ltd
Barras Bridge, Newcastle upon Tyne NE1 7RH
Website: www.northernstage.co.uk
e-mail: info@northernstage.co.uk
Fax: 0191-261 8093   Tel: 0191-232 3366

NORTHUMBERLAND THEATRE COMPANY (NTC)
(Touring Regionally & Nationally)
The Playhouse, Bondgate Without
Alnwick, Northumberland NE66 1PQ
Website: www.ntc-touringtheatre.co.uk
e-mail: admin@ntc-touringtheatre.co.uk
Fax: 01665 605837   Tel: 01665 602586

NUFFIELD THEATRE
(Touring & Projects)
University Road, Southampton SO17 1TR
Website: www.nuffieldtheatre.co.uk
e-mail: laura.cooney@nuffieldtheatre.co.uk
Fax: 023-8031 5511   Tel: 023-8031 5500

OLD TYME PLAYERS THEATRE COMPANY
(Music Hall, Revues - Locally Based)
35 Barton Court Avenue, Barton on Sea, Hants BH25 7EP
Website: www.oldetymeplayers.co.uk
e-mail: oldetymeplayers@tiscali.co.uk   Tel: 01425 612830

ONATTI THEATRE COMPANY
9 Field Close, Warwick, Warwickshire CV34 4QD
Website: www.onatti.co.uk
e-mail: info@onatti.co.uk
Fax: 0870 1643629   Tel: 01926 495220

OPEN STAGE PRODUCTIONS
49 Springfield Road, Moseley
Birmingham B13 9NN
e-mail: info@openstage.co.uk   Tel/Fax: 0121-777 9086

ORMSGARD! DARK AGES THEATRE
12 Carleton Close
Great Yeldham, Essex CO9 4QJ
Website: www.ormsgard.org
e-mail: pete@gippeswic.demon.co.uk   Tel: 01787 238257

OXFORDSHIRE TOURING THEATRE COMPANY
The Annexe
SS Mary & John School
Meadow Lane, Oxford OX4 1TJ
Website: www.ottc.org.uk
e-mail: info@ottc.oxfordshire.co.uk
Fax: 01865 247266   Tel: 01865 249444

PASCAL THEATRE COMPANY
35 Flaxman Court, Flaxman Terrace
Bloomsbury, London WC1H 9AR
Website: www.pascal-theatre.com
e-mail: pascaltheatreco@aol.com   Tel: 020-7383 0920

PAUL'S THEATRE COMPANY
Ardleigh House
42 Ardleigh Green Road
Hornchurch, Essex RM11 2LG
Website: www.paulstheatreschool.co.uk
e-mail: info@paulstheatreschool.co.uk   Tel: 01708 447123

PEOPLE'S THEATRE COMPANY The
12E High Street
Egham, Surrey TW20 9EA
Website: www.ptc.org.uk
e-mail: admin@ptc.org.uk   Tel: 01784 470439

PHANTOM CAPTAIN The
618B Finchley Road, London NW11 7RR
Website: www.phantomcaptain.netfirms.com
e-mail: lambhorn@gmail.com   Tel: 020-8455 4564

PLAYTIME THEATRE COMPANY
18 Bennells Avenue
Whitstable, Kent CT5 2HP
Website: www.playtimetheatre.co.uk
e-mail: playtime@dircon.co.uk
Fax: 01227 266648   Tel: 01227 266272

PRIME PRODUCTIONS
54 Hermiston Village, Currie EH14 4AQ
Website: www.primeproductions.co.uk
e-mail: primeproductions@talktalk.net
                          Tel/Fax: 0131-449 4055

PROTEUS THEATRE COMPANY
(Multimedia and Cross-art Form Work)
Queen Mary's College
Cliddesden Road
Basingstoke, Hampshire RG21 3HF
Website: www.proteustheatre.com
e-mail: info@proteustheatre.com   Tel: 01256 354541

PURSUED BY A BEAR PODUCTIONS
Farnham Maltings
Bridge Square, Farnham GU9 7QR
Website: www.pursuedbyabear.co.uk
e-mail: pursuedbyabear@yahoo.co.uk   Tel: 01252 745445

Q20 THEATRE COMPANY
19 Wellington Crescent, Shipley
West Yorkshire BD18 3PH
e-mail: info@q20theatre.co.uk   Tel: 0845 1260632

QUICKSILVER THEATRE
The Glasshouse
4 Enfield Road, London N1 5AZ
Website: www.quicksilvertheatre.org
e-mail: talktous@quicksilvertheatre.org
Fax: 020-7254 3119   Tel: 020-7241 2942

RIDING LIGHTS THEATRE COMPANY
Friargate Theatre
Lower Friargate, York YO1 9SL
Website: www.ridinglights.org
e-mail: info@rltc.org
Fax: 01904 651532   Tel: 01904 655317

SALTMINE THEATRE COMPANY
St James House, Trinity Road
Dudley, West Midlands DY1 1JB
Website: www.saltmine.org
e-mail: creative@saltmine.org   Tel: 01384 454807

SCRATCH PRODUCTIONS
64 York Road, Bridgwater
Somerset TA6 6EE
Website: www.scratchproductions.org.uk
e-mail: markscott.ison@yahoo.co.uk   Tel: 01278 422681

SPANNER IN THE WORKS
PO Box 239, Sidcup DA15 0DP
Website: www.spannerintheworks.org.uk
e-mail: info@spannerintheworks.org.uk
                          Mobile: 07850 313986

SPARE TYRE THEATRE COMPANY
Contact: Bonnie Mitchell (General Manager)
(Community Drama & Music Projects)
Hampstead Town Hall
213 Haverstock Hill
London NW3 4QP
Website: www.sparetyretheatrecompany.co.uk
e-mail: info@sparetyretheatrecompany.co.uk
                          Tel/Fax: 020-7419 7007

SPECTACLE THEATRE
Coleg Morgannwg, Rhondda
Llwynypia, Tonypandy CF40 2TQ
Website: www.spectacletheatre.co.uk
e-mail: info@spectacletheatre.co.uk
Fax: 01443 439640   Tel: 01443 430700

SPONTANEITY SHOP The
85-87 Bayham Street
London NW1 0AG
Website: www.the-spontaneity-shop.com
e-mail: info@the-spontaneity-shop.com
                          Tel: 020-7788 4080

STABLES GALLERY & ARTS CENTRE The
The Hayloft, Gladstone Park
Dollis Hill Lane, London NW2 6HT
e-mail: stablesgallery@msn.com   Tel: 020-8452 8655

TAG CITIZENS
Citizens' Theatre
119 Gorbals Street, Glasgow G5 9DS
Website: www.tag-theatre.co.uk
e-mail: info@tag-theatre.co.uk
Fax: 0141-429 7374   Tel: 0141-429 5561

TAKING FLIGHT THEATRE COMPANY
79 Kings Road
Canton, Cardiff CF11 9DB
Website: www.takingflighttheatre.com
e-mail: takingflighttheatre@yahoo.co.uk
                          Tel: 029-2064 5505

TARA ARTS GROUP
356 Garratt Lane
London SW18 4ES
Website: www.tara-arts.com
Fax: 020-8870 9540
Tel: 020-8333 4457

THEATRE AND
Church Hall, St James Road
Marsh, Huddersfield HD1 4QA
Website: www.theatreand.com
e-mail: clare@theatreand.com
Fax: 01484 532962
Tel: 01484 532967

THEATRE EXPRESS MANAGEMENT
Contact: By Post
Spindle Cottage, Allens Farm
Digby Fen, Billinghay, Lincoln LN4 4DT
e-mail: info@theatre-express.com

THEATRE IN EDUCATION TOURS (TIE TOURS)
PO Box 433, Weston Super Mare
Somerset BS24 0WY
Website: www.actionwork.com
e-mail: admin@actionwork.com
Tel: 01934 815163

THEATRE IS, ...
The Innovation Centre
College Lane, Hatfield AL10 9AB
Website: www.theatreis.org
e-mail: info@theatreis.org
Tel: 01707 281100

THEATRE OF LITERATURE The
(Dramatised Readings)
51 The Cut, London SE1 8LF
e-mail: info@calderpublications.com
Fax: 020-7928 5930
Tel: 020-7633 0599

THEATRE PECKHAM
Havil Street, London SE5 7SD
Website: www.theatrepeckham.co.uk
e-mail: admin@theatrepeckham.co.uk
Tel: 020-7708 5401

THEATRE WORKSHOP
34 Hamilton Place
Edinburgh EH3 5AX
Website: www.theatre-workshop.com
Fax: 0131-220 0112
Tel: 0131-225 7942

THEATR POWYS
The Drama Centre, Tremont Road
Llandrindod Wells, Powys LD1 5EB
Website: www.theatrpowys.co.uk
e-mail: theatr.powys@powys.gov.uk
Fax: 01597 824381
Tel: 01597 824444

THIRD PARTY PRODUCTIONS Ltd
87 St Thomas' Road
Hastings, East Sussex TN34 3LD
Website: www.thirdparty.org.uk
e-mail: gleave@thirdparty.org.uk
Mobile: 07768 694211
Mobile: 07768 694212

TIME OF OUR LIVES MUSIC THEATRE Ltd
5 Monkhams Drive
Woodford Green, Essex IG8 0LG
Website: www.toolmusictheatre.co.uk
e-mail: dympna@toolmusictheatre.co.uk
Tel/Fax: 020-8491 6695

TOBACCO FACTORY THEATRE
Raleigh Road, Southville, Bristol BS3 1TF
Website: www.tobaccofactory.com
e-mail: theatre@tobaccofactory.com
Fax: 0117-902 0162
Tel: 0117-902 0345

TRADING FACES
(Mask & Physical Theatre)
3 Bicton, Clun, Shropshire SY7 8NF
Website: www.tradingfaces.org.uk
e-mail: admin@tradingfaces.org.uk
Tel: 01588 640150

TRICYCLE THEATRE
269 Kilburn High Road, London NW6 7JR
Website: www.tricycle.co.uk
e-mail: admin@tricycle.co.uk
Fax: 020-7328 0795
Tel: 020-7372 6611

WAREHOUSE THEATRE COMPANY
Dingwall Road, Croydon CR0 2NF
Website: www.warehousetheatre.co.uk
e-mail: info@warehousetheatre.co.uk
Fax: 020-8688 6699
Tel: 020-8681 1257

WIGAN PIER THEATRE COMPANY
Wigan Leisure & Culture Trust
Elizabeth House, Pottery Road, Wigan WN3 4BD
Website: www.wiganpier.net
e-mail: mpj.green@@wlct.org
Tel: 01942 7486919

WINCHESTER HAT FAIR, FESTIVAL OF STREET THEATRE
5A Jewry Street, Winchester
Hampshire SO23 8RZ
Website: www.hatfair.co.uk
e-mail: info@hatfair.co.uk
Tel: 01962 849841

WOMEN & THEATRE BIRMINGHAM Ltd
220 Moseley Road
Highgate, Birmingham B12 0DG
e-mail: info@womenandtheatre.co.uk
Fax: 0121-446 4280
Tel: 0121-440 4203

Y TOURING THEATRE COMPANY
One KX, 120 Cromer Street, London WC1H 8BS
Website: www.ytouring.org.uk
e-mail: d.jackson@ytouring.org.uk
Fax: 020-7520 3099
Tel: 020-7520 3092

YELLOW EARTH THEATRE
3rd Floor, 18 Rupert Street, London W1D 6DE
Website: www.yellowearth.org
e-mail: admin@yellowearth.org
Fax: 020-7287 3141
Tel: 020-7734 5988

YORICK INTERNATIONALIST THEATRE ENSEMBLE
(Yorick Theatre & Film)
4 Duval Court, 36 Bedfordbury
Covent Garden, London WC2N 4DQ
e-mail: yorickx@hotmail.com
Tel/Fax: 020-7836 7637

YOUNG VIC THEATRE
66 The Cut, London SE1 8LZ
Website: www.youngvic.org
e-mail: info@youngvic.org
Fax: 020-7922 2801
Tel: 020-7922 2800

YWT
(Touring Theatre in Health Education)
Leeds Media Centre
21 Savile Mount, Leeds LS7 3HZ
Website: www.yorkshirewomentheatre.com
e-mail: admin@ywtheatre.com
Fax: 0113-200 7033
Tel: 0113-200 7200

ZIP THEATRE
Newhampton Arts Centre
Dunkley Street, Wolverhampton WV1 4AN
Website: www.ziptheatre.co.uk
e-mail: cathy@ziptheatre.co.uk
Fax: 01902 572251
Tel: 01902 572250

ACTION TRANSPORT THEATRE COMPANY
(New Writing, Professional Production for, by and with
Young People)
Whitby Hall, Stanney Lane
Ellesmere Port, Cheshire CH65 9AE
Website: www.actiontransporttheatre.co.uk
e-mail: info@actiontransporttheatre.co.uk
Tel: 0151-357 2120

ACTIONWORK
(Theatre & Film Productions with Young People)
PO Box 433, Weston-super-Mare, Somerset BS24 0WY
Website: www.actionwork.com
e-mail: admin@actionwork.com   Tel: 01934 815163

ARTY-FACT THEATRE COMPANY Ltd
18 Weston Lane, Crewe, Cheshire CW2 5AN
Website: www.arty-fact.co.uk
Fax: 07020 982098   Tel: 07020 962096

ASHCROFT YOUTH THEATRE
Ashcroft Academy of Dramatic Art, Malcolm Primary
School, Malcolm Road, Penge, London SE20 8RH
Website: www.ashcroftacademy.com
e-mail: geraldi.gillma@btconnect.com
Mobile: 07799 791586   Tel: 0844 8005328

BARKING DOG THEATRE COMPANY
14 Leaside Mansions, Fortis Green, London N10 3EB
Website: www.barkingdog.co.uk
e-mail: mike@barkingdog.co.uk   Tel: 020-8883 0034

BECK THEATRE
Grange Road, Hayes, Middlesex UB3 2UE
Website: www.becktheatre.org.uk
BO: 020-8561 8371   Tel: 020-8561 7506

BIG WOODEN HORSE THEATRE COMPANY Ltd
30 Northfield Road, West Ealing, London W13 9SY
Website: www.bigwoodenhorse.com
e-mail: info@bigwoodenhorse.com   Tel: 020-8567 8431

BIRMINGHAM STAGE COMPANY The
Contact: Neal Foster (Actor/Manager)
Philip Compton (Executive Producer)
Suite 228, The Linen Hall
162 Regent Street, London W1B 5TB
Website: www.birminghamstage.net
e-mail: info@birminghamstage.net
Fax: 020-7437 3395   Tel: 020-7437 3391

BITESIZE THEATRE COMPANY
8 Green Meadows, New Broughton, Wrexham LL11 6SG
Website: www.bitesizetheatre.co.uk
Fax: 01978 358315   Tel: 01978 358320

BLAH BLAH BLAH THEATRE COMPANY The
The West Park Centre, Spen Lane, Leeds LS16 5BE
Website: www.blahs.co.uk
e-mail: admin@blahs.co.uk   Tel: 0113-274 0030

BLUE MOON THEATRE COMPANY
20 Sandpiper Road, Blakespool Park
Bridgwater, Somerset TA6 5QU
Website: www.bluemoontheatre.co.uk
e-mail: info@bluemoontheatre.co.uk Tel/Fax: 01278 458253

BLUNDERBUS THEATRE COMPANY Ltd
The Studio, Ollerton Primary School, Whinney Lane
New Ollerton, Newark, Notts NG22 9TH
Website: www.blunderbus.co.uk
e-mail: admin@blunderbus.co.uk
Fax: 01623 869559   Tel: 01623 835888

BOOSTER CUSHION THEATRE COMPANY
75 How Wood, Park Street, St Albans, Herts AL2 2RW
Website: www.booster-cushion.co.uk
e-mail: boostercushion@hotmail.com
Fax: 01727 872597   Tel: 01727 873874

BORDERLINE THEATRE COMPANY
Contact: Eddie Jackson (Producer)
North Harbour Street, Ayr KA8 8AA
Website: www.borderlinetheartre.co.uk
e-mail: enquiries@borderlinetheatre.co.uk
Fax: 01292 618685   Tel: 01292 281010

BRIDGE HOUSE THEATRE
(Visiting Companies, School Productions, Own Productions)
Warwick School Site, Myton Road, Warwick CV34 6PP
Website: www.bridgehousetheatre.co.uk
Fax: 01926 776476   Tel: 01926 776437

BRIEF CANDLE THEATRE
Peel House, Brimington Road
Chesterfield, Derbyshire S41 7UG
Website: www.briefcandle.co.uk
e-mail: office@briefcandle.co.uk   Tel: 01246 556161

CAUGHT IN THE ACT
Conygree House, Church Street
Kingham, Oxfordshire OX7 6YA
Website: www.caughtintheact.co.uk
e-mail: cita@caughtintheact.co.uk   Tel/Fax: 01608 659555

CHAIN REACTION THEATRE COMPANY
Three Mills Studios, Sugar House Yard
Sugar House Lane, London E15 2QS
Website: www.chainreactiontheatre.co.uk
e-mail: mail@chainreactiontheatre.co.uk
Tel/Fax: 020-8534 0007

CHALKFOOT THEATRE ARTS
Contact: Philip Dart (Artistic Director)
Central Studios, 36 Park Place, Margate, Kent CT9 1LE
Website: www.chalkfoot.org.uk
e-mail: mail@chalkfoot.org.uk   Tel: 01843 280077

CHICKENSHED
Contact: Mary Ward MBE (Artistic Director)
Chase Side, Southgate, London N14 4PE
Website: www.chickenshed.org.uk
e-mail: info@chickenshed.org.uk
Minicom: 020-8350 0676   Tel: 020-8351 6161

CIRCUS MANIACS YOUTH CIRCUS
(International Award-Winning Youth Circus Company)
Office 8A, The Kingswood Foundation
Britannia Road, Kingswood, Bristol BS15 8DB
e-mail: info@circusmaniacs.com
Mobile: 07977 247287   Tel/Fax: 0117-947 7042

CLWYD THEATR CYMRU THEATRE FOR YOUNG PEOPLE
Contact: Education Administator
Mold, Flintshire CH7 1YA
Website: www.ctctyp.co.uk
e-mail: education@clwyd-theatr-cymru.co.uk
Fax: 01352 701558   Tel: 01352 701575

COMPLETE WORKS CREATIVE COMPANY Ltd The
Contact: Phil Evans (Artistic Director)
The Old Truman Brewery, 91 Brick Lane, London E1 6QL
Website: www.tcw.org.uk
e-mail: info@tcw.org.uk
Fax: 0870 1431979   Tel: 0870 1431969

CRAGRATS Ltd
The Mill, Dunford Road, Holmfirth, Huddersfield HD9 2AR
Website: www.cragrats.com
e-mail: info@cragrats.com
Fax: 01484 686212   Tel: 01484 686451

CTC THEATRE
Arts Centre, Vane Terrace
Darlington, County Durham DL3 7AX
Website: www.ctctheatre.org.uk
e-mail: ctc@ctctheatre.org.uk
Fax: 01325 369404   Tel: 01325 352004

DAYLIGHT THEATRE
66 Middle Street, Stroud
Gloucestershire GL5 1EA   Tel: 01453 763808

DONNA MARIA COMPANY
16 Bell Meadow, Dulwich, London SE19 1HP
Website: www.donna-marias-world.co.uk
e-mail: info@donnamariasworld.co.uk   Tel: 020-8670 7814

DRAGON DRAMA
(Theatre Company, Tuition, Workshops, Parties)
347 Hanworth Road, Surrey TW12 3EJ
Website: www.dragondrama.co.uk
e-mail: info@dragondrama.co.uk   Tel/Fax: 020-8255 8356

EUROPA CLOWN THEATRE SHOW
36 St Lukes Road, Tunbridge Wells, Kent TN4 9JH
Website: www.clownseuropa.co.uk   Tel: 01892 537964

EUROPEAN THEATRE COMPANY The
39 Oxford Avenue, London SW20 8LS
Website: www.europeantheatre.co.uk
e-mail: admin@europeantheatre.co.uk
Fax: 020-8544 1999   Tel: 020-8544 1994

FUSE: NEW THEATRE FOR YOUNG PEOPLE
Contact: Michael Quirke (General Manager)
Kathy McArdle (Artistic Producer)
13 Hope Street, Liverpool L1 9BH
Website: www.fusetheatre.com
e-mail: info@fusetheatre.com   Tel/Fax: 0151-708 0877

FUTURES THEATRE COMPANY
St John's Crypt, 73 Waterloo Road, London SE1 8UD
Website: www.futurestheatrecompany.co.uk
e-mail: info@futurestheatrecompany.co.uk
Fax: 020-7928 6724   Tel: 020-7928 2832

GAZEBO TIE COMPANY Ltd
Bilston Town Hall, Church Street
Bilston, West Midlands WV14 0AP
Website: www.gazebotie.org
e-mail: info@gazebotie.org
Fax: 01902 497244   Tel: 01902 497222

GRANT Derek ORGANISATION Ltd
13 Beechwood Road, West Moors, Dorset BH22 0BN
Website: www.derekgrant.co.uk
e-mail: admin@derekgrant.co.uk   Tel: 01202 855777

GREENWICH & LEWISHAM YOUNG PEOPLES' THEATRE (GLYPT)
Royal Laboratory Office, No 1 Street
Royal Arsenal West, Woolwich, London SE18 6ST
Website: www.glypt.co.uk
e-mail: postbox@glypt.co.uk
Fax: 020-8317 8595   Tel: 020-8854 1316

GROUP 64 YOUTH THEATRE
Putney Arts Theatre, Ravenna Road, London SW15 6AW
Website: www.putneyartstheatre.org.uk
Fax: 020-8788 6940   Tel: 020-8788 6935

GWENT TIE COMPANY
The Drama Centre Pen-y-pound
Abergavenny, Monmouthshire NP7 5UD
Website: www.gwenttheatre.com
e-mail: gwenttie@uwclub.net
Fax: 01873 853910   Tel: 01873 853167

HALF MOON YOUNG PEOPLE'S THEATRE
43 White Horse Road, London E1 0ND
Website: www.halfmoon.org.uk
e-mail: admin@halfmoon.org.uk
Fax: 020-7709 8914   Tel: 020-7265 8138

HOXTON HALL YOUTH ARTS CENTRE
130 Hoxton Street, London N1 6SH
Website: www.hoxtonhall.co.uk
e-mail: info@hoxtonhall.co.uk
Fax: 020-7729 3815   Tel: 020-7684 0060

IMAGE MUSICAL THEATRE
23 Sedgeford Road, Shepherd's Bush, London W12 0NA
Website: www.imagemusicaltheatre.co.uk
e-mail: brian@imagemusicaltheatre.co.uk
Fax: 020-8749 9294   Tel: 020-8743 9380

IMPACT ON LEARNING
Impact Universal, Hopebank House
Woodhead Road, Honley, Huddersfield HD9 6PF
Website: www.impactonlearning.com
e-mail: rosie.perkin@impactonlearning.com
Fax: 01484 660088   Tel: 01484 660077

INDIGO MOON THEATRE
35 Waltham Court, Beverley, East Yorkshire HU17 9JF
Website: www.indigomoontheatre.com
e-mail: info@indigomoontheatre.com   Mobile: 07855 328552

INTERPLAY THEATRE
Armley Ridge Road, Leeds LS12 3LE
Website: www.interplayleeds.co.uk
e-mail: info@interplayleeds.co.uk   Tel: 0113-263 8556

KINETIC THEATRE COMPANY Ltd
Suite H, The Jubilee Centre
Lombard Road, Wimbledon, London SW19 3TZ
Website: www.kinetictheatre.co.uk
e-mail: paul@kinetictheatre.co.uk
Fax: 020-8286 2645   Tel: 020-8286 2613

KOMEDIA
44-47 Gardner Street, Brighton BN1 1UN
Website: www.komedia.co.uk/brighton
e-mail: info@komedia.co.uk
Fax: 01273 647102   Tel: 01273 647100

LEIGHTON BUZZARD YOUTH THEATRE
6 Hillside Road, Leighton Buzzard LU7 3BU
e-mail: sarah.cavender@tesco.net   Tel: 01525 377222

LITTLE ACTORS THEATRE COMPANY
16 Hawthorn Road, Parkgate, Cheshire CH64 6SX
e-mail: info@littleactorstheatre.com
Fax: 0870 9157551   Tel: 0151-336 4302

M6 THEATRE COMPANY
Studio Theatre, Hamer C. P. School
Albert Royds Street, Rochdale OL16 2SU
Website: www.m6theatre.co.uk
e-mail: info@m6theatre.co.uk
Fax: 01706 712601   Tel: 01706 355898

MAGIC CARPET THEATRE
18 Church Street, Sutton-on-Hull HU7 4TS
Website: www.magiccarpettheatre.com
e-mail: admin@magiccarpettheatre.com
Fax: 01482 787362   Tel: 01482 709939

NATIONAL ASSOCIATION OF YOUTH THEATRES (NAYT)
Arts Centre, Vane Terrace, Darlington
County Durham DL3 7AX
Website: www.nayt.org.uk
e-mail: nayt@btconnect.com
Fax: 01325 363313   Tel: 01325 363330

NATIONAL STUDENT DRAMA FESTIVAL
Aberdeen Centre, 22-24 Highbury Grove, London N5 2DQ
Website: www.nsdf.org.uk
e-mail: admin@nsdf.org.uk   Tel: 020-7354 8070

NATIONAL YOUTH MUSIC THEATRE The
2-4 Great Eastern Street, London EC2A 3NW
Website: www.nymt.org.uk
e-mail: enquiries@nymt.org.uk
Fax: 0870 9033785   Tel: 020-7422 8290

NATIONAL YOUTH THEATRE OF GREAT BRITAIN
443-445 Holloway Road, London N7 6LW
Website: www.nyt.org.uk
e-mail: info@nyt.org.uk
Fax: 020-7281 8246   Tel: 020-7281 3863

NETTLEFOLD The
West Norwood Library Centre
1 Norwood High Street, London SE27 9JX
e-mail: thenettlefold@lambeth.gov.uk   Tel: 020-7926 8070

OILY CART
(Create work for the under 5's and young people 3-19 with
complex disabilities or ASD)
Smallwood School Annexe
Smallwood Road, London SW17 0TW
Website: www.oilycart.org.uk
e-mail: oilies@oilycart.org.uk
Fax: 020-8672 0792   Tel: 020-8672 6329

ONATTI THEATRE COMPANY
Contact: Andrew Bardwell (Artistic Director)
9 Field Close, Warwick, Warwickshire CV34 4QD
Website: www.onatti.co.uk
e-mail: info@onatti.co.uk
Fax: 0870 1643629   Tel: 01926 495220

PANDEMONIUM TOURING PARTNERSHIP
228 Railway Street, Cardiff CF24 2NJ   Tel: 029-2047 2060

PANDORA'S BOX THEATRE COMPANY
(National Touring Young Children's Theatre)
43 Fallsbrook Road, London SW16 6DU
Website: www.pandorasboxtheatre.co.uk
e-mail: info@pandorasboxtheatre.co.uk
                                      Tel/Fax: 020-8769 8710

PAUL'S THEATRE COMPANY
Ardleigh House, 42 Ardleigh Green Road
Hornchurch, Essex RM11 2LG
Website: www.paulstheatreschool.co.uk
e-mail: info@paulstheatreschool.co.uk   Tel: 01708 447123

PIED PIPER COMPANY
(In association with The Yvonne Arnaud Theatre Guildford)
1 Lilian Place, Coxcombe Lane
Chiddingfold, Surrey GU8 4QA
Website: www.piedpipertheatre.co.uk
e-mail: twpiedpiper@aol.com   Tel/Fax: 01428 684022

PILOT THEATRE
York Theatre Royal, St Leonard's Place, York YO1 7HD
Website: www.pilot-theatre.com
e-mail: info@pilot-theatre.com
Fax: 01904 656378   Tel: 01904 635755

PLAY HOUSE The
(Language Alive!/Catalyst Theatre/Project)
Longmore Street, Birmingham B12 9ED
Website: www.theplayhouse.org.uk
e-mail: info@theplayhouse.org.uk
Fax: 0121-464 5713   Tel: 0121-464 5712

PLAYTIME THEATRE COMPANY
18 Bennells Avenue, Whitstable, Kent CT5 2HP
Website: www.playtimetheatre.co.uk
e-mail: playtime@dircon.co.uk
Fax: 01227 266648   Tel: 01227 266272

POLKA THEATRE
240 The Broadway, Wimbledon SW19 1SB
Website: www.polkatheatre.com
e-mail: admin@polkatheatre.com
Fax: 020-8545 8365   Tel: 020-8545 8320

Q20 THEATRE COMPANY
19 Wellington Crescent, Shipley, West Yorkshire BD18 3PH
e-mail: info@q20theatre.co.uk   Tel: 0845 1260632

QUAKER YOUTH THEATRE
Ground Floor, 1 The Lodge
1046 Bristol Road, Birmingham B29 6LJ
Website: www.leaveners.org
e-mail: qyt@leaveners.org
Fax: 0121-414 0090   Tel: 0121-414 0099

QUANTUM THEATRE
Contact: Michael Whitmore, Jessica Selous
(Artistic Directors)
The Old Button Factory
1-11 Bannockburn Road, Plumstead, London SE18 1ET
Website: www.quantumtheatre.co.uk
e-mail: office@quantumtheatre.co.uk   Tel: 020-8317 9000

QUICKSILVER THEATRE COMPANY
(National Touring - New Writing for the under 12's
Participatory Outreach Projects)
4 Enfield Road, London N1 5AZ
Website: www.quicksilvertheatre.org
e-mail: talktous@quicksilvertheatre.org
Fax: 020-7254 3119   Tel: 020-7241 2942

RAINBOW BIGBOTTOM & Co Ltd
The Studio, 1A Park View
Stanley Avenue, Chesham, Bucks HP5 2JF
Website: www.rainbowbigbottom.com
e-mail: laneatrainbows@aol.com
Mobile: 07778 106552   Tel: 01494 771029

REDROOFS THEATRE COMPANY
Contact: By Post
The Novello Theatre
Sunninghill, Nr Ascot, Berkshire SL5 9NE
Website: www.novellotheatre.co.uk

ROUND The
34 Lime Street, Ouseburn
Newcastle Upon Tyne NE1 2PQ
Website: www.the-round.com
e-mail: info@the-round.com   Tel: 0191-260 5605

ROUNDABOUT THEATRE IN EDUCATION
Nottingham Playhouse
Wellington Circus, Nottingham NG1 5AF
e-mail: roundabout@nottinghamplayhouse.co.uk
Fax: 0115-947 5759   Tel: 0115-947 4361

ROYAL & DERNGATE
19-21 Guildhall Road, Northampton NN1 1DP
Website: www.royalandderngate.co.uk
e-mail: education@ntt.org   Tel: 01604 627566

ROYAL COURT YOUNG WRITERS PROGRAMME
(Playwriting Projects for Young People aged 13-25)
Royal Court Theatre, Sloane Square, London SW1W 8AS
Website: www.royalcourttheatre.com
e-mail: ywp@royalcourttheatre.com
Fax: 020-7565 5001   Tel: 020-7565 5050

SCOTTISH YOUTH THEATRE
The Old Sheriff Court, 105 Brunswick Street, Glasgow G1 1TF
Website: www.scottishyouththeatre.org
e-mail: info@scottishyouththeatre.org
Fax: 0141-552 7615   Tel: 0141-552 3988

SEAHORSE THEATRE & PARTY COMPANY
Ealing House, 33 Hanger Lane, London W5 3HJ
e-mail: revampevents@aol.com   Tel: 020-8997 3355

SHAKESPEARE 4 KIDZ THEATRE COMPANY The
42 Station Road East, Oxted, Surrey RH8 0PG
Website: www.shakespeare4kidz.com
e-mail: theatre@shakespeare4kidz.com
Fax: 01883 730384   Tel: 01883 723444

SHAKESPEAREWORKS
22 Chilswell Road, Oxford OX1 4PJ
Website: www.shakespeareworks.co.uk
e-mail: info@shakespeareworks.co.uk   Tel/Fax: 01865 241281

SHARED EXPERIENCE YOUTH THEATRE
13 Riverside House, 27-29 Vauxhall Grove, London SW8 1SY
Website: www.sharedexperience.org.uk
e-mail: admin@sharedexperience.org.uk
Fax: 020-7735 0374   Tel: 020-7587 1596

SHEFFIELD THEATRES
Contact: Sue Burley (Education Administrator)
55 Norfolk Street, Sheffield S1 1DA
www.sheffieldtheatres.co.uk/creativedevelopmentprogramme
Fax: 0114-249 6003   Tel: 0114-249 5999

SOLOMON THEATRE COMPANY
Penny Black, High Street
Damerham, Fordingbridge, Hants SP6 3EU
Website: www.solomon-theatre.co.uk
e-mail: office@solomon-theatre.co.uk   Tel/Fax: 01725 518760

SPECTACLE THEATRE
Coleg Morgannwg, Rhondda
Llwynypia, Tonypandy CF40 2TQ
Website: www.spectacletheatre.co.uk
e-mail: info@spectacletheatre.co.uk
Fax: 01443 423080   Tel: 01443 430700

STOPWATCH THEATRE COMPANY
Unit 318 Solent Business Centre
Millbrook Road West
Southampton SO15 0HW
Website: www.stopwatchtheatre.com
e-mail: info@stopwatchtheatre.com   Tel: 023-8078 3800

STORYTELLERS THEATRE COMPANY The
Bridge Farm, 249 Hawes Side Lane
Blackpool FY4 4AA
Website: www.pendleproductions.co.uk
e-mail: admin@pendleproductions.co.uk
Fax: 01253 792930   Tel: 01253 839375

SUPPORT ACT PRODUCTIONS
Contact: Ian McCracken
243A Lynmouth Avenue
Morden, Surrey SM4 4RX
Website: www.supportact.co.uk
e-mail: info@supportact.co.uk   Tel: 0845 0940796

TEAM PLAYERS THEATRE COMPANY
Lingfield Countryside Centre
Mount Pleasant Way
Coulby Newham, Middlesbrough TS8 0XF
Website: www.teamplayerstheatre.com
e-mail: info@teamplayerstheatre.com
Fax: 01642 577121   Tel: 01642 592648

THEATRE ALIBI
(Adult & Young People)
Northcott Studio Theatre
Emmmanuel Road, Exeter EX4 1EJ
Website: www.theatrealibi.co.uk
e-mail: info@theatrealibi.co.uk   Tel/Fax: 01392 217315

THEATRE AND
Church Hall, St James Road
Marsh, Huddersfield HD1 4QA
Website: www.theatreand.com
e-mail: clare@theatreand.com
Fax: 01484 532962   Tel: 01484 532967

THEATRE CENTRE
(National Touring & New Writing for Young Audiences)
Shoreditch Town Hall
380 Old Street, London EC1V 9LT
Website: www.theatre-centre.co.uk
e-mail: admin@theatre-centre.co.uk
Fax: 020-7739 9741   Tel: 020-7729 3066

THEATRE IS.......
The Innovation Centre
College Lane, Hatfield AL10 9AB
Website: www.theatreis.org
e-mail: info@theatreis.org   Tel: 01707 281100

THEATRE NA N'OG
Unit 3
Millands Road Industrial Estate, Neath SA11 1NJ
Website: www.theatr-nanog.co.uk
e-mail: drama@theatr-nanog.co.uk
Fax: 01639 647941   Tel: 01639 641771

THEATRE WORKOUT Ltd
13A Stratheden Road, Blackheath, London SE3 7TH
Website: www.theatreworkout.co.uk
e-mail: enquiries@theatreworkout.co.uk   Tel: 020-8144 2290

THEATR IOLO Ltd
The Old School Building, Cefn Road
Mynachdy, Cardiff CF14 3HS
Website: www.theatriolo.com
e-mail: info@theatriolo.com
Fax: 029-2052 2225   Tel: 029-2061 3782

TICKLISH ALLSORTS SHOW
57 Victoria Road, Wilton, Salisbury, Wiltshire SP2 0DZ
Website: www.ticklishallsorts.co.uk
e-mail: garynunn@ntlworld.com   Tel/Fax: 01722 744949

TIE ACTION WORK
PO Box 433, Weston-Super-Mare
Somerset BS24 0WY
Website: www.actionwork.com
e-mail: admin@actionwork.com   Tel: 01934 815163

TOURING TALES THEATRE COMPANY Ltd
Suite 228 The Linen Hall
162 Regent Street, London W1B 5TB
Website: www.birminghamstage.net
e-mail: info@birminghamstage.net
Fax: 020-7437 3395   Tel: 020-7437 3391

TRICYCLE THEATRE
Contact: Gillian Christie (Education Director)
269 Kilburn High Road, London NW6 7JR
Website: www.tricycle.co.uk
e-mail: education@tricycle.co.uk   Tel/Fax: 020-7372 6611

TWISTING YARN THEATRE
Alhambra Theatre
Morley Street, Bradford BD7 1AJ
Website: www.bradford-theatres.co.uk
e-mail: twisting-yarn@bradford.gov.uk
Fax: 01274 437571   Tel: 01274 437490

UNICORN THEATRE
147 Tooley Street, London SE1 2HZ
Website: www.unicorntheatre.com
e-mail: admin@unicorntheatre.com
Fax: 020-7645 0550   Tel: 020-7645 0500

WEST YORKSHIRE PLAYHOUSE
(Touring Company)
Playhouse Square
Quarry Hill, Leeds LS2 7UP
e-mail: gail.mcintyre@wyp.org.uk   Tel: 0113-213 7225

WIZARD THEATRE
Contact: Leon Hamilton (Director), Emmy Bradbury
(Company Manager)
175 Royal Crescent
Ruislip, Middlesex HA4 0PN
Website: www.wizardtheatre.co.uk
e-mail: admin@wizardtheatre.co.uk   Tel: 0800 5832373

YOUNG SHAKESPEARE COMPANY
Contact: Christopher Geelan, Sarah Gordon
(Artistic Directors)
31 Bellevue Road, Friern Barnet, London N11 3ET
e-mail: youngshakespeare@mac.com
Fax: 020-8368 6713   Tel: 020-8368 4828

AUSTRIA
VIENNA
Vienna's English Theatre
(See website for casting requirements)
UK Representative: VM Theatre Productions Ltd
16 The Street, Ash, Canterbury, Kent CT3 2HJ
Website: www.englishtheatre.at   Tel/Fax: 01304 813330
Casting: Vanessa Mallatratt

DENMARK
COPENHAGEN
The English Theatre of Copenhagen
London Toast Theatre, Kochsvej 18, 1812 Fred C.
Copenhagen, Denmark
Website: www.londontoast.dk
e-mail: mail@londontoast.dk   Tel: + 45 33 22 8686
Artistic Director: Vivienne McKee
Administrator: Soren Hall

FRANCE
PARIS
ACT Company
25 avenue Mal Leclerc, 92240 Malakoff, France
Website: www.actheatre.com
e-mail: andrew@actheatre.com   Tel: + 33 1 46 56 20 50
Artistic Director: Andrew Wilson
Administrator: Anne Wilson

FRANCE
LYON
Theatre From Oxford (Touring Europe & Beyond)
B.P. 10, F-42750 St-Denis-de-Cabanne
e-mail: theatre.oxford@virgin.net
Contact: Robert Southam (By Post)

GERMANY
FRANKFURT
The English Theatre
Kaiserstrasse 34, 60329, Frankfurt, Germany
Website: www.english-theatre.org
e-mail: mail@english-thearte.org
Fax: + 49 69 242 316 14   Tel: + 49 69 242 316 15
Contact: Daniel John Nicolai

GERMANY
HAMBURG
The English Theatre of Hamburg
Lerchenfeld 14, 22081 Hamburg, Germany
Website: www.englishtheatre.de
Fax: + 49 40 227 7927   Tel: + 49 40 227 7089
Contact: Robert Rumpf, Clifford Dean

GERMANY
TOURING GERMANY
White Horse Theatre
Boerdenstrasse 17
59494 Soest-Muellingsen, Germany
e-mail: theatre@whitehorse.de
Fax: + 49 29 21 33 93 36   Tel: + 49 29 21 33 93 39
Contact: Peter Griffith, Michael Dray

HUNGARY
BUDAPEST
Merlin International Theatre
Gerloczy Utca 4
1052 Budapest, Hungary
e-mail: angol@merlinszinhaz.hu
Fax: + 36 1 2660904   Tel: + 36 1 3179338
Contact: Laszlo Magacs

ICELAND
REYKJAVIK
Light Nights - The Summer Theatre
The Travelling Theatre, Baldursgata 37
IS-101 Reykjavik, Iceland   Tel: + 354 551 9181
Artistic Director: Kristine G Magnus

ITALY
SANREMO
THEATRINO & MELTING POT THEATRE - ACLE
Via Roma 54, 18038 Sanremo (IM), Italy
Website: www.acle.org
e-mail: info@acle.org
Fax: + 39 0184 509996   Tel: + 39 0184 506070

SWITZERLAND
TANNAY
Simply Theatre
Chemin des Couleuvres 8B, 1295 Tannay, Switzerland
Website: www.simplytheatre.com
e-mail: info@simplytheatre.com
Fax: + 41 22 8600159   Tel: + 41 22 8600518

UNITED KINGDOM
WARWICK
Onatti Theatre Company
9 Field Close, Warwick
Warwickshire CV34 4QD
Website: www.onatti.co.uk
e-mail: info@onatti.co.uk
Fax: 0870 1643629   Tel: 01926 495220
Contact: Andrew Bardwell

ADELPHI
Strand, London WC2E 7NN
Manager: --------------------
Stage Door: 020-7836 1166
Box Office: 0870 8955598

ALDWYCH
Aldwych, London WC2B 4DF
Manager: 020-7836 5537
Stage Door: 020-7836 5537
Box Office: 020-7389 3367
Website: www.aldwychtheatre.co.uk

ALMEIDA
Almeida Street, London N1 1TA
Manager: 020-7288 4900
Stage Door: --------------------
Box Office 020-7359 4404

AMBASSADORS
West Street
London WC2H 9ND
Manager: 020-7395 5410
Stage Door: 020-7395 5400
Box Office: 020-7395 5405
Website: www.theambassadorstheatre.co.uk
e-mail: boxofficemanager@theambassadorstheatre.co.uk

APOLLO
Shaftesbury Avenue, London W1D 7EZ
Manager: 020-7494 5834
Stage Door: 020-7851 2711
Box Office: 0870 8901107
e-mail: enquiries@nimaxtheatres.com

APOLLO VICTORIA
17 Wilton Road, London SW1V 1LG
Manager: 020-7834 6318
Stage Door: 020-7630 9943
Box Office: 0870 4000650
Website: www.getlive.co.uk

ARTS
6-7 Great Newport Street
London WC2H 7JB
Manager: 020-7836 2132
Stage Door: 020-7836 2132
Box Office: 0844 8471608
Website: www.artstheatrelondon.com

BARBICAN
Barbican, London EC2Y 8DS
Manager: 020-7628 3351
Stage Door: 020-7628 3351
Box Office: 0845 1207511
Website: www.barbican.org.uk

BLOOMSBURY
15 Gordon Street
London WC1H 0AH
Manager: 020-7679 2777
Stage Door: 020-7679 2922
Box Office: 020-7388 8822
Website: www.thebloomsbury.com
e-mail: blooms.theatre@ucl.ac.uk

BUSH
Shepherds Bush Green
London W12 8QD
Manager: 020-8743 3584
Stage Door: --------------------
BO: 020-7610 4224
Website: www.bushtheatre.co.uk
e-mail: info@bushtheatre.co.uk

CAMBRIDGE
Earlham Street
Seven Dials
Covent Garden, London WC2H 9HU
Manager: 020-7850 8711
Stage Door: 020-7850 8710
Box Office: 020-7850 8715

COLISEUM (English National Opera)
St Martin's Lane
London WC2N 4ES
Manager: 020-7836 0111
Stage Door: 020-7845 9397
Box Office: 0870 1450200

COMEDY
Panton Street, London SW1Y 4DN
Manager: 020-7321 5310
Stage Door: 020-7321 5300
Box Office: 0870 0606637

CRITERION
2 Jermyn Street
Piccadilly, London SW1Y 4XA
Manager: 020-7839 8811
Stage Door: 020-7839 8811
Box Office: 0844 8471778
Website: www.criterion-theatre.com
e-mail: admin@criterion-theatre.co.uk

DOMINION
268-269 Tottenham Court Road
London W1T 7AQ
Manager: --------------------
Stage Door: 020-7927 0900
Box Office: 0870 7490587
Website: www.dominiontheatrelondon.org.uk

DONMAR WAREHOUSE
41 Earlham Street
London WC2H 9LX
Manager: 020-7240 4882
Stage Door: 020-7438 9200
Box Office: 0870 060 6624
Website: www.donmarwarehouse.com
e-mail: office@donmarwarehouse.com

DRURY LANE
Theatre Royal
Catherine Street
London WC2B 5JF
Manager: --------------------
Stage Door: 020-7850 8790
Box Office: 020-7494 5060

DUCHESS
Catherine Street, London WC2B 5LA
Manager: 020-7632 9601
Stage Door: 020-7632 9600
Box Office: 0844 4124659
e-mail: enquiries@nimaxtheatres.com

DUKE OF YORK'S
St Martin's Lane, London WC2N 4BG
Manager: 020-7836 4615
Stage Door: 020-7836 4615
Box Office: 0870 0606623

FORTUNE
Russell Street
Covent Garden, London WC2B 5HH
Manager: 020-7010 7901
Stage Door: 020-7010 7901
Box Office: 0870 0606626

GARRICK
Charing Cross Road
London WC2H 0HH
Manager: 020-7520 5692
Stage Door: 020-7520 5690
Box Office: 020-7520 5693
e-mail: enquiries@nimaxtheatres.com

GIELGUD
Shaftesbury Avenue
London W1D 6AR
Manager: 020-7292 1321
Stage Door: 020-7292 1320
Box Office: 020-7812 7480

HACKNEY EMPIRE
291 Mare Street, London E8 1EJ
Manager: 020-8510 4500
Stage Door: 020-8510 4500
Box Office: 020-8985 2424
Website: www.hackneyempire.co.uk
e-mail: info@hackneyempire.co.uk

HAMMERSMITH APOLLO
Queen Caroline Street
London W6 9QH
Manager: -------------------
Stage Door: -------------------
Box Office: 0844 8444748
Website: www.hammersmithapollo.net

HAMPSTEAD
Eton Avenue, Swiss Cottage
London NW3 3EU
Manager: 020-7449 4200
Stage Door: -------------------
Box Office: 020-7722 9301
Website: www.hampsteadtheatre.com
e-mail :   info@hampsteadtheatre.com

HER MAJESTY'S
Haymarket, London SW1Y 4QL
Manager: 020-7850 8750
Stage Door: 020-7850 8750
Box Office: 0844 4122707

LONDON PALLADIUM
Argyll Street, London W1F 7TF
Manager: 020-7850 8777
Stage Door: 020-7850 8770
Box Office: 0870 8901108

LYCEUM
21 Wellington Street
London WC2E 7RQ
Manager: 020-7420 8100
Stage Door: 020-7420 8100
Box Office: 0844 8440005

LYRIC
29 Shaftesbury Avenue
London W1D 7ES
Manager: 020-7494 5840
Stage Door: 020-7494 5841
Box Office: 020-7494 5842
e-mail: enquiries@nimaxtheatres.com

LYRIC HAMMERSMITH
King Street, London W6 0QL
Manager: -------------------
Stage Door: -------------------
Box Office: 0871 2211722
Website: www.lyric.co.uk
e-mail: enquiries@lyric.co.uk

NATIONAL
South Bank
Upper Ground
London SE1 9PX
Manager: 020-7452 3280
Stage Door: 020-7452 3333
Box Office: 020-7452 3000
Website: www.nationaltheatre.org.uk

NEW LONDON
Drury Lane
London WC2B 5PW
Manager: 020-7242 9802
Stage Door: 020-7242 9802
Box Office: 0870 8900141

NEW PLAYERS
The Arches
Off Villiers Street
London WC2N 6NG
Manager: 020-7930 5868
Stage Door: -------------------
Box Office: -------------------
Website: www.newplayerstheatre.com
e-mail: info@newplayerstheatre.com

NOEL COWARD (Previously Albery)
85 St Martin's Lane
London WC2N 4AA
Manager: 020-7759 8011
Stage Door: 020-7759 8010
Box Office: -------------------

NOVELLO (Previously STRAND)
Aldwych, London WC2B 4LD
Manager: 020-7759 9611
Stage Door: 020-7759 9611
Box Office: 0870 9500935

OLD VIC
The Cut, London SE1 8NB
Manager: 020-7928 2651
Stage Door: 020-7928 2651
Box Office: 0870 0606628
Website: www.oldvictheatre.com
e-mail: info@oldvictheatre.com

OPEN AIR
Inner Circle, Regent's Park
London NW1 4NR
Manager: 020-7935 5756
Stage Door: 020-7935 5756
Box Office: 0844 8264242
Website: www.openairtheatre.org

PALACE
Shaftesbury Avenue
London W1D 5AY
Manager: 020-7434 0088
Stage Door: 020-7434 0088
Box Office: 0870 8955579
Website: www.rutheatres.com
e-mail: info@rutheatres.com

PEACOCK
(For Administration SEE SADLER'S WELLS)
Portugal Street, Kingsway
London WC2A 2HT
Manager: 020-7863 8918
Stage Door: 020-7863 8268
Box Office: 0844 4124322
Website: www.sadlerswells.com
e-mail: info@sadlerswells.com

PHOENIX
110 Charing Cross Road
London WC2H 0JP
Manager: 020-7438 9610
Stage Door: 020-7438 9600
Box Office: 020-7438 9605

PICCADILLY
Denman Street, London W1D 7DY
Manager: 020-7478 8810
Stage Door: 020-7478 8800
Box Office: 020-7478 8805

PLAYHOUSE
Northumberland Avenue, London WC2N 5DE
Manager: 020-7839 4292
Stage Door: 020-7839 4292
Box Office: 020-7839 4401

PRINCE EDWARD
28 Old Compton Street, London W1D 4HS
Manager: 020-7440 3021
Stage Door: 020-7440 3020
Box Office: 020-7447 5459
Website: www.delfont-mackintosh.com

PRINCE OF WALES
Coventry Street, London W1D 6AS
Manager: 020-7766 2101
Stage Door: 020-7766 2100
Box Office: 0870 8500393
Website: www.delfont-mackintosh.com

QUEEN'S
51 Shaftesbury Avenue, London W1D 6BA
Manager: 020-7292 1351
Stage Door: 020-7292 1350
Box Office: 0870 9500930

RIVERSIDE STUDIOS
Crisp Road, Hammersmith, London W6 9RL
Manager: 020-8237 1000
Stage Door: 020-8237 1000
Box Office: 020-8237 1111
Website: www.riversidestudios.co.uk
e-mail: info@riversidestudios.co.uk

ROYAL COURT
Sloane Square, London SW1W 8AS
Manager: 020-7565 5050
Stage Door: 020-7565 5050
Box Office: 020-7565 5000
Website: www.royalcourttheatre.com
e-mail: info@royalcourttheatre.com

ROYAL OPERA HOUSE
Covent Garden, London WC2E 9DD
Manager: 020-7240 1200
Stage Door: 020-7240 1200
Box Office: 020-7304 4000

SADLER'S WELLS
Rosebery Avenue, London EC1R 4TN
Manager: 020-7863 8034
Stage Door: 020-7863 8198
Box Office: 0870 7377737
Website: www.sadlerswells.com
e-mail: info@sadlerswells.com

SAVOY
Strand, London WC2R 0ET
Manager: -------------------
Stage Door: 020-7845 6050
Box Office: 0870 1648787

SHAFTESBURY
210 Shaftesbury Avenue
London WC2H 8DP
Manager: 020-7379 3345
Stage Door: 020-7379 3345
Box Office: 020-7379 5399
e-mail: info@toc.dltentertainment.co.uk

SHAKESPEARE'S GLOBE
21 New Globe Walk
Bankside, London SE1 9DT
Manager: 020-7902 1400
Stage Door: 020-7902 1400
Box Office: 020-7401 9919
Website: www.shakespeares-globe.org
e-mail: info@shakespearesglobe.com

SOHO
21 Dean Street
London W1D 3NE
Manager: 020-7287 5060
Stage Door: -------------------
Box Office: 020-7478 0100
Website: www.sohotheatre.com

ST MARTIN'S
West Street, London WC2H 9NZ
Manager: 020-7497 0578
Stage Door: 020-7836 1086
Box Office: 0870 1628787

THEATRE ROYAL
Haymarket, London SW1Y 4HT
Manager: 020-7930 8890
Stage Door: 020-7930 8890
Box Office: 0845 4811870

TRICYCLE
269 Kilburn High Road
London NW6 7JR
Manager: 020-7372 6611
Stage Door: 020-7372 6611
Box Office: 020-7328 1000
Website: www.tricycle.co.uk
e-mail: info@tricycle.co.uk

VAUDEVILLE
404 Strand, London WC2R 0NH
Manager: 020-7836 1820
Stage Door: 020-7836 3191
Box Office: 0870 8900511

VICTORIA PALACE
Victoria Street
London SW1E 5EA
Manager: 020-7828 0600
Stage Door: 020-7834 2781
Box Office: 0844 2485000

WYNDHAM'S
Charing Cross Road
London WC2H 0DA
Manager: 020-7759 8077
Stage Door: 020-7759 8010
Box Office: 0870 9500925

YOUNG VIC
66 The Cut, London SE1 8LZ
Manager: 020-7922 2800
Stage Door: 020-7922 2800
Box Office: 020-7922 2922
Website: www.youngvic.org
e-mail: info@youngvic.org

ALBANY The
Douglas Way
Deptford, London SE8 4AG
Fax: 020-8469 2253
BO: 020-8692 4446   Admin 020-8692 0231

ARCOLA THEATRE
Contact: Mehmet Ergen (Artistic Director)
27 Arcola Street
Dalston, (Off Kingsland High Street)
London E8 2DJ
e-mail: info@arcolatheatre.com
Fax/Admin: 020-7503 1645   BO: 020-7503 1646
Route: Victoria Line to Highbury & Islington, then North
London Line to Dalston Kingsland (Main Line) - 5 min walk.
Buses: 38 or 242 from West End, 149 from London Bridge or
30, 67, 76, 243

ARTSDEPOT
5 Nether Street, Tally Ho Corner
North Finchley, London N12 0GA
Website: www.artsdepot.co.uk
e-mail: info@artsdepot.co.uk   BO: 020-8369 5454

BAC
Lavender Hill, London SW11 5TN
Website: www.bac.org.uk
e-mail: mailbox@bac.org.uk
Fax: 020-7978 5207
BO: 020-7223 2223   Admin: 020-7223 6557
Route: Victoria or Waterloo (Main Line) to Clapham
Junction then 5 min walk or Northern Line to Clapham
Common then 20 min walk

BARONS COURT THEATRE
'The Curtain's Up'
28A Comeragh Road
West Kensington, London W14 9HR
Fax: 020-7602 0235   Admin/BO: 020-8932 4747
Route: West Kensington or Barons Court tube

BATES Tristan THEATRE
Contact: Laura Kriefman (Theatre Manager)
(adjoining The Actors Centre)
1A Tower Street, London WC2H 9NP
Website: www.tristanbatestheatre.co.uk
e-mail: tbt@actorscentre.co.uk
Fax: 020-7240 3896
BO: 020-7240 6283   Admin: 020-7632 8010

BECK THEATRE
Grange Road, Hayes, Middlesex UB3 2UE
Website: www.becktheatre.org.uk
BO: 020-8561 8371   Admin: 020-8561 7506
Route: Metropolitan Line to Uxbridge then buses 427 or
607 to Theatre or Paddington (Main Line) to Hayes
Harlington then buses 90, H98 or 195 (10 min)

BEDLAM THEATRE
11B Bristo Place, Edinburgh EH1 1EZ
Website: www.bedlamtheatre.co.uk
e-mail: info@bedlamtheatre.co.uk
Admin/Fax: 0131-225 9873   BO: 0131-225 9893

BELLAIRS PLAYHOUSE
Millmead Terrace, Guildford GU2 4YT
Website: www.gsauk.org
e-mail: enquiries@gsauk.org
BO: 01483 444789   Admin: 01483 560701 (Mon-Fri)

BLACKHEATH HALLS
23 Lee Road
Blackheath, London SE3 9RQ
Website: www.blackheathhalls.com
e-mail: programming@blackheathhalls.com
Fax: 020-8852 5154   Tel: 020-8318 9758

BLOOMSBURY THEATRE
15 Gordon Street, Bloomsbury, London WC1H 0AH
Website: www.thebloomsbury.com
e-mail: blooms.theatre@ucl.ac.uk
BO: 020-7388 8822   Admin: 020-7679 2777
Route: Tube to Euston, Euston Square or Warren Street

BORLASE THEATRE The
Sir William Borlase's Grammar School
West Street, Marlow SL7 2BR
Website: www.swbgs.com
e-mail: mhartley@swbgs.com   Tel: 01628 816500

BRENTWOOD THEATRE
Contact: Mark P. Reed (Theatre Administrator)
15 Shenfield Road, Brentwood, Essex CM15 8AG
Website: www.brentwood-theatre.org
SD: 01277 226658   BO: 01277 200305
Route: Liverpool Street (Main Line) to Shenfield, then 15
min walk

BRIDEWELL THEATRE The
St Bride Foundation, Bride Lane
Fleet Street, London EC4Y 8EQ
Website: www.bridewelltheatre.org
e-mail: admin@bridewelltheatre.co.uk
Fax: 020-7353 1547   Admin: 020-7353 3331
Route: District & Circle Line to Blackfriars, Circle Line to
St Paul's. City Thameslink Capital Connect. Fifteen different
bus routes

BROADWAY STUDIO THEATRE The
Contact: Martin Costello (Director)
Catford, London SE6 4RU
Website: www.broadwaytheatre.org.uk
e-mail: martin@broadwaytheatre.org.uk
BO: 020-8690 0002   Admin: 020-8690 1000
Route: Charing Cross to Catford Bridge

BROADWAY The
Broadway, Barking IG11 7LS
Website: www.thebroadwaybarking.com
e-mail: admin@thebroadwaybarking.com
Fax: 020-8507 5611
BO: 020-8507 5607   Admin: 020-8507 5610

CAMDEN PEOPLE'S THEATRE
Contact: Matt Ball (Artistic Director)
58-60 Hampstead Road, London NW1 2PY
Website: www.cptheatre.co.uk
e-mail: admin@cptheatre.co.uk
Fax: 020-7813 3889   Tel: 020-7419 4841
Route: Victoria or Northern Line to Warren Street,
Metropolitan or Circle Line to Euston Square (2 min walk
either way)

CANAL CAFE THEATRE The
Contact: Emma Taylor (Artistic Director)
The Bridge House, Delamere Terrace
Little Venice, London W2 6ND
Website: www.canalcafetheatre.com
e-mail: mail@canalcafetheatre.com
Fax: 020-7266 1717
BO: 020-7289 6054   Admin: 020-7289 6056

CHATS PALACE ARTS CENTRE
Contact: Sarah Wickens
42-44 Brooksby's Walk, Hackney, London E9 6DF
Website: www.chatspalace.com
e-mail: info@chatspalace.com   Tel: 020-8533 0227

CHELSEA THEATRE
World's End Place, King's Road, London SW10 0DR
e-mail: admin@chelseatheatre.org.uk
Fax: 020-7352 2024   Tel: 020-7349 7811
Route: District or Circle Line to Sloane Square then short
bus ride 11 or 22 down King's Road

CHICKENSHED
Contact: Mary Ward MBE (Artistic Director)
Chase Side, Southgate
xLondon N14 4PE
Website: www.chickenshed.org.uk
e-mail: info@chickenshed.org.uk
Fax: 020-8292 0202
Minicom: 020-8350 0676　　　　　　　　BO: 020-8292 9222
Route: Piccadilly Line to Oakwood, turn left outside tube &
walk 8 min down Bramley Road or take 307 bus. Buses 298,
299, 699 or N19. Car parking available & easy access
parking by reservation

CHRIST'S HOSPITAL THEATRE
Contact: Jeff Mayhew (Director)
Horsham, West Sussex RH13 7LW
e-mail: jm@christs-hospital.org.uk
BO: 01403 247434　　　　　　　　Admin: 01403 247435

CHURCHILL The
Contact: Derek Nicholls (Chief Executive)
High Street, Bromley, Kent BR1 1HA
Website: www.churchilltheatre.co.uk
Fax: 020-8290 6968
BO: 0870 0606620　　　　　　　　Tel: 020-8464 7131

CLUB FOR ACTS & ACTORS The
Contact: Mark Wynter, Malcolm Knight
(Concert Artistes Association)
20 Bedford Street, London WC2E 9HP
Website: www.thecaa.org
e-mail: office@thecaa.org　　　　Admin: 020-7836 3172
Route: Piccadilly or Northern Line to Leicester Square then
few mins walk

COCHRANE THEATRE
Contact: Deirdre Malynn
Southampton Row, London WC1B 4AP
e-mail: info@cochranetheatre.co.uk
BO: 020-7269 1606　　　　　　　　Admin: 020-7269 1600
Route: Central or Piccadilly Line to Holborn then 3 min
walk

COCKPIT THEATRE
Gateforth Street, London NW8 8EH
Website: www.cockpittheatre.org.uk
e-mail: admin@cockpittheatre.org.uk
Fax: 020-7258 2921
BO: 020-7258 2925　　　　　　　　Admin: 020-7258 2920
Route: Tube to Marylebone/Edgware Road then short walk
or bus 139 to Lisson Grove & 6, 8 or 16 to Edgware Road

CORBETT THEATRE
(East 15 Acting School)
Hatfields, Rectory Lane, Loughton IG10 3RY
Website: www.east15.ac.uk
e-mail: east15@essex.ac.uk
Fax: 020-8508 7521　　　　BO & Admin: 020-8508 5983
Route: Central Line (Epping Branch) to Debden then 6 min
walk

COURTYARD THEATRE The
Contact: June Abbott, Tim Gill (Joint Artistic Directors)
Bowling Green Walk
40 Pitfield Street, London N1 6EU
Website: www.thecourtyard.org.uk
e-mail: info@thecourtyard.org.uk
BO: 0870 1630717　　　　　　　　Admin/Fax: 020-7251 6018

CROYDON CLOCKTOWER
Katharine Street, Croydon CR9 1ET
Website: www.croydonclocktower.org.uk
e-mail: arts@croydon.gov.uk
Fax: 020-8253 1003
BO: 020-8253 1030　　　　　　　　Tel: 020-8253 1037

CUSTARD FACTORY
Gibb Street
Digbeth, Birmingham B9 4AA
Website: www.custardfactory.co.uk
e-mail: info@custardfactory.co.uk
Fax: 0121-604 8888　　　　　　　　Tel: 0121-224 7777

DARTFORD ORCHARD THEATRE
Contact: Vanessa Hart
Home Gardens, Dartford, Kent DA1 1ED
Website: www.orchardtheatre.co.uk
Fax: 01322 227122
BO: 01322 220000　　　　　　　　Admin: 01322 220099
Route: Charing Cross (Main Line) to Dartford

DIORAMA ARTS CENTRE
(Hire Venue)
5-7 Euston Centre, London NW1 3JG
Website: www.diorama-arts.org.uk
e-mail: admin@diorama-arts.org.uk
Fax: 020-7813 3116　　　　　　　　Admin: 020-7916 5467
Route: Circle & District Line to Great Portland Street then
5 min walk, or Victoria/Northern line to Warren Street then
1 min walk

DRILL HALL The
16 Chenies Street, London WC1E 7EX
Website: www.drillhall.co.uk
e-mail: box.office@drillhall.co.uk
Fax: 020-7307 5062　　　　　　　　BO: 020-7307 5060
Route: Northern Line to Goodge Street then 1 min walk

EDINBURGH FESTIVAL FRINGE
180 High Street, Edinburgh EH1 1QS
Website: www.edfringe.com
e-mail: admin@edfringe.com
Fax: 0131-226 0016　　　　　　　　Tel: 0131-226 0026

EDINBURGH UNIVERSITY THEATRE COMPANY
(See BEDLAM THEATRE)

EMBASSY THEATRE & STUDIOS
(The Central School of Speech & Drama)
64 Eton Avenue
Swiss Cottage, London NW3 3HY
Website: www.cssd.ac.uk
e-mail: enquiries@cssd.ac.uk　　　　Tel: 020-7722 8183
Route: Jubilee Line to Swiss Cottage then 1 min walk

ETCETERA THEATRE CLUB
Contact: Zena Barrie, Michelle Flower (Directors)
Oxford Arms, 265 Camden High Street, London NW1 7BU
Website: www.etceteratheatre.com
e-mail: etc@etceteratheatre.com
Fax: 020-7482 0378　　　　　　　　Admin/BO: 020-7482 4857

FAIRFIELD HALLS
Ashcroft Theatre & Concert Hall
Park Lane, Croydon CR9 1DG
Website: www.fairfield.co.uk
e-mail: info@fairfield.co.uk
BO: 020-8688 9291　　　　　　　　Admin & SD: 020-8681 0821
Route: Victoria & London Bridge (Main Line) to East
Croydon then 5 min walk

FINBOROUGH THEATRE
Contact: Neil McPherson (Artistic Director)
The Finborough
118 Finborough Road
London SW10 9ED
Website: www.finboroughtheatre.co.uk
e-mail: admin@finboroughtheatre.co.uk
Fax: 020-7835 1853
BO: 020-7373 3842　　　　　　　　Admin: 020-7244 7439
Route: District or Piccadilly Line to Earls Court then 5 min
walk. Buses 74, 328, C1, C3, 74 then 3 min walk

GATE THEATRE
Contact: Carrie Cracknell & Natalie Abrahami (Artistic Directors)
Above Prince Albert Pub, 11 Pembridge Rd, London W11 3HQ
Website: www.gatetheatre.co.uk
e-mail: gate@gatetheatre.co.uk
Fax: 020-7221 6055
BO: 020-7229 0706   Admin: 020-7229 5387
Route: Central, Circle or District Line to Notting Hill Gate
then 1 min walk

GBS THEATRE (George Bernard Shaw)
Malet Street, London WC1E 7JN
Website: www.radaenterprises.org
e-mail: bookings@rada.ac.uk
BO: 020-7908 4800   Tel: 020-7908 4754

GIELGUD John THEATRE
Malet Street, London WC1E 7JN
Website: www.radaenterprises.org
e-mail: bookings@rada.ac.uk
BO: 020-7908 4800   Tel: 020-7908 4754

GREENWICH PLAYHOUSE
Contact: Alice de Sousa
Greenwich BR Station Forecourt
189 Greenwich High Road, London SE10 8JA
Website: www.galleontheatre.co.uk
e-mail: alice@galleontheatre.co.uk
Fax: 020-8310 7276   Tel: 020-8858 9256
Route: Main Line from Charing Cross, Waterloo East or
London Bridge, DLR to Greenwich

GREENWICH THEATRE
Contact: James Haddrell (Executive Director)
Crooms Hill, Greenwich, London SE10 8ES
Website: www.greenwichtheatre.org.uk
e-mail: info@greenwichtheatre.org.uk
Fax: 020-8858 8042
BO: 020-8858 7755   Admin: 020-8858 4447
Route: Jubilee Line (change Canary Wharf) then DLR to
Greenwich Cutty Sark, 3 min walk or Charing Cross (Main
Line) to Greenwich, 5 min walk

GUILDHALL SCHOOL OF MUSIC & DRAMA
Silk Street, Barbican, London EC2Y 8DT
e-mail: info@gsmd.ac.uk
Fax: 020-7256 9438   Tel: 020-7628 2571
Route: Hammersmith & City, Circle or Metropolitan line to
Barbican or Moorgate (also served by Northern line) then 5
min walk

HACKNEY EMPIRE THEATRE
291 Mare Street, Hackney, London E8 1EJ
BO: 020-8985 2424   Press/Admin: 020-8510 4500
Route: North London Line to Hackney Central

HEN & CHICKENS THEATRE
Unrestricted View, Above Hen & Chickens Theatre Bar,
109 St Paul's Road, Islington, London N1 2NA
Website: www.henandchickens.com
e-mail: james@henandchickens.com   Tel: 020-7704 2001
Route: Victoria Line or Main Line to Highbury & Islington
directly opposite station

ICA THEATRE
(No CVs, Venue only)
The Mall, London SW1Y 5AH
Website: www.ica.org.uk
Fax: 020-7873 0051
BO: 020-7930 3647   Admin: 020-7930 0493
Route: Nearest stations Piccadilly & Charing Cross

JACKSONS LANE
269A Archway Road, London N6 5AA
Website: www.jacksonslane.org.uk
e-mail: reception@jacksonslane.org.uk   Tel: 020-8340 5226

JERMYN STREET THEATRE
Contact: Penny Horner (General Manager)
16B Jermyn Street, London SW1Y 6ST
Website: www.jermynstreettheatre.co.uk
Fax: 020-7287 3232
BO: 020-7287 2875   Admin: 020-7434 1443

JERWOOD VANBRUGH THEATRE
Malet Street, London WC1E 7JN
Website: www.radaenterprises.org
e-mail: bookings@rada.ac.uk
BO: 020-7908 4800   Tel: 020-7908 4754

KING'S HEAD THEATRE
115 Upper Street
Islington, London N1 1QN
Website: www.kingsheadtheatre.org
BO: 0870 890 0149   Admin: 020-7226 8561
Route: Northern Line to Angel then 5 min walk. Approx
halfway between Angel and Highbury & Islington tube
stations

KING'S LYNN CORN EXCHANGE
Tuesday Market Place
King's Lynn, Norfolk PE30 1JW
Website: www.kingslynncornexchange.co.uk
e-mail: entertainment_admin@west-norfolk.gov.uk
Fax: 01553 762141
BO: 01553 764864   Admin: 01553 765565

KOMEDIA
Contact: David Lavender (Artistic Director, Theatre &
Comedy), Marina Kobler, Laurence Hill (Artistic Directors,
Music, Cabaret & Children's Theatre)
44-47 Gardner Street, Brighton BN1 1UN
Website: www.komedia.co.uk/brighton
e-mail: info@komedia.co.uk
Fax: 01273 647102
BO: 01273 647100   Tel: 01273 647101

LANDMARK ARTS CENTRE
Ferry Road, Teddington Lock, Middlesex TW11 9NN
Website: www.landmarkartscentre.org
e-mail: info@landmarkartscentre.org
Fax: 020-8977 4830   Tel: 020-8977 7558

LANDOR THEATRE The
Contact: Robert McWhir (Artistic Director)
70 Landor Road, London SW9 9PH
Website: www.landortheatre.co.uk
e-mail: info@landortheatre.co.uk   Admin/BO: 020-7737 7276
Route: Northern Line Clapham North then 2 min walk

LEICESTER SQUARE THEATRE
5 Leicester Place, London WC2H 7BP
Website: www.leicestersquaretheatre.com
BO: 0844 8472475   Tel: 0870 8993335

LEIGHTON BUZZARD THEATRE
Lake Street, Leighton Buzzard
Bedfordshire LU7 1RX
Website: www.leightonbuzzardtheatre.co.uk
BO: 01582 818801   Tel: 01582 818800

LILIAN BAYLIS THEATRE
(Information: Sadler's Wells Theatre)
Rosebery Avenue, London EC1R 4TN
Website: www.sadlerswells.com
e-mail: info@sadlerswells.com
BO: 0844 4124300   SD: 020-7863 8198

LIVE THEATRE
27 Broad Chare, Quayside
Newcastle upon Tyne NE1 3DQ
Website: www.live.org.uk
e-mail: info@live.org.uk
Fax: 0191-232 2224
BO: 0191-232 1232   Admin: 0191-261 2694

MACOWAN THEATRE
(LAMDA)
1-2 Logan Place, London W8 6QN
Website: www.lamda.org.uk
Fax: 020-7370 1980 Tel: 020-7244 8744
Route: District or Piccadilly Line to Earl's Court then 6 min walk

MADDERMARKET THEATRE
Contact: Michael Lyas (General Manager)
St John's Alley, Norwich NR2 1DR
Website: www.maddermarket.co.uk
e-mail: mmtheatre@btconnect.com
Fax: 01603 661357
BO: 01603 620917 Admin: 01603 626560

MENIER CHOCOLATE FACTORY
53 Southwark Street, London SE1 1RU
Website: www.menierchocolatefactory.com
e-mail: office@menierchocolatefactory.com
Fax: 020-7378 1713
Tel: 020-7378 1712 BO: 020-7906 7060

MILLFIELD ARTS CENTRE
Silver Street, London N18 1PJ
Website: www.millfieldtheatre.co.uk
e-mail: info@millfieldtheatre.co.uk
Fax: 020-8807 3892
BO: 020-8807 6680 Admin: 020-8803 5283
Route: Liverpool Street (Main Line) to Silver Street or tube to Turnpike Lane then bus 144, 15 min to Cambridge Roundabout

MYERS STUDIO THEATRE The
Contact: Trevor Mitchell (General Manager & Artistic Director)
The Epsom Playhouse, Ashley Ave, Epsom, Surrey KT18 5AL
Website: www.epsomplayhouse.co.uk
e-mail: tmitchell@epsom-ewell.gov.uk
Fax: 01372 726228
BO: 01372 742555 Tel: 01372 742226

NADINE'S WINDOW
(Showcase Theatre Company)
Website: www.myspace.com/nadineswindow
e-mail: nadineswindow@yahoo.co.uk

NETTLEFOLD The
West Norwood Library Centre
1 Norwood High Street, London SE27 9JX
e-mail: thenettlefold@lambeth.gov.uk
Fax: 020-7926 8071
Admin/BO: 020-7926 8070
Route: Victoria, West Croydon or London Bridge (Main Line) to West Norwood then 2 min walk, or tube to Brixton then buses 2, 196, 322, 432, or buses 68, 468

NEW END THEATRE
27 New End, Hampstead, London NW3 1JD
Website: www.newendtheatre.co.uk
Fax: 020-7794 4044
BO: 0870 0332733 Admin: 020-7472 5800
Route: Northern Line to Hampstead then 2 min walk off Heath Street

NEW PLAYERS THEATRE The
(Formerly The Players Theatre)
The Arches, Villiers Street
London WC2N 6NG Tel: 020-7930 5868

NEW WIMBLEDON THEATRE & STUDIO
The Broadway, Wimbledon, London SW19 1QG
Website: www.newwimbledontheatre.co.uk
Fax: 020-8543 6637
BO: 0870 0606646 Admin: 020-8545 7900
Route: Main Line or District Line to Wimbledon, then 3 min walk. Buses 57, 93, 155

NORTHBROOK THEATRE The
Contact: Dave Manley (Theatre Co-ordinator)
Littlehampton Road, Goring-by-Sea
Worthing, West Sussex BN12 6NU
Website: www.northbrooktheatre.co.uk
e-mail: box.office@nbcol.ac.uk
Fax: 01903 606141 BO/Admin: 01903 606162

NORWICH PUPPET THEATRE
St James, Whitefriars, Norwich NR3 1TN
Website: www.puppettheatre.co.uk
e-mail: info@puppettheatre.co.uk
Fax: 01603 617578
BO: 01603 629921 Admin: 01603 615564

NOVELLO THEATRE The
(Redroofs Theatre Company)
2 High Street, Sunninghill
Nr Ascot, Berkshire Tel: 01344 620881
Route: Waterloo (Main Line) to Ascot then 1 mile from station

OLD RED LION THEATRE PUB
Contact: Helen Devine (Theatre Manager)
418 St John Street, Islington, London EC1V 4NJ
BO: 020-7837 7816 Admin: 020-7833 3053
Route: Northern Line to Angel then 1 min walk

ORANGE TREE
Contact: Sam Walters (Artistic Director)
1 Clarence Street, Richmond TW9 2SA
e-mail: admin@orangetreetheatre.co.uk
Fax: 020-8332 0369
BO: 020-8940 3633 Admin: 020-8940 0141
Route: District Line, Waterloo (Main Line) or North London Line are virtually opposite station

OVAL HOUSE THEATRE
52-54 Kennington Oval, London SE11 5SW
Website: www.ovalhouse.com
e-mail: info@ovalhouse.com
Fax: 020-7820 0990
BO: 020-7582 7680 Admin: 020-7582 0080
Route: Northern Line to Oval then 1 min walk, Victoria Line & Main Line to Vauxhall then 10 min walk

PAVILION THEATRE
Marine Road, Dun Laoghaire, County Dublin, Ireland
Website: www.paviliontheatre.ie
e-mail: info@paviliontheatre.ie
Fax: 353 1 663 6328 Tel: 353 1 231 2929

PENTAMETERS
Theatre Entrance in Oriel Place
28 Heath Street, London NW3 6TE
Website: www.pentameters.co.uk
BO/Admin: 020-7435 3648
Route: Northern Line to Hampstead then 1 min walk. Buses 268, 46

PLACE The
(Main London Venue for Contemporary Dance)
17 Duke's Road, London WC1H 9PY
Website: www.theplace.org.uk
e-mail: theatre@theplace.org.uk
BO: 020-7387 0031 Admin: 020-7380 1268
Route: Northern or Victoria Line to Euston or King's Cross then 5 min walk (Opposite rear of St Pancras Church)

PLEASANCE ISLINGTON
Contact: Anthony Alderson
Carpenters Mews, North Road, London N7 9EF
Website: www.pleasance.co.uk
e-mail: info@pleasance.co.uk
Fax: 020-7700 7366
BO: 020-7609 1800 Admin: 020-7619 6868
Route: Piccadilly Line to Caledonian Road, turn left, walk 50 yds, turn left into North Road, 2 min walk. Buses 17, 91, 259, N91, 393

POLISH THEATRE
(Polish Social & Cultural Association Ltd)
238-246 King Street, London W6 0RF
BO: 020-8741 0398   Admin: 020-8741 1940
Route: District Line to Ravenscourt Park, or District,
Piccadilly or Metropolitan Lines to Hammersmith then 7
min walk. Buses 27, 267, 190, 391, H91

POLKA THEATRE
240 The Broadway, Wimbledon SW19 1SB
Website: www.polkatheatre.com
e-mail: admin@polkatheatre.com
Fax: 020-8545 8365
BO: 020-8543 4888   Admin: 020-8545 8320
Route: Waterloo (Main Line) or District Line to Wimbledon
then 10 min walk. Northern Line to South Wimbledon then
10 min walk. Tram to Wimbledon, Buses 57, 93, 219, 493

PRINCESS THEATRE HUNSTANTON
The Green, Hunstanton
Norfolk PE36 5AH
Website: www.princesstheatrehunstanton.co.uk
Fax: 01485 534463
BO: 01485 532252   Admin: 01485 535937

PUTNEY ARTS THEATRE
Ravenna Road, Putney SW15 6AW
Website: www.putneyartstheatre.org.uk
e-mail: info@putneyartstheatre.org.uk
Fax: 020-8788 6940   Tel: 020-8788 6943

QUEEN'S THEATRE
Contact: Bob Carlton (Artistic Director)
Billet Lane, Hornchurch, Essex RM11 1QT
Website: www.queens-theatre.co.uk
e-mail: info@queens-theatre.co.uk
Fax: 01708 462363
BO: 01708 443333   SD/Admin 01708 462362
Route: District Line to Hornchurch, Main Line to
Romford/Gidea Park. 15 miles from West End take A13,
A1306 then A125 or A12 then A127

QUESTORS THEATRE EALING The
12 Mattock Lane, London W5 5BQ
Website: www.questors.org.uk
e-mail: enquiries@questors.org.uk
Fax: 020-8567 2275
BO: 020-8567 5184   Admin: 020-8567 0011
Route: Central or District Line to Ealing Broadway then 5
min walk. Buses 207, 83, 65

RED LADDER THEATRE COMPANY Ltd
3 St Peter's Buildings
York Street, Leeds LS9 8AJ
Website: www.redladder.co.uk
e-mail: rod@redladder.co.uk
Fax: 0113-245 5351   Tel: 0113-245 5311

RICHMOND THEATRE
Contact: Karin Gartzke
The Green, Richmond, Surrey TW9 1QJ
Website: www.richmondtheatre.net
e-mail: richmondstagedoor@theambassadors.com
Fax: 020-8948 3601
BO: 0870 0606651   Admin & SD: 020-8940 0220
Route: 20 minutes from Waterloo (South West Trains) or
District Line or Silverlink to Richmond then 2 min walk

RIDWARE THEATRE
Contact: Alan & Margaret Williams (Venue only. No resident
performing company)
Wheelwright's House, Pipe Ridware
Rugeley, Staffs WS15 3QL
e-mail: al@christmas-time.com   Tel: 01889 504380

RIVERSIDE STUDIOS
Crisp Road, London W6 9RL
Website: www.riversidestudios.co.uk
e-mail: info@riversidestudios.co.uk
BO: 020-8237 1111   Admin: 020-8237 1000
Route: District, Piccadilly or Hammersmith & City Line to
Hammersmith then 5 min walk. Buses 9, 10, 27, 33, 72, 190,
209, 211, 266, 267, 283, 295, 391, 419

ROSEMARY BRANCH THEATRE
2 Shepperton Road
London N1 3DT
Website: www.rosemarybranch.co.uk
e-mail: cecilia@rosemarybranch.co.uk   Tel: 020-7704 6665
Route: Tube to Bank, Moorgate or Old Street (exit 5), then
No 21, 76 or 141 bus to Baring Street, or 271 bus from
Highbury and Islington.

ROSE THEATRE
24-26 High Street
Kingston upon Thames, Surrey KT1 1HL
Website: www.rosetheatrekingston.org
e-mail: admin@rosetheatrekingston.org
Fax: 020-8546 8783   Tel: 020-8546 6983

SCOTTISH STORYTELLING CENTRE
(Netherbow Theatre)
43-45 High Street, Edinburgh EH1 1SR
Website: www.scottishstorytellingcentre.co.uk
                    Tel: 0131-556 9579

SHADY DOLLS THEATRE COMPANY
9 Upper Handa Walk, London N1 2RG
Website: www.shadydolls.com
e-mail: info@shadydolls.com   Mobile: 07796 353531

SHAW THEATRE The
100-110 Euston Road, London NW1 2AJ
Fax: 020-7388 7555
BO: 0871 5943123   Admin: 020-7388 2555

SOUTH HILL PARK ARTS CENTRE
Bracknell, Berkshire RG12 7PA
Website: www.southhillpark.org.uk
e-mail: admin@southhillpark.org.uk
BO: 01344 484123   Admin & SD: 01344 484858
Route: Waterloo (Main Line) to Bracknell then 10 min bus
ride or taxi rank at station

SOUTH LONDON THEATRE
(Bell Theatre & Prompt Corner)
2A Norwood High Street
London SE27 9NS
Website: www.southlondontheatre.co.uk
e-mail: southlondontheatre@yahoo.co.uk
                    Tel: 020-8670 3474
Route: Victoria or London Bridge (Main Line) to West
Norwood then 2 min walk, or Victoria Line to Brixton then
buses 2, 68, 196, 322

SOUTHWARK PLAYHOUSE
Contact: Chris Smyrnios (Chief Executive), Ellie Jones
(Artistic Director)
Shipwright Yard, Corner of Tooley Street & Bermondsey
Street, London SE1 2TF
Website: www.southwarkplayhouse.co.uk
e-mail: admin@southwarkplayhouse.co.uk
BO: 0844 8471656   Admin: 020-7407 0234
Route: Trains to London Bridge, Jubilee/Northern Line to
London Bridge. Buses 47, 381, RV1, N47, N381. River service
to London Bridge City

SPACE ARTS CENTRE The
269 Westferry Road, London E14 3RS
Website: www.space.org.uk
e-mail: info@space.org.uk   Tel: 020-7515 7799

TABARD THEATRE
Contact: Collin Hilton, Fred Perry (Artistic Directors),
Simon Reilly (Theatre Manager)
2 Bath Road, London W4 1LW
Website: www.tabardtheatre.co.uk
e-mail: info@tabardtheatre.co.uk
Fax: 020-8994 6985   Tel: 020-8995 6035

THEATRE 503
The Latchmere Pub
503 Battersea Park Road
London SW11 3BW
Website: www.theatre503.com
e-mail: info@theatre503.com   BO: 020-7978 7040
Route: Victoria or Waterloo (Main Line) to Clapham
Junction then 10 min walk or buses 44, 219, 319, 344, 345 or
tube to South Kensington then buses 49 or 345 or tube to
Sloane Square then bus 319

THEATRE OF ALL POSSIBILITIES
Contact: Kathlin Gray (Artistic Director)
24 Old Gloucester Street, London WC1N 3AL
Website: www.allpossibilities.org
e-mail: engage@allpossibilities.org   Tel: 020-7242 9831

THEATRE ROYAL STRATFORD EAST
Contact: Kerry Michael (Artistic Director)
Gerry Raffles Square, London E15 1BN
Website: www.stratfordeast.com
e-mail: theatreroyal@stratfordeast.com
Fax: 020-8534 8381
BO: 020-8534 0310   Admin: 020-8534 7374
Route: Central or Jubilee Line to Stratford then 2 min walk

THEATRO TECHNIS
Contact: George Eugeniou (Artistic Director)
26 Crowndale Road, London NW1 1TT
Website: www.theatrotechnis.com
e-mail: info@theatrotechnis.com
BO & Admin: 020-7387 6617
Route: Northern Line to Mornington Crescent then 3 min
walk

TRICYCLE THEATRE
Contact: Nicolas Kent (Artsitic Director), Mary Lauder
(General Manager)
269 Kilburn High Road, London NW6 7JR
Website: www.tricycle.co.uk
e-mail: admin@tricycle.co.uk
Fax: 020-7328 0795
BO: 020-7328 1000   Admin: 020-7372 6611
Route: Jubilee Line to Kilburn then 5 min walk or buses 16,
189, 32 pass the door, 98, 31, 206, 316, 332 pass nearby

TRON THEATRE
63 Trongate, Glasgow G1 5HB
Website: www.tron.co.uk
e-mail: casting@tron.co.uk
Fax: 0141-552 6657
BO: 0141-552 4267   Admin: 0141-552 3748

UNION THEATRE The
Contact: Sasha Regan (Artistic Director), Ben De Wynter
(Associate Director), Thom Southerland (Resident
Director), Steve Miller (Technical Director), Paul Flynn (All
Casting Enquiries)
204 Union Street
Southwark, London SE1 0LX
Website: www.uniontheatre.org
e-mail: sasha@uniontheatre.freeserve.co.uk
                                Tel/Fax: 020-7261 9876
Route: Jubilee Line to Southwark then 2 min walk

UPSTAIRS AT THE GATEHOUSE
(Ovation Theatres Ltd)
The Gatehouse Pub
Corner of Hampstead Lane/North Road
London N6 4BD
Website: www.upstairsatthegatehouse.com
e-mail: events@ovationproductions.com
BO: 020-8340 3488   Admin: 020-8340 3477
Route: Northern Line to Highgate then 10 min walk. Buses
143, 210, 214, 271

WAREHOUSE THEATRE
Contact: Ted Craig (Artistic Director)
Dingwall Road
Croydon CR0 2NF
Website: www.warehousetheatre.co.uk
e-mail: info@warehousetheatre.co.uk
Fax: 020-8688 6699
BO: 020-8680 4060   Admin: 020-8681 1257
Route: Adjacent to East Croydon (Main Line). Direct from
Victoria (15 min), Clapham Junction (10 min) or by First
Capital Connect from West Hampstead, Kentish Town,
Kings Cross, Blackfriars & London Bridge

WATERMANS
40 High Street
Brentford TW8 0DS
Website: www.watermans.org.uk
e-mail: info@watermans.org.uk
Fax: 020-8232 1030
BO: 020-8232 1010   Admin: 020-8232 1020
Route: Buses: 237, 267, 65, N9. Tube: Gunnersbury or South
Ealing. Main Line: Kew Bridge then 5 min walk, Gunnersbury
then 10 min walk, or Brentford

WESTRIDGE (OPEN CENTRE)
(Drawing Room Recitals)
Star Lane
Highclere
Nr Newbury
Berkshire RG20 9PJ   Tel: 01635 253322

WHITE BEAR THEATRE
(Favours New Writing)
138 Kennington Park Road
London SE11 4DJ
Website: www.whitebeartheatre.co.uk
e-mail: info@whitebeartheatre.co.uk
                                Admin/BO: 020-7793 9193
Route: Northern Line to Kennington (2 min walk)

WILTONS MUSIC HALL
Graces Alley
Off Ensign Street
London E1 8JB
Website: www.wiltons.org.uk
Fax: 0871 2532424   Tel: 020-7702 9555
Route: Tube: Under 10 minutes walk from Aldgate East (exit
for Leman Street)/Tower Hill. DLR: Shadwell or Tower
Gateway. Car: Follow the yellow AA signs to Wiltons Music
Hall from the Highway, Aldgate or Tower Hill

WIMBLEDON STUDIO THEATRE
(See NEW WIMBLEDON THEATRE & STUDIO)

WYCOMBE SWAN
St Mary Street
High Wycombe
Buckinghamshire HP11 2XE
Website: www.wycombeswan.co.uk
e-mail: enquiries@wycombeswan.co.uk
BO: 01494 512000   Admin: 01494 514444

ABERDEEN
His Majesty's Theatre
Rosemount Viaduct, Aberdeen AB25 1GL
Box Office: 01224 641122
Stage Door: 01224 337673
Admin: 0845 2708200
Website: www.boxofficeaberdeen.com
e-mail: info@hmtheatre.com

ABERYSTWYTH
Aberystwyth Arts Centre
University of Wales
Aberystwyth SY23 3DE
Box Office: 01970 623232
Stage Door: 01970 624239
Admin: 01970 622882
Website: www.aber.ac.uk/artscentre
e-mail: ggo@aber.ac.uk

ASHTON-UNDER-LYNE
Tameside Hippodrome
Oldham Road
Ashton-under-Lyne OL6 7SE
Box Office: 0870 6021175
Stage Door: ------------------
Admin: 0161-330 2095
Website: www.livenation.co.uk/tameside

AYR
Gaiety Theatre
Carrick Street
Ayr KA7 1NU
Box Office: 01292 611222
Stage Door: --------------------
Admin: 01292 617400
Website: www.gaietytheatre.co.uk
e-mail: gaiety.theatre@south-ayrshire.gov

BACUP
Royal Court Theatre
Rochdale Road
Bacup OL13 9NR
Box Office: 01706 874080
Stage Door: ------------------
Admin: ------------------

BASINGSTOKE
The Haymarket Theatre
Wote Street
Basingstoke RG21 7NW
Box Office: 01256 844244
Stage Door: 01256 819797
Admin: 01256 819797
Website: www.haymarket.org.uk
e-mail: info@haymarket.org.uk

BATH
Theatre Royal
Sawclose, Bath BA1 1ET
Box Office: 01225 448844
Stage Door: 01225 448815
Admin: 01225 448815
Website: www.theatreroyal.org.uk
e-mail: forename.surname@theatreroyal.org.uk

BELFAST
Grand Opera House
Great Victoria Street, Belfast BT2 7HR
Box Office: 028-9024 1919
Stage Door: 028-9024 0411
Admin: 028-9024 0411
Website: www.goh.co.uk
e-mail: info@goh.co.uk

BILLINGHAM
Forum Theatre
Town Centre, Billingham TS23 2LJ
Box Office: 01642 552663
Stage Door: ------------------
Admin: 01642 551389
Website: www.forumtheatrebillingham.co.uk
e-mail: forumtheatre@btconnect.com

BIRMINGHAM
Alexandra Theatre
Station Street, Birmingham B5 4DS
Box Office: 0870 6077533
Stage Door: 0121-230 9102
Admin: 0121-643 5536
Website: www.livenation.co.uk/birmingham

BIRMINGHAM
Hippodrome
Hurst Street, Birmingham B5 4TB
Box Office: 0844 3385000
Stage Door: 0121-689 3020
Admin: 0870 7305555

BLACKPOOL
Grand Theatre National Theatre of Variety
33 Church Street, Blackpool FY1 1HT
Box Office: 01253 290190
Stage Door: 01253 743218
Admin: 01253 290111
Website: www.blackpoolgrand.co.uk
e-mail: box@blackpoolgrand.co.uk

BLACKPOOL
Opera House
Church Street, Blackpool FY1 1HW
Box Office: 0844 8561111
Stage Door: 01253 625252 ext 148
Admin: 01253 625252
Website: www.blackpoollive.com

BOURNEMOUTH
Pavilion Theatre
Westover Road, Bournemouth BH1 2BU
Box Office: 0844 5763000
Stage Door: 01202 451863
Admin: 01202 456400
Website: www.bic.co.uk

BRADFORD
Alhambra Theatre
Morley Street, Bradford BD7 1AJ
Box Office: 01274 432000
Stage Door: 01274 432375
Admin: 01274 432375
Website: www.bradford-theatres.co.uk
e-mail: administration@ces.bradford.gov.uk

BRADFORD
Theatre in the Mill
University of Bradford,
Shearbridge Road, Bradford BD7 1DP
Box Office: 01274 233200
Stage Door: 01274 233187
Admin: 01274 233185
Website: www.bradford.ac.uk/theatre
e-mail: theatre@bradford.ac.uk

BRIGHTON
Theatre Royal
New Road, Brighton BN1 1SD
Box Office: 0870 0606650
Stage Door: 01273 764400
Admin: 01273 764400
Website: www.theambassadors.com/theatreroyal
e-mail: brightontheatremanager@theambassadors.com

BRIGHTON
The Dome, Corn Exchange & Pavilion Theatres
29 New Road, Brighton BN1 1UG
Box Office: 01273 709709
Stage Door: 01273 261550
Admin: 01273 700747
Website: www.brightondome.org
e-mail: info@brightondome.org

BRISTOL
Hippodrome
St Augustines Parade
Bristol BS1 4UZ
Box Office: 0844 847 2335
Stage Door: 0117-302 3251
Admin: 0117-302 3310
Website: www.bristolhippodrome.org.uk

BROXBOURNE (Herts)
Broxbourne Civic Hall
High Street, Hoddesdon, Herts EN11 8BE
Box Office: 01992 441946
Stage Door: ----------------
Admin: 01992 441931
Website: www.broxbourne.gov.uk/whatson
e-mail: civic.leisure@broxbourne.gov.uk

BURY ST EDMUNDS
Theatre Royal
Westgate Street
Bury St Edmunds IP33 1QR
Box Office: 01284 769505
Stage Door: 01284 755127
Admin: 01284 755127
Website: www.theatreroyal.org
e-mail: admin@theatreroyal.org

BUXTON
Buxton Opera House
Water Street, Buxton SK17 6XN
Box Office: 0845 1272190
Stage Door: 01298 72524
Admin: 01298 72050
Website: www.buxtonoperahouse.org.uk
e-mail: admin@boh.org.uk

CAMBERLEY
The Camberley Theatre
Knoll Road, Camberley, Surrey GU15 3SY
Box Office: 01276 707600
Stage Door: ----------------
Admin: 01276 707512
Website: www.camberleytheatre.biz
e-mail: camberleytheatre@surreyheath.gov.uk

CAMBRIDGE
Cambridge Arts Theatre Trust Ltd
6 St Edward's Passage, Cambridge CB2 3PJ
Box Office: 01223 503333
Stage Door: 01223 578933
Admin: 01223 578903
Website: www.cambridgeartstheatre.com
e-mail: info@cambridgeartstheatre.com

CAMBRIDGE
Mumford Theatre
Anglia Ruskin University, East Road, Cambridge CB1 1PT
Box Office: 0845 1962320
Stage Door: 0845 1962848
Admin: 0845 1962848
e-mail: mumford@anglia.ac.uk

CANTERBURY
Gulbenkian Theatre
University of Kent, Canterbury CT2 7NB
Box Office: 01227 769075
Stage Door: ----------------
Admin: 01227 827861
Website: www.gulbenkiantheatre.co.uk
e-mail: gulbenkian@kent.ac.uk

CANTERBURY
The Marlowe Theatre
The Friars, Canterbury CT1 2AS
Box Office: 01227 787787
Stage Door: 01227 763262
Admin: 01227 763262
Website: www.marlowetheatre.com
e-mail: mark.everett@canterbury.gov.uk

CARDIFF
New Theatre
Park Place, Cardiff CF10 3LN
Box Office: 029-2087 8889
Stage Door: 029-2087 8900
Admin: 029-2087 8787
Website: www.newtheatrecardiff.co.uk

CARDIFF
Wales Millennium Centre
Bute Place, Cardiff CF10 5AL
Box Office: 0870 0402000
Stage Door: 029-2063 4700
Admin: 029-2063 6400
Website: www.wmc.org.uk

CHELTENHAM
Everyman Theatre
Regent Street, Cheltenham GL50 1HQ
Box Office: 01242 572573
Stage Door: 01242 512515
Admin: 01242 512515
Website: www.everymantheatre.org.uk
e-mail: admin@everymantheatre.org.uk

CHICHESTER
Festival Theatre
Oaklands Park, Chichester PO19 6AP
Box Office: 01243 781312
Stage Door: 01243 784437
Admin: 01243 784437
Website: www.cft.org.uk
e-mail: admin@cft.org.uk

CRAWLEY
The Hawth
Hawth Avenue, Crawley, West Sussex RH10 6YZ
Box Office: 01293 553636
Stage Door: ------------------
Admin: 01293 552941
Website: www.hawth.co.uk
e-mail: info@hawth.co.uk

CREWE
Lyceum Theatre
Heath Street, Crewe CW1 2DA
Box Office: 01270 537333
Stage Door: 01270 537336
Admin: 01270 537243

DARLINGTON
Civic Theatre
Parkgate, Darlington DL1 1RR
Box Office: 01325 486555
Stage Door: ------------------
Admin: 01325 387775
Website: www.darlingtonarts.co.uk

DUBLIN
Gaiety Theatre
South King Street, Dublin 2
Box Office: 00 353 1 6771717
Stage Door: 00 353 1 6795622
Admin: 00 353 1 6795622
Website: www.gaietytheatre.com

DUBLIN
Gate Theatre
1 Cavendish Row, Dublin 1
Box Office: 00 353 1 8744045
Stage Door: ------------------
Admin: 00 353 1 8744368
Website: www.gate-theatre.ie
e-mail: info@gate-theatre.ie

DUBLIN
Olympia Theatre
72 Dame Street, Dublin 2
Box Office: 00 353 1 6793323
Stage Door: 00 353 1 6771400
Admin: 00 353 1 6725883
Website: www.olympia.ie
e-mail: info@olympia.ie

EASTBOURNE
Congress Theatre
Admin: Winter Garden, Compton Street, Eastbourne BN21 4BP
Box Office: 01323 412000
Stage Door: 01323 410048
Admin: 01323 415500
Website: www.eastbournetheatres.co.uk
e-mail: theatres@eastbourne.gov.uk

EASTBOURNE
Devonshire Park Theatre
Admin: Winter Garden, Compton Street, Eastbourne BN21 4BP
Box Office: 01323 412000
Stage Door: 01323 410074
Admin: 01323 415500
Website: www.eastbournetheatres.co.uk
e-mail: theatres@eastbourne.gov.uk

EDINBURGH
King's Theatre
2 Leven Street, Edinburgh EH3 9LQ
Box Office: 0131-529 6000
Stage Door: 0131-229 3416
Admin: 0131-662 1112
Website: www.eft.co.uk
e-mail: empire@eft.co.uk

EDINBURGH
Playhouse Theatre
18-22 Greenside Place, Edinburgh EH1 3AA
Box Office: 0870 6063424
Stage Door: 0131-524 3324
Admin: 0131-524 3333
Website: www.livenation.co.uk/edinburgh

GLASGOW
King's Theatre
297 Bath Street, Glasgow G2 4JN
Box Office: 0141-240 1111
Stage Door: 0141-240 1300
Admin: 0141-240 1300
Website: www.kings-glasgow.co.uk

GLASGOW
Theatre Royal
282 Hope Street, Glasgow G2 3QA
Box Office: 0870 0606647
Stage Door: 0141-332 3321
Admin: 0141-332 3321
Website: www.theatreroyalglasgow.com

GRAYS THURROCK
Thameside Theatre
Orsett Road, Grays Thurrock RM17 5DX
Box Office: 0845 3005264
Stage Door: ------------------
Admin: 01375 382555
Website: www.thurrock.gov.uk/theatre
e-mail: mallinson@thurrock.gov.uk

HARLOW
The Playhouse
Playhouse Square, Harlow CM20 1LS
Box Office: 01279 431945
Stage Door: ------------------
Admin: 01279 446760
Website: www.playhouseharlow.com
e-mail: playhouse@harlow.gov.uk

HARROGATE
Harrogate International Centre
Kings Road, Harrogate HG1 5LA
Box Office: 0845 1308840
Stage Door: ------------------
Admin: 01423 500500
Website: www.harrogateinternationalcentre.co.uk
e-mail: sales@harrogateinternationalcentre.co.uk

HASTINGS
White Rock Theatre
White Rock
Hastings TN34 1JX
Box Office:	01424 462288
Stage Door:	------------------
Admin:	01424 462280
Website:	www.whiterockhastings.org.uk

HAYES (Middlesex)
Beck Theatre
Grange Road
Hayes, Middlesex UB3 2UE
Box Office:	020-8561 8371
Stage Door:	-------------------
Admin:	020-8561 7506
Website:	www.becktheatre.org.uk

HIGH WYCOMBE
Wycombe Swan
St Mary Street
High Wycombe HP11 2XE
Box Office:	01494 512000
Stage Door:	01494 514444
Admin:	01494 514444
Website:	www.wycombeswan.co.uk
e-mail:	enquiries@wycombeswan.co.uk

HUDDERSFIELD
Cragrats Ltd
The Mill, Dunford Road
Holmfirth, Huddersfield HD9 2AR
Stage Door:	------------------
BO:	------------------
Admin:	01484 686451
Website:	www.cragrats.com
e-mail:	info@cragrats.com

HUDDERSFIELD
Lawrence Batley Theatre
Queen Street
Huddersfield HD1 2SP
Box Office:	01484 430528
Stage Door:	01484 484501
Admin:	01484 484412
Website:	www.lawrencebatleytheatre.co.uk
e-mail:	theatre@lbt-uk.org

HULL
Hull New Theatre
Kingston Square
Hull HU1 3HF
Box Office:	01482 226655
Stage Door:	01482 318300
Admin:	01482 613818
e-mail:	theatre.management@hullcc.gov.uk

HULL
Hull Truck Theatre
Spring Street, Hull HU2 8RW
Box Office:	01482 323638
Stage Door:	------------------
Admin:	01482 224800
Website:	www.hulltruck.co.uk
e-mail:	admin@hulltruck.co.uk

ILFORD
Kenneth More Theatre
Oakfield Road
Ilford IG1 1BT
Box Office:	020-8553 4466
Stage Door:	020-8553 4465
Admin:	020-8553 4464
Website:	www.kenneth-more-theatre.co.uk
e-mail:	kmtheatre@aol.com

IPSWICH
Sir John Mills Theatre (Hire Only)
Gatacre Road
Ipswich IP1 2LQ
Box Office:	01473 211498
Stage Door:	------------------
Admin:	01473 218202
Website:	www.easternangles.co.uk
e-mail:	admin@easternangles.co.uk

JERSEY
Opera House
Gloucester Street
St Helier, Jersey JE2 3QR
Box Office:	01534 511115
Stage Door:	----------------
Admin:	01534 511100
Website:	www.jerseyoperahouse.co.uk
e-mail:	ian@jerseyoperahouse.co.uk

KIRKCALDY
Adam Smith Theatre
Bennochy Road, Kirkcaldy KY1 1ET
Box Office:	01592 583302
Stage Door:	------------------
Admin:	01592 583301

LEATHERHEAD
The Leatherhead Theatre
7 Church Street
Leatherhead, Surrey KT22 8DN
Box Office:	01372 365141
Stage Door:	------------------
Admin:	01372 365130
Website:	www.the-theatre.org
e-mail:	info@the-theatre.org

LEEDS
City Varieties Music Hall
Swan Street, Leeds LS1 6LW
Box Office:	0845 6441881
Stage Door:	------------------
Admin:	0845 1260696
Website:	www.cityvarieties.co.uk
e-mail:	info@cityvarieties.co.uk

LEEDS
Grand Theatre & Opera House
46 New Briggate
Leeds LS1 6NZ
Box Office:	0844 8482700
Stage Door:	0113-245 6014
Admin:	0113-245 6014
Website:	www.leedsgrandtheatre.com
e-mail:	boxoffice@leedsgrandtheatre.com

LICHFIELD
The Lichfield Garrick
Castle Dyke,, Lichfield WS13 6HR
Box Office: 01543 412121
Stage Door: -----------------
Admin: 01543 412110
Website: www.lichfieldgarrick.com

LINCOLN
Theatre Royal
Clasketgate, Lincoln LN2 1JJ
Box Office: 01522 525555
Stage Door: ------------------
Admin: 01522 523303
Website: www.theatreroyallincoln.com
e-mail: trl@dial.pipex.com

LIVERPOOL
Empire Theatre
Lime Street, Liverpool L1 1JE
Box Office: 0844 8472525
Stage Door: 0151-708 3200
Admin: 0151-708 3200
Website: www.liverpoolempire.org.uk

LLANDUDNO
Venue Cymru
Promenade, Llandudno, Conwy, North Wales LL30 1BB
Tel: 01492 879771
Box Office: 01492 872000
Website: www.venuecymru.co.uk
e-mail: info@venuecymru.co.uk

MALVERN
Malvern Theatres (Festival & Forum Theatres)
Grange Road, Malvern WR14 3HB
Box Office: 01684 892277
Stage Door: ------------------
Admin: 01684 569256
Website: www.malvern-theatres.co.uk
e-mail: post@malvern-theatres.co.uk

MANCHESTER
Manchester Apollo
Stockport Road, Ardwick Green, Manchester M12 6AP
Box Office: 0844 4777677
Stage Door: 0161-273 2416
Admin: 0161-273 6921
Website: www.livenation.co.uk

MANCHESTER
Opera House
Quay Street, Manchester M3 3HP
Box Office: 0844 8472328
Stage Door: 0161-828 1700
Admin: 0161-828 1700
Website: www.palaceandoperahouse.org.uk

MANCHESTER
Palace Theatre
Oxford Street, Manchester M1 6FT
Box Office: 0870 4013000
Stage Door: 0161-245 6600
Admin: 0161-245 6600
Website: www.manchesterpalace.org.uk

MARGATE
Theatre Royal
Addington Street
Margate, Kent CT9 1PW
Box Office: 0845 1301786
Stage Door: 01843 293397
Admin: 01843 293397
Website: www.theatreroyalmargate.com

MILTON KEYNES
Milton Keynes Theatre
500 Marlborough Gate
Central Milton Keynes MK9 3NZ
Box Office: 0870 0606652
Stage Door: 01908 547500
Admin: 01908 547500
Website: www.miltonkeynestheatre.com

NEWARK
Palace Theatre
Appletongate, Newark NG24 1JY
Box Office: 01636 655755
Stage Door: ------------------
Admin: 01636 655750
Website: www.palacenewark.com
e-mail: kevan.jackson@nsdc.info

NEWCASTLE UPON TYNE
Northern Stage
Barras Bridge
Haymarket
Newcastle upon Tyne NE1 7RH
Box Office: 0191-230 5151
Stage Door: ------------------
Admin: 0191-232 3366
Website: www.northernstage.co.uk
e-mail: info@northernstage.co.uk

NEWCASTLE UPON TYNE
Theatre Royal
Grey Street
Newcastle upon Tyne NE1 6BR
Box Office: 0844 8112121
Stage Door: 0191-244 2500
Admin: 0191-244 2500

NORTHAMPTON
Royal & Derngate Theatres
19-21 Guildhall Road
Northampton NN1 1DP
Box Office: 01604 624811
Stage Door: 01604 626222
Admin: 01604 626222
Website: www.royalandderngate.co.uk
e-mail: postbox@royalandderngate.co.uk

NORWICH
Theatre Royal
Theatre Street, Norwich NR2 1RL
Box Office: 01603 630000
Stage Door: 01603 598500
Admin: 01603 598500
Website: www.theatreroyalnorwich.co.uk

NOTTINGHAM
Theatre Royal & Royal Concert Hall
Theatre Square, Nottingham NG1 5ND
Box Office:	0115-989 5555
Stage Door:	0115-989 5500
Admin:	0115-989 5500
Website:	www.royalcentre-nottingham.co.uk
e-mail:	enquiry@royalcentre-nottingham.co.uk

OXFORD
New Theatre
George Street, Oxford OX1 2AG
Box Office:	0870 6077484
Stage Door:	01865 320760
Admin:	01865 320760

OXFORD
Oxford Playhouse
Beaumont Street, Oxford OX1 2LW
Box Office:	01865 305305
Stage Door:	01865 305301
Admin:	01865 305300
Website:	www.oxfordplayhouse.com
e-mail:	admin@oxfordplayhouse.com

POOLE
Lighthouse, Poole's Centre for The Arts
Kingland Road, Poole BH15 1UG
Box Office:	0844 4068666
Stage Door:	------------------
Admin:	------------------
Website:	www.lighthousepoole.co.uk

READING
The Hexagon
Queen's Walk, Reading RG1 7UA
Box Office:	0118-960 6060
Stage Door:	0118-939 0018
Admin:	0118-939 0123

RICHMOND (N Yorks)
Georgian Theatre Royal
Victoria Road, Richmond, North Yorkshire DL10 4DW
Box Office:	01748 825252
Stage Door:	------------------
Admin:	01748 823710
Website:	www.georgiantheatreroyal.co.uk

RICHMOND (Surrey)
Richmond Theatre
The Green, Richmond, Surrey TW9 1QJ
Box Office:	0870 0606651
Stage Door:	020-8940 0220
Admin:	020-8940 0220
Website:	www.richmondtheatre.net

SHEFFIELD
Sheffield Theatres - Crucible, Lyceum & Crucible Studio
55 Norfolk Street, Sheffield S1 1DA
Box Office:	0114-249 6000
Stage Door:	0114-249 5999
Admin:	0114-249 5999
Website:	www.sheffieldtheatres.co.uk
e-mail:	info@sheffieldtheatres.co.uk

SHERINGHAM
The Little Theatre
2 Station Road
Sheringham
Norfolk NR26 8RE
BO:	01263 822347
Stage Door:	01263 826173
Admin:	01263 822117
Website:	www.sheringhamlittletheatre.com
e-mail:	enquiries@sheringhamlittletheatre.com

SOUTHAMPTON
The Mayflower
Commercial Road
Southampton SO15 1GE
Box Office:	023-8071 1811
Stage Door:	------------------
Admin:	023-8071 1800
Website:	www.mayflower.org.uk
e-mail:	info@mayflower.org.uk

SOUTHEND
Southend Theatres (Cliffs Pavilion, Palace & Dixon Theatres)
Cliffs Pavilion, Station Road
Westcliff-on-Sea
Essex, SS0 7RA
Box Office:	01702 351135
Stage Door:	01702 347394
Admin:	01702 390657
Website:	www.southendtheatres.org.uk
e-mail:	info@southendtheatres.org.uk

ST ALBANS
Abbey Theatre
Holywell Hill
St Albans AL1 2DL
Box Office:	01727 857861
Stage Door:	------------------
Admin:	01727 847472
Website:	www.abbeytheatre.org.uk
e-mail:	manager@abbeytheatre.org.uk

ST ALBANS
Alban Arena
Civic Centre
St Albans AL1 3LD
Box Office:	01727 844488
Stage Door:	------------------
Admin:	01727 861078
Website:	www.alban-arena.co.uk
e-mail:	alban.arena@leisureconnection.co.uk

ST HELENS
Theatre Royal
Corporation Street
St Helens WA10 1LQ
Box Office:	01744 756000
Stage Door:	------------------
Admin:	01744 756333
Website:	www.sthelenstheatreroyal.co.uk

STAFFORD
Stafford Gatehouse Theatre
Eastgate Street, Stafford ST16 2LT
Box Office: 01785 254653
Stage Door: ------------------
Admin: 01785 253595
Website: www.staffordgatehousetheatre.co.uk
e-mail: gatehouse@staffordbc.gov.uk

STEVENAGE
Gordon Craig Theatre
Arts & Leisure Centre, Lytton Way, Stevenage SG1 1LZ
Box Office: 0870 0131030
Stage Door: 01438 242629
Admin: 01438 242679
Website: www.gordon-craig.co.uk
e-mail: gordoncraig@stevenage-leisure.co.uk

SUNDERLAND
Sunderland Empire
High Street West, Sunderland SR1 3EX
Box Office: 0870 6021130
Stage Door: 0191-566 1050
Admin: 0191-566 1040

SWANAGE
Mowlem Theatre
Shore Road, Swanage BH19 1DD
Box Office: 01929 422239
Stage Door: ------------------
Admin: ------------------

TAMWORTH
Assembly Rooms
Corporation Street
Tamworth B79 7BX
Box Office: 01827 709618
Stage Door: ------------------
Admin: 01827 709620

TEWKESBURY
The Roses
Sun Street, Tewkesbury GL20 5NX
Box Office: 01684 295074
Stage Door: ------------------
Admin: 01684 290734
e-mail: admin@rosestheatre.org

TORQUAY
Babbacombe Theatre
Babbacombe Downs, Torquay TQ1 3LU
Box Office: 01803 328385
Stage Door: 01803 328385
Admin: 01803 322233
Website: www.babbacombe-theatre.com
e-mail: mail@matpro-show.biz

TORQUAY
Princess Theatre
Torbay Road, Torquay TQ2 5EZ
Box Office: 0844 8472315
Stage Door: 01803 290068
Admin: 01803 290288
Website: www.livenation.co.uk/torquay

TRURO
Hall For Cornwall
Back Quay, Truro, Cornwall TR1 2LL
Box Office: 01872 262466
Stage Door: 01872 262465
Admin: 01872 262465
Website: www.hallforcornwall.co.uk
e-mail: admin@hallforcornwall.org.uk

WINCHESTER
Theatre Royal
21-23 Jewry Street, Winchester SO23 8SB
Box Office: 01962 840440
Stage Door: ------------------
Admin: 01962 844600
Website: www.theatre-royal-winchester.co.uk
e-mail: comms@theatre-royal-winchester.co.uk

WOLVERHAMPTON
Grand Theatre
Lichfield Street, Wolverhampton WV1 1DE
Box Office: 01902 429212
Stage Door: 01902 573320
Admin: 01902 573300
Website: www.grandtheatre.co.uk
e-mail: marketing@grandtheatre.co.uk

WORCESTER
Swan Theatre
The Moors
Worcester WR1 3EF
Box Office: 01905 611427
Stage Door: ------------------
Admin: 01905 726969
Website: www.worcesterlive.co.uk
e-mail: chris@worcesterlive.co.uk

WORTHING
Connaught Theatre
Union Place
Worthing BN11 1LG
Box Office: 01903 206206
Stage Door: ------------------
Admin: 01903 231799
Website: www.worthingtheatres.co.uk

YEOVIL
Octagon Theatre
Hendford, Yeovil BA20 1UX
Box Office: 01935 422884
Stage Door: ------------------
Admin: 01935 845900
Website: www.octagon-theatre.co.uk
e-mail: octagontheatre@southsomerset.gov.uk

YORK
Grand Opera House
Cumberland Street
York YO1 9SW
Box Office: 0844 8472322
Stage Door: ------------------
Admin: 01904 678700
Website: www.grandoperahouseyork.org.uk

AUTHENTIC PUNCH & JUDY
Contact: John Styles (Puppets, Booths & Presentations)
42 Christchurch Road
Sidcup
Kent DA15 7HQ
Website: www.johnstylesentertainer.co.uk
Tel/Fax: 020-8300 3579

BUCKLEY Simon
(Freelance Puppeteer/Presenter)
12 College Green
55-57 Barrington Road
London SW9 7JG
Website: www.simonbuckley.co.uk
e-mail: puppet.buckley@virgin.net   Mobile: 07976 290351

COMPLETE WORKS CREATIVE COMPANY Ltd The
Contact: Phil Evans (Artistic Director)
The Old Truman Brewery
91 Brick Lane
London E1 6QL
Website: www.tcw.org.uk
e-mail: info@tcw.org.uk
Fax: 0870 1431979   Tel: 0870 1431969

CORNELIUS & JONES
49 Carters Close
Sherington
Newport Pagnell
Buckinghamshire MK16 9NW
Website: www.corneliusjones.com
e-mail: admin@corneliusjones.com   Tel/Fax: 01908 612593

DYNAMIC NEW ANIMATION
Unit 13, The Watermark
Ribbleton Lane
Preston PR1 5EZ
Website: www.dynamicnewanimation.co.uk
e-mail: info@dynamicnewanimation.co.uk
Mobile: 07976 946003   Tel: 01772 253100

INDIGO MOON THEATRE
35 Waltham Court
Beverley
East Yorkshire HU17 9JF
Website: www.indigomoontheatre.com
e-mail: info@indigomoontheatre.com Mobile: 07855 328552

JACOLLY PUPPET THEATRE
Kirkella Road
Yelverton
West Devon PL20 6BB
Website: www.jacolly-puppets.co.uk
e-mail: theatre@jacolly-puppets.co.uk   Tel: 01822 852346

LITTLE ANGEL THEATRE
14 Dagmar Passage
Cross Street
London N1 2DN
Website: www.littleangeltheatre.com
e-mail: info@littleangeltheatre.com   Tel: 020-7226 1787

MAJOR MUSTARD'S TRAVELLING SHOW
1 Carless Avenue
Harborne
Birmingham B17 9EG
e-mail: mm@majormustard.com   Tel: 0121-426 4329

NORWICH PUPPET THEATRE
St James
Whitefriars
Norwich NR3 1TN
Website: www.puppettheatre.co.uk
e-mail: info@puppettheatre.co.uk
Fax: 01603 617578   Tel: 01603 615564

PEKKO'S PUPPETS
Contact: Stephen Novy (Director)
92 Stanley Avenue
Greenford
Middlesex UB6 8NP   Tel: 020-8575 2311

POM POM PUPPETS
9 Fulham Park Gardens
London SW6 4JX   Mobile: 07974 175247

PROFESSOR PATTEN'S PUNCH & JUDY
(Puppetry & Magic)
14 The Crest
Goffs Oak
Herts EN7 5NP
Website: www.dennispatten.co.uk   Tel: 01707 873262

PUPPET THEATRE WALES
22 Starling Road, St Athan
Vale of Glamorgan CF62 4NJ
Website: www.puppettheatrewales.com
e-mail: puppetwales@aol.com   Tel: 01446 790634

TALK TO THE HAND PRODUCTIONS
(Custom Characters Created and Performed)
Studio 277
Wimbledon Art Studios
Riverside Yard, Riverside Road
Earlsfield, London SW17 0BB
Website: www.talktothehandproductions.com
e-mail: info@talktothehandproductions.com
Mobile: 07813 682293   Mobile: 07855 421454

TICKLISH ALLSORTS SHOW
57 Victoria Road
Wilton, Salisbury
Wiltshire SP2 0DZ
Website: www.ticklishallsorts.co.uk
e-mail: garynunn@ntlworld.com   Tel/Fax: 01722 744949

TOPPER Chris PUPPETS
(Puppets Created & Performed)
75 Barrows Green Lane
Widnes
Cheshire WA8 3JH
Website: www.christopperpuppets.co.uk
e-mail: christopper@ntlworld.com   Tel: 0151-424 8692

ALDEBURGH
Summer Theatre (July & August) The Jubilee Hall
Crabbe Street, Aldeburgh IP15 5BW
BO: 01728 453007/454022 (Evening)
　　　　　　　　Admin: (Oct-May) 020-7724 5432
　　　　　　　　Admin: (June-Sept) 01502 723077
Website: www.southwoldtheatre.org

BELFAST
Lyric Theatre
55 Ridgeway Street, Belfast BT9 5FB
Fax: 028-9038 1395
BO: 028-9038 1081　　　Admin: 028-9038 5685
Website: www.lyrictheatre.co.uk
e-mail: info@lyrictheatre.co.uk
Production Manager: Marianne Crosslé
Administration Manager: Clare Gault
Executive Director: Michael Diskin
Finance Manager: David McIlwrath

BIRMINGHAM
Birmingham Stage Company
The Old Rep Theatre, Station Street, Birmingham B5 4DY
BO: 0121-303 2323　　　Admin: 0121-643 9050
Website: www.birminghamstage.net
e-mail: info@birminghamstage.net
Actor/Manager: Neal Foster

BIRMINGHAM
Birmingham Stage Company
London Office:
Suite 228 The Linen Hall
162 Regent Street, London W1B 5TB
Fax: 020-7437 3395　　　Admin: 020-7437 3391
Website: www.birminghamstage.net
e-mail: info@birminghamstage.net
Actor/Manager: Neal Foster
Executive Producer: Philip Compton

BIRMINGHAM
Repertory Theatre
Centenary Square, Broad Street, Birmingham B1 2EP
Press Office: 0121-245 2075
BO: 0121-236 4455　　　Tel: 0121-245 2000
e-mail: info@birmingham-rep.co.uk
Artistic Director: Rachel Kavanaugh
Executive Director: Stuart Rogers

BOLTON
Octagon Theatre
Howell Croft South, Bolton BL1 1SB
Fax: 01204 556502
BO: 01204 520661　　　Admin: 01204 529407
Artistic Director: Mark Babych
Executive Director: John Blackmore
Head of Administration: Lesley Etherington
Head of Production: Lesley Chenery

BRISTOL
Theatre Royal and Studio
(Closed for refurbishment December 2008 - Mid 2009)
Bristol Old Vic, King Street, Bristol BS1 4ED
Fax: 0117-949 3996　　　Tel: 0117-949 3993
Website: www.bristol-old-vic.co.uk
e-mail: admin@bristol-old-vic.co.uk

CARDIFF
Sherman Cymru
Senghennydd Road CF24 4YE
Fax: 029-2064 6902
BO: 029-2064 6900　　　Tel: 029-2064 6901
Director: Chris Ricketts
General Manager: Margaret Jones

CHICHESTER
Chichester Festival Theatre
Oaklands Park, Chichester
West Sussex PO19 6AP
Fax: 01243 787288
BO: 01243 781312　　　SD & Admin: 01243 784437
Website: www.cft.org.uk
e-mail: admin@cft.org.uk
Artistic Director: Jonathan Church
Executive Director: Alan Finch
Theatre Manager: Janet Bakose

CHICHESTER
Minerva Theatre at Chichester Festival Theatre
Oaklands Park
Chichester, West Sussex PO19 6AP
Fax: 01243 787288
BO: 01243 781312　　　SD & Admin: 01243 784437
Website: www.cft.org.uk
e-mail: admin@cft.org.uk
Theatre Manager: Janet Bakose
Artistic Director: Jonathan Church
Executive Director: Alan Finch

COLCHESTER
Mercury Theatre
Balkerne Gate
Colchester, Essex CO1 1PT
Fax: 01206 769607
BO: 01206 573948　　　Admin: 01206 577006
Website: www.mercurytheatre.co.uk
e-mail: info@mercurytheatre.co.uk
Chief Executive: Dee Evans
General Manager: Adrian Grady

COVENTRY
Belgrade Main Stage & B2 Auditorium
Belgrade Square, Coventry
West Midlands CV1 1GS
BO: 024-7655 3055　　　Admin: 024-7625 6431
Website: www.belgrade.co.uk
e-mail: admin@belgrade.co.uk
Artistic Director & CEO: Hamish Glen
Executive Director: Joanna Reid
Director of Marketing: Antony Flint

DUBLIN
Abbey Theatre Amharclann na Mainistreach
26 Lower Abbey Street, Dublin 1, Ireland
Fax: 00 353 1 872 9177
BO: 00 353 1 878 7222　　　Admin: 00 353 1 887 2200
Website: www.abbeytheatre.ie
e-mail: info@abbeytheatre.ie
Director: Fiach MacConghail

DUNDEE
Dundee Repertory Theatre
Tay Square, Dundee DD1 1PB
Fax: 01382 228609
BO: 01382 223530　　　Admin: 01382 227684
Website: www.dundeereptheatre.co.uk
Artistic Directors: James Brining, Dominic Hill
Executive Director: Graeme Wallace

EDINBURGH
Royal Lyceum Theatre Company
30B Grindlay Street, Edinburgh EH3 9AX
Fax: 0131-228 3955
BO: 0131-248 4848　　　SD & Admin: 0131-248 4800
Website: www.lyceum.org.uk
e-mail: info@lyceum.org.uk
Artistic Director: Mark Thomson

EDINBURGH
Traverse Theatre
(New Writing, Own Productions, Touring & Visiting
Companies)
10 Cambridge Street
Edinburgh EH1 2ED
Fax: 0131-229 8443
BO: 0131-228 1404   Admin: 0131-228 3223
Website: www.traverse.co.uk
e-mail: admin@traverse.co.uk
Artistic Director: Dominic Hill
Administrative Director: Mike Griffiths

EXETER
Exeter Northcott Theatre
Stocker Road
Exeter, Devon EX4 4QB
Fax: 01392 223996
BO: 01392 493493   Admin: 01392 223999
Website: www.northcott-theatre.co.uk
Executive Director: Kate Tyrrell

FRINTON
Frinton Summer Theatre
(July-Sept)
The McGrigor Hall, Fourth Avenue
Frinton-on-Sea, Essex CO13 9EB
BO: 01255 674443 (July-Sept Only)
e-mail: ed.max@frintonsummertheatre.co.uk
Producer/Artistic Director: Edward Max

GLASGOW
Citizens Theatre
Gorbals, Glasgow G5 9DS
Fax: 0141-429 7374
BO: 0141-429 0022   Admin: 0141-429 5561
Website: www.citz.co.uk
e-mail: info@citz.co.uk
Artistic Directors: Jeremy Raison, Guy Hollands
Administrative Director: Anna Staples

GUILDFORD
Yvonne Arnaud Theatre
Millbrook, Guildford
Surrey GU1 3UX
Fax: 01483 564071
BO: 01483 440000   Admin: 01483 440077
Website: www.yvonne-arnaud.co.uk
e-mail: yat@yvonne-arnaud.co.uk
Director: James Barber

HARROGATE
Harrogate Theatre
(Mainly Co-productions, Touring & Visiting Companies)
Oxford Street
Harrogate HG1 1QF
Fax: 01423 563205
Admin: 01423 502710   BO: 01423 502116
Website: www.harrogatetheatre.co.uk
e-mail: info@harrogatetheatre.co.uk
Chief Executive: David Bown

HULL
Hull Truck Theatre
Spring Street, Hull HU2 8RW
Fax: 01482 581182
Tel: 01482 224800
Website: www.hulltruck.co.uk
e-mail: admin@hulltruck.co.uk
Artistic Directors: John Godber & Gareth Tudor Price
Executive Director: Joanne Gower
Associate Director: Nick Lane

IPSWICH
The New Wolsey Theatre
Civic Drive, Ipswich, Suffolk IP1 2AS
Admin Fax: 01473 295910
BO: 01473 295900   Admin: 01473 295911
Website: www.wolseytheatre.co.uk
e-mail: info@wolseytheatre.co.uk
Artistic Director: Peter Rowe
Chief Executive: Sarah Holmes

KESWICK
Theatre by the Lake, Lakeside, Keswick, Cumbria CA12 5DJ
Fax: 017687 74698
BO: 017687 74411   Admin: 017687 72282
Website: www.theatrebythelake.com
e-mail: enquiries@theatrebythelake.com
Artistic Director: Ian Forrest

LANCASTER
The Dukes, Moor Lane, Lancaster, Lancashire LA1 1QE
Fax: 01524 598519
BO: 01524 598500   Admin: 01524 598505
Website: www.dukes-lancaster.org
e-mail: info@dukes-lancaster.org
Director: Joe Sumsion

LEEDS
The West Yorkshire Playhouse
Playhouse Square, Quarry Hill, Leeds LS2 7UP
Fax: 0113-213 7250
BO: 0113-213 7700   Admin: 0113-213 7800
Website: www.wyp.org.uk
Artistic Director (Chief Executive): Ian Brown
Producer: Henrietta Duckworth

LEICESTER
Leicester Theatre Trust, Suite 1A, Rutland Centre
56 Halford Street, Leicester LE1 1TQ
Fax: 0870 7065241   Admin: 0116-253 0021
Website: www.curveonline.co.uk
e-mail: enquiries@leicestertheatretrust.co.uk
Artistic Director: Paul Kerryson
Chief Executive: Ruth Eastwood

LIVERPOOL
Everyman & Playhouse Theatres
Everyman: 13 Hope Street, Liverpool L1 9BH
Playhouse: Williamson Square, Liverpool L1 1EL
Fax: 0151-709 0398
BO: 0151-709 4776   Admin: 0151-708 0338
Website: www.everymanplayhouse.com
e-mail: reception@everymanplayhouse.com
Artistic Director: Gemma Bodinetz
Executive Director: Deborah Aydon

MANCHESTER
Contact Theatre Company
Oxford Road, Manchester M15 6JA
Fax: 0161-274 0640
BO: 0161-274 0600   Admin: 0161-274 0623
Website: www.contact-theatre.org
e-mail: info@contact-theatre.org
Chief Executive/Artistic Director: John Edward McGrath

MANCHESTER
Library Theatre Company
St Peter's Square, Manchester M2 5PD
Fax: 0161-228 6481
BO: 0161-236 7110   Admin: 0161-234 1913
Website: www.librarytheatre.com
e-mail: ltcadmin@manchester.gov.uk
Artistic Director: Chris Honer
General Manager: Adrian J. P. Morgan

MANCHESTER
Royal Exchange Theatre
St Ann's Square, Manchester M2 7DH
Fax: 0161-832 0881
BO: 0161-833 9833   Admin: 0161-833 9333
Website: www.royalexchange.co.uk
Artistic Directors: Braham Murray, Gregory Hersov &
Sarah Frankcom
Executive Director: Paul Clay
Producer (Studio): Richard Morgan
Casting Director: Jerry Knight-Smith

MILFORD HAVEN
Torch Theatre
St Peter's Road
Milford Haven, Pembrokeshire SA73 2BU
Fax: 01646 698919
BO: 01646 695267   Admin: 01646 694192
Website: www.torchtheatre.co.uk
e-mail: info@torchtheatre.co.uk
Artistic Director: Peter Doran

MOLD
Clwyd Theatr Cymru
(Repertoire, 4 Weekly, also touring)
Mold, Flintshire, North Wales CH7 1YA
Fax: 01352 701558
BO: 0845 3303565   Admin: 01352 756331
Website: www.clwyd-theatr-cymru.co.uk
e-mail: admin@clwyd-theatr-cymru.co.uk

MUSSELBURGH
The Brunton Theatre
(Annual programme of Theatre, Dance, Music, Comedy &
Children's Work)
Ladywell Way, Musselburgh EH21 6AA
Fax: 0131-653 5265
BO: 0131-665 2240   Admin: 0131-665 9900
General Manager: Lesley Smith

NEWBURY
Watermill Theatre
(4-8 Weekly) (Feb-Jan)
Bagnor, Nr Newbury
Berkshire RG20 8AE
Fax: 01635 523726
BO: 01635 46044   Admin: 01635 45834
Website: www.watermill.org.uk
e-mail: admin@watermill.org.uk
Artistic & Executive Director: Hedda Beeby
General Manager: Clare Lindsay

NEWCASTLE UPON TYNE
Northern Stage (Theatrical Productions) Ltd
Barras Bridge, Newcastle upon Tyne NE1 7RH
Fax: 0191-261 8093
BO: 0191-230 5151   Admin: 0191-232 3366
Website: www.northernstage.co.uk
e-mail: info@northernstage.co.uk
Chief Executive: Erica Whyman

NEWCASTLE-UNDER-LYME
New Vic Theatre
(3-4 Weekly)
Etruria Road, Newcastle-under-Lyme
Staffordshire ST5 0JG
Fax: 01782 712885
BO: 01782 717962   Tel: 01782 717954
Website: www.newvictheatre.org.uk
e-mail: casting@newvictheatre.org.uk
Artistic Director: Theresa Heskins
Managing Director: Nick Jones

NORTHAMPTON
Royal & Derngate Theatres
Guildhall Road, Northampton
Northamptonshire NN1 1DP
TIE: 01604 655740
BO: 01604 624811   Admin: 01604 626222
Chief Executive: Martin Sutherland
Artistic Director: Laurie Sansom
Associate Director: Dani Parr

NOTTINGHAM
Nottingham Playhouse
(3/4 Weekly)
(Nottingham Playhouse Trust Ltd)
Wellington Circus, Nottingham NG1 5AL
Fax: 0115-947 5759
BO: 0115-941 9419   Admin: 0115-947 4361
Website: www.nottinghamplayhouse.co.uk
Chief Executive: Stephanie Sirr
Artistic Director: Giles Croft
Director, Roundabout and Education: Andrew Breakwell

OLDHAM
Coliseum Theatre
(3-4 Weekly)
Fairbottom Street, Oldham, Lancashire OL1 3SW
Fax: 0161-624 5318
BO: 0161-624 2829   Admin: 0161-624 1731
Website: www.coliseum.org.uk
e-mail: mail@coliseum.org.uk
Chief Executive: Kevin Shaw

PERTH
Perth Theatre
(2-3 Weekly)
Horsecross Arts, 185 High Street, Perth PH1 5UW
Fax: 01738 624576
BO: 0845 6126328   Admin: 01738 472700
Website: www.horsecross.co.uk
e-mail: info@horsecross.co.uk
Artistic Director: Ian Grieve
Head of Planning & Resources: Paul Hackett
Chief Executive: Jane Spiers

PETERBOROUGH
Key Theatre
(Touring & Occasional Seasonal)
Embankment Road, Peterborough, Cambridgeshire PE1 1EF
Fax: 01733 567025
BO: 01733 552439   Admin: 01733 552437
e-mail: key.theatre@peterborough.gov.uk

PITLOCHRY
Pitlochry Festival Theatre
Pitlochry, Perthshire PH16 5DR
Fax: 01796 484616
BO: 01796 484626   Admin: 01796 484600
Website: www.pitlochry.org.uk
e-mail: admin@pitlochry.org.uk
Chief Executive/Artistic Director: John Durnin

PLYMOUTH
Theatre Royal & Drum Theatre
Royal Parade, Plymouth, Devon PL1 2TR
Fax: 01752 230506
BO: 01752 267222   Admin: 01752 668282
Website: www.theatreroyal.com
e-mail: info@theatreroyal.com
Artistic Director: Simon Stokes
Chief Executive: Adrian Vinken

READING
The Mill at Sonning Theatre
(5-6 Weekly)
Sonning Eye, Reading RG4 6TY
BO: 0118-969 8000
Admin: 0118-969 6039
Artistic Director: Sally Hughes
Assistant Administrator: Ann Seymour

SALISBURY
Playhouse & Salberg Studio
(3-4 Weekly)
Malthouse Lane
Salisbury, Wiltshire SP2 7RA
Fax: 01722 421991
BO: 01722 320333
Admin: 01722 320117
Website: www.salisburyplayhouse.com
e-mail: info@salisburyplayhouse.com
Artistic Director: Philip Wilson
Executive Director: Michelle Carwardine-Palmer

SCARBOROUGH
Stephen Joseph Theatre
(Repertoire/Repertory)
Westborough, Scarborough
North Yorkshire YO11 1JW
Fax: 01723 360506
BO: 01723 370541
Admin: 01723 370540
e-mail: enquiries@sjt.uk.com
Artistic Director: Alan Ayckbourn
Executive Director: Stephen Wood

SHEFFIELD
Crucible, Studio & Lyceum Theatres
55 Norfolk Street
Sheffield S1 1DA
Fax: 0114-249 6003
BO: 0114-249 6000
Admin: 0114-249 5999
Website: www.sheffieldtheatres.co.uk
e-mail: info@sheffieldtheatres.co.uk
Chief Executive: Angela Galvin

SHERINGHAM
Summer Repertory
The Little Theatre
2 Station Road
Sheringham, Norfolk NR26 8RE
BO: 01263 822347
Website: www.sheringhamlittletheatre.com
e-mail: enquiries@sheringhamlittletheatre.com
Producer: Sheringham Little Theatre
Artistic Director: Debbie Thompson

SIDMOUTH
Manor Pavilion Theatre
(Weekly) (July-Sept)
Manor Road, Sidmouth
Devon EX10 8RP
BO: 01395 579977 (Season Only
Tel: 020-7636 4343 Charles Vance

SOUTHAMPTON
Nuffield Theatre
(Sept-July, Sunday Night Concerts, Tours)
University Road
Southampton SO17 1TR
Fax: 023-8031 5511
BO: 023-8067 1771
Admin: 023-8031 5500
Website: www.nuffieldtheatre.co.uk
Artistic Director: Patrick Sandford
Executive Director: Kate Anderson

SOUTHWOLD
Summer Theatre
(July-Sept)
St Edmund's Hall
Cumberland Road, Southwold IP18 6JP
Admin: (Oct-May) 020-7724 5432
Admin: (June-Sept) 01502 723077
Website: www.southwoldtheatre.org
e-mail: jill@southwoldtheatre.org
Producer: Jill Freud & Company

ST ANDREWS
Byre Theatre
(Not producing, Co-productions only)
Abbey Street, St Andrews KY16 9LA
Fax: 01334 475370
BO: 01334 475000
Admin: 01334 475000
Website: www.byretheatre.com
e-mail: enquiries@byretheatre.com
Chief Executive: Jacqueline McKay

STRATFORD-UPON-AVON
Royal Shakespeare Company & Courtyard Theatre
Southern Lane
Stratford-upon-Avon CV37 6BB
Fax: 01789 294810
BO: 0844 8001110
Admin: 01789 296655
Website: www.rsc.org.uk
e-mail: info@rsc.org.uk

WATFORD
Watford Palace Theatre
(3-4 Weekly) Weds 2.30pm, Sat 3pm
20 Clarendon Road
Watford, Herts WD17 1JZ
Fax: 01923 819664
BO: 01923 225671
Admin: 01923 810300
Website: www.watfordtheatre.co.uk
e-mail: melody@watfordtheatre.co.uk
Artistic Director & Chief Executive: Brigid Larmour
Executive Director: Anne Gallacher

WINDSOR
Theatre Royal
Thames Street, Windsor
Berkshire SL4 1PS
Fax: 01753 831673
BO: 01753 853888
Admin: 01753 863444
Website: www.theatreroyalwindsor.co.uk
e-mail: info@theatreroyalwindsor.co.uk
Director: Angela Edwards

WOKING
New Victoria Theatre, The Ambassadors
Peacocks Centre
Woking GU21 6GQ
SD: 01483 545855
BO: 0870 0606645
Admin: 01483 545800
Website: www.theambassadors.com/woking
e-mail: boxoffice@theambassadors.com

YORK
Theatre Royal
St Leonard's Place, York YO1 7HD
Fax: 01904 550164
BO: 01904 623568
Admin: 01904 658162
Website: www.yorktheatreroyal.co.uk
e-mail: admin@yorktheatreroyal.co.uk
Artistic Director: Damian Cruden
Chief Executive: Daniel Bates

Unions, Professional Guilds and Associations

UNTIED KINGDOM
BROADCASTING ENTERTAINMENT CINEMATOGRAPH &
THEATRE UNION (BECTU) (Formerly BETA & ACTT)
373-377 Clapham Road, London SW9 9BT
e-mail: smacdonald@bectu.org.uk
Fax: 020-7346 0901   Tel: 020-7346 0900

CASTING DIRECTORS' GUILD
50 Sandringham Avenue, London SW20 8JY
Website: www.thecdg.co.uk
e-mail: info@thecdg.co.uk

DIRECTORS GUILD OF GREAT BRITAIN
Top Floor, Julian House, 4 Windmill Street, London W1T 2HZ
Website: www.dggb.org
e-mail: info@dggb.org
Fax: 020-7580 9132   Tel: 020-7580 9131

EQUITY inc Variety Artistes' Federation
Guild House, Upper St Martin's Lane, London WC2H 9EG
Website: www.equity.org.uk
e-mail: info@equity.org.uk
Fax: 020-7379 7001   Tel: 020-7379 6000

(Midlands)
Office 1, Steeple House, Percy Street, Coventry CV1 3BY
e-mail: info@midlands-equity.org.uk   Tel/Fax: 024-7655 3612

(North West & Isle of Man)
Conavon Court, 12 Blackfriars Street, Salford M3 5BQ
e-mail: info@manchester-equity.org.uk
Fax: 0161-839 3133   Tel: 0161-832 3183

(Scotland & Northern Ireland)
114 Union Street, Glasgow G1 3QQ
e-mail: igilchrist@glasgow.equity.org.uk
Fax: 0141-248 2473   Tel: 0141-248 2472

(Wales & South West)
Transport House, 1 Cathedral Road, Cardiff CF11 9SD
e-mail: info@cardiff-equity.org.uk
Fax: 029-2023 0754   Tel: 029-2039 7971

FILM ARTISTS ASSOCIATION
(Amalgamated with BECTU)
373-377 Clapham Road, London SW9
Website: www.bectu.org.uk
Fax: 020-7346 0925   Tel: 020-7346 0900

INTERNATIONAL FEDERATION OF ACTORS (FIA)
Guild House, Upper St Martin's Lane, London WC2H 9EG
Website: www.fia-actors.com
e-mail: office@fia-actors.com
Fax: 020-7379 8260   Tel: 020-7379 0900

MUSICIANS' UNION
60-62 Clapham Road, London SW9 0JJ
Website: www.musiciansunion.org.uk
Fax: 020-7582 9805   Tel: 020-7582 5566

NASAA - NATIONAL ASSOCIATION OF SUPPORTING
ARTISTES AGENTS
Website: www.nasaa.org.uk
e-mail: info@nasaa.org.uk

NORTH AMERICAN ACTORS ASSOCIATION
Contact: By phone or e-mail only
Website: www.naaa.org.uk
e-mail: americanactors@aol.com   Mobile: 07873 371891

[CONTACTS 2009]

PERSONAL MANAGERS' ASSOCIATION Ltd
PO Box 63819, London N1P 1HL
Website: www.thepma.com
e-mail: info@thepma.com
Tel: 0845 6027191

WRITERS' GUILD OF GREAT BRITAIN The
15 Britannia Street
London WC1X 9JN
Website: www.writersguild.org.uk
e-mail: admin@writersguild.org.uk
Fax: 020-7833 4777
Tel: 020-7833 0777

BELGIUM
ACV/TRANSCOM - CULTUUR
Steenstraat 29, 1000 Brussels
Website: www.acvcultuur.be
e-mail: jpvandervurst.transcom@acv-csc.be
Fax: 00 32 2 514 1836
Tel: 00 32 2 289 0830

CENTRALE GÉNÉRALE DES SERVICES PUBLICS
Place Fontainas 9-11, 1000 Brussels
Website: www.cgsp-culture.be
e-mail: mylene.paon@cgsp.be
Fax: 00 32 2 508 5902
Tel: 00 32 2 508 5811

DENMARK
DAF - DANSK ARTIST FORBUND
Vendersgade 24
1363 Copenhagen K
Website: www.artisten.dk
e-mail: artisten@artisten.dk
Fax: 00 45 33 33 73 30
Tel: 00 45 33 32 66 77

DANSK SKUESPILLERFORBUND
Sankt Knuds Vej 26
1903 Frederiksberg C
Website: www.skuespillerforbundet.dk
e-mail: dsf@skuespillerforbundet.dk
Fax: 00 45 33 24 81 59
Tel: 00 45 33 24 22 00

FINLAND
SUOMEN NÄYTTELIJÄLIITTO
Meritullinkatu 33
00170 Helsinki
Finland
Website: www.nayttelijaliitto.fi
e-mail: toimisto@nayttelijaliitto.fi
Fax: 00 358 9 2511 2139
Tel: 00 353 9 2511 2135

FRANCE
SYNDICAT FRANÇAIS DES ARTISTES-INTERPRÈTES
1 rue Janssen, 75019 Paris
Website: www.sfa-cgt.fr
e-mail: info@sfa-cgt.fr
Fax: 00 33 1 53 25 09 01
Tel: 00 33 1 53 25 09 09

GERMANY
GENOSSENSCHAFT DEUTSCHER BUEHNENANGEHOERIGER
Feldbrunnenstrasse 74
20148 Hamburg
Website: www.buehnengenossenschaft.de
e-mail: gdba@buehnengenossenschaft.de
Fax: 00 49 40 45 93 52
Tel: 00 49 40 44 51 85

What are performers' unions?

The unions listed over the next few pages exist to protect and improve the rights, interests and working conditions of performers. They offer very important services to their members, such as advice on pay and conditions, help with contracts and negotiations, legal support and welfare advice. To join a performers' union there is usually a one-off joining fee and then an annual subscription fee calculated in relation to an individual's total yearly earnings. Equity is the main actors' union in the UK. See www.equity.org.uk and page 412 for more details.

Do similar organisations exist for other sectors of the entertainment industry?

In addition to representation by trade unions, some skills also have professional bodies and guilds which complement the work of trade unions. These include directors, producers, stage managers, designers and casting directors. Please also see the 'Organisations' section of this book for these and other listings.

What is the FIA?

The FIA (International Federation of Actors) www.fia-actors.com is an organisation which represents performers' trades unions, guilds and associations from all around the world. It tackles the same issues as individual actors' unions, but on an international rather than local level.

I'm a professionally trained actor from overseas and I want to work in the UK. How do I get started?

As with all forms of employment, to work as an actor in the UK you will need to have a relevant work permit / working visa. You might want to visit http://www.bia.homeoffice.gov.uk/workingintheuk for full information. You may also wish to join the UK's actors' union, Equity. For more information please visit their website www.equity.org.uk. If you can prove that you have relevant professional acting training and/or experience, you can also apply to join Spotlight to promote yourself to casting opportunities.

I am a UK resident and I want to work as an actor elsewhere in Europe. Where do I start?

A good starting point would be to contact the actors' union in the country in which you are hoping to work for information on their employment legislation. Contact details for performers' unions in Europe can be found over the next few pages or obtained from the FIA www.fia-actors.com, who in most cases will be able to advise on what criteria you need to fulfil to be eligible for work.

What are English Speaking Theatres?

English Speaking Theatres can provide British actors with an opportunity to work abroad in theatre. These companies vary greatly in terms of the plays they put on and the audiences they attract: they may aim to teach English to schoolchildren; help audiences develop an appreciation of English plays; or may exist simply because there is a demand for English speaking entertainment. Some are based in one venue while others tour round the country. Actors may be employed for an individual production or, especially if touring, for a series of plays. Performers interested in the possibility of working for this type of theatre company should refer to the 'Theatre - English Speaking in Europe' section for listings.

I am a UK resident and I want to work as an actor in the USA. Where do I start?

To work in America you will need a Green Card, a visa which entitles the holder to live and work there permanently as an immigrant, but you will not qualify for one unless you are sponsored by a prospective employer in the US or a relative who is a US citizen. It would be worth visiting the US Embassy's website www.usembassy.org.uk/cons_new/visa/index.html or the US Department of State's Bureau of Consular Affairs website http://travel.state.gov/visa/visa_1750.html for information about the criteria you must meet and the fees you will have to pay. Relocation companies and legal services tailored to helping performers move to America can be found in the 'Accountants, Insurance & Law' section of Contacts.

Don't expect to be granted immediate entry to the USA. There is a limit to the number of people who can apply for immigrant status every year, so you could be on the waiting list for several years depending on the category of your application. If your previous experience demonstrates that you have what is classed as "exceptional ability" you may be given priority - this would mean your level of ability was significantly above average and that your entry to the US would be of benefit to its national economy, cultural or educational interests, or welfare. See the websites above for more details. You should also enter the Green Card Lottery at www.greencard.co.uk for a chance to fast-track the processing of your application, although your visa will still have to be approved.

Finding employment from outside the USA will be difficult. You might want to try signing with an American talent agent to submit you for work, although there is huge competition for agents. Try the Association of Talent Agents (ATA) www.agentassociation.com for US agent details. You could also view the Talent Managers Association's website www.talentmanagers.org if you are looking for a personal manager, although they will not put you forward for work. See the 'Agents & Personal Managers' section for advice on how to target and approach agents. The most effective way to gain an American agent's interest would be to get a personal referral from an industry contact, such as a casting director or acting coach. You should also promote yourself as you would with Spotlight by signing up with casting directories such as www.breakdownservices.com.

Acting employment in America is divided into union work and non-union work. The major actors' unions are SAG www.sag.org, AEA www.actorsequity.org, and AFTRA www.aftra.com. As with any other union they protect and enhance the rights of their members and offer various services and benefits. You will only become eligible for membership once you have provided proof of a contract for a job which comes under a particular union's jurisdiction. Non-members can work on union jobs if a producer is willing to employ them. You can join more than one union, but once you have joined at least one you will be unable to accept any non-union work.

You may have to begin your career in America with non-union work, as experience or union membership in the UK does not make you eligible to join a union in the US. Work ungoverned by the unions could include student and independent films, small stage productions, commercials, voice-overs, extra work, and so on. You are unlikely to be paid well as non-union contracts are not governed by the minimum wages set by the unions but you will be able to build on your CV and begin making yourself known in the US acting industry.

Martin McGrath is the Campaigns & Publications Officer at Equity, the trade union for the UK entertainment industry. He works to provide a voice of authority for performers and the industry in general.

We at Equity take our role as an advocate very seriously. As the events of recent months have demonstrated, when our members choose to make their voices heard on an issue Equity can have a dramatic impact on policy decisions made at the highest levels.

Take, for example, the issue of funding for the arts in England. In the run-up to the government's spending review we were told that a reduction in funding was unavoidable. Organisations across the arts were preparing for a below-inflation settlement that could have meant serious cuts.

Equity was not prepared to simply sit back and accept that such an outcome was inevitable. Through our members, and enlisting the support of the wider public, we began a campaign to persuade ministers that money spent supporting the arts was not just a cultural benefit but an investment that delivered economic growth in an industry where the UK leads the world. We argued our case with ministers, MPs and civil servants and we demonstrated the popularity of arts funding by encouraging supporters to write to their MP and to ministers with a postcard campaign.

The result was so successful that some MPs were so deluged that they pleaded with us to stop the mailings.

And when the government announced its spending review the arts were one of the very few sectors to enjoy an above-inflation settlement. When the result was announced the government was quick to concede the important role of Equity's campaign in swaying its decision.

Then, when Arts Council England took the government's settlement and announced dramatic cuts of funding to some of the country's most innovative and exciting theatres, Equity members again took up arms forcing the Arts Council into an embarrassing rethink and preserving funding for a number of organisations.

But Equity does more than simply react to events. We can also play a central role in constructing the framework that will shape our industry's future.

Over the last year Equity has been conducting a major campaign of consultation and education amongst our members about the dramatic impact of new technology on broadcasting. Our "TV is Changing" campaign **(www.tvischanging.com)** demonstrates how Equity is able to look ahead, identifying challenges and opportunities and developing strategies to shape the emerging digital broadcasting landscape in ways that protect our members' interests while ensuring that our industry remains competitive and able to respond to the opportunities presented by this era of dramatic change.

In developing our policies and setting out our vision, Equity is keen, whenever possible, to work together with interested parties across the industry. While we have a duty to defend our members' interests our goal is to do that through cooperation rather than confrontation.

Whether you are a performer requiring support and advice or a professional who shares our concerns about the future of our industry, Equity is a powerful voice to have on your side and the persuasive partner making the case for properly funded, high-quality arts and entertainment industry in the UK.

For more information about Equity contact:

Post: Equity, Guild House, Upper St Martin's Lane, London WC2H 9EG
Telephone: 020-7379 6000
Online: www.equity.org.uk
e-mail: info@equity.org.uk

GREECE
HAU - HELLENIC ACTORS' UNION
33 Kaniggos Street
106 82 Athens
Website: www.sei.gr
e-mail: support@sei.gr
Fax: 00 30 210 380 8651 Tel: 00 30 210 383 3742

IRELAND
IEG - IRISH EQUITY GROUP
SIPTU
Liberty Hall
Dublin 1
Website: www.irishequity.ie
e-mail: equity@siptu.ie
Fax: 00 353 1 874 3691 Tel: 00 353 1 858 6403

ITALY
SINDACATO ATTORI ITALIANO
Via Ofanto 18
00198 Rome
Website: www.cgil.it/sai-slc
e-mail: sai-slc@cgil.it
Fax: 00 39 06 854 6780 Tel: 00 39 06 841 7303

LUXEMBOURG
ONOFHANGEGE GEWERKSCHAFTSBOND LETZEBUERG
60 bd. Kennedy
B.P. 149
L-4002 Esch/Alzette
Website: www.ogb-l.lu
e-mail: ogbl@ogbl.lu
Fax: 00 352 541 620 Tel: 00 352 540 545-1

NETHERLANDS
FNV - KUNSTEN INFORMATIE EN MEDIA
Jan Tooropstraat 1
Postbus 9354
1006 AJ Amsterdam
Website: www.fnv.nl/kiem
e-mail: algemeen@fnv-kiem.nl
Fax: 00 31 20 355 3737 Tel: 00 31 20 355 3636

NORWAY
NSF - NORSK SKUESPILLERFORBUND
Welhavensgate 3
0166 Oslo
Website: www.skuespillerforbund.no
e-mail: nsf@skuespillerforbund.no
Fax: 00 47 21 02 71 91 Tel: 00 47 21 02 71 90

PORTUGAL
STE - SINDICATO DOS TRABALHADORES DE ESPECTÁCULOS
Rua da Fe 23, 2do piso
1150-149 Lisbon
e-mail: startistas@mail.telepac.pt
Fax: 00 351 21 885 3787 Tel: 00 351 21 885 2728

SPAIN
CC.OO. COMISIONES OBRERAS-COMUNICACIÓN Y TRANSPORTE
Plaza Cristino Martos 4
6A Planta
28015 Madrid
Website: www.fct.ccoo.es
e-mail: medios@fct.ccoo.es
Fax: 00 34 91 548 1613 Tel: 00 34 91 540 9295

FAEE - FEDERACIÓN DE ARTISTAS DEL ESTADO ESPAÑOL
C/ Montera 34
1ro Piso
28013 Madrid
Website: www.faee.net
e-mail: faee@wanadoo.es
Fax: 00 34 91 522 6055 Tel: 00 34 91 522 2804

SWEDEN
TF TEATERFÖRBUNDET
Kaplansbacken 2A
Box 12 710
112 94 Stockholm
Website: www.teaterforbundet.se
e-mail: info@teaterforbundet.se
Fax: 00 46 8 653 9507 Tel: 00 46 8 441 1300

UNITED STATES OF AMERICA
AFTRA
(American Federation of Television & Radio Artists)
260 Madison Avenue
New York NY 10016
Website: www.aftra.com
Fax: (212) 545-1238 Tel: (212) 532-0800

5757 Wilshire Boulevard
9th Floor
Los Angeles CA 90036
Website: www.aftra.com
Fax: (323) 634-8246 Tel: (323) 634-8100

S A G
(Screen Actors Guild)
7th Floor
5757 Wilshire Boulevard
Los Angeles
CA 90036-3600
Website: www.sag.org Tel: (323) 954-1600

360 Madison Avenue
12th Floor
New York NY 10017
Website: www.sag.org
e-mail: nymember@sag.org
Fax: (212) 944-6774 Tel: (212) 944-1030

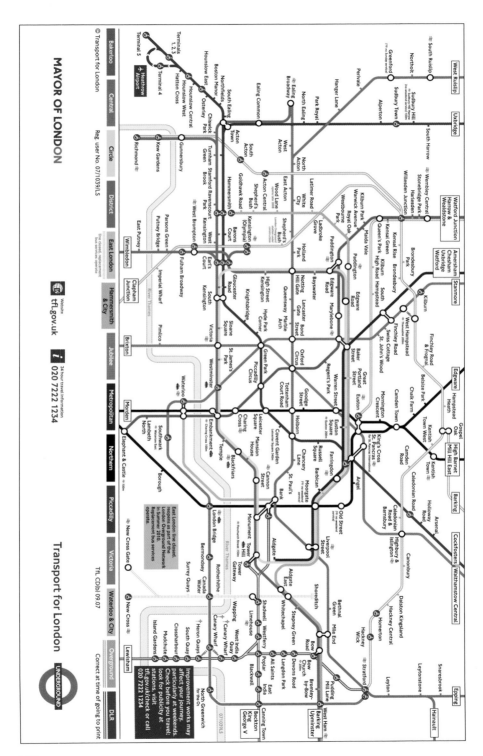

Index To Advertisers

PHOTOGRAPHERS

Q

R